International Baccalaureate Biology Higher Level

Introduction

Welcome to the International Baccalaureate Higher Level Biology Revision Guide, 2011 edition.

This covers every aspect of the Higher Level course in a format that is clear, colourful and simple to follow. Key points, facts and principles are listed for easy learning, and diagrams are designed to make them easy to learn. Remember that a clear diagram provides an instant essay plan therefore helping you to gain the extra two marks for clarity and organisation.

In the margin are shaded boxes that give the heading for the section being covered.
These help you to find sections quickly.

Cell Theory

Many Assessment Statements begin with "State ----". These statements are in pale blue boxes.

These boxes contain Statements.

There are also many Assessment Statements asking you to define something. These Definitions are in Appendix 2 on page 227.

Define gene mutation.

This is **your** revision book, so dotted throughout the notes are question boxes. These contain simple questions such as definitions, statements or revision of some particular point. You should be able to complete these. In addition to these there are longer Revision boxes.

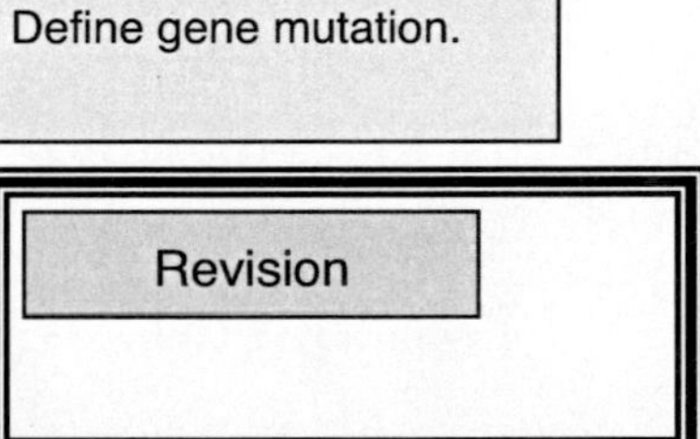
Revision

At the end of each topic there are a number of multiple choice questions to allow you to test your factual knowledge. Remember that when you answer multiple choice questions NEVER choose the first one that sounds right. Examiners sometimes put in a trick answer as A or B. Always read ALL four answers and try to think of the reason why the other three are wrong.The answers are in Appendix 5. There are 7 genetics problems in Topic 4 and a further 11 in Topic 10. The worked answers are in Appendix 6.

Every assessment statement in the syllabus starts with a Command Term and so it is essential that you understand what these mean as you will be expected to apply them in your answers to exam questions. There are three levels of depth of treatment and are all given in Appendix 1 on page 226. Appendix 9 on page 241 has model answers for essays using some of these Command Terms.

Thanks to my colleagues Tony and Arabella Stuart who helped to refine the text, and also to my students for trialling the multiple choice questions and their advice on the layout.

I would greatly value any feedback on this revision guide so that later editions can continue to help students throughout the world. Please feel free to email me at Oxford Study Courses – osc@osc-ib.com.

Ashby Merson-Davies.

Contents

Topic 1

Statistical Analysis

Mean

Calculating the mean of a set of values

The mathematical symbols used have been standardised.
Each measurement or value from a sample is given the symbol x.
The sum of all measurements is written as $\sum x$. ($\sum$ is the Greek letter sigma).

The number of values in the sample is n.

The mean of the sample is x-bar, $\bar{x}$

The mean = sum of all samples / sample size

$$\bar{x} = \frac{\sum x}{n}$$

Error bars are a graphical representation of the variability of data.

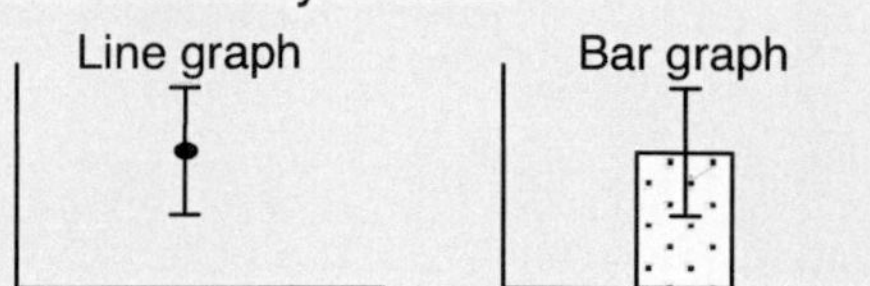
Line graph
Bar graph

Standard Deviation

Standard deviation of a set of values

More information on graphs and statistics is available in the OSC Student Guide for Internal Assessment.

Standard deviation is used to summarise the spread of values around the mean.

68% of the values fall within plus and minus one standard deviation of the mean.

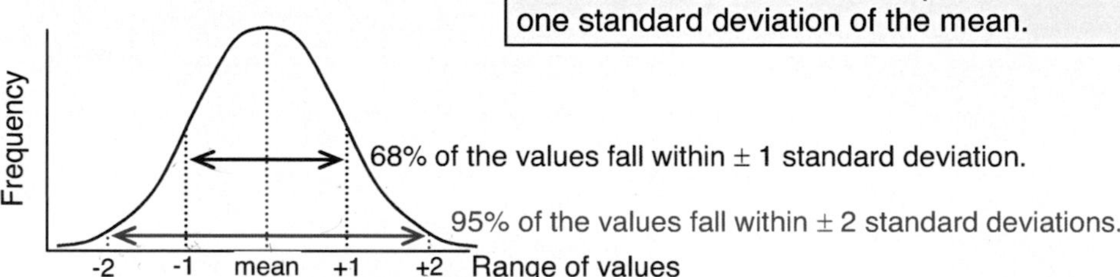
Frequency
68% of the values fall within ± 1 standard deviation.
95% of the values fall within ± 2 standard deviations.
-2
-1
mean
+1
+2
Range of values

Standard deviation can only be applied to a normal or near normal distribution, so the larger the sample the better. The standard rule is that 68% of the data falls within + or – one standard deviation, and 95% falls within + or – two standard deviations.

Example

Let us say the mean is 30 seconds and the standard deviation is 5 seconds.

68% of the values will fall within the times of 25 to 35 seconds, and 95% of the values will fall within the times of 20 to 40 seconds.

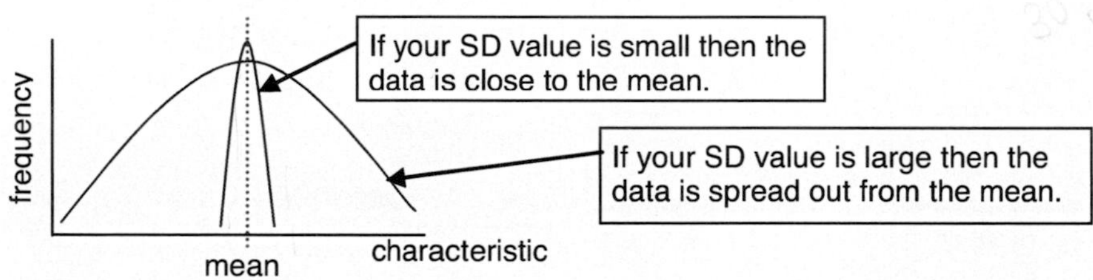
If your SD value is small then the data is close to the mean.
If your SD value is large then the data is spread out from the mean.
frequency
mean
characteristic

The SD is considered to be small if it is less than 33% of the mean.

The standard deviation can be used to help decide if the difference between two means is significant. Look at the data below taken from two investigations.

Data Set 1	Mean	Standard deviation
% red flowers pollinated	25	12
% white flowers pollinated	79	12

Data Set 2	Mean	Standard deviation
% germination in red light	47	18
% germination in blue light	62	25

In Data Set 1 the standard deviation is the same value but for the red flowers it is large (greater than 33% of the mean) and for the white flowers it is small. This tells us that there is much variation for the red flowers but very little for the white. The difference between the means is 54%, which is large, and there is no overlap of the data. (25 + 12 does not overlap with 79 – 12). This indicates that there is a significant difference between the means.

In Data Set 2 though both standard deviations are large as they are greater than 33% of the mean. 47 + 18 = 65 and 62 – 25 = 37. This means that there is a great deal of overlap between the two sets and we cannot be so confident that the difference of 15% between the two means is significant. We would need to use a statistical test such as the Student t-test described below to see if this difference of 15% is significant.

Checking for Normal Distribution

The simplest way to check if your data follows a normal distribution is to do a tally chart.

Note that the numbers for the independent variable are consecutive even though there may not be values in some groups.

Pulse rate / beats min^{-1}	Number of pupils
65	I
66	III
67	I
68	
69	II
70	
71	IIIIII

Clearly this is not a normal distribution, probably because the sample is too small.

This distribution is very slightly skewed, but it is good enough.

This is a good normal distribution.

Size class of leaves / cm	Shaded site	Sunny site
2.5 – 3.0		II
3.0 – 3.5		IIIII I
3.5 – 4.0	II	IIIII IIII
4.0 – 4.5	IIIII	IIII
4.5 – 5.0	IIIII II	II
5.0 – 5.5	IIIII	
5.5 – 6.0	I	
6.0 – 6.5	I	
6.5 – 7.0	I	

Calculating the standard deviation of a set of values

The symbol for standard deviation is **s**. There are different formulae that can be used depending on the data that you have collected. Sometimes you can group your data into frequencies and use the frequency formula, but the one below uses individual data.

- ❖ Remember that standard deviation has the same units as the data values.

Set out your data as in the table on the right.

Sum the values of x and x^2.
$\sum x = 111.2$ and $\sum x^2 = 549.96$

Substitute the values of $\sum x$ and $\sum x^2$ into the equation for standard deviation.

$$s = \sqrt{\frac{\sum x^2 - ((\sum x)^2 / n)}{n-1}}$$

$$s = \sqrt{\frac{549.96 - (111.2^2 / 23)}{23-1}}$$

$$s = \sqrt{\frac{549.96 - 537.63}{22}} = 0.7487cm$$

$$s = 0.75cm$$

Leaf n	Width / cm x	$Width^2$ x^2
1	4.5	20.25
2	5.0	25.00
3	4.5	20.25
4	4.4	19.36
5	4.5	etc
6	4.7	
7	4.8	
8	6.4	
9	4.4	
10	4.3	
11	5.1	
12	3.8	
13	3.6	
14	5.5	
15	5.3	
16	4.8	
17	4.5	
18	5.7	
19	4.1	
20	6.5	
21	5.4	
22	5.4	
23	4.0	
Σ	111.2	549.69

The square of the standard deviation, s^2, is called the variance, and you will come across this in the t-test in the next section.

Alternatively you can use your calculator, or quicker still, an Excel spreadsheet as in the table below.

	Data set 1	Data set 2
	16	41
	18	45
	19	81
	15	86
	15	99
	17	60
	18	58
Mean	16.86	67.14
St. dev.	1.57	21.87

1.57 is small relative to the mean of 16.86 (9.3%), so this is a small value for s.

21.87 is large relative to the mean of 67.14 (32.6%), so this is a large value for s.

Place cursor in cell below set of data;
Click on fx (Insert formula);
Select a category – Statistical;
Select a function – AVERAGE;
Check the selected cells are correct;
Click OK;
Repeat for standard deviation;
Select a category – Statistical;
Select a function – STDEV;
Check the selected cells are correct;
Click OK;
Select the cells with the mean and standard deviations;
Click Format;
Click Cells;
Click Number;
Select category Number;
Choose 1 or 2 decimal places as appropriate;
Click OK.

Remember that if the standard deviation is less than 33% of the mean then you can call that a small standard deviation..

If you are using standard deviation to compare the spread of data then simply look at the relative percentage values. In this example 21.87% is clearly very much bigger than 9.3%.

Student t-test

Student t-test

This test is the one to use if the data –

- Is unmatched;
- Is at the interval level, ie true measurements such as length, mass, volume;
- Has a minimum sample size of 10 for each data set;
- Has a normal distribution;
- Has similar variances.

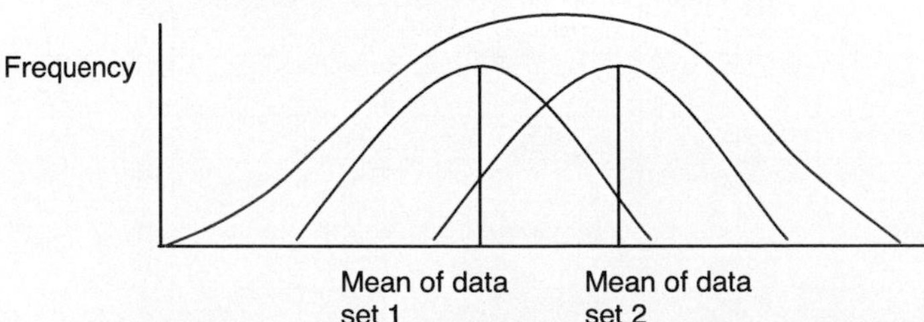
Frequency
Mean of data set 1
Mean of data set 2

Here are two sets of data with different mean values. However is there a significant difference between these means or could the two samples simply come from a single set of data as shown by the red line? The t-test will tell you.

It is a powerful test in that it can distinguish marginal differences between the sets of data, though the smaller the sample size the larger the difference between the means has to be to be detected. A sample size of 10 really is the absolute minimum and ideally you should have 15 or more. There does not need to be the same number of values in each data set. While collecting the data, or after collection, you will need to check the distribution. Use the frequency tally system given earlier. You may be able to exclude obvious outliers in order to obtain a normal distribution.
All you need to know for the theory papers is how to deduce the significance of a calculated value for t.

Lets assume that in an investigation the number of samples in both data sets is 15, and the calculated value for t is 3.42.

Step 1	Method	Example
Calculate the degrees of freedom.	Add the number of values in each data set together and subtract 2	15 + 15 – 2 = 28 Degrees of freedom = 28
Step 2		
Find the critical value for t. The table of critical values is on page 228.	Look on the table of critical values along the row for the degrees of freedom and find the value corresponding to a probability value of 5% or 0.05.	The critical value for 28 degrees of freedom is 2.05
Step 3		
Determine the significance.	Compare the critical value with the calculated value – is it larger or smaller?	The calculated value for t is 3.42. This is bigger than the critical value of 2.05 and so there is a significant difference between the means.

Key points

- Degrees of freedom is the sum of the two sets of data minus 2;
- The critical value is always the 5% or 0.05 value;
- If the calculated value of t is greater than the critical value for t then there is a significant difference between the means.

Correlations

Correlations

Very often it looks as though two variables, V1 and V2, may be linked. For example, light intensity and vegetation density; water temperature and snail movement. Two sets of data can be collected and a scattergraph drawn along with the line of best fit. There may be no correlation, a positive one or a negative one.

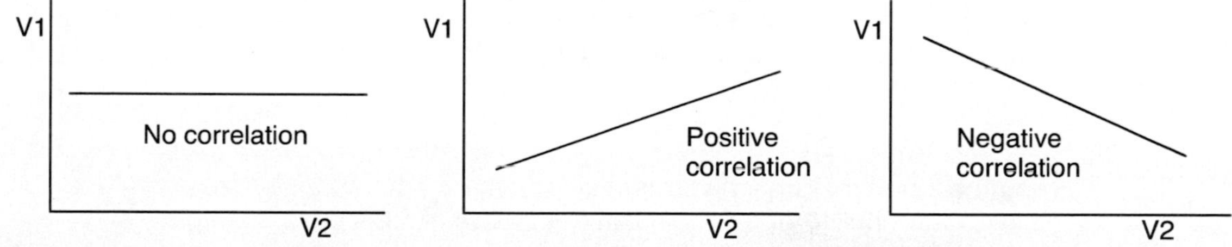
V1
No correlation
V2
V1
Positive correlation
V2
V1
Negative correlation
V2

However the existance of a correlation does not establish that there is a causal relationship between the two variables. In the first example above a positive correlation would seem reasonable since there is more light for photosynthesis. In the second example, even if we found a correlation, we could not be sure that the snail movement was linked to the water temperature as this could have changed some other factor which in turn altered the snail movement. Therefore further experimentation would be required.

What % of the values fall within 1 standard deviation of the mean?

What are the units for standard deviation?

How do you calculate degrees of freedom for the t-test?

Under which % column do you look up the critical value?

Self-Test Quiz on Topic 1

1. A student wanted to find out if there was a significant difference in the surface area of ivy leaves on opposited sides of a wall. She collected 10 leaves from each side and calculated a t value of 1.66. Is there a significant difference?

2. On a holiday to a rocky shore a student noticed that the barnacles on the rocks more exposed to waves looked smaller than those on more sheltered parts of the rocks. She measured the diameter of 26 barnacles at each site and calculated a t value of 2.53. Is there a significant difference?

3a. Students on a tropical ecology course were observing a nest of leaf cutter ants in the rainforest. Trails led into the nest from different directions.

Leaf cutter ants photographed in Honduras by the author.

One student noticed that the leaf samples coming in along one trail seemed smaller than those on a different trail. He collected 30 samples from each trail and calculated a t value of 2.23. Is there a significant difference?

3b. He thought that maybe the ants were different sizes and smaller ants carried smaller leaves. He collected 15 ants from one trail and 12 from the other and calculated a t value of 1.19. Was he right?

3c. Another student suggested that maybe the smaller leaves were thicker and so had the same mass as the larger leaves. She weighed 22 samples from one trail and 19 from the other and calculated a t value of 1.28. Was she right?

4. A student calculated the mean and standard deviation for a set of measurements of light transmission through an extract of anthocyanin, a red plant pigment. She found the mean value was 47% with a standard deviation of 13%. Was she right in stating that the standard deviation was very small?

5. Standard deviation can be applied to a population with a normal distribution. In this case
   a. 68% of the population falls within ± 1 standard deviation of the mean,
   b. 95% of the population falls within ± 1 standard deviation of the mean,
   c. 68% of the population fits under the curve,
   d. 68% of the population falls within ± 2 standard deviation of the mean.

6. Population A has a standard deviation of 2.7 units and population B has a standard deviation of 3.2 units. It can be deduced that
   a. Population A is smaller than population B.
   b. The mean value of population B is greater than the mean value of population A;
   c. Population B shows greater variation than population A;
   d. The sampling procedure used for population A was different from that used for population B.

Topic 2

Cells

Cell Theory

Cell Theory

The cell theory states that -

- Cells are the smallest units of life.
- Living organisms are composed of cells.
- Cells come from pre-existing cells.

Points for discussion

- A cell is a functional unit of cytoplasm surrounded by a membrane and containing genetic material.
- Most multicellular organisms do contain many cells that conform to this cell structure – liver, pancreas, nerve, leucocytes; palisade, epidermal, cortex.
  - Skeletal muscle tissue and many fungi do not have separate cells as the nuclei are spread around in a single mass of cytoplasm.
  - Many plant cells have holes in their walls called plasmodesmata. The plasma membranes and cytoplasm of adjacent cells are continuous through these holes. This makes some plant tissues similar to muscle tissue and fungi in that a single mass of cytoplasm has several nuclei.
  - Mature red blood cells in humans do not have a nucleus.
  - The water transport cells in plants (xylem) are dead and have lost their end walls.
  - The food transport cells in plants (phloem) have lost their nucleus and the cytoplasm is very changed.
  - Surface skin cells of mammals have lost their cytoplasm and nucleus.
  - Hair, nails, feathers, bone, cartilage, waxy cuticle are not cells but are made by cells.
- We could therefore say that organisms are made up of cells and modified cells and cell products.
- Some organisms, bacteria and unicells, (also called acellular, meaning 'without cells') consist of a single cell that carries out all the functions of living.
- This has led to a modification of the cell theory called the **organismal theory**.
- A jar of jam left unopened will stay good for years, but if it is left open for a short while fungi soon start to grow on its surface. This shows that life will not spontaneously appear in the jam.

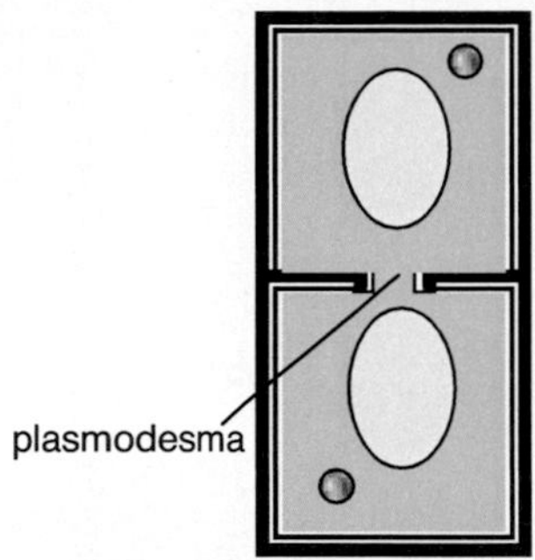
plasmodesma

Unicellular organisms carry out all the functions of life –

- metabolism;
- response;
- homeostasis;
- growth;
- reproduction,
- nutrition.

What do you understand by the cell theory?

What do you understand by the organismal theory?

Size Units and Relative Sizes

Size Units and Relative Sizes

You need to know the relative units. Start with 1 metre and go down 1000, or 10^{-3}, each time.

10^{-3} of a metre = a **millimetre** or **mm**.
10^{-6} of a metre or 10^{-3} of a millimetre = a **micrometre** or **μm**.
10^{-9} of a metre or 10^{-6} of a millimetre or 10^{-3} of a micrometre = a **nanometre** or **nm**.

Relative Sizes

Molecules	Membrane thickness	Viruses	Bacteria	Organelles	Cells
1nm	10nm	100nm	1μm	Upto 10μm	Upto 100μm

Calculating Magnification

Magnification

A scale bar is a short line usually drawn on an electron micrograph that will allow you to calculate the magnification of the photograph. An example is shown on the right.

Using a scale bar to calculate magnification. (See photo on right.)

1. Measure the scale bar on the photograph in mm with your ruler.
   15mm
2. Convert these mm into the same units as the scale bar using the information above.
   15mm = 15000µm
3. Divide this number by the number on the scale bar.
   15000 ÷ 5 = 3000

Therefore magnification = 3000x.

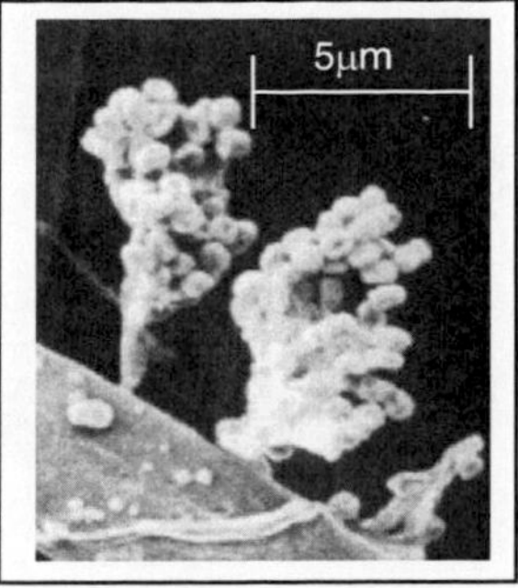
5µm

Determine the magnification of these scale bars. The answers are at the bottom of the page.

a. 2µm

b. 3µm

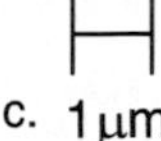

c. 1µm

An alternative is that the electron micrograph states the magnification. From this you can calculate the actual size.

How many micrometres in a millimetre?

22mm = µm

Example.
The 'cell' on the right has been magnified 750x. Calculate its actual size.

1. Measure a dimension of the cell.
   41mm
2. Divide this by the magnification.
   41 ÷ 750 = 0.055mm
3. Convert to a sensible unit.
   0.055mm x 1000 = 55µm

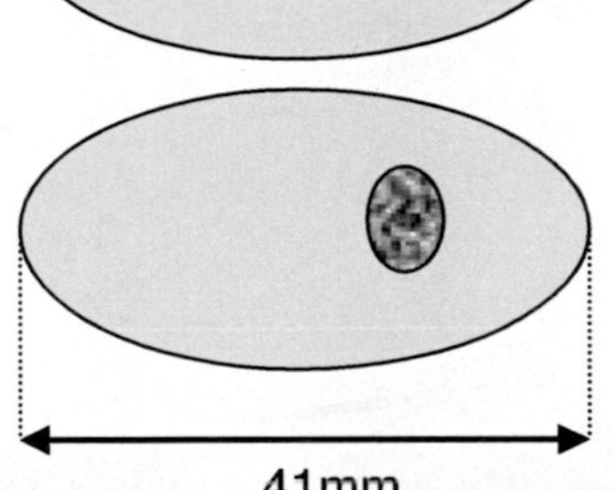

41mm

Calculate the size of these. The answers are at the bottom of the page.

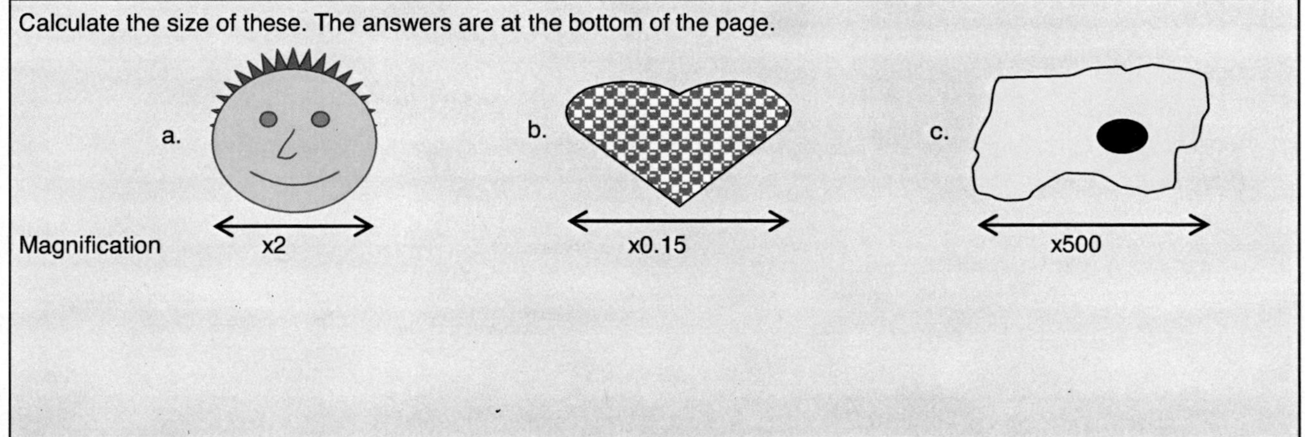
a.
b.
c.
Magnification
x2
x0.15
x500

Answers
a. 11mm b. 200mm c. 62 micrometres

Answers
a. 7500x b. 7000x c. 5000x

Surface Area and Volume

Surface Area to Volume Ratio

Principle

- As an organism increases in size its surface area to volume ratio decreases. This can easily be seen by comparing the following cubes.

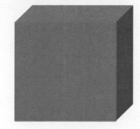

Dimensions	1x1x1
Surface area	$6cm^2$
Volume	$1cm^3$
SA :V ratio	6 : 1

Dimensions	2x2x2
Surface area	$24cm^2$
Volume	$8cm^3$
SA :V ratio	3 : 1

Dimensions	3x3x3
Surface area	$54cm^2$
Volume	$27cm^3$
SA :V ratio	2 : 1

The metabolism of a cell is linked to its mass:volume ratio, whereas it is the surface area that provides the exchange surface for heat and substances. The more cytoplasm the more heat and waste products generated, and the greater the demand for oxygen and nutrients. However the models above show that the relative surface area decreases as the 'organism' gets bigger. Thus organisms and cells develop strategies to cope with this problem. Examples are –

- Plant cells develop a large central vacuole;
- Intestinal cells have microvilli;
- Leaf palisade cells are column shaped;
  - Elephants and the Desert Fox have large ears; the Polar Bear has small ears.
  - The wall of the small intestine is very folded.

Emergent Properties

Emergent Properties

Multicellular organisms show emergent properties.

Emergent properties arise from the interaction of component parts: the whole organism is greater than the sum of its parts. For example an organisms that can carry out temperature homeostasis by using hair or feathers, sweating, changing blood flow, can exploit more habitats than ones that cannot.

Differentiation

Differentiation

Key points

- This means to become different and therefore specialise in a particular function.
- Cells in a multicellular organism are produced by mitosis;
- Hence each cells has all the chromosomes and all the genes;
- Most of these genes will be switched off as they will code for functions that the cell does not do, eg. liver cells will have the genes for eye cells, stomach cells, brain cells etc switched off;
- The genes that are switched on are those associated with 'house-keeping' such as respiraion to keep the cell alive, and those associated with its specialist function.

List the three steps in determining magnification from a scale bar.

1.

2.

3.

Stem Cells

Therapeutic Use of Stem Cells

Stem cells retain the capacity to divide and to have the ability to differentiate along different pathways.

Key points

- Leukemia is a cancer of white blood cells or leukocytes;
- Leukocytes are made in the bone marrow from multipotent adult stem cells;
- The leukocytes are released into the blood stream to fight off infection;
- Leukemia is when these cells grow abnormally;
- Chemotherapy is used to kill all the bone marrow cells, the normal cells as well as the abnormal ones;
- A sample of donor bone marrow containing stem cells is introduced into the patient's blood;
- The stem cells migrate to the bone marrow and start to produce healthy leukocytes.

Prokaryotic Cells

Prokaryotic Cells

Structure	Function
Cell wall	Protection.
Plasma membrane	Controls the transfer of substances in and out of the cell.
Cytoplasm	Site of metabolic activities.
Plasmid	Small rings of DNA.
Ribosomes	Site of protein synthesis.
Nucleoid	Contains naked DNA which is the store of genetic information.
Pili	Short hair-like structures which can be changed in length; Used for - • adhering to surfaces and other bacteria; • exchanging DNA with other bacteria during conjugation.
Flagella	Long threads used for swimming, which requires energy.

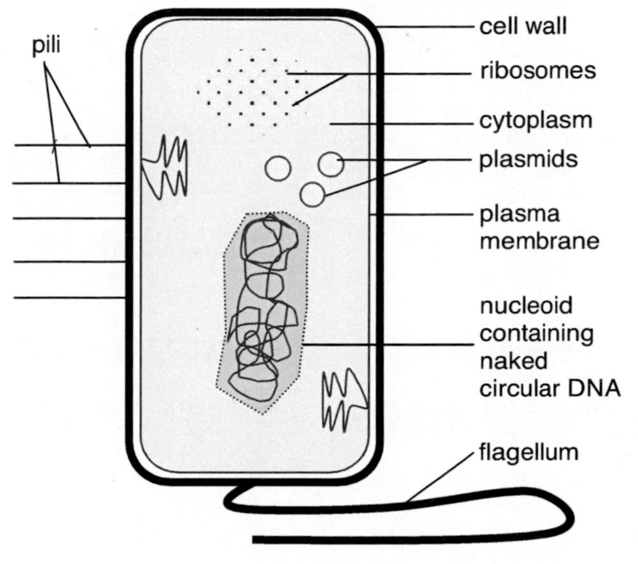
pili
cell wall
ribosomes
cytoplasm
plasmids
plasma membrane
nucleoid containing naked circular DNA
flagellum

Example – *Escherichia coli or E. coli*

Electron micrographs of prokaryotic cells are shown in Appendix 4 on p119.

Prokaryotic cells divide by binary fission.

Name 3 cell types that do not fit the description of a typical cell.

How many nanometres in a micrometre?

How many micrometres in a millimetre?

How many nanometres in a millimetre?

Eukaryotic Cells

Eukaryotic Animal Cell

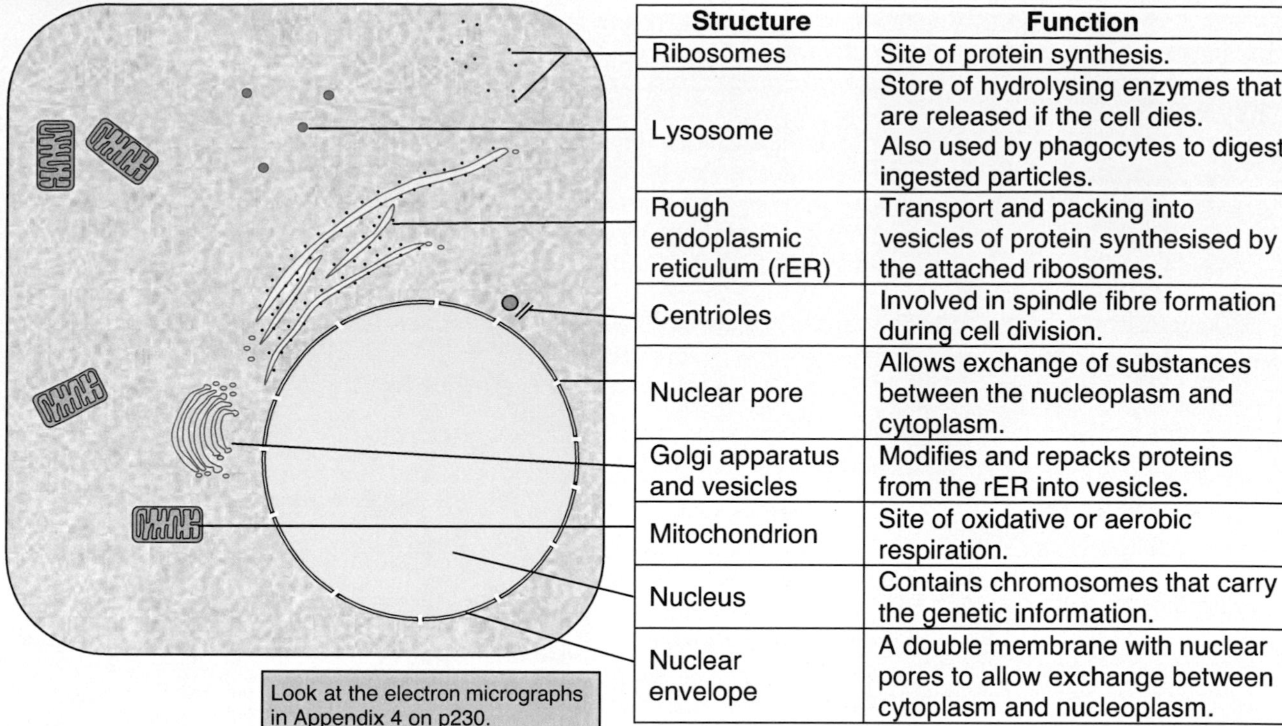

Structure	Function
Ribosomes	Site of protein synthesis.
Lysosome	Store of hydrolysing enzymes that are released if the cell dies. Also used by phagocytes to digest ingested particles.
Rough endoplasmic reticulum (rER)	Transport and packing into vesicles of protein synthesised by the attached ribosomes.
Centrioles	Involved in spindle fibre formation during cell division.
Nuclear pore	Allows exchange of substances between the nucleoplasm and cytoplasm.
Golgi apparatus and vesicles	Modifies and repacks proteins from the rER into vesicles.
Mitochondrion	Site of oxidative or aerobic respiration.
Nucleus	Contains chromosomes that carry the genetic information.
Nuclear envelope	A double membrane with nuclear pores to allow exchange between cytoplasm and nucleoplasm.

Look at the electron micrographs in Appendix 4 on p230.

Prokaryotic and Eukaryotic Cells

Comparing Prokaryotic and Eukaryotic Cells

Prokaryotic Cell	Eukaryotic Cell
Naked DNA.	DNA wrapped around proteins.
DNA in cytoplasm.	DNA enclosed by a nuclear envelope.
DNA circular.	DNA linear.
No membrane bound structures.	Membrane bound structures such as mitochondria, endoplasmic reticulum and Golgi apparatus present which compartmentalize functions.
Plasmids present.	No plasmids.
Ribosomes smaller (70S).	Ribosomes larger (80S).

Plant and Animal Cells

Differences between Plant and Animal Cells

Plant Cells	Animal Cells
Cellulose cell wall.	No cellulose cell wall.
Mature cells usually contain a large central vacuole	No large central vacuole but small vacuoles may be present in the cytoplasm.
No cholesterol in the plasma membrane.	Cholesterol in the plasma membrane.
No centrioles.	Centrioles present.
Store starch.	Store glycogen.
May contain chloroplasts.	Never contain chloroplasts.

Extracellular Components

Extracellular Components

Plant Cells	Animal Cells
The cellulose cell wall - ▪ Maintains shape; ▪ Prevents excessive water uptake by osmosis; ▪ Supports plant against force of gravity.	Secreted glycoproteins form the extra-cellular matrix which functions in – ▪ Support – bone and cartilage cells are embedded in the matrix; ▪ Adhesion – skin cells sit on a sheet of proteoglycan (protein + polysaccharide); ▪ Movement.

Plasma Membrane

Membranes

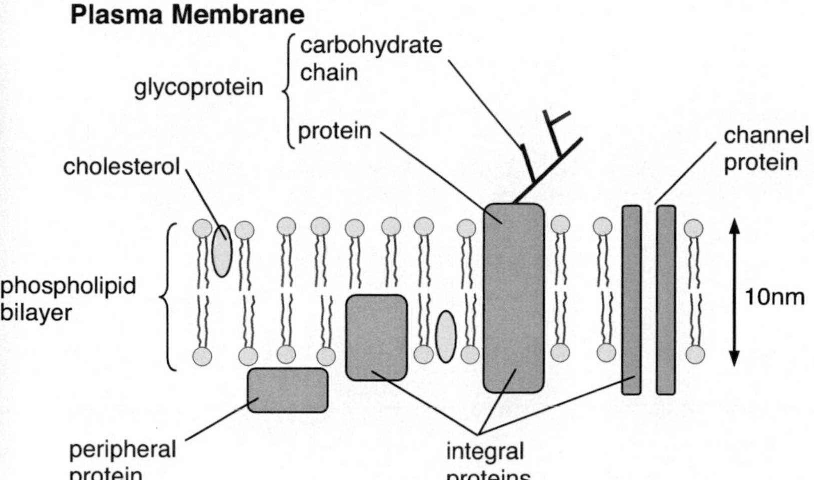

glycoprotein
carbohydrate chain
protein
cholesterol
channel protein
phospholipid bilayer
10nm
peripheral protein
integral proteins

Functions of membrane proteins
• Hormone receptor } can be glycoproteins • Active transport • Diffusion channel • Electron carrier • Immobilised enzymes • Cell adhesion • Cell-to-cell communication

Hydro means water; phobic means hate; philic means like (think phi**<u>lic</u>** and **<u>lik</u>**e)
Look at the simple diagram below.

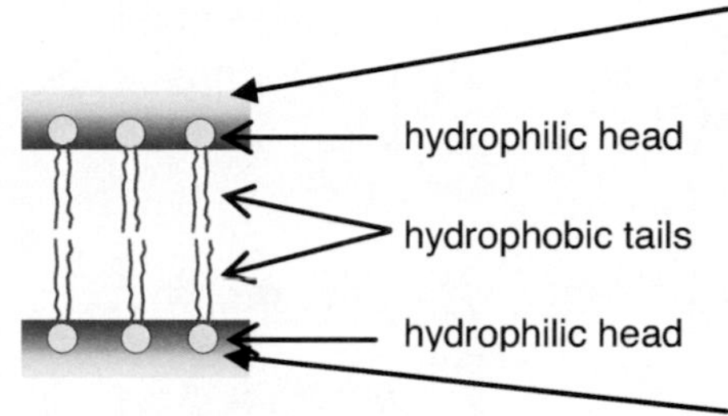

Water based environment eg blood, tissue fluid, river.
hydrophilic head
hydrophobic tails
hydrophilic head
Water based cytoplasm

The more saturated the tails the less flexible the membrane; (See page 30 for information about saturated and unsaturated fatty acids).
Cholesterol also reduces flexibility.

Key points

- There is always a water solution on each side of a membrane and so there must be a hydro<u>philic</u> part next to the solution.
- If there was only one phospholipid molecule then the hydrophobic tails would be next to water.
- The hydrophilic part will always want to remain in contact with the water solution due to the hydrogen bonds which form between the head and water molecules.
- The hydrophobic tails will want to remain in contact with each other due to the hydrophobic interactions and therefore form a lipid bilayer.
- The major force causing the formation of the bilayer is the hydrophobic interaction.

Simple Diffusion and Facilitated Diffusion

Diffusion

Key facts

- Passive, therefore no energy from ATP is used.
- The substance always moves from a high concentration to a low concentration using molecular kinetic energy.
- A membrane is not essential.

Define diffusion.

Many substances move through air and liquids such as cytoplasm, blood and tissue fluid by diffusion.
Some substances such as water, urea, lipids and steroid hormones can diffuse through the phospholipid bilayer of membranes. (It does sound odd that water can given that the core of the membrane is hydrophobic, but it is slow).
Other substances cannot pass through the phospholipid bilayer and so have to pass through protein channels that have a hydrophilic core. This is called **facilitated diffusion**. (To facilitate means to make easier). The channels are specific and so have a binding site for the transported substance.
Sometimes these channels are gated to control the flow of the particular substance.
Neurons contain both open and gated facilitated channels. (See page 100).

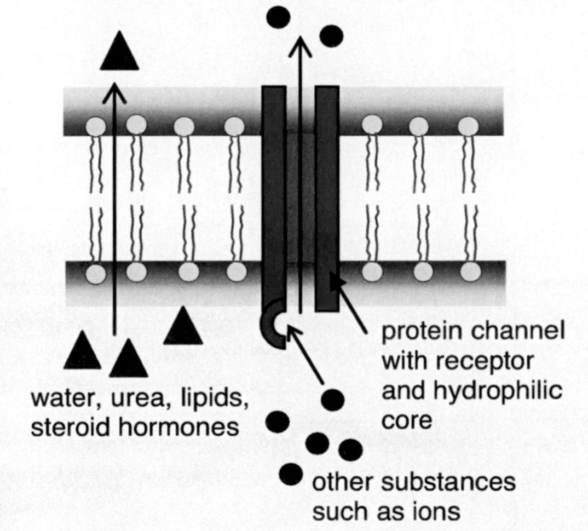

protein channel with receptor and hydrophilic core
water, urea, lipids, steroid hormones
other substances such as ions

Osmosis

Osmosis

Key Facts
- Diffusion of water.
- Passive, therefore no energy is used.
- The water always moves from a high concentration of water (lower solute concentration) to a lower concentration of water (higher solute concentration).
- A membrane is essential.
- Water moves only by osmosis/diffusion, never by active transport.

Active Transport

Active Transport

Key facts
- Always uses energy from ATP.
- ATP hydrolysed to ADP + Pi.
- Transports against a concentration gradient.
- Requires an integral protein transporter in the membrane.
- Transport of substance requires a change in shape of the protein.
- The protein transporter has a specific binding site for the transported substance.
- Some pumps transport two substances, either in the same direction (symport)or in opposite directions (antiport). An example of a symport is the Na^+:K^+:Cl^- pump in the kidney – see page 208. An example of an antiport is the Na^+:K^+ pump in neurons – see pages 99 - 100.

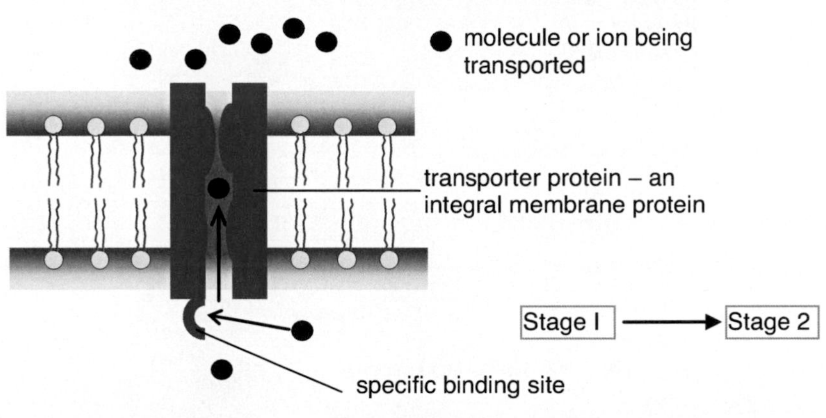
molecule or ion being transported
transporter protein – an integral membrane protein
specific binding site
Stage I
Stage 2

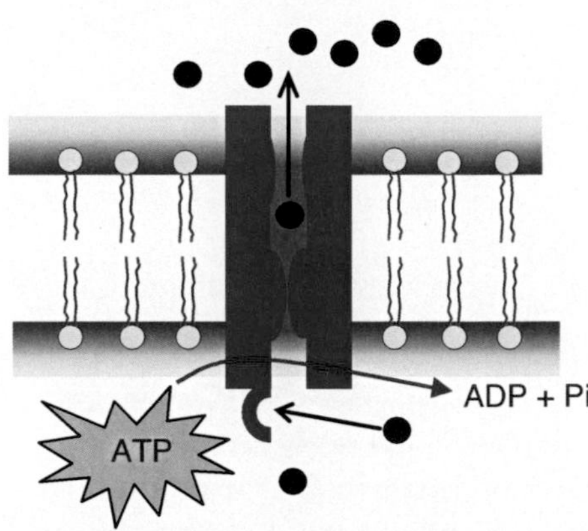
ADP + Pi
ATP

Define osmosis.

List three differences between plant and animal cells.

List five functions of membrane proteins.

What is the name given to a membrane protein that is combined with a carbohydrate?

Where is cholesterol found in a membrane?

What does hydrophobic mean?

What is the name given to proteins that sit on the surface of the membrane?

Endocytosis and Exocytosis

Endocytosis and Exocytosis

Key facts

- Phagocytosis takes in particles.
- Pinocytosis takes in solution.
- Phagocytosis and pinocytosis are both forms of endocytosis.
- Energy from ATP is required.
- In endocytosis the plasma membrane folds inwards to form a vesicle which buds off.
- Exocytosis removes substances from the cell. This includes secretion.
- In exocytosis a vesicle in the cytoplasm joins to the plasma membrane.

Transport Vesicles

Transport
Vesicles

Key facts

- Vesicles bud off rER;
- Vesicles move through cytoplasm and join onto one side of the Golgi apparatus;
- Vesicles bud off other side of Golgi apparatus;
- Vesicle may move to plasma membrane for secretion of contents;
- Vesicle may remain in cytoplasm as a lysosome and fuse with a phagocytic vesicle.

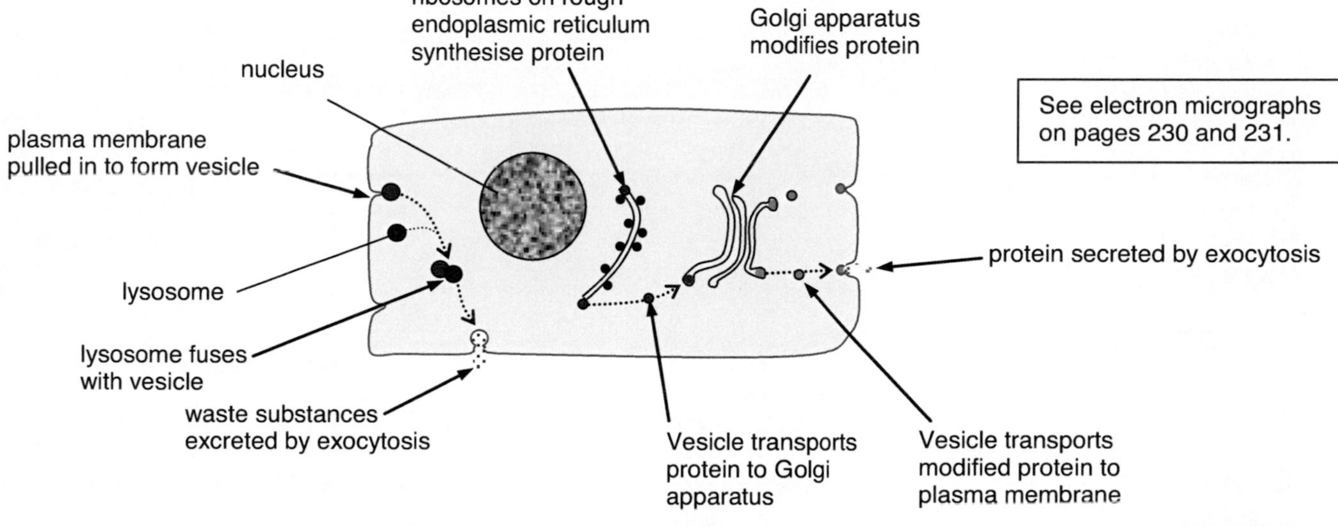
ribosomes on rough endoplasmic reticulum synthesise protein
Golgi apparatus modifies protein
nucleus
plasma membrane pulled in to form vesicle
protein secreted by exocytosis
lysosome
lysosome fuses with vesicle
waste substances excreted by exocytosis
Vesicle transports protein to Golgi apparatus
Vesicle transports modified protein to plasma membrane

See electron micrographs on pages 230 and 231.

Membrane Fluidity

Membrane Fluidity

Key facts

- The phospholipids are held together by mutual attraction and not by chemical bonds;
- The hydrophobic tails are flexible;
- This allows the membrane to bend easily, break and rejoin;
- Unsaturated fatty acid chains make a membrane more fluid;
- Cholesterol makes a membrane less fluid by reducing the movement of the hydrophobic tails.

Revision Prokaryotic Cells

Complete the 4 shaded boxes.

Structure	Function
Pili	
	Locomotion.
	Protein synthesis.
	Store of genetic information.

Revision Organelles and Functions

Complete the 6 shaded boxes.

Structure	Function
Nucleus	
	Site of protein synthesis.
	Stores hydrolysing enzymes; Digests ingested particles.
Golgi apparatus	
	Transport and packing into vesicles of synthesised protein.
Mitochondrion	

Revision Transport

Complete the 8 shaded boxes of key features for each of the three types of transport.

Diffusion	Osmosis	Active transport
With the concentration gradient.		
	Transports water.	
		Requires a membrane
	Does not require ATP.	

Revision Prokaryotic and Eukaryotic Cells

Complete the 9 shaded boxes below.

Feature	Prokaryotic cell	Eukaryotic cell
DNA	Enclosed in envelope or not enclosed?	Enclosed in envelope or not enclosed?
DNA	Naked.	
DNA	Circular or linear?	Circular or linear?
Mitochondria	Present or Absent?	Present or Absent?
Size of ribosomes		

One route for vesicles in a cell is from the .... to the .... and then to the plasma membrane.

The Cell Cycle

The Cell Cycle

The cell division cycle consists of
- ⇒ Interphase – G_1, S and G_2,
- ⇒ mitosis or M phase,
- ⇒ cytokinesis.

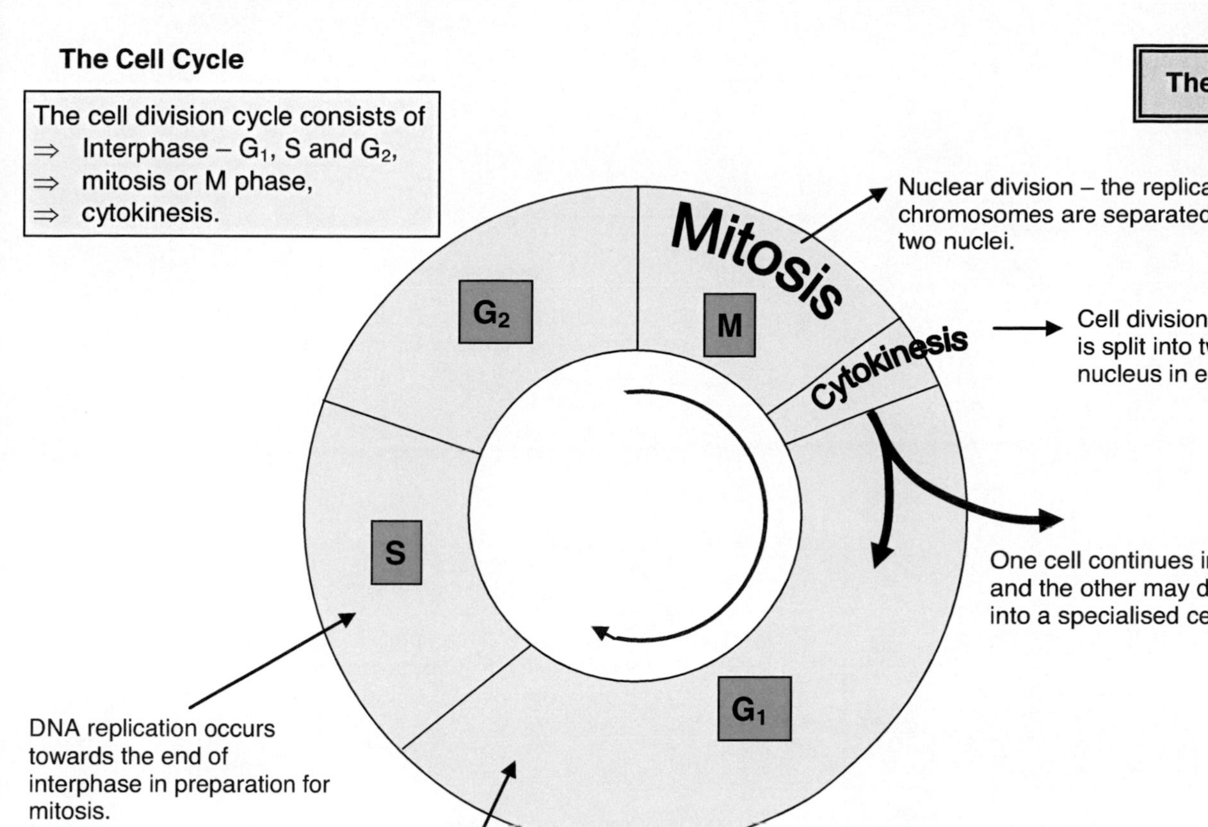

Mitosis
Nuclear division – the replicated chromosomes are separated into two nuclei.
Cytokinesis
Cell division – the cell is split into two, one nucleus in each part.
One cell continues in the cycle and the other may differentiate into a specialised cell.
G2
M
S
G1
DNA replication occurs towards the end of interphase in preparation for mitosis.

Cell activities –
- transcription;
- translation;
- synthesis of other molecules.

Interphase is divided into 3 subphases –
- **G_1** (Gap 1) – longest phase; synthesis of biochemicals (protein, mRNA, tRNA); replication of organelles;
- **S** (Synthesis) – DNA replication;
- **G_2** (Gap 2) – synthesis of microtubule components; centrioles in animals cells replicate; mitochondria and chloroplasts replicate.

Interphase is an active period in the life of a cell when many metabolic reactions occur, including protein synthesis, DNA replication and an increase in the number of mitochondria and chloroplasts.

Mitosis

Mitosis

Phase	Key points
Prophase	• Replicated DNA undergoes supercoiling (multiple coiling) and becomes visible under the light microscope; • Spindle microtubules start to form; • Nuclear envelope breaks down.
Metaphase	• Chromosomes move to central plate (equator) of cell; • Microtubule network completed; • Microtubules attach to centromeres.
Anaphase	• Centromeres split; • Microtubules contract; • Chromosomes pulled to opposite poles.
Telophase	• Chromosomes uncoil; • Spindle microtubules break down; • Nuclear envelope reforms. (*This is effectively the opposite of prophase*)

Note –
There are three key points for each phase.

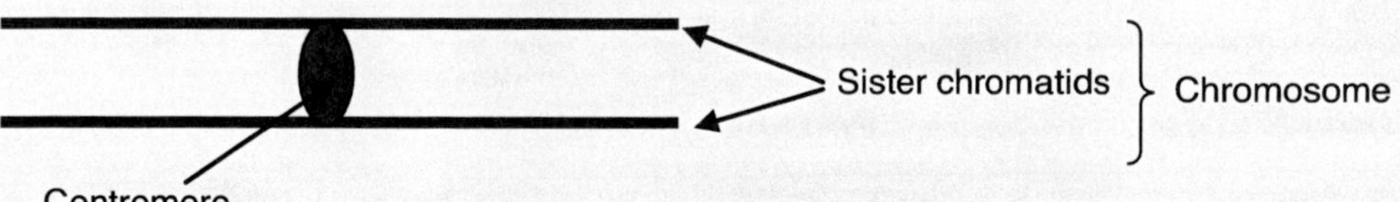

Sister chromatids
Chromosome
Centromere

Note –
The two DNA molecules formed by replication are called sister chromatids until the centromere splits at the start of anaphase. After this they are individual chromosomes.

Cell with one pair of chromosomes at interphase

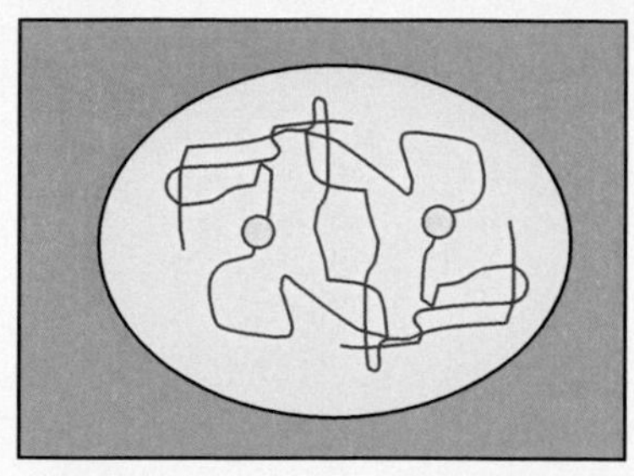

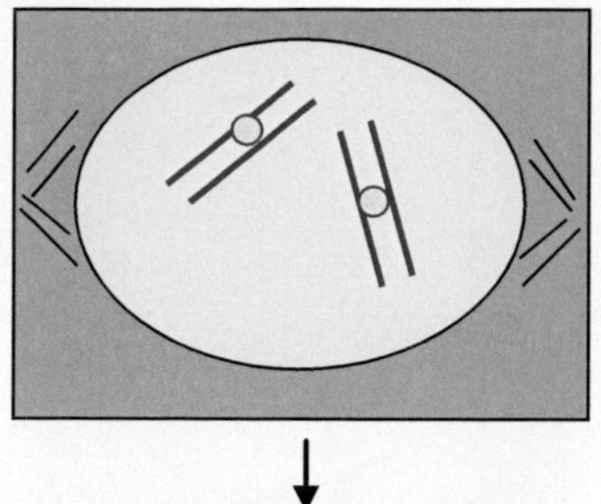

Prophase

⇒ Replicated DNA undergoes supercoiling and becomes visible under the light microscope;

⇒ Spindle microtubules start to form (from centrioles in animal cells);

⇒ Nuclear envelope breaks down.

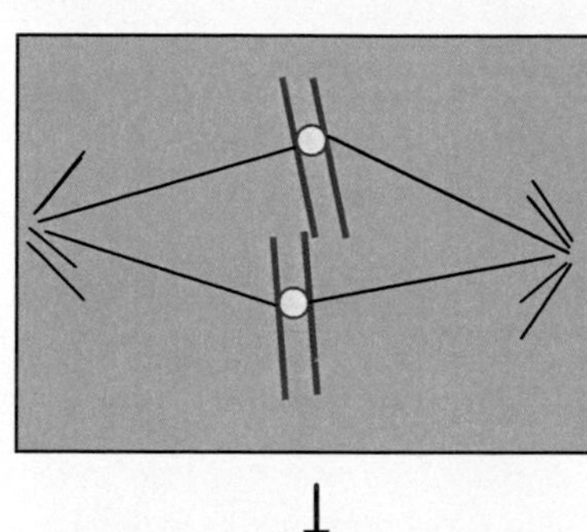

Metaphase

⇒ Microtubule network completed;

⇒ Microtubules attach to centromeres;

⇒ Chromosomes move to central plate (equator) of cell.

Remember – There are three key points for each phase.

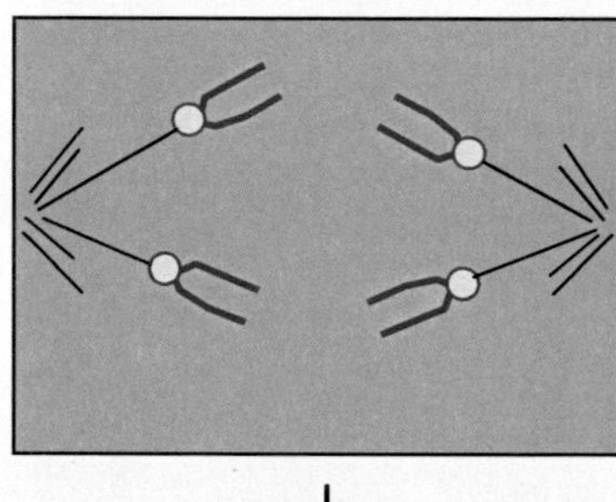

Anaphase

⇒ Centromeres split;

⇒ Microtubules contract;

⇒ Chromosomes pulled to opposite poles.

A chromosome consists of a pair of sister chromatids, but as soon as the centromere splits the chromatids become chromosomes.

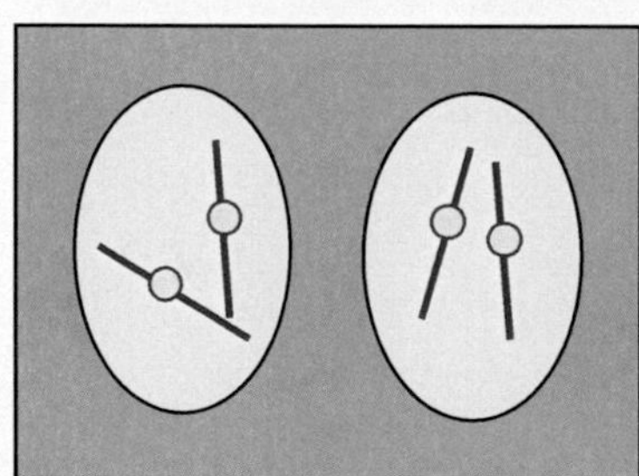

Telophase

⇒ Chromosomes uncoil;

⇒ Spindle microtubules break down;

⇒ Nuclear envelope reforms.

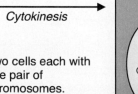

Cytokinesis

Two cells each with one pair of chromosomes.

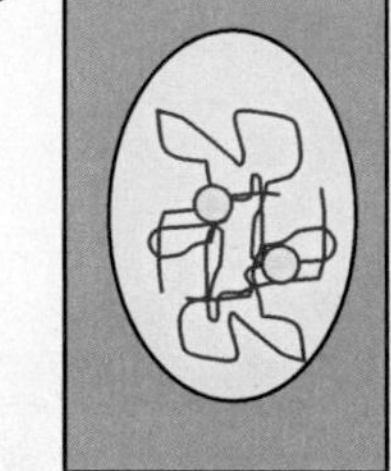

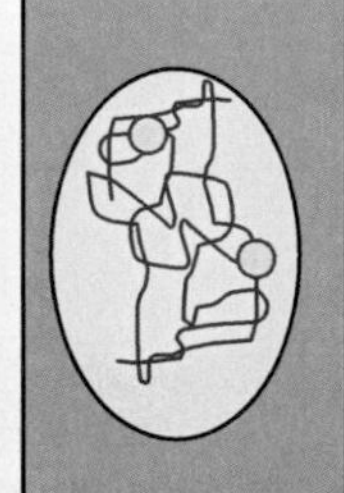

Mitosis is involved in –

- Asexual reproduction;
- Embryonic development;
- Growth;
- Tissue repair.

Tumours are caused by uncontrolled cell division. They can occur in any tissue or organ of both plants and animals.

Producing Identical Nuclei

Producing
Identical Nuclei

Key steps

- DNA produces exact copies – sister chromatids;
- Aligning at metaphase.

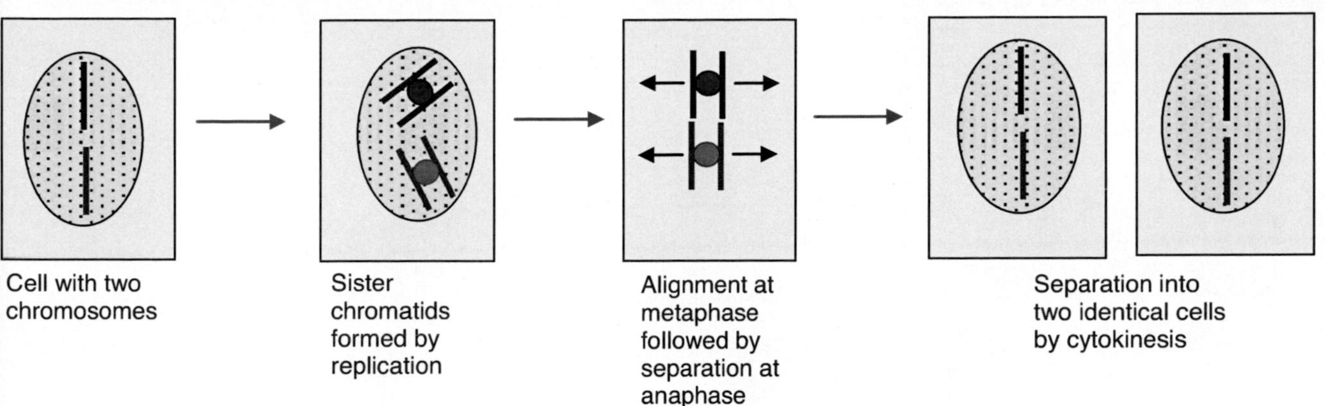

Cell with two chromosomes

Sister chromatids formed by replication

Alignment at metaphase followed by separation at anaphase

Separation into two identical cells by cytokinesis

The sequence above shows how the process of mitosis produces identical nuclei.

List the sequence of phases in mitosis.

Name the phase after mitosis when the cell divides into two.

What structures attach to the centromere?

List the sequence of subphases in interphase.

Label the diagram.

.... } ....

....

Complete the three boxes.

Phase	Description
G_1	
S	
G_2	

Revision
Mitosis

Use these blank boxes to practise your drawings and labels.

Drawing	Name of stage	Key points
	Prophase	1. Supercoiling of DNA. 2. 3.
		1. 2. 3.
		1. 2. 3.
	Telophase	1. Chromosomes uncoil. 2. 3.

Self-Test Quiz on Topic 2

1. The cell theory states that
   a. living organisms are composed of cells,
   b. cells come from pre-existing cells,
   c. cells are the smallest unit of life,
   d. all of the above.

2. The 'cell' drawn below has been magnified 500x. What is its actual diameter?
   a. 100μm,
   b. 50μm,
   c. 25μm,
   d. 500μm.

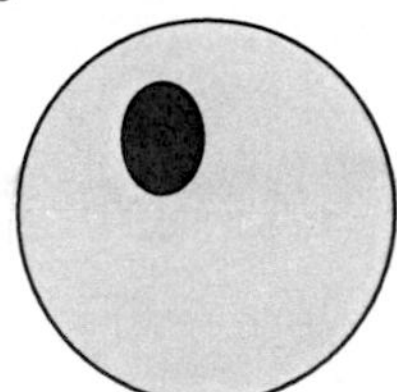

3. Which line in the table is correct?

	Molecules	Membrane thickness	Viruses	Bacteria	Organelles	Cells
a.	1μm	10nm	1μm	Upto 10μm	10nm	Upto 100μm
b.	10nm	1μm	100nm	100nm	Upto 10μm	Upto 100μm
c.	1nm	10nm	Upto 10μm	1μm	Upto 100μm	100nm
d.	1nm	10nm	100nm	1μm	Upto 10μm	Upto 100μm

4. A description of emergent properties could include
   a. cell growth is in an outward direction,
   b. germinating seeds emerge above the soil,
   c. stem cells emerge by differentiating into specialised cells,
   d. specialised groups of cells interact to form a functional unit better than the individual cells.

5. The diagram below shows part of a cell membrane. Which molecule is an integral protein?
   a. One
   b. Two
   c. Three
   d. Four.

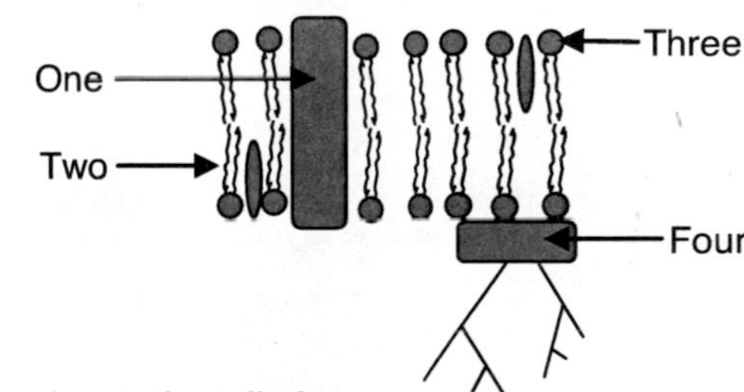
One
Two
Three
Four

6. A characteristic of both prokaryotic and eukaryotic cells is
   a. possession of a nucleus,
   b. circular DNA molecules in the cytoplasm,
   c. ribosomes in the cytoplasm,
   d. presence of membranous cytoplasmic organelles.

7. The main molecules forming membranes are
   a. phospholipids and proteins,
   b. lipids and polysaccharides,
   c. carbohydrates and lipids,
   d. lipids.

8. The diagram below shows part of a cell membrane. Which molecule is a glycoprotein?
   a. One
   b. Two
   c. Three
   d. Four.

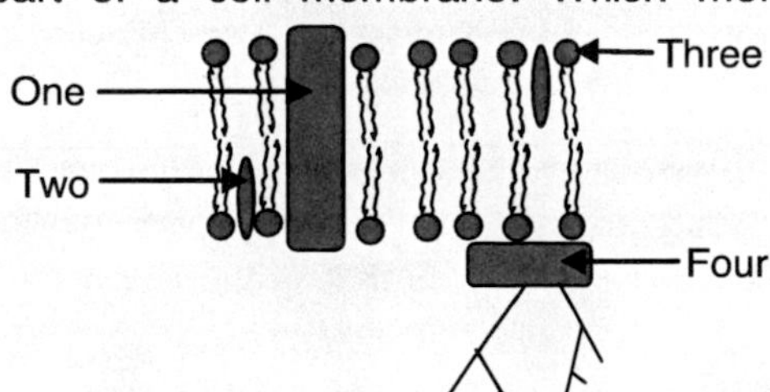
One
Two
Three
Four

9. Which of the following statements is correct?
   a. Active transport uses energy from ATP to transfer molecules across a membrane against a concentration gradient.
   b. Diffusion is the movement of water from a concentrated solution to a weak solution.
   c. Osmosis requires energy from ATP.
   d. Molecules can only diffuse across a membrane.

10. Which of the following statements is correct?
   a. A phospholipid has hydrophobic regions at both ends of the molecule.
   b. A membrane is made up of two layers of protein with a hydrophobic core.
   c. Proteins embedded in a membrane can act as transport channels.
   d. The presence of cholesterol in a membrane is harmful.

11. The scale bar shows a magnification of
   a. x400,
   b. x4000,
   c. x20,
   d. x1000.

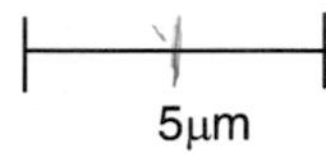
5μm

12. Which is the best description of vesicle movement within a cell?
   a. from the plasma membrane to the Golgi apparatus,
   b. from the Golgi apparatus to the rER,
   c. from the plasma membrane to the rER,
   d. from the rER to the Golgi apparatus.

13. Facilitated diffusion means
   a. The transfer of substances through an integral protein channel in a membrane against a concentration gradient.
   b. Using ATP to facilitate the diffusion of substances from one part of a cell to another.
   c. Using a protein carrier and energy to diffuse substances rapidly down a concentration gradient.
   d. The diffusion of substances through an integral protein channel in a membrane.

14. As a cell increases in size
   a. the surface area to volume ratio decreases,
   b. the surface area to volume ratio increases,
   c. the surface area to volume ratio does not change,
   d. the surface area to volume ratio begins to decrease only after the cell reaches a certain size.

15. A micrometre is
   a. 10^{-6} of a metre,
   b. 10^{-3} of a metre,
   c. 10^{-4} of a millimetre,
   d. twice the size of a nanometre.

16. In a prokaryotic cell the pili
   a. are required for the cell to respire,
   b. are sensory receptors,
   c. are used for locomotion,
   d. are used to attach the cell to other objects.

17. In a prokaryotic cell
   a. the ribosomes are found on the rough endoplasmic reticulum,
   b. the ribosomes are smaller than in the eukaryotic cell,
   c. the lysosomes contain digestive enzymes,
   d. the nucleus contains a single linear molecule of naked DNA.

18. In multicellular organisms cells differentiate because
    a. some of their genes are expressed but not others,
    b. some genes are lost from the nucleus,
    c. not all genes are passed on when the cell reproduces,
    d. the nucleus is lost.

19. Which of the following statements is correct?
    a. Animal cells are round whereas plant cells are square.
    b. Plant cell walls are enclosed in membrane.
    c. Both plant and animal cells have 80S ribosomes.
    d. Animal cells contain more organelles than plant cells.

20. The data in the table below shows the normal concentration of two ions inside and outside the nerve cell of a squid.

	Concentration / mmoles dm^{-3}	
Ions	Inside	Outside
Potassium K^+	0.400	0.020
Chloride Cl^-	0.120	0.560

This information shows that
    a. potassium ions diffuse into nerve cells whereas chloride ions diffuse out,
    b. osmosis creates diffusion gradients for these two ions,
    c. potassium ions are moved out of the cell by active transport whereas chloride ions are actively moved in.
    d. chloride ions are moved out of the cell by active transport whereas potassium ions are actively moved in.

21. Which of the following events occurs during mitosis?
    a. DNA replication,
    b. replication of organelles,
    c. Splitting of the centromeres.
    d. Formation of the cell wall.

22. Tumours can occur
    a. in tissues of plants and animals,
    b. in plant tissues only,
    c. in animal tissues only,
    d. in human tissues only.

23. During which phase of mitosis do the replicated DNA molecules get pulled apart?
    a. Prophase.
    b. Metaphase.
    c. Anaphase.
    d. Telophase.

24. During which phase of mitosis do the microtubules attach to the centromere?
    a. Prophase.
    b. Metaphase.
    c. Anaphase.
    d. Telophase.

25. Which is the correct sequence of phases in the cell cycle?
    a. G_1, S, G_2, mitosis, cytokinesis.
    b. G_1, G_2, S, mitosis, cytokinesis.
    c. mitosis, G_1, S, G_2, cytokinesis.
    d. mitosis, G_1, G_2, S, cytokinesis.

Topic 3

The Chemistry of Life

Chemical Elements

Chemical Elements

The most frequently occurring elements in organisms are -
- Carbon,
- Hydrogen,
- Oxygen,
- Nitrogen

Organisms require a variety of other elements including -
- Sulfur,
- Calcium,
- Phosphorus,
- Iron,
- Sodium.

Element	Function		
	Prokaryotes	**Plants**	**Animals**
Sulfur	Proteins	Proteins	Proteins
Calcium	Flagella movement	Forms cell plate during cytokinesis	Shells, bones and teeth; Vescicle fusion to membranes
Phosphorus	Nucleic acids and ATP	Nucleic acids and ATP	Nucleic acids and ATP
Iron	Cytochrome – used in respiration	Cytochromes – used in mitochondrial respiration	Cytochromes – used in mitochondrial respiration; Haemoglobin
Sodium		Main cation in cytoplasm	Transmission of nerve impulses

Water

Water

Key facts

- Water is a polar molecule – it has negative and positive ends (poles);
- The oxygen atom has a slight negative charge;
- The hydrogen atoms each have a slight positive charge;
- The positive and negative charges on different molecules attract each other;
- This attraction forms hydrogen bonds ••••••
- This is called cohesion;
- Water has a high specific heat, ie it can store a large amount of heat;
- The polarity of water allows it to dissolve other polar molecules such as sugars and amino acids;
- Other substances form ions in water and dissolve, eg sodium chloride (salt) forms sodium ions Na^+ and chloride ions Cl^-.

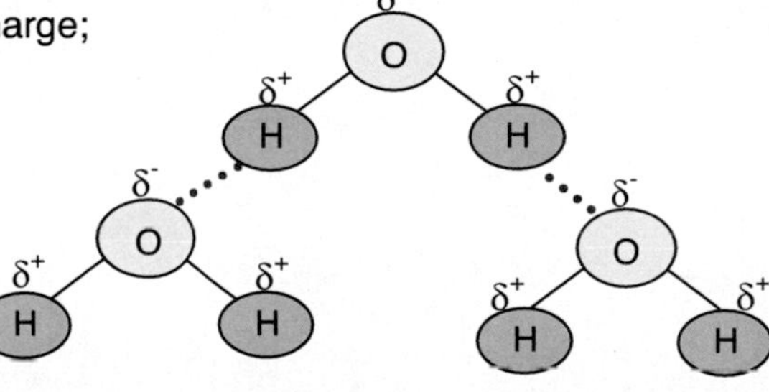

δ-
O
δ+
H
δ+
H
δ-
O
δ+
H
δ+
H
δ-
O
δ+
H
δ+
H

Organisms and Properties of Water

Organisms and Water

Coolant

Property of water
- Water requires a high input of energy to break the hydrogen bonds and turn it from the liquid state to the vapour state.
- Evaporation of water off the surface of an organism allows it to lose heat.

Value to organisms
- Plants in deserts increase transpiration when in danger of over-heating;
- Mammals sweat for thermoregulation.

Medium for Metabolic Reactions

Property of water

- Water is a good <u>solvent</u> due to its polarity.
- <u>Liquid</u> between 0 and 100^0C, the temperatures in most regions of the Earth.

Value to organisms

- Watery habitat dissolves substances that can be absorbed by organisms;
- Watery cytoplasm dissolves substances;
- Metabolic reactions can take place easily between substances dissolved in a liquid medium.

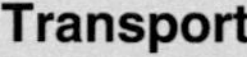

Transport

Property of water

- Water has a <u>high specific heat</u> allowing it to store heat energy.

Value to organisms

- Heat transport – blood can transfer heat from hot regions of the body to cooler regions for temperature regulation.

Property of water

- Water is a good <u>solvent</u> due to its polarity.
- Water is quite a dense medium.

Value to organisms

- Watery habitat dissolves ions that can be absorbed by organism;
- Soluble excretory products eg urea, can be removed;
- Substances can be transported within cells in the cytoplasm;
- Substances can be transported around an organism in its circulatory system;
- The density of water allows it to support large particles, eg blood cells, fat droplets, which are transported by mass flow.

Property of water

- <u>Cohesion</u> - hydrogen bonds link water molecules together;

Value to organisms

- As water molecules evaporate from the surface of a leaf further water molecules are pulled from behind creating the transpiration stream in the xylem. Dissolved substances are transported in the transpiration stream.

Why is water called a polar molecule?

Draw a diagram to show hydrogen bonding between water molecules.

State the four most frequently occurring elements in organisms.

State one role in organisms for –

Calcium

Iron

Sodium

Phosphorus

Sulfur

Give two reasons why the solvent properties of water are of value to organisms.

Explain why water can act as a coolant.

Organic and Inorganic

Organic and Inorganic

- Organic compounds are those that contain carbon and are found in living organisms.
- They do not though include carbonates, hydrogencarbonates and oxides of carbon.

Ribose and Glucose

Identifying Molecules

Ribose and Glucose

Carbon 5 in ribose and carbon 6 in glucose may be shown as CH_2OH.

ribose

Common features -

- Ring structure;
- One carbon is outside the ring;
- Formula $C_nH_{2n}O_n$ where n = 5 for ribose and 6 for glucose;
- Carbon atoms numbered clockwise starting next to the oxygen.
- Last carbon not in ring;
- Each carbon has 4 bonds;
- Each pink bond on a carbon is for an OH or hydroxyl group;
- Each black bond is for a hydrogen.

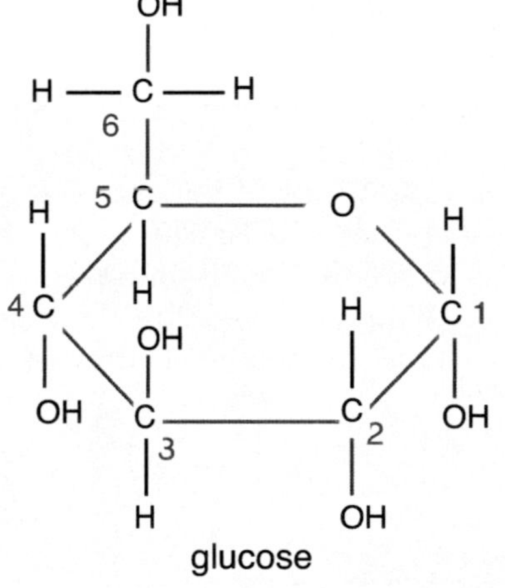
OH
H
C
H
6
5 C
O
H
H
4 C
H
OH
H
C 1
OH
C
C
2
OH
3
H
OH
glucose

Amino Acids

Amino Acids

Key features

- The formula for an amino acid can be written in a variety of ways. Always look for the **nitrogen** as the key atom.
- There are 20 amino acids used in proteins.
- They all have a common part shown in black.
- The **R** group, or side group, is variable and the key to protein function.
- The R group can be neutral, or have a positive or negative charge.
- The R group can be hydrophobic or hydrophilic.

Three different ways of writing the structure of an amino acid.

$NH_2CHRCOOH$

$NH_2-CH(R)-COOH$

Fatty Acids

Fatty Acids

$O{=}C(OH){-}(CH_2)_n{-}CH_3$ HOOC — $(CH_2)_n$ — CH_3 CH_3 — $(CH_2)_n$ — COOH

Three different ways of writing the structure of a fatty acid.

Key features -

- At one end is a CH_3 group;
- At the other end is a COOH or carboxylic acid group;
- In the carboxylic acid group the oxygen is joined to the carbon with a double bond;
- Between these end groups is a variable number of CH or CH_2 groups;
- The number of these intermediate groups is typically between 12 and 22;
- A CH group means there is a double bond between adjacent carbons; $-\overset{|}{\underset{H}{C}}{=}\overset{|}{\underset{H}{C}}-$
- Double bonds mean the fatty acid is unsaturated;
- If there are a large number of double bonds the fatty acid is called polyunsaturated.

Carbohydrates

Carbohydrates

Monosaccharides
Glucose
Galactose
Fructose

Disaccharides
Maltose = glucose + glucose
Lactose = glucose + galactose
Sucrose = glucose + fructose

Polysaccharides
Starch, Glycogen, Cellulose = poly-glucose

Functions in animals -

- **Glucose – broken down in respirationto release energy.**
- **Lactose – sugar in milk produced by mammals.**
- **Glycogen – energy store in liver and skeletal muscles.**

Functions in plants -

- **Fructose – energy source and component of sucrose.**
- **Sucrose – unreactive and so transported around the plant.**
- **Cellulose – main component of cell wall.**

Lipids

Lipids

Functions of Lipids
⇒ Cuticle on leaf to prevent water loss;
⇒ Thermal insulation in animals as sub-cutaneous fat;
⇒ Energy store in plants and animals;
⇒ Oil on fur or feathers for water-proofing;
⇒ Main component of myelin sheath of neurons;
⇒ Buoyancy in aquatic animals as lipids are less dense than water.

Energy Storage

Carbohydrates and Lipids as Energy Stores

Carbohydrates
⇒ 17kJ of energy released per gram;
⇒ Easily built up for storage;
⇒ Easily broken down to release energy quickly;
⇒ Glycogen in animals: starch in plants;
⇒ Both of these converted to glucose when energy required.

Lipids
⇒ 38kJ of energy released per gram – over twice as much;
⇒ hence more efficient as energy store;
⇒ storage efficiency increased because lipids are hydrophobic and less mass is taken up storing water;
⇒ Metabolic pathways to build up and break down more complex and therefore slower;
⇒ Converted to fatty acids and glycerol when energy required;
⇒ Both of these converted to acetyl CoA.

Distinguish between organic and inorganic compounds.

List three examples of - monosaccharides disaccharides polysaccharides.

State one function in animals of - glucose lactose glycogen.

State one function in plants of - fructose sucrose cellulose.

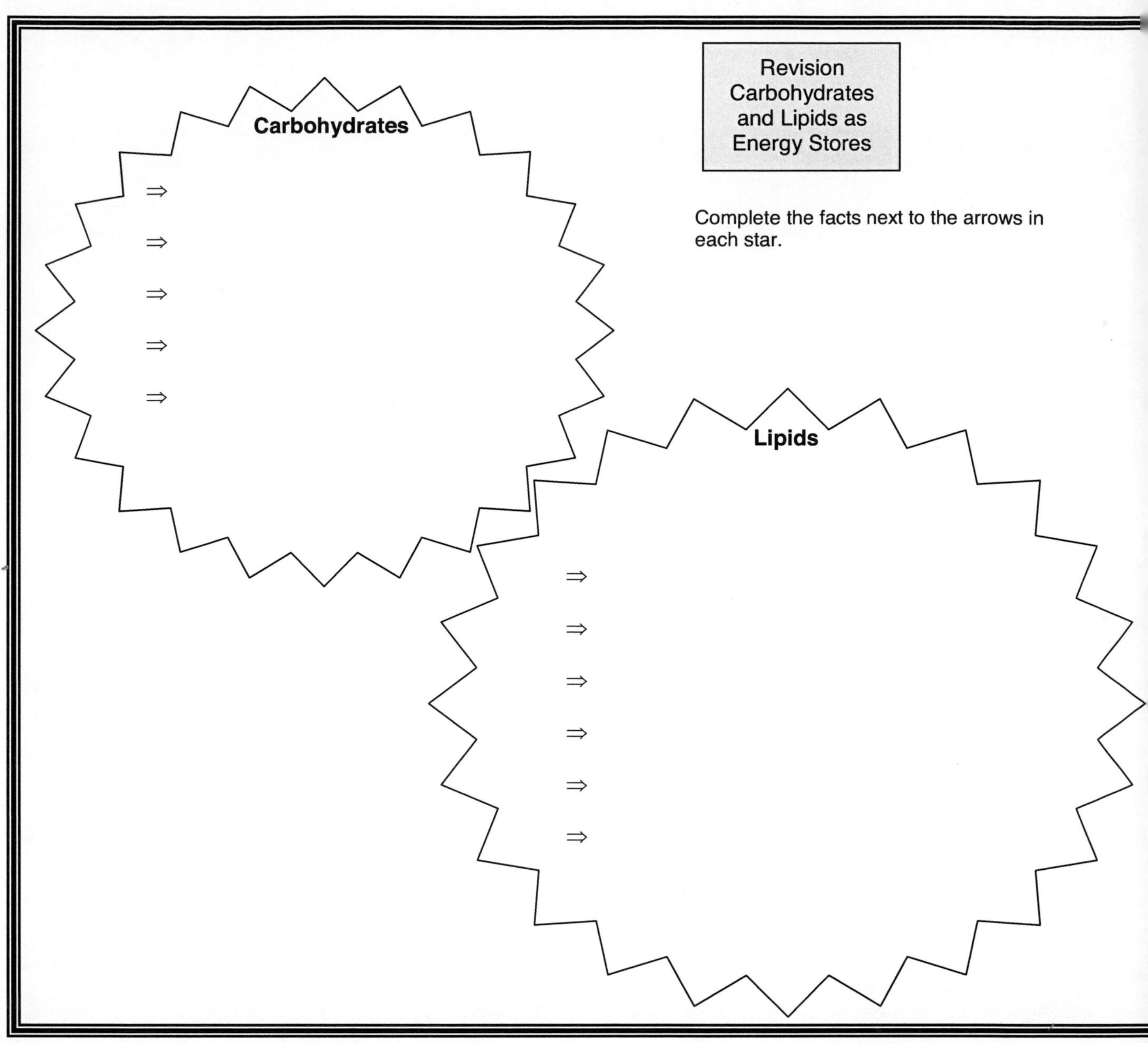
Revision
Carbohydrates
and Lipids as
Energy Stores
Complete the facts next to the arrows in each star.
Carbohydrates
⇒
⇒
⇒
⇒
⇒
Lipids
⇒
⇒
⇒
⇒
⇒
⇒

Draw the general structure of an amino acid.

Draw the general structure of a fatty acid.

State three functions of lipids.

Draw the general structure of ribose.

Draw the general structure of glucose.

Condensation and Hydrolysis

Condensation and Hydrolysis

These two opposite reactions are widespread in biochemistry and function on the same principle.

- In condensation two units are **joined** together with the **release** of water.
- In hydrolysis two units are **separated using** water – remember 'hydro' means water and 'lysis' means to split.

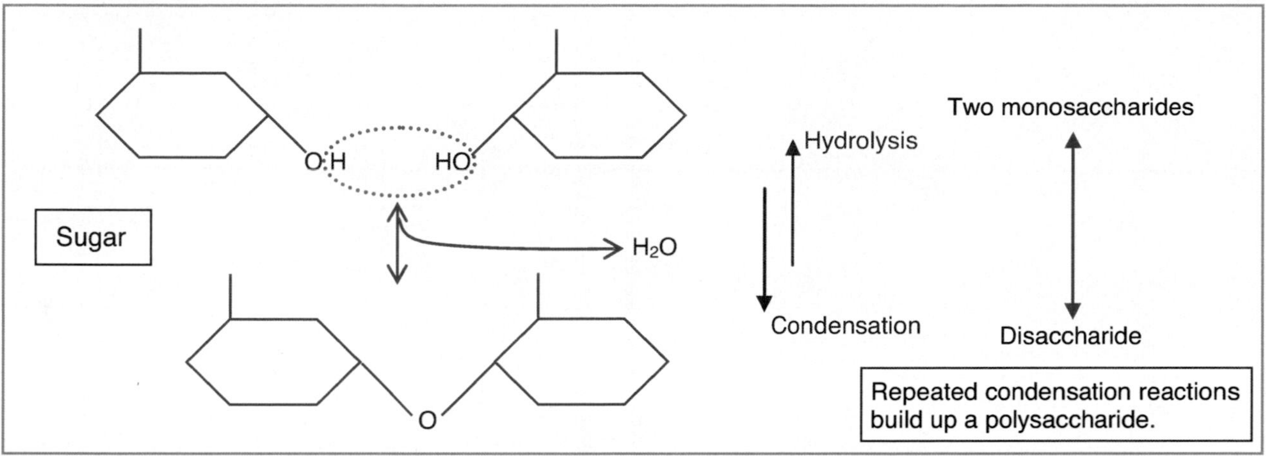

Sugar
O H
HO
H_2O
O
Hydrolysis
Condensation
Two monosaccharides
Disaccharide
Repeated condensation reactions build up a polysaccharide.

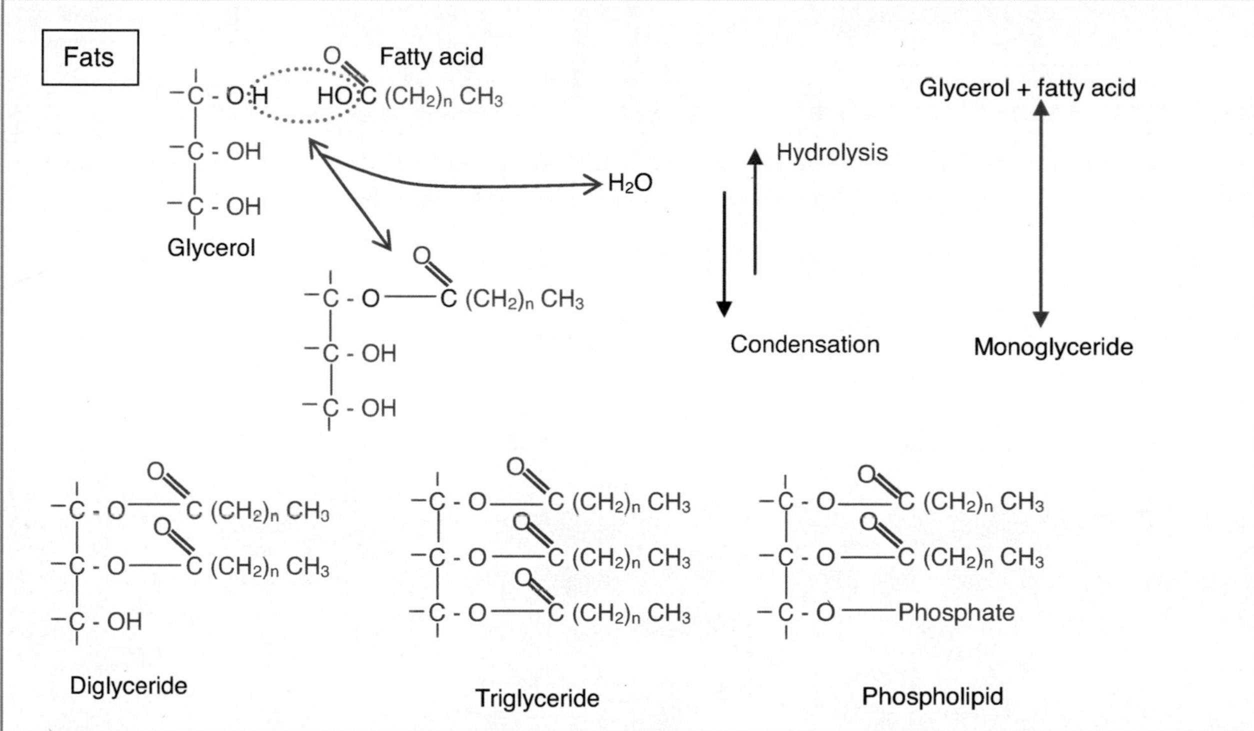

Fats
Fatty acid
-C - OH HO C $(CH_2)_n$ CH_3
-C - OH
-C - OH
Glycerol
H_2O
-C - O — C $(CH_2)_n$ CH_3
-C - OH
-C - OH
Hydrolysis
Condensation
Glycerol + fatty acid
Monoglyceride
Diglyceride
Triglyceride
Phosphate
Phospholipid

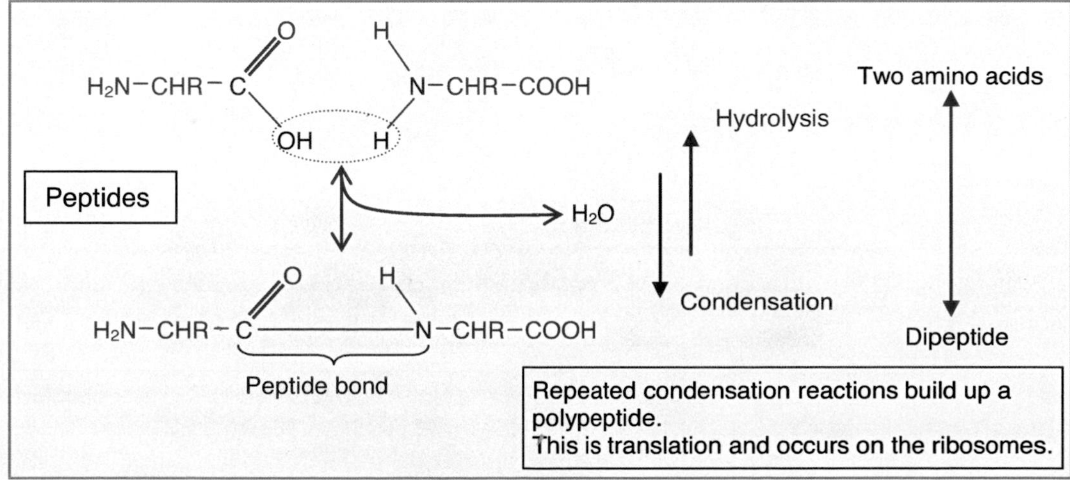

Peptides
H_2N−CHR−C
N−CHR−COOH
OH H
H_2O
Peptide bond
Hydrolysis
Condensation
Two amino acids
Dipeptide
Repeated condensation reactions build up a polypeptide.
This is translation and occurs on the ribosomes.

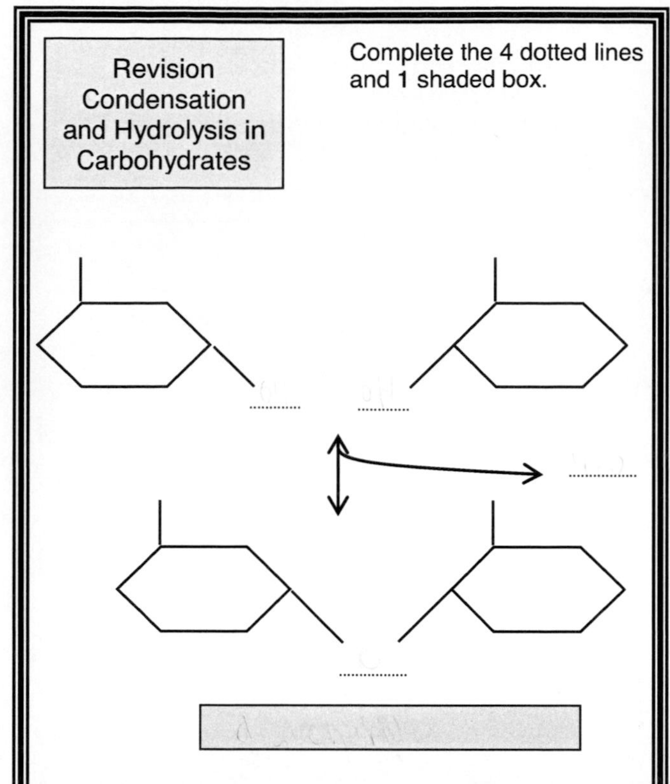

Revision
Condensation
and Hydrolysis in
Carbohydrates
Complete the 4 dotted lines
and 1 shaded box.

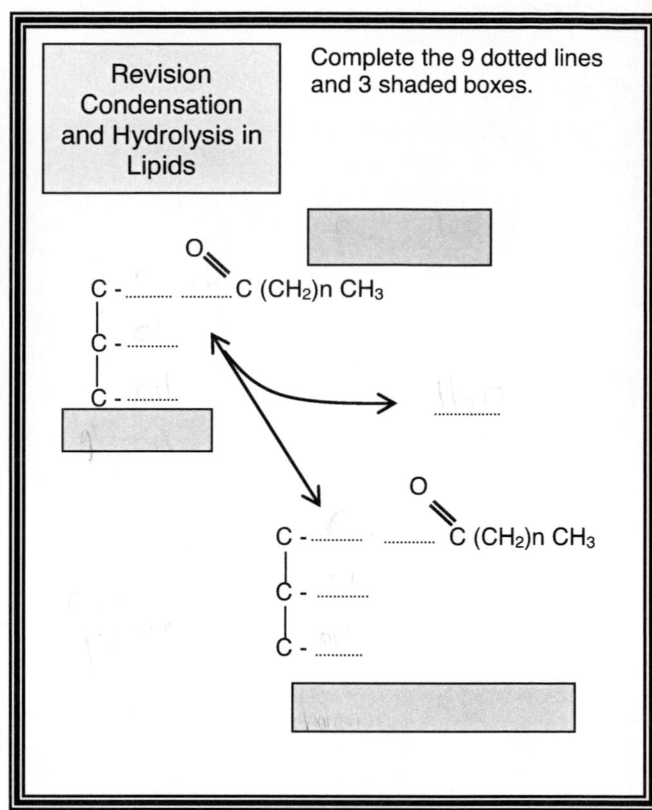

Revision
Condensation
and Hydrolysis in
Lipids
Complete the 9 dotted lines
and 3 shaded boxes.
O
C -
C (CH2)n CH3
C -
C -
O
C -
C (CH2)n CH3
C -
C -

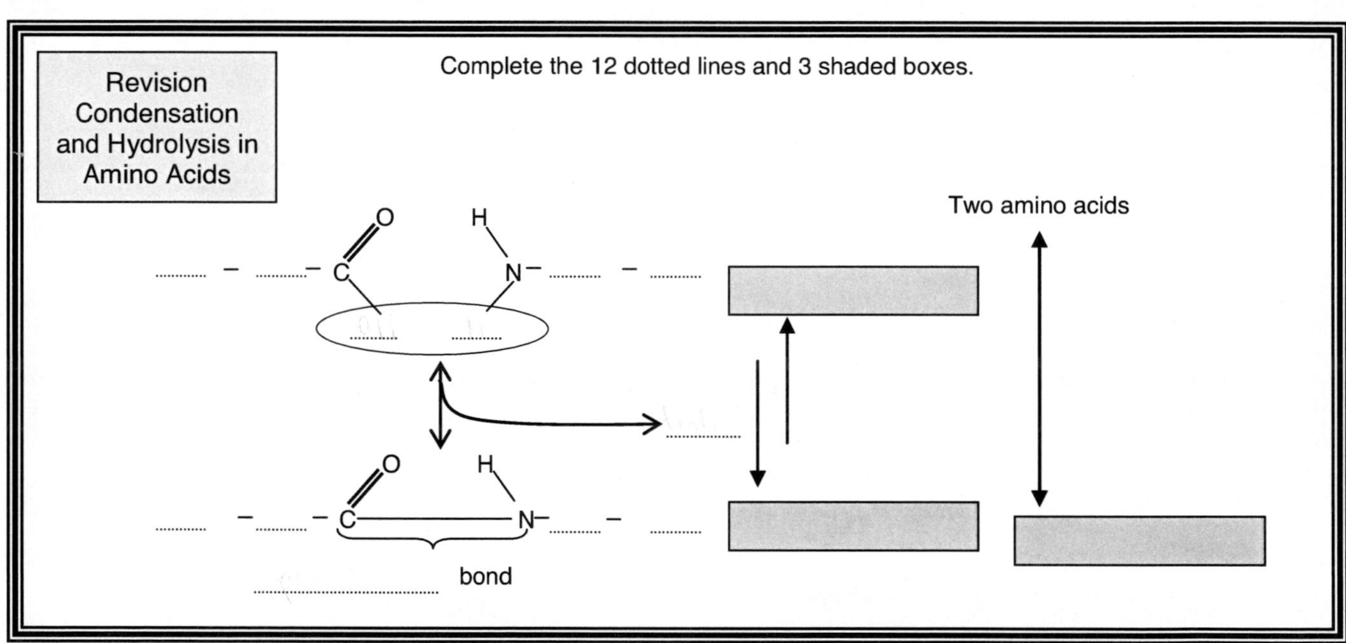

Revision
Condensation
and Hydrolysis in
Amino Acids
Complete the 12 dotted lines and 3 shaded boxes.
O
H
C
N
Two amino acids
O
H
C
N
bond

DNA Structure

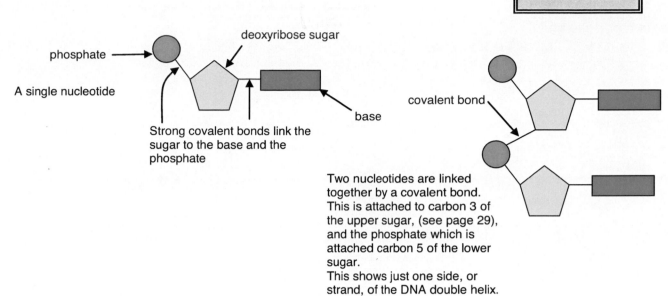

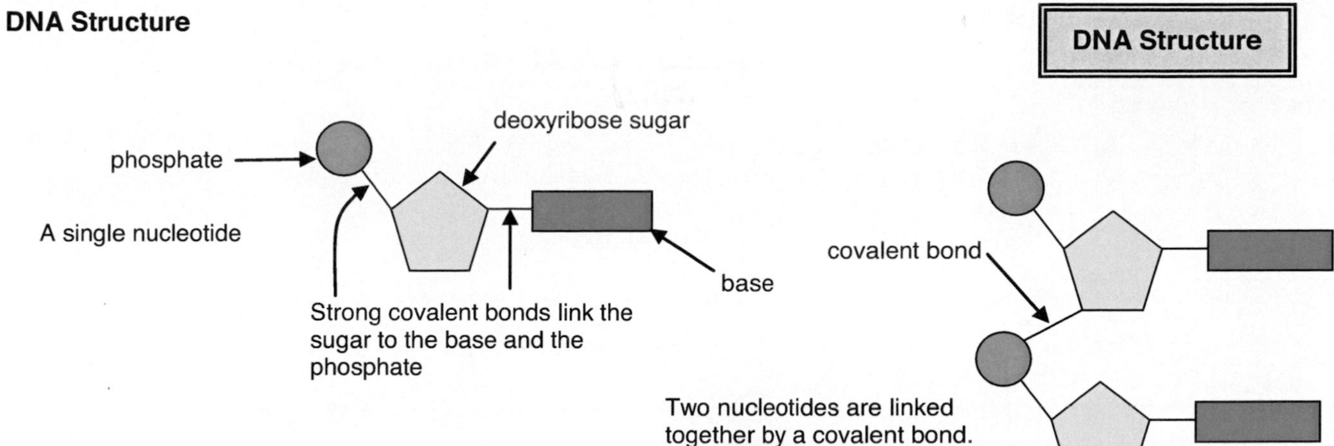
phosphate
deoxyribose sugar
A single nucleotide
base
Strong covalent bonds link the sugar to the base and the phosphate
covalent bond
Two nucleotides are linked together by a covalent bond. This is attached to carbon 3 of the upper sugar, (see page 29), and the phosphate which is attached carbon 5 of the lower sugar.
This shows just one side, or strand, of the DNA double helix.

Key features

- Complementary base pairing;
- A with T;
- C with G.

Use a simple game to link the bases, eg **A**pple **T**art and **C**hocolate **G**ateau; or A and T are 'straight' letters and C and G are 'curly' letters.

The four DNA bases are –

- **A**denine
- **T**hymine
- **C**ytosine
- **G**uanine

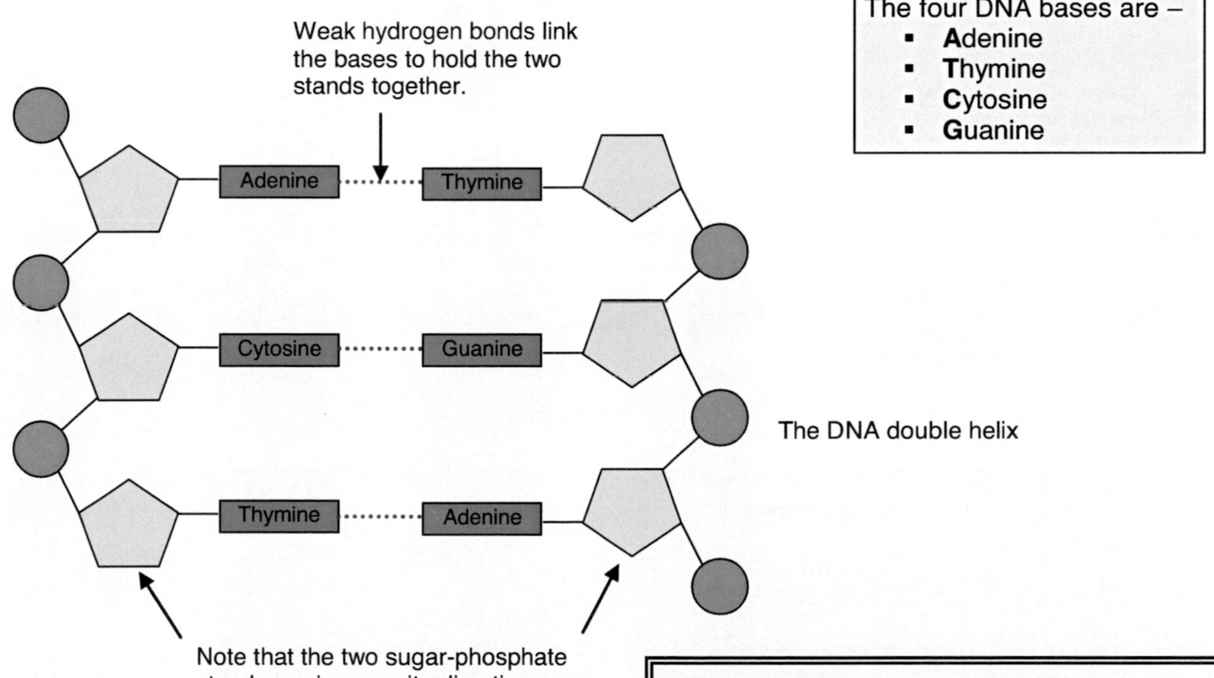
Weak hydrogen bonds link the bases to hold the two stands together.
Adenine
Thymine
Cytosine
Guanine
Thymine
Adenine
The DNA double helix

Note that the two sugar-phosphate stands run in opposite directions. They are described as being antiparallel.

NB. In an exam you should draw 4 nucleotides showing both base pairs by name. Label all the covalent bonds and the 3 nucleotide components as shown in blue on the diagrams at the top of the page, the hydrogen bonds and the antiparallel strands.

The diagram above deliberately has 6 nucleotides in order to show that bases can pair either way, but this is unnecessary in the exam and would be a waste of time.

DNA Replication

DNA Replication

DNA replication is semi-conservative.

- Remember that the ending –ase (usually) indicates an enzyme.
- DNA is a *helix* so it is unwound by the enzyme *helicase*.
- A polymer is a molecule made up of repeating units. DNA is a polymer of nucleotides and hence the enzyme that makes it is a *polymerase*.

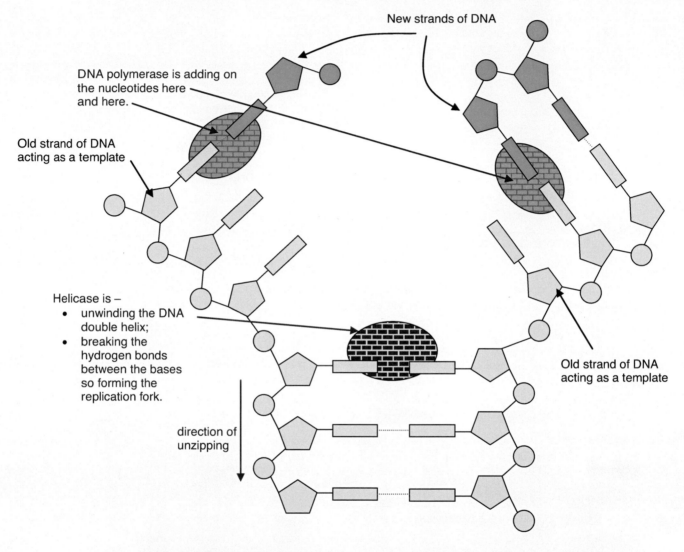

New strands of DNA

DNA polymerase is adding on the nucleotides here and here.

Old strand of DNA acting as a template

Helicase is –
- unwinding the DNA double helix;
- breaking the hydrogen bonds between the bases so forming the replication fork.

direction of unzipping

Old strand of DNA acting as a template

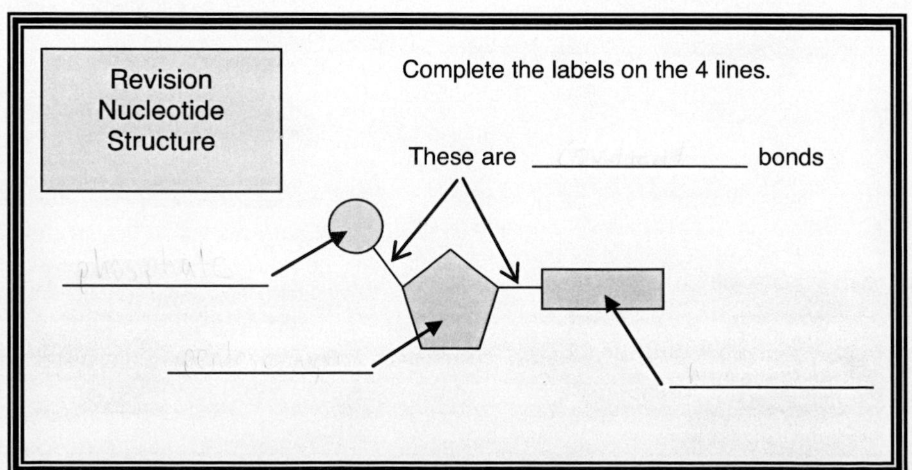

Revision Nucleotide Structure
Complete the labels on the 4 lines.
These are ______ bonds

The previous diagram is far too complex to draw in an exam so a simple stick diagram is sufficient.

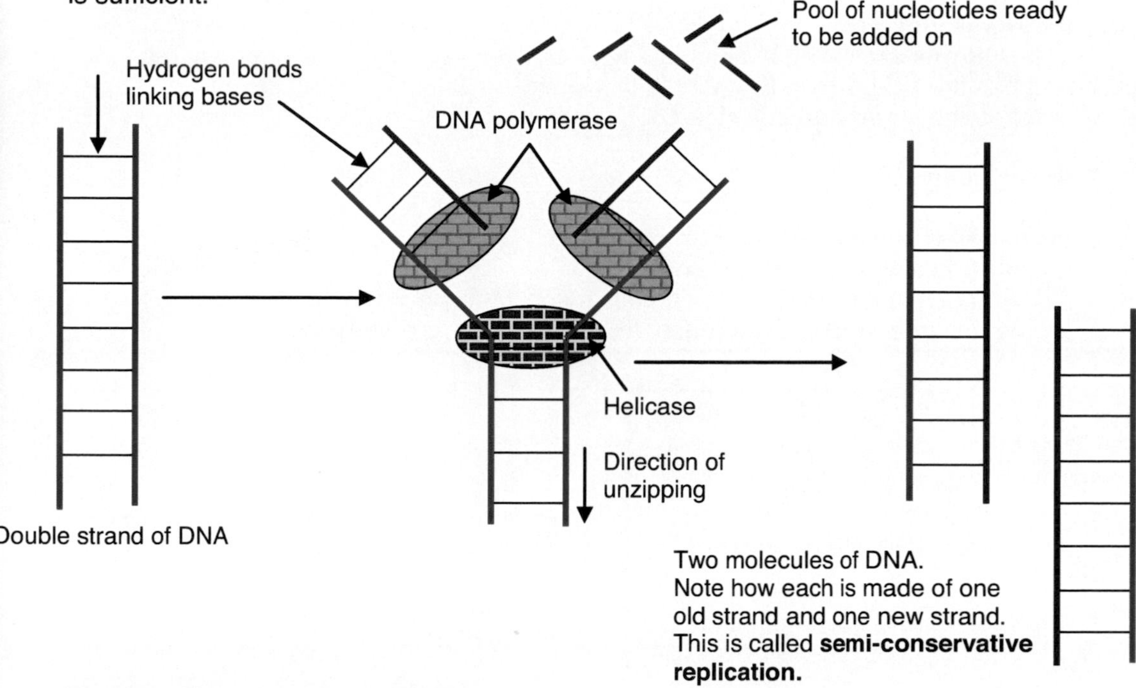
Pool of nucleotides ready to be added on
Hydrogen bonds linking bases
DNA polymerase
Helicase
Direction of unzipping
Double strand of DNA

Two molecules of DNA. Note how each is made of one old strand and one new strand. This is called **semi-conservative replication.**

The Significance of Base Pairing

Significance of Base Pairing

Key points

- DNA carries the genetic code.
- The code is the linear sequence of bases.
- Thus this sequence must be preserved.
- In the original double helix of DNA an A is paired with a T, and a C is paired with a G.
- When the new strand is built onto the original, an A on the original strand will have a T on the new strand in the same way that it was paired with a T on the original.

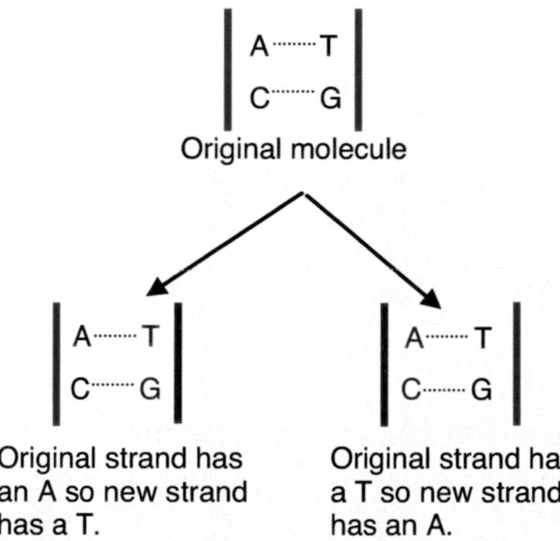
A T
C G
Original molecule
A T
C G
A T
C G

Original strand has an A so new strand has a T.

Original strand has a T so new strand has an A.

The replicated molecules have the same base sequence as the original.

Is DNA replication conservative or semi-conservative?

What type of bond forms between bases?

What type of bond forms between the sugar and the base?

What type of bond forms between the sugar and the phosphate?

Name the four bases in DNA.

How do the bases pair up?

RNA

RNA

Differences with DNA

- It is **single stranded**, but can fold back on itself to form double stranded regions;
- It has the base **uracil** (U) instead of thymine;
- It has the sugar **ribose** instead of deoxyribose;

Transcription

Transcription

Differences with DNA replication

- Only one side of the DNA is copied.
- RNA nucleotides are used. (There is a pool of these in the nucleoplasm).
- The enzyme is RNA polymerase. (RNA, like DNA, is a polymer)

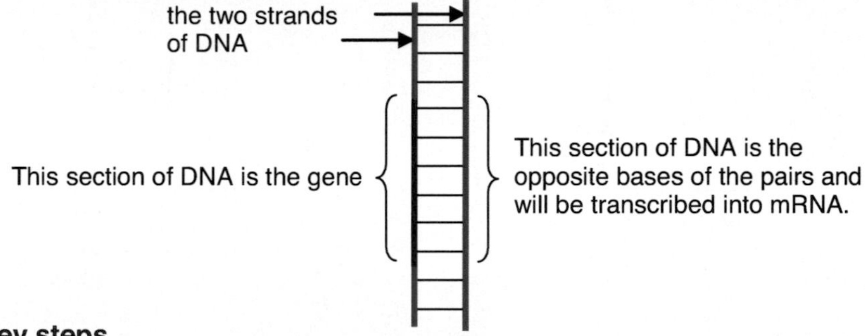

the two strands
of DNA
This section of DNA is the gene
This section of DNA is the
opposite bases of the pairs and
will be transcribed into mRNA.

Key steps

- DNA unzipped by RNA polymerase.
- RNA polymerase builds mRNA by base pairing mRNA nucleotides onto the strand of the DNA opposite to the gene.
- Uracil (U) is used instead of thymine(T).
- mRNA released and leaves the nucleus.

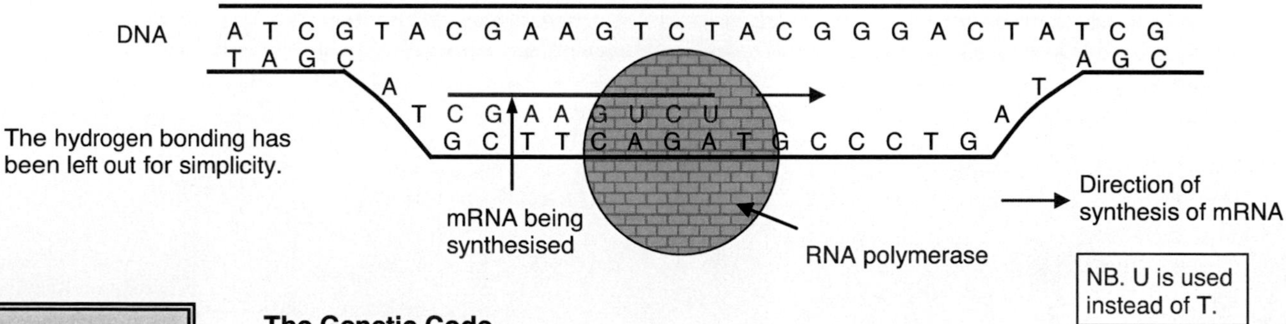

DNA
A T C G T A C G A A G T C T A C G G G A C T A T C G
T A G C
A G C
A
T
T C G A A G U C U
A
G C T T C A G A T G C C C T G
The hydrogen bonding has
been left out for simplicity.
mRNA being
synthesised
RNA polymerase
Direction of
synthesis of mRNA
NB. U is used
instead of T.

The Genetic Code

The Genetic Code

Key points

- The codon triplet is messenger RNA and not DNA.
- Groups of 3 RNA bases code for 1 amino acid.
- The table has 64 codons but only 61 of these code for amino acids.
- The remaining three are stop codons. They do not have an amino acid and so mark the end of the 'message' on the mRNA.
- All but two amino acids have more than one codon. This is called **degeneracy**.
- All organisms use the same code so it is called **universal**.

You will not be expected to memorise the codon table but you are expected to know how to use it. The complete mRNA codon table is given in Appendix 8 on page 240.

Name the two enzymes involved in DNA replication, stating what each does.

1.

2.

Name the enzyme involved in transcription and it's function.

List three differences between DNA and RNA.

Translation

Translation

How can you stop getting muddled up between transcription and translation? Think of language. Think of DNA as a 'language' of nucleotides, and protein as a 'language' of amino acids.
Transcribe means to copy in the same language. Thus in transcription you go from the nucleotide 'language' of DNA to the nucleotide 'language' of mRNA.
Translate means to change into a different language. Thus in translation you go from the nucleotide 'language' of mRNA to the amino acid 'language' of a polypeptide.

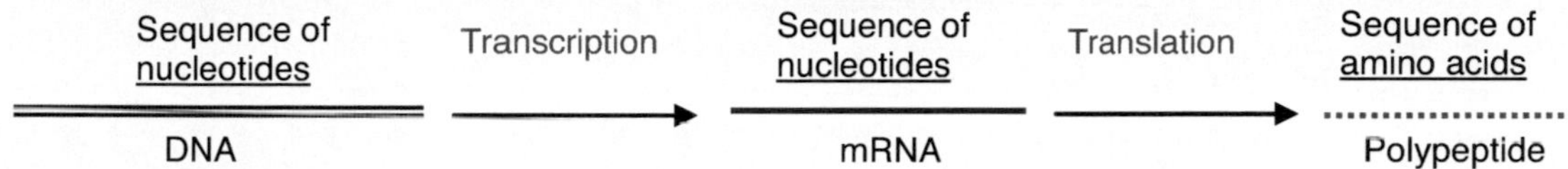
Sequence of nucleotides
Transcription
Sequence of nucleotides
Translation
Sequence of amino acids
DNA
mRNA
Polypeptide

Key components and terms

- mRNA
- codon
- tRNA carrying its specific amino acid
- anticodon
- ribosome
- peptide bond

Key steps

This is illustrated on the next page. Remember that ribosomes may be free in the cytoplasm or attached to endoplasmic reticulum forming rER.

1. mRNA moves from nucleus and attaches to ribosome in cytoplasm.
2. First tRNA with amino acid joins to first codon by base pairing codon and anticodon.
3. Second tRNA with amino acid joins to second codon by base pairing codon and anticodon.
4. The two amino acids are now alongside each other and a peptide bond forms between them.
5. Ribosome shifts along one mRNA triplet.
6. In comes the third tRNA and step 4 is repeated.
7. Steps 5 and 6 now keep repeating until the stop codon is reached.
8. mRNA and ribosome separate and the completed polypeptide breaks free.

A simple representation of a tRNA molecule with an amino acid attached.

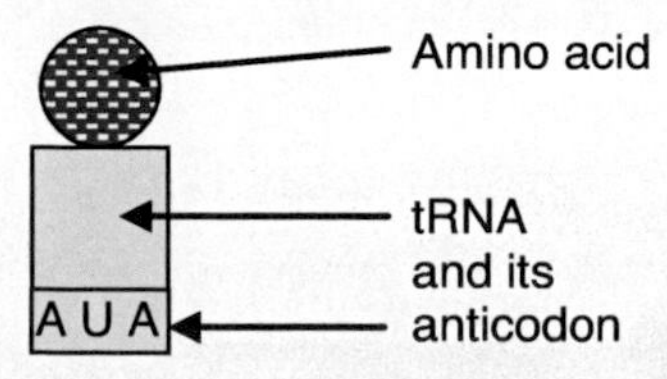
Amino acid
tRNA and its anticodon
A U A

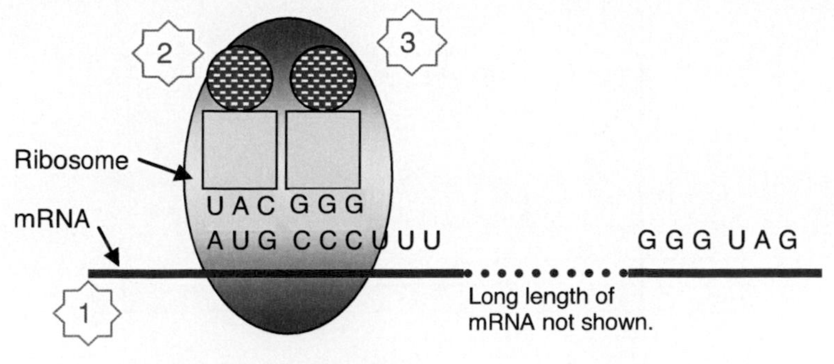
2
3
Ribosome
mRNA
UAC GGG
AUG CCCUUU
GGG UAG
1
Long length of mRNA not shown.

1. mRNA moves from nucleus and attaches to ribosome in cytoplasm at the start codon.
2. First tRNA with amino acid joins to start codon AUG by base pairing codon and anticodon.
3. Second tRNA with amino acid joins to second codon by base pairing codon and anticodon.

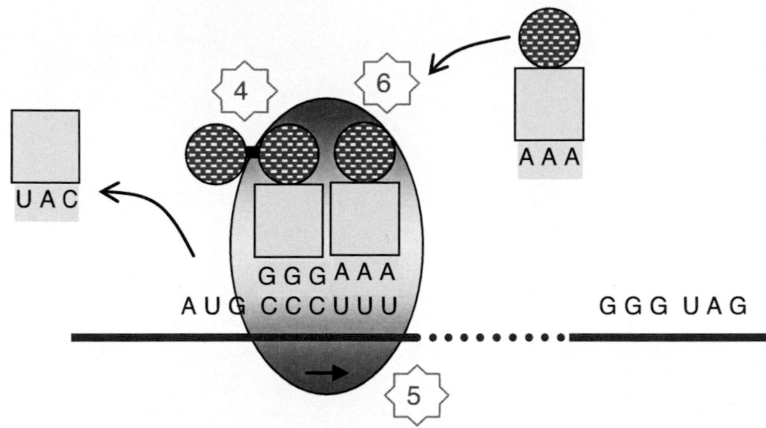
4
6
AAA
UAC
GGG AAA
AUG CCCUUU
GGG UAG
5

4. The two amino acids are now alongside each other and a peptide bond forms between them.
5. Ribosome shifts along one mRNA triplet and first tRNA is released.
6. In comes the third tRNA and step 4 is repeated.

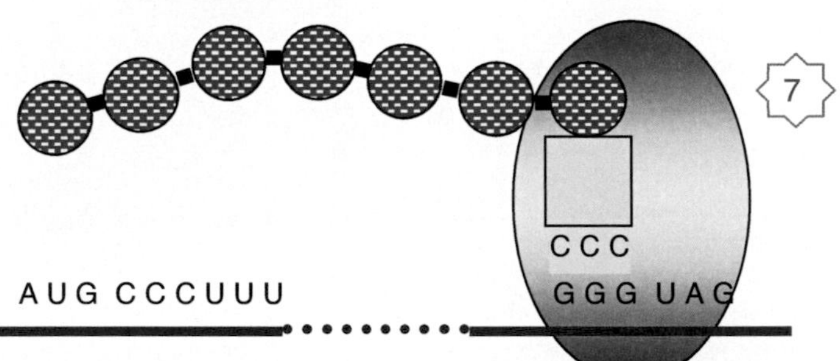
7
CCC
AUG CCCUUU
GGG UAG

7. Steps 5 and 6 now keep repeating until the stop codon UAG is reached.

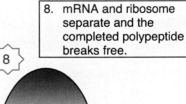

8. mRNA and ribosome separate and the completed polypeptide breaks free.

8

AUG CCCUUU GGG UAG

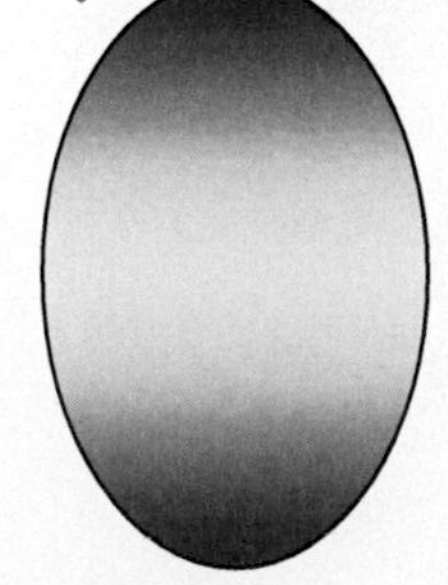

Tip: Use simple codons such as CCC or AAA – much easier to base pair and less likely to make mistakes. Always, though, include adenine A so you can show it pairs with uracil U.

You do not need to know any codons. However you could remember that AUG is the start codon (A starts the alphabet) and the similar one UAG is a stop codon (U is near the end of the alphabet).

One Gene – One Polypeptide

One Gene - One Polypeptide

Points for discussion

- A gene used to be thought of as the code for one polypeptide.
- The processes of transcription and translation, because of the precision of base pairing, (firstly DNA to mRNA and secondly anticodon to codon), do not permit more than one specific polypeptide to be made from the mRNA that came from the gene; One particular mRNA molecule may be translated into a very large number of polypeptides but they are all exactly the same;
- Some genes are transcribed but not translated, eg. those for tRNA and rRNA;
- Three recent discoveries are –
    - A polypeptide may require two or more genes, each synthesising a different part of the polypeptide, eg. the β chain of HCG requires six genes;
    - The mRNA from a gene may be broken into sections and the sections joined in different ways. Each of these will be translated into a different polypeptide.
    - A single mRNA can have many starting places for translation and so code for several polypeptides.

How many bases code for one amino acid?

3

Name the two types of RNA used in translation.

Determine the sequence of amino acids from the following DNA base sequence. The codon table is on page 240. The answer is at the bottom of the page.

T A C C C C A G G A A G A A C G G C A T C

State the names of the five nucleic acid bases.

Which of these is not found in DNA?

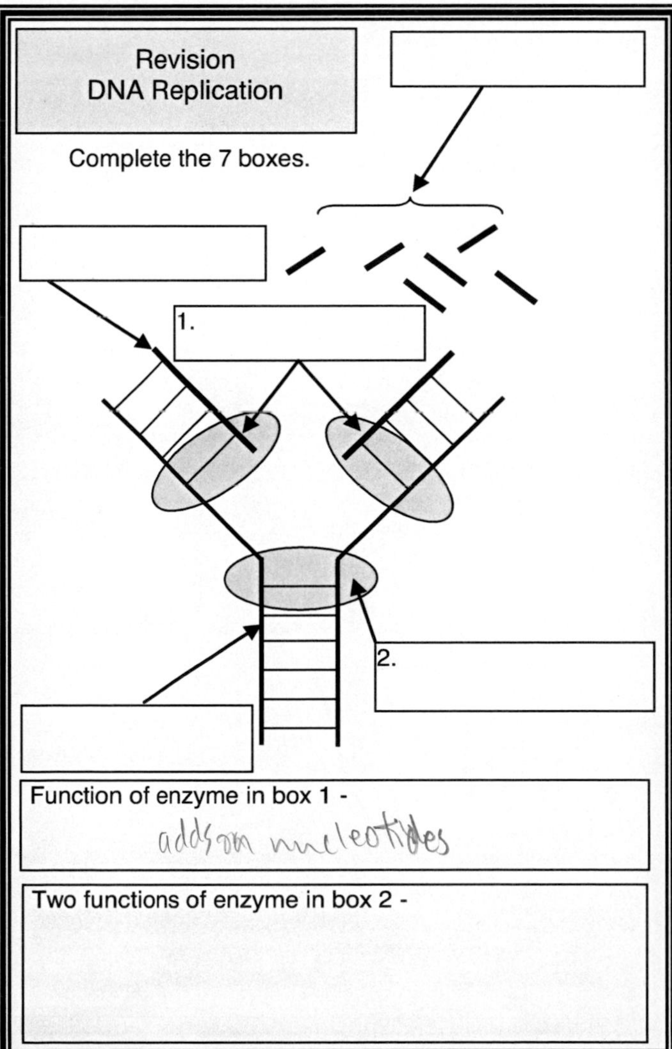
Revision
DNA Replication
Complete the 7 boxes.
1.
2.
Function of enzyme in box 1 -
adds on nucleotides
Two functions of enzyme in box 2 -

methionine - glycine - serine - phenyl-alanine - leucine - proline

Enzymes

Enzymes

Lock and Key Model of Enzyme Action.

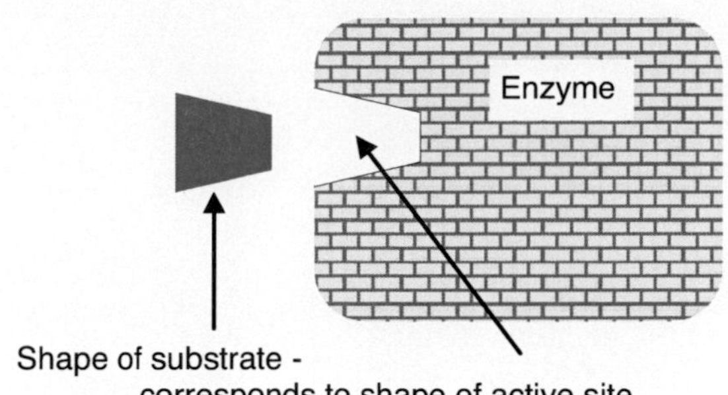
Enzyme
Shape of substrate -
corresponds to shape of active site.

Key points

- Enzymes are large molecules folded to form a three-dimensional globular structure;
- The folding creates a specifically shaped three-dimensional 'pocket' on the surface into which the substrate or substrates can fit;
- The shape of the active site matches the shape of the substrate(s);
- This brings substrates together in the correct orientation;
- The bonds in the substrate(s) are weakened making a reaction easier.

Factors Affecting Enzyme Action

Factors Affecting Enzyme Action

Key background points

- Enzymes are proteins.
- They are large, complex folded molecules held in shape by, mostly, weak bonds.
- Increasing temperature makes atoms and molecules move more quickly.

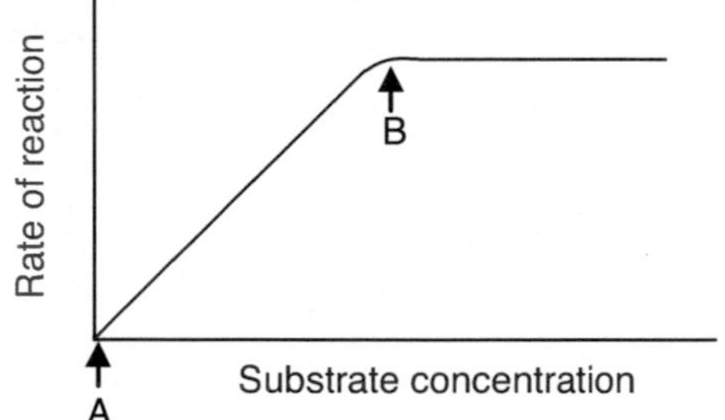
Rate of reaction
B
A
Substrate concentration

- We assume here that the amount of enzyme is fixed and therefore the number of active sites is constant.
- As substrate concentration increases between A and B more collisions occur with enzyme molecules and so more reactions occur.
- At point B all the active sites are occupied by substrate at any one time and so there can be no further increase in reaction rate.

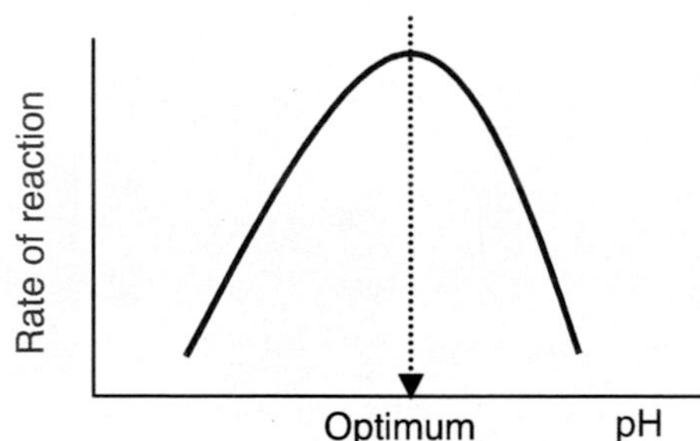
Rate of reaction
Optimum
pH

- Enzymes are large protein molecules folded into a complex three-dimensional shape.
- This shape is held in place by bonds and these are strongest at the optimum pH.
- Changing the pH affects these bonds and so the shape of the molecule, and hence the active site, changes.
- If the substrate can no longer bind to the active site then the reaction rate drops.
- Note the symmetry of the curve.

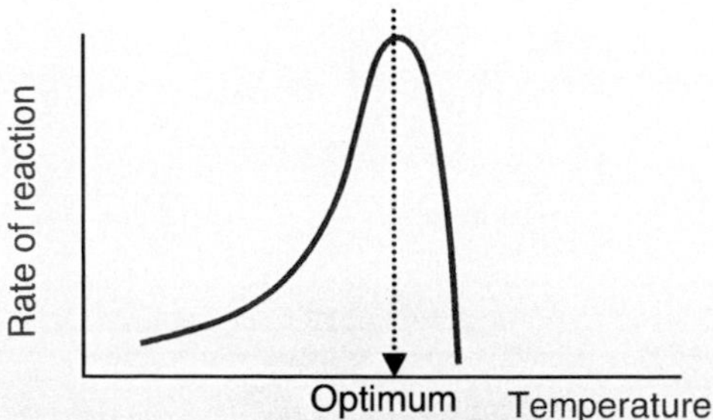
Rate of reaction
Optimum
Temperature

- Note the asymmetry of this curve compared to the pH one.
- There is an approximately exponential increase (see yellow box below) up to the optimum temperature and then a sharp drop.
- Temperature increases the molecular movement and so in the solution the molecules collide more frequently and with more energy.
- This makes it more likely that the reaction occurs.
- However beyond the optimum temperature the amino acids within the protein are moving so much that weak bonds are broken and the molecule begins to fall apart.
- Once again the shape of the active site no longer fits the shape of the substrate and the reaction cannot take place.

- During the exponential period the rate of reaction doubles for every 10^0C rise in temperature;
- In this case the temperature coefficient $Q_{10} = 2$;
- The Q_{10} value can be up to 3, ie the rate triples for every 10^0C rise in temperature.

State two reasons that support the one gene one polypeptide hypothesis.

State two reasons that go against the one gene one polypeptide hypothesis.

Define enzyme.

Define active site.

Define denaturation.

Draw a diagram to show the lock and key principle of enzyme action.

Enzymes in Biotechnology

Enzymes in Biotechnology

Production of Lactose-free Milk

Key points

- Many adults are intolerant of the lactose in milk.
- This is because as they get older the gene producing lactase gets switched off.
- Lactose is a disaccharide and cannot be absorbed by the gut.
- The lactose then gets fermented by bacteria in the large intestine resulting in nausea, abdominal pain and diarrhoea.
- Milk is treated with lactase and this breaks down the lactose to the monosaccharides glucose and galactose which are easily absorbed by the gut.
- Lactase is obtained from the fungus *Kluyveromyces lactis.*
- The lactase is often immobilised and the milk passed over it. This prevents the lactase from being in the product and is more economical as the lactase can be used repeatedly.
- Lactose-free milk is also used in the production of ice cream as lactose crystallises when cold and makes the ice cream granular. The glucose and galactose remain dissolved and so the ice cream is smoother.
- In yoghurt production bacteria ferment lactose slowly but ferment glucose and galactose much more quickly making production faster.
- Lactose is not a sweet tasting sugar whereas glucose and galactose are. By changing the lactose into these two sugars foods such as yoghurt and ice cream made from lactose-free milk need less added sugar to make them taste sweet.

Revision
Enzyme Reaction Rates

Draw in the lines for these three graphs and state key points in the box alongside each graph..

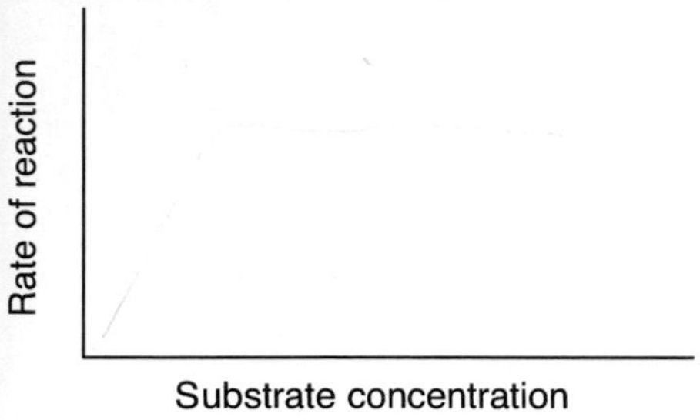

Rate of reaction

Substrate concentration

Rate of reaction

pH

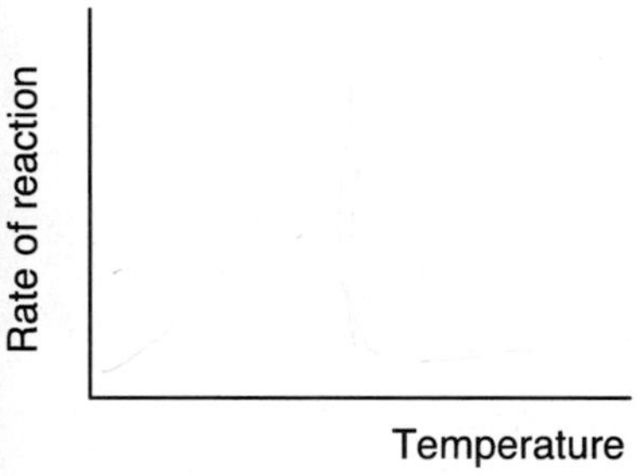

Rate of reaction

Temperature

State 5 key points relating to the production of lactose-free milk.

Revision Transcription

Complete the 3 missing names on the dotted lines.

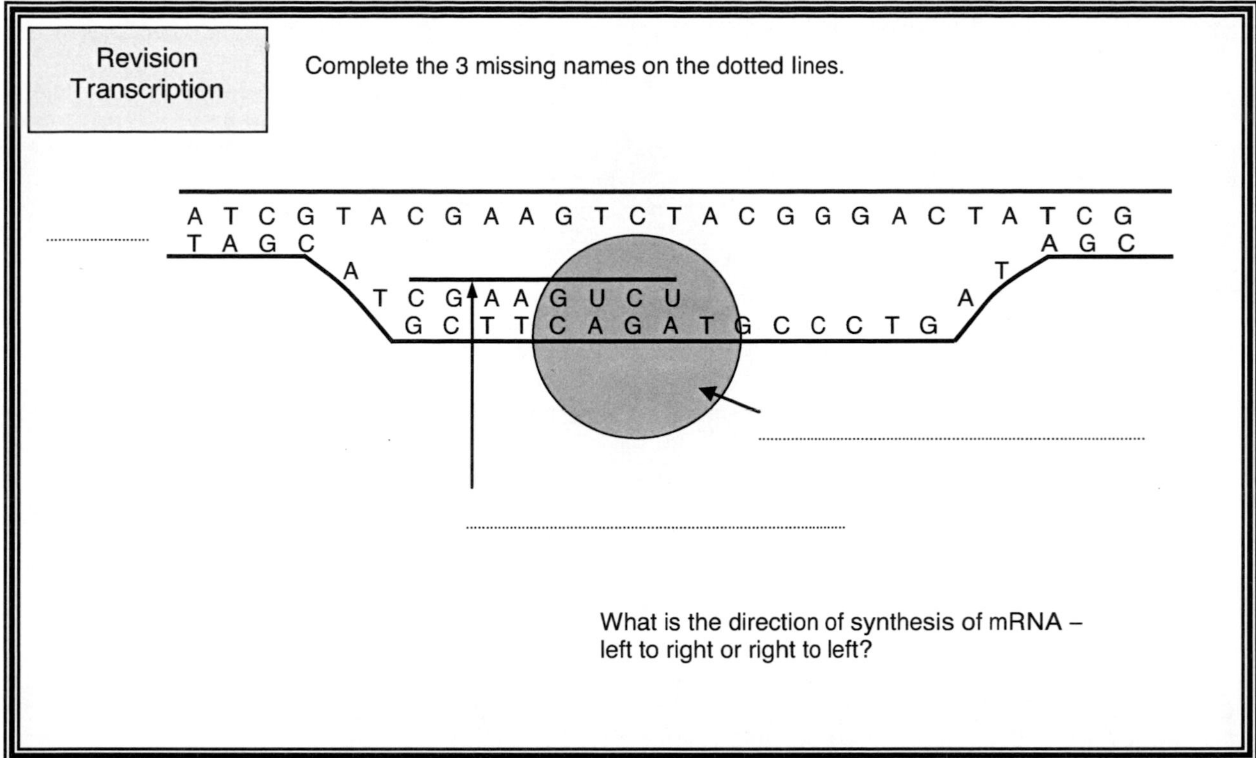

A T C G T A C G A A G T C T A C G G G A C T A T C G
T A G C
A G C
A
T
T C G A A G U C U
A
G C T T C A G A T G C C C T G

What is the direction of synthesis of mRNA – left to right or right to left?

Revision Translation

Complete the 7 missing names on the dotted lines.
Fill in the bases in the two boxes indicated by the solid arrows.

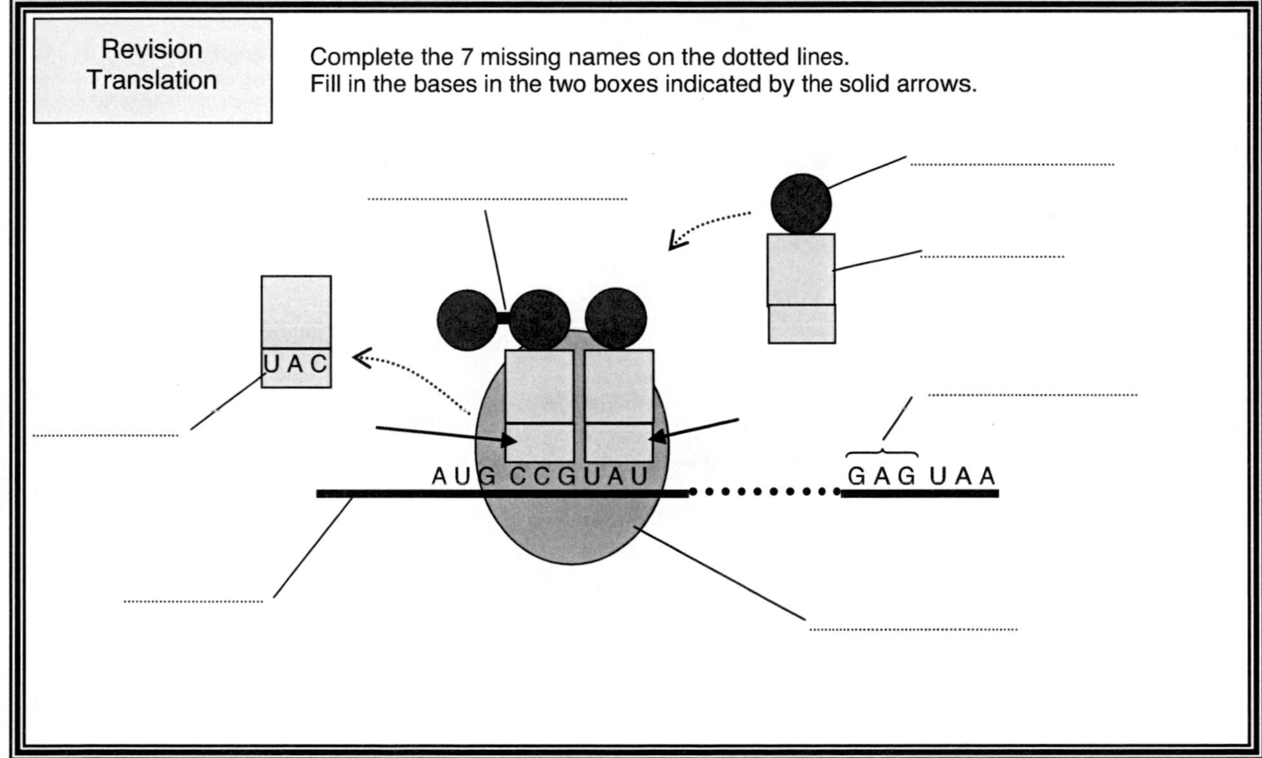

UAC
AUG CCG UAU
GAG UAA

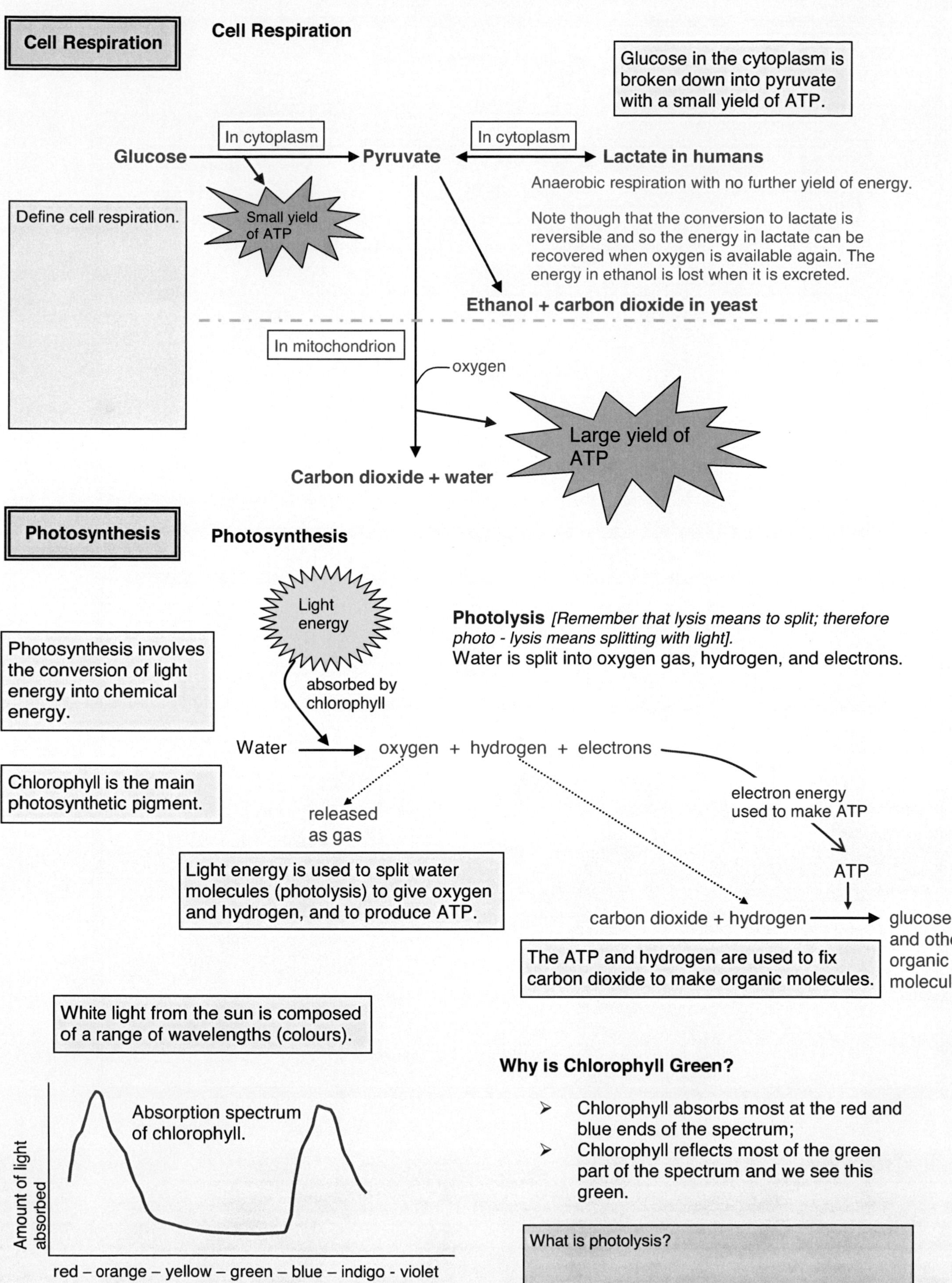
Cell Respiration
Cell Respiration
Glucose in the cytoplasm is broken down into pyruvate with a small yield of ATP.
In cytoplasm
In cytoplasm
Glucose
Pyruvate
Lactate in humans
Anaerobic respiration with no further yield of energy.
Note though that the conversion to lactate is reversible and so the energy in lactate can be recovered when oxygen is available again. The energy in ethanol is lost when it is excreted.
Define cell respiration.
Small yield of ATP
Ethanol + carbon dioxide in yeast
In mitochondrion
oxygen
Large yield of ATP
Carbon dioxide + water
Photosynthesis
Photosynthesis
Light energy
Photolysis [Remember that lysis means to split; therefore photo - lysis means splitting with light].
Water is split into oxygen gas, hydrogen, and electrons.
Photosynthesis involves the conversion of light energy into chemical energy.
absorbed by chlorophyll
Water
oxygen + hydrogen + electrons
Chlorophyll is the main photosynthetic pigment.
released as gas
electron energy used to make ATP
ATP
Light energy is used to split water molecules (photolysis) to give oxygen and hydrogen, and to produce ATP.
carbon dioxide + hydrogen
glucose and other organic molecules
The ATP and hydrogen are used to fix carbon dioxide to make organic molecules.
White light from the sun is composed of a range of wavelengths (colours).
Why is Chlorophyll Green?
Chlorophyll absorbs most at the red and blue ends of the spectrum;
Chlorophyll reflects most of the green part of the spectrum and we see this green.
Absorption spectrum of chlorophyll.
Amount of light absorbed
red – orange – yellow – green – blue – indigo - violet
What is photolysis?

Measuring Photosynthesis

Measuring Photosynthesis

Remember the simple word equation -
carbon dioxide + water + light energy → oxygen + glucose
Substances on the left decrease whereas those on the right increase so we can measure these. (Measuring water is difficult).

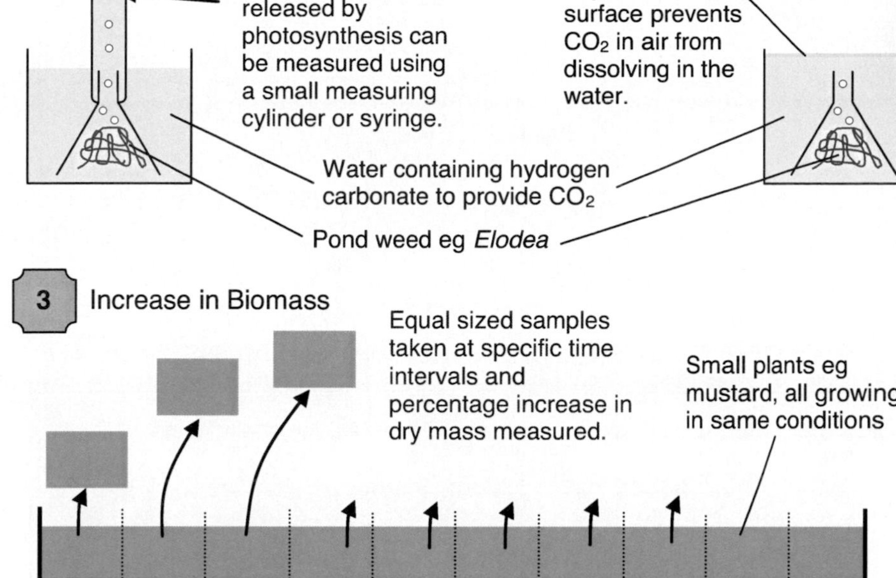

1
Production of Oxygen
Volume of oxygen released by photosynthesis can be measured using a small measuring cylinder or syringe.
2
Uptake of Carbon Dioxide
Layer of oil on surface prevents CO2 in air from dissolving in the water.
As carbon dioxide is taken up out of solution by photosynthesis the pH increases. This can be measured by a pH probe.
Water containing hydrogen carbonate to provide CO2
Pond weed eg Elodea
3
Increase in Biomass
Equal sized samples taken at specific time intervals and percentage increase in dry mass measured.
Small plants eg mustard, all growing in same conditions

With all three measurements the values are relative since respiration is occuring all the time. This uses up some of the oxygen and sugar (biomass) produced by photosynthesis and provides some of the carbon dioxide required for photosynthesis.

The Effect of Light Intensity, Carbon Dioxide Concentration, and Temperature on Photosynthesis

Effect of External Factors

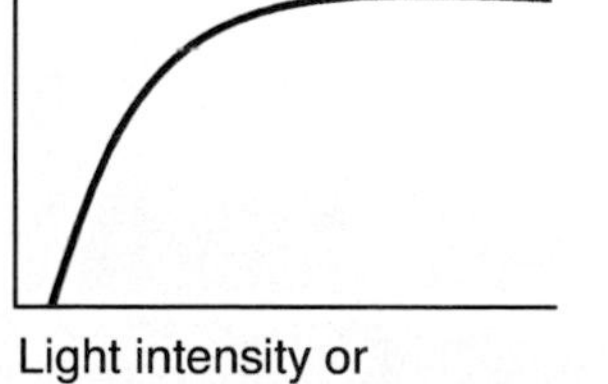

Rate of photosynthesis
Light intensity or carbon dioxide concentration

1. **Light Intensity**
   As the intensity increases there comes a point when all the chlorophyll molecules are saturated and cannot accept any more light.
   A minimum intensity is required before photosynthesis starts.

2. **Carbon Dioxide**
   This is a substrate for an enzyme controlled reaction, and once all the enzyme active sites are used up the reaction cannot go faster. (Refer back to the section on enzymes).
   A minimum concentration of carbon dioxide is required before photosynthesis starts.

3. **Temperature**
   The shape of the graph should be familiar. (Refer back to the section on enzymes, page 42). Many of the reactions of photosynthesis are enzyme controlled and hence the rate of photosynthesis shows the same shape.

Rate of photosynthesis

Temperature

Name the main photosynthetic pigment.

Which colours in the spectrum are absorbed most during photosynthesis?

Name the two substances needed to fix carbon dioxide in photosynthesis.

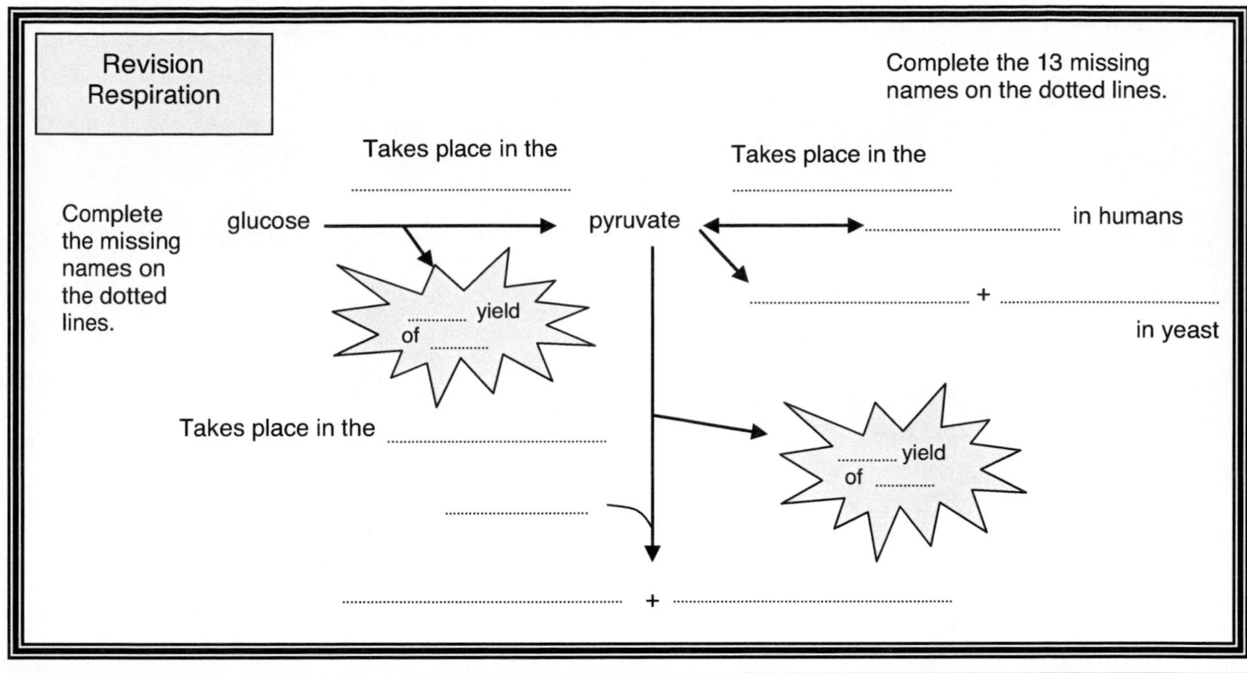
Revision
Respiration
Complete the 13 missing names on the dotted lines.
Takes place in the
Takes place in the
Complete the missing names on the dotted lines.
glucose
pyruvate
in humans
yield of
+
in yeast
Takes place in the
yield of
+

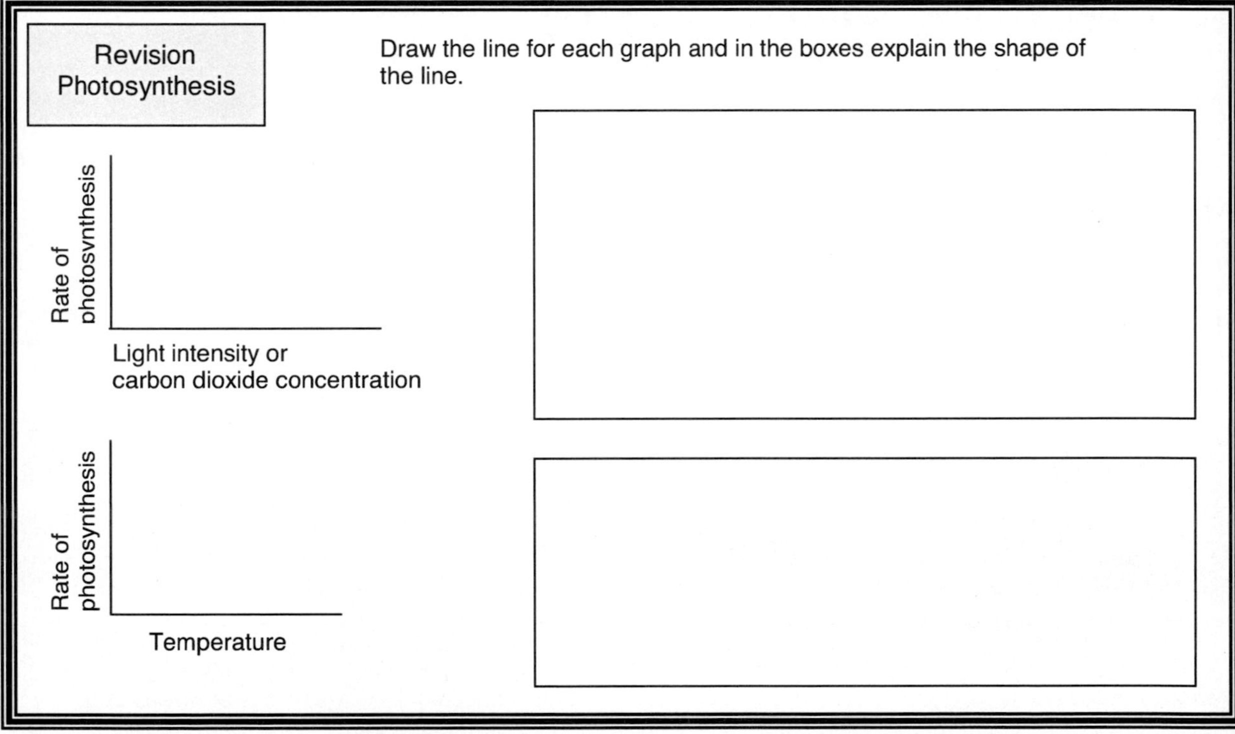
Revision
Photosynthesis
Draw the line for each graph and in the boxes explain the shape of the line.
Rate of photosynthesis
Light intensity or
carbon dioxide concentration
Rate of photosynthesis
Temperature

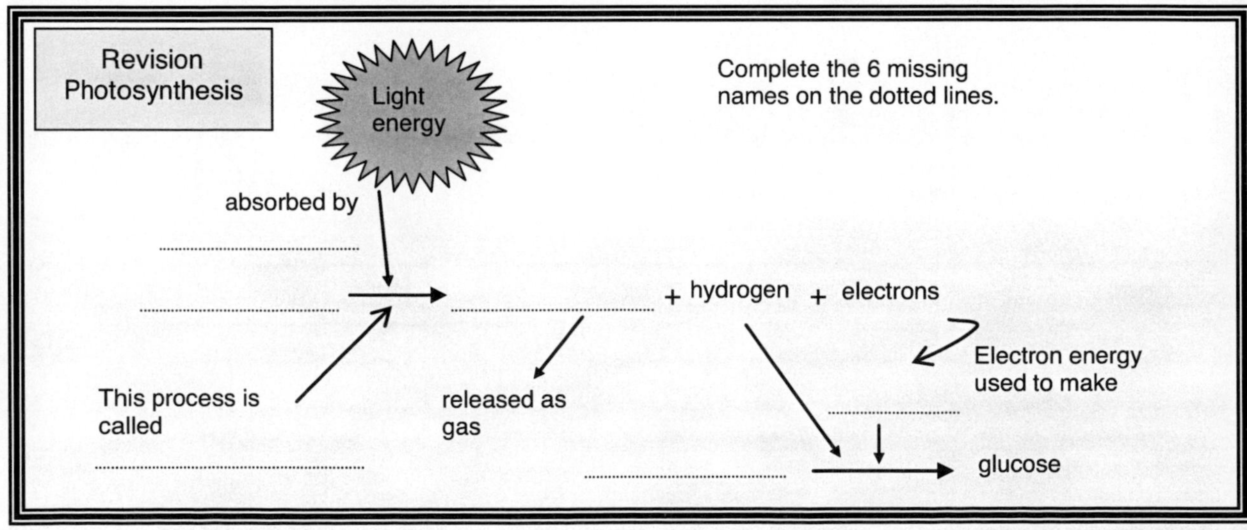
Revision
Photosynthesis
Light energy
Complete the 6 missing names on the dotted lines.
absorbed by
+ hydrogen + electrons
Electron energy used to make
This process is called
released as gas
glucose

Self-Test Quiz on Topic 3

1. Which line in the table is correct?

	Monosaccharide	Disaccharide	Polysaccharide
a.	galactose	maltose	glycogen
b.	glucose	starch	galactose
c.	fructose	galactose	starch
d.	glucose	fructose	cellulose

2. The four most frequently occurring elements in organisms are
   a. hydrogen, nitrogen, oxygen, sulfur,
   b. carbon, hydrogen, oxygen, nitrogen,
   c. carbon, nitrogen, oxygen, calcium,
   d. carbon, nitrogen, hydrogen, sodium.

3. Hydrogen bonding is,
   a. only found in water,
   b. an attraction between molecules,
   c. a bond between hydrogen atoms,
   d. formed during a condensation reaction.

4. Cohesion between water molecules means that
   a. water is a good solvent,
   b. substances can diffuse in water,
   c. osmosis can occur within a cell,
   d. a transpiration stream can occur in plants.

5. Carbohydrates, lipids, proteins and nucleic acids **all** contain the elements
   a. nitrogen and oxygen,
   b. carbon, hydrogen and nitrogen,
   c. hydrogen, carbon and oxygen,
   e. nitrogen, carbon and oxygen.

6. The term organic can be described as
   a. the element carbon,
   b. a compound containing water,
   c. a compound containing carbon,
   d. a compound that dissolves in water.

7. Which one of the following represents the general structure of an amino acid?

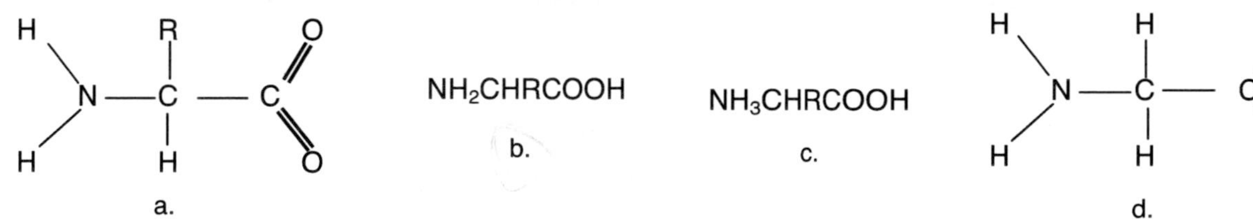
H
R
O
N
C
C
H
H
O
a.
$NH_2CHRCOOH$
b.
$NH_3CHRCOOH$
c.
H
H
R
N
C
C
H
H
O
d.

8. Which of the following represents the basic structure of the sugar ribose?

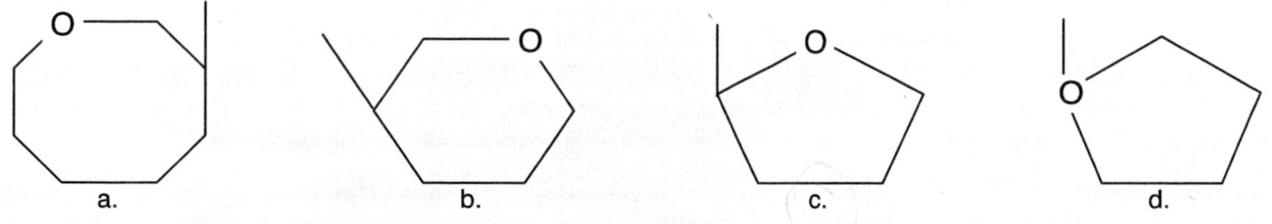
O
a.
O
b.
O
c.
O
d.

9. Translation is
   a. the formation of a polypeptide from DNA,
   b. the formation of a polypeptide from RNA,
   c. the formation of a molecule of RNA from a molecule of DNA,
   d. the formation of a molecule of DNA from a molecule of DNA.

10. Polymerisation occurs in carbohydrates due to
    a. repeated condensation reactions,
    b. hydrogen bonding,
    c. bonding to proteins to form glycoproteins,
    e. repeated hydrolysis reactions.

11. The number of carbon atoms in glycerol is
    a. dependent upon the size of the fatty acids,
    b. n,
    c. 3,
    d. 6.

12. The active site of an enzyme is
    a. the region of the molecule where the substrate can bind,
    b. the place where the protein is folded,
    c. the position of the sulphur containing amino acids,
    d. the only region of the molecule that is denatured when heated.

13. Which of the following represents a fatty acid?

```
     H   H   H   O             H         H              H   H   H   O             H   H   O
     |   |   |   ||            |         |              |   |   |   ||            |   |   ||
 N — C — C — C — C         H — C — C — C = O        H — C — C — C — C     O = C — C — C — N
     |   |   |   |             |   |                    |   |   |   |           |   |   |
     H   H   H   OH            H   H                    H   H   H   OH          H   H   H

         a.                        b.                         c.                     d.
```

14. Denaturation can be defined as
    a. breakdown of a protein into its amino acids,
    b. loss of the functional properties of a protein,
    c. failure of an enzyme to catalyse its reaction,
    d. breakdown of the phospholipid bilayer of a membrane.

15. A molecule of DNA
    a. is made up from two strands of nucleotides linked by covalent bonds,
    b. contains five different types of base,
    c. has the bases linked to sugar molecules via phosphate,
    d. differs from RNA because it contains the base thymine.

16. During complementary base pairing
    a only identical bases pair up,
    b thymine links with uracil,
    c adenine can link with either uracil or thymine.
    d guanine links with thymine.

17. In aerobic cell respiration
    a. pyruvate is broken down in the cytoplasm,
    b. the conversion of pyruvate to carbon dioxide and water yields a large amount of ATP,
    c. glucose is broken down to pyruvate in the mitochondrion,
    d. glucose can be converted to lactate with the formation of a large amount of ATP.

18. Photolysis is the
    a. splitting of water by light energy,
    b. splitting of light by water,
    c. conversion of ATP to glucose,
    d. absorption of light by chlorophyll.

19. Which of the following graphs represents the effect of light intensity on the rate of photosynthesis?

a.
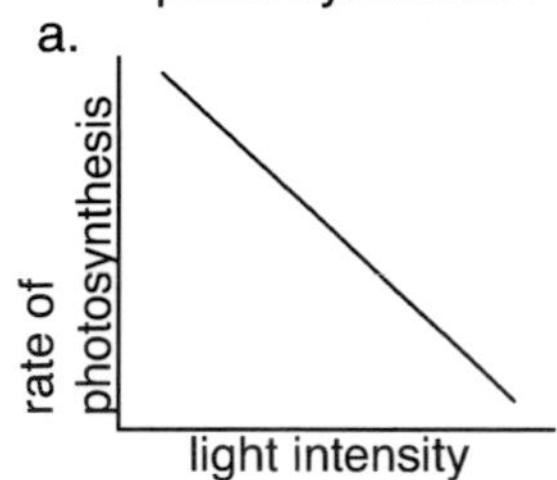
rate of photosynthesis
light intensity

b.
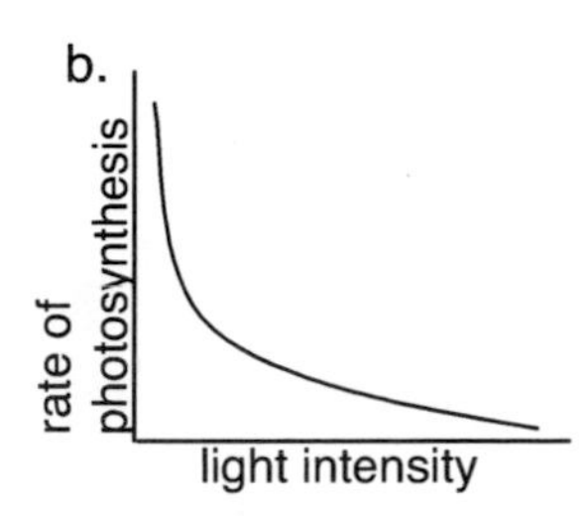
rate of photosynthesis
light intensity

c.
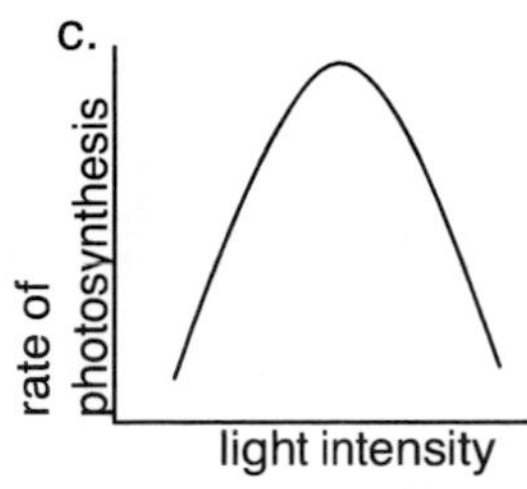
rate of photosynthesis
light intensity

d.
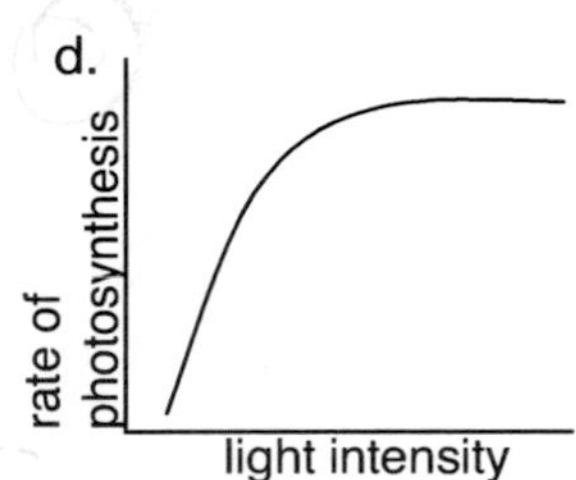
rate of photosynthesis
light intensity

20. If a beam of white light is shone through a solution of chlorophyll and the emerging beam split into colours by a prism, which colour or colours will be largely missing?
    a. red, blue and green,
    b. green,
    c. red and blue,
    d. red and green.

21. During photosynthesis which statement best describes how carbohydrate molecules are made.
    a. carbon and oxygen from carbon dioxide + hydrogen from water + energy from ATP.
    b. ATP + light energy + oxygen from water.
    c. light energy + carbon and oxygen from carbon dioxide.
    d. energy from ATP + hydrogen and oxygen from water + carbon from carbon dioxide.

22. Carbohydrates differ from lipids in that
    a. carbohydrates produce more energy per gram than triglycerides,
    b. triglycerides contain the element nitrogen whereas carbohydrates do not.
    c. triglycerides can be used for thermal insulation as well as energy release,
    d. triglycerides form ring structures whereas carbohydrates do not.

23. Which of the following represents the effect of pH on the rate of an enzyme controlled reaction?

a.
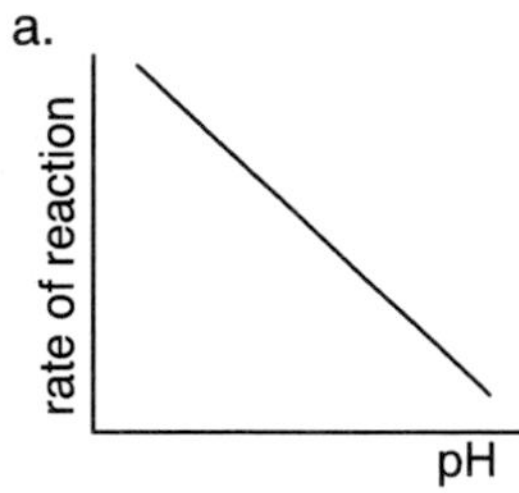
rate of reaction
pH

b.
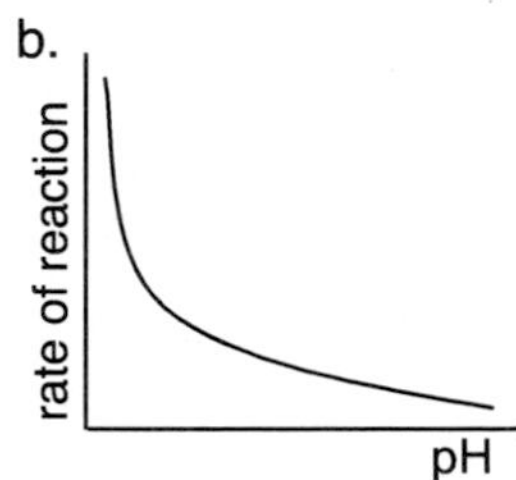
rate of reaction
pH

c.
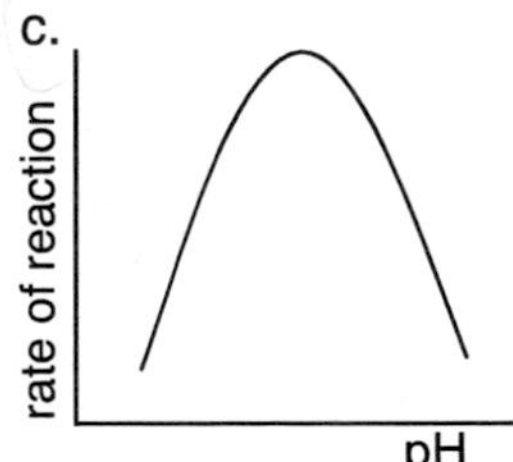
rate of reaction
pH

d.
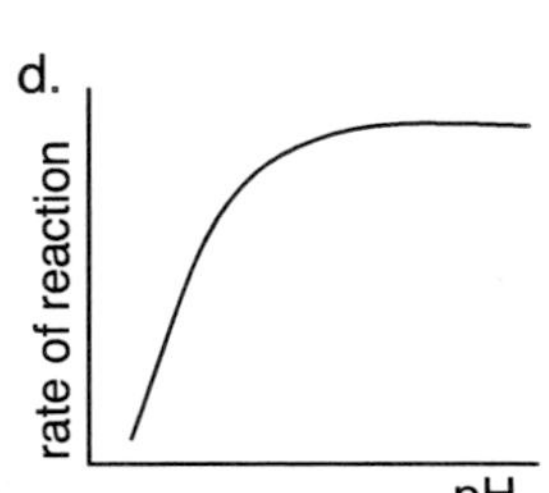
rate of reaction
pH

24. Which of the following represents a nucleotide?

a.
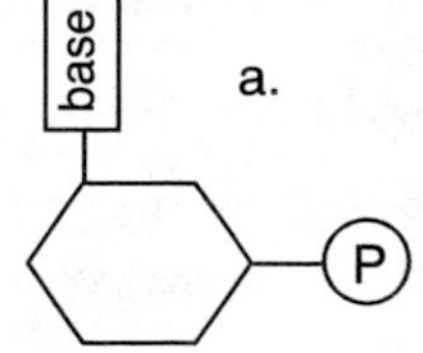
base
P

b.
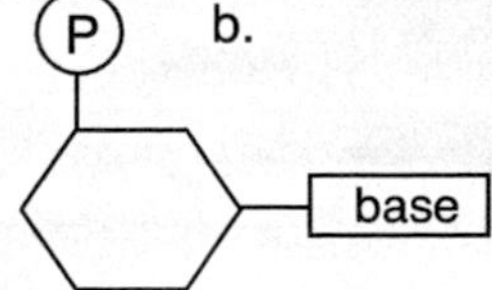
P
base

c.
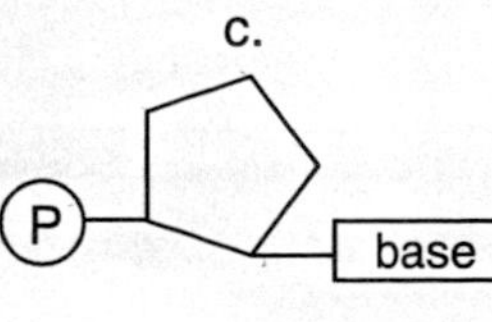
P
base

d.
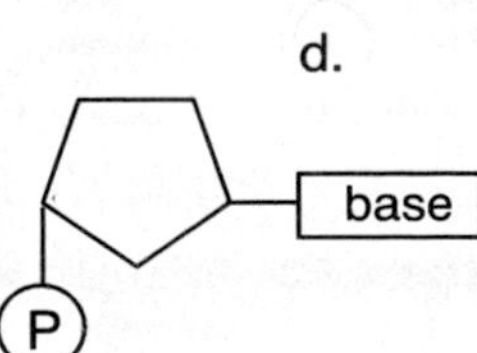
base
P

25. A growing plant is enclosed in a clear plastic bag. The rate of photosynthesis can be measured by
    a. an increase in the carbon dioxide concentration of the air in the bag,
    b. a decrease in the carbon dioxide concentration of the air in the bag,
    c. a decrease in biomass over a set time period,
    d. a decrease in the oxygen concentration of the air in the bag,

26. Water is a good solvent because
    a. it is a polar molecule and can form hydrogen bonds,
    b. it is transparent,
    c. it has a high surface tension,
    d. it has a high specific heat.

27. The number of carbons in the ring region of glucose is
    a. 6,
    b. 5,
    c. 4,
    d. 3.

28. The source of oxygen released during photosynthesis is
    a. water,
    b. carbon dioxide,
    c. chlorophyll,
    d. glucose.

29. The function of helicase during DNA replication is
    a. unwinding the double helix,
    b. unwinding the double helix and adding new nucleotides,
    c. unwinding the double helix and breaking the hydrogen bonds between bases,
    d. adding new nucleotides.

30. DNA polymerase is the enzyme required for
    a. joining two amino acids during translation,
    b. adding a nucleotide to the end of a DNA strand,
    c. adding a nucleotide to the end of an RNA strand,
    d. polymerisation of DNA during both transcription and translation.

31. Which of these cell organelles is required for translation?
    a. Ribosomes.
    b. Endoplasmic reticulum.
    c. Golgi apparatus.
    d. Vesicles.

Topic 4

Genetics

Chromosomes

Chromosomes, Genes, Alleles and Mutations

Eukaryotic chromosomes are made of DNA and protein.

Sickle-cell Anaemia

Sickle Cell Anaemia – a Base Substitution Mutation

Key points

- Caused by a mutation in one of the haemoglobin genes;
- An amino acid called glutamic acid has been replaced by one called valine;
- The triplet GAG in the gene has mutated to GTG;
- The triplet in the opposite strand, CTC, becomes CAC;
- This is the triplet that is transcribed, so in the mRNA GAG becomes GUG;
- GAG would be translated into glutamic acid but GUG is translated into valine.

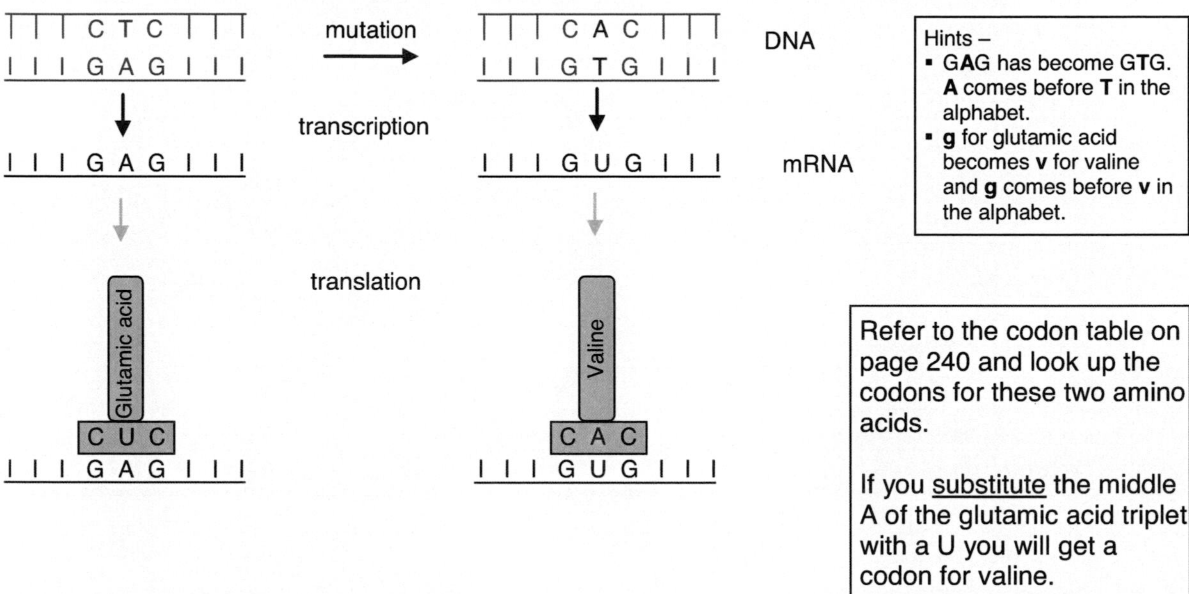

C T C
G A G
mutation
C A C
G T G
DNA
transcription
G A G
G U G
mRNA
translation
Glutamic acid
C U C
G A G
Valine
C A C
G U G
Hints –
▪ GAG has become GTG. A comes before T in the alphabet.
▪ g for glutamic acid becomes v for valine and g comes before v in the alphabet.
Refer to the codon table on page 240 and look up the codons for these two amino acids.
If you substitute the middle A of the glutamic acid triplet with a U you will get a codon for valine.

Define gene.

Define allele.

Define genome.

Define gene mutation.

State the two components of a eukaryotic chromosome.

In the sickle cell mutation the normal amino acid ____________________ has been replaced with the amino acid ____________________.

This is because in the gene there has been a ____________________ mutation causing _____ to become _____.

Revision Mitosis

Drawing	Name of stage	Key points
	Prophase	1. Supercoiling of DNA. 2. 3.
		1. 2. 3.
		1. 2. 3.
	Telophase	1. Chromosomes uncoil. 2. 3.

Meiosis

Meiosis

Diploid
- Two sets of chromosomes in a nucleus;
- The chromosomes are in pairs;
- Each parent contributed one of the pair.

Haploid
- One set of chromosomes in a nucleus;
- Only one member of each pair of chromosomes.

Define homologous chromosomes.

Meiosis is a reduction division. The chromosome number is halved from the diploid number to the haploid number so a diploid nucleus forms from 1 to 4 haploid nuclei.

Phase	Key Points
Prophase I	Supercoiling of chromosomes. Replicated chromosomes pair up in their homologous pairs to form a bivalent. This is called synapsis. Crossing over may occur.*[1] Spindle fibre network of microtubules start to form. Nuclear envelope begins to break down.
Metaphase I	Spindle fibre network complete. Bivalents line up on equator in a random way.*[2] Centromere attached to microtubules.
Anaphase I	Microtubules contract separating homologous pairs to opposite poles. Centromeres do **not** split.
Telophase I	These stages often merge with each other because they are opposite. The spindle fibre network breaks down and two new ones begin to form, often at right angles to the first one.
Cytokinesis I	*First cell division starts.*
Prophase II	
Metaphase II	Chromatids line up on equator. Centromeres attached to microtubules.
Anaphase II	Centromeres **do** split and sister chromosomes pulled to opposite poles.
Telophase II	Spindle fibre network breaks down. Nuclear envelope reforms. Chromosomes uncoil.
Cytokinesis II	*Second cell division into four haploid cells.*

*[1] *[2] Both of these are important in producing genetic variety.

Since you have studied mitosis you already know most of meiosis. Meiosis has two phases, but the names are the same as in mitosis with I or II added. Likewise the key facts for each stage are very similar. On the diagrams on the next page I have kept the same pattern as in mitosis but indicated in blue where the five differences are.

Cell with two pairs of chromosomes

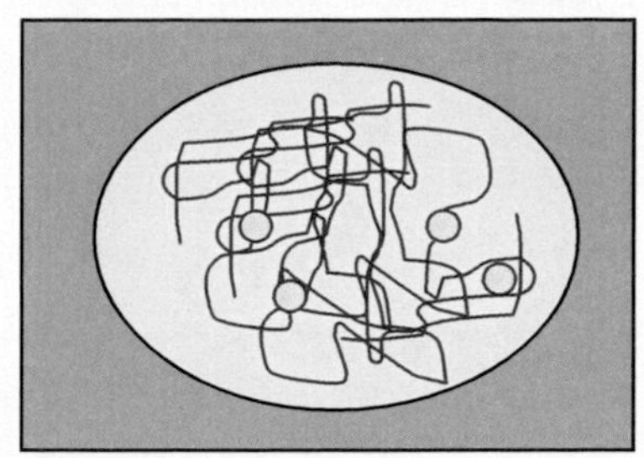

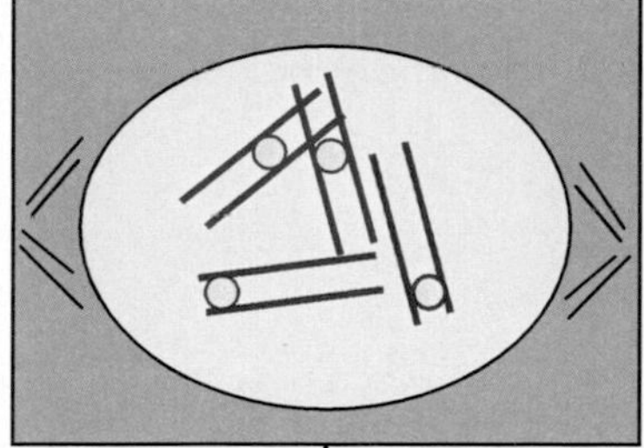

Prophase I

- Replicated DNA undergoes supercoiling and becomes visible under the light microscope;
- Spindle microtubules start to form;

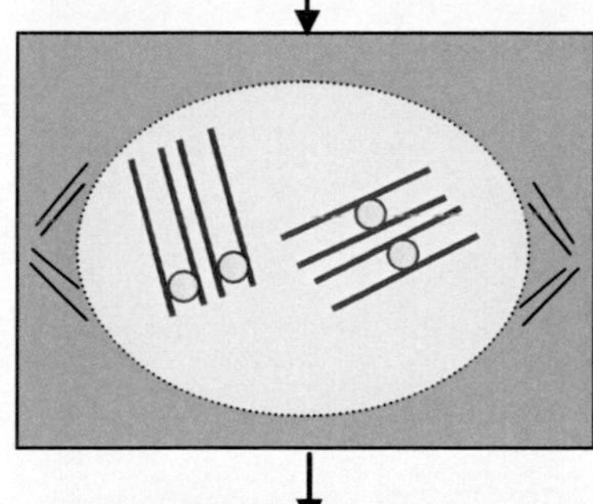

Later Prophase I

- Homologous chromosomes line up as pairs called bivalents. This is called synapsis. (This is a difference from mitosis).
- Crossing over may occur between non-sister chromatids within the bivalent leading to exchange of genetic material. (This is a difference from mitosis).
- Nuclear envelope breaks down.

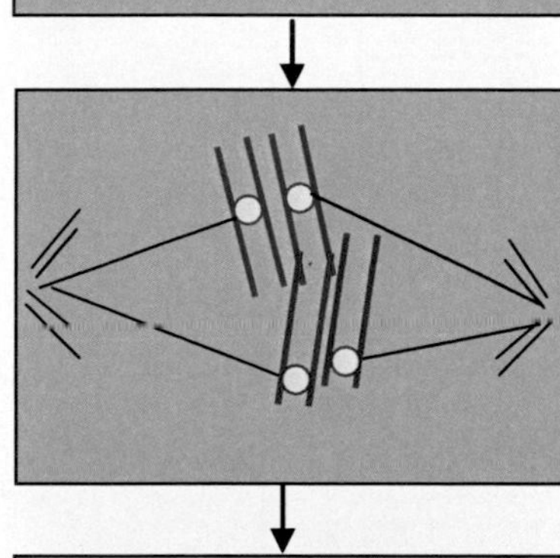

Metaphase I

- Microtubule network completed;
- Microtubules attach to centromeres;
- Bivalents move to central plate (equator) of cell. (This is a difference from mitosis).

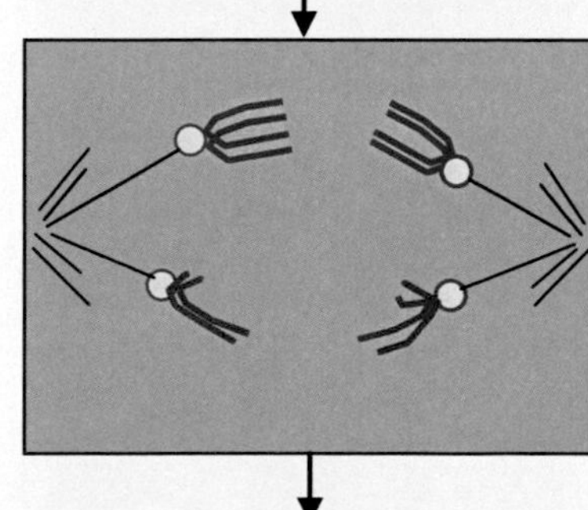

Anaphase I

- Centromeres <u>do not</u> split; (This is a difference from mitosis).
- Microtubules contract;
- Homologous chromosomes pulled to opposite poles. (This is a difference from mitosis).

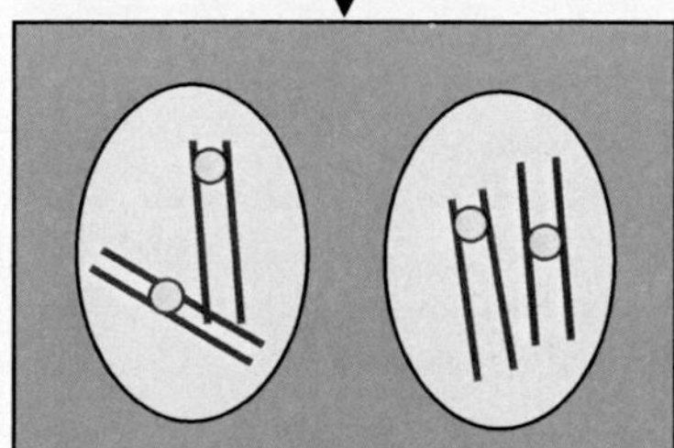

Telophase I

- Chromosomes uncoil;
- Spindle microtubules break down;
- Nuclear envelope reforms.

Note how each cell contains one chromosome from each homologous pair. The chromosome number has been halved so this is called a <u>reduction division</u>.

(There is no S phase) → Second division

Cytokinesis I

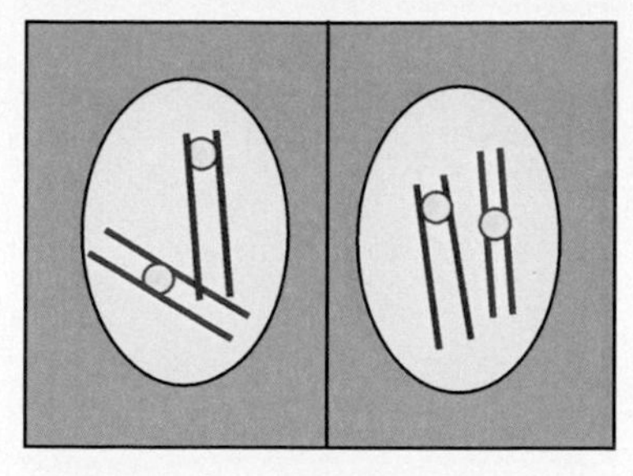

Each of these cells then undergoes the second division of meiosis.
Only one is shown below for simplicity.
The second division is very similar to mitosis.

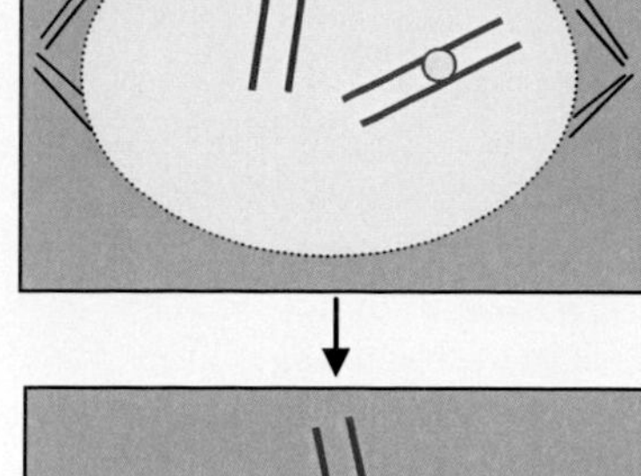

Prophase II

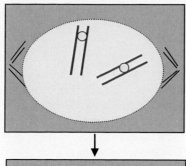

- The amount of supercoiling depends on the amount of uncoiling during telophase I;
- Spindle microtubules start to form;
- Nuclear envelope breaks down at end of prophase II.

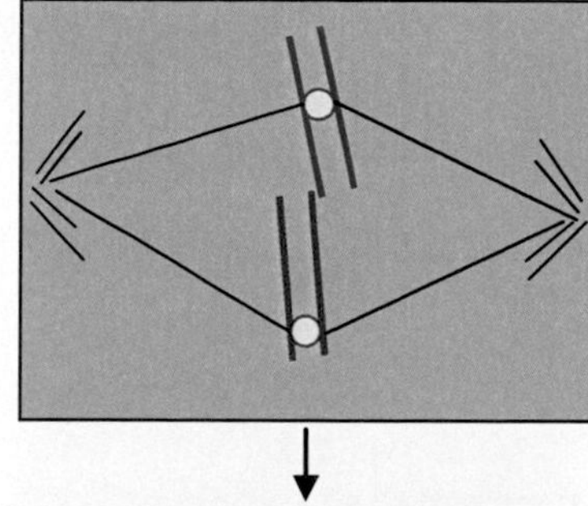

Metaphase II

- Chromosomes move to central plate (equator) of cell;
- Microtubule network completed;
- Microtubules attach to centromeres.

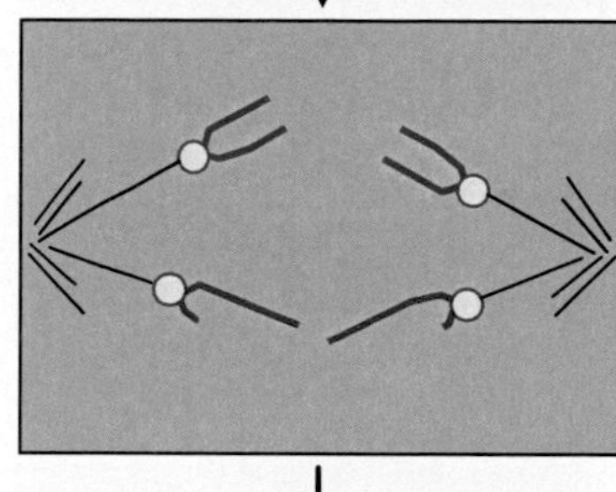

Anaphase II

- Centromeres **do** split;
- Microtubules contract;
- Chromosomes pulled to opposite poles.

A chromosome consists of a pair of sister chromatids, but as soon as the centromere splits the chromatids become chromosomes.

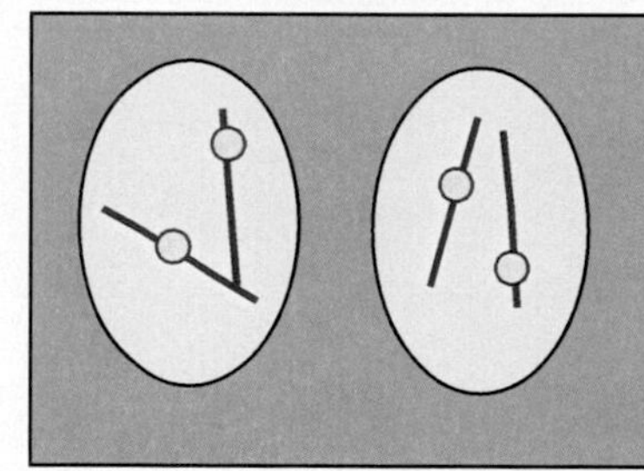

Telophase II

- Chromosomes uncoil;
- Spindle microtubules break down;
- Nuclear envelope reforms.

Cytokinesis II in both cells

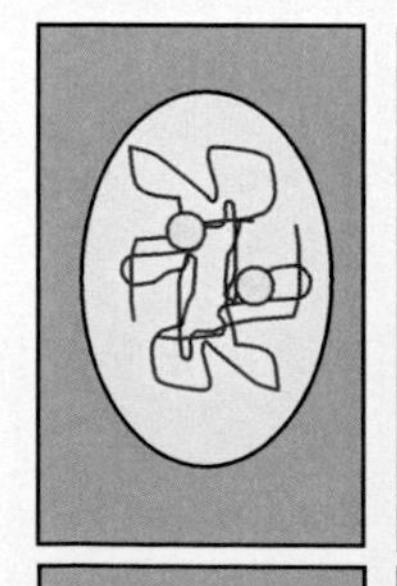
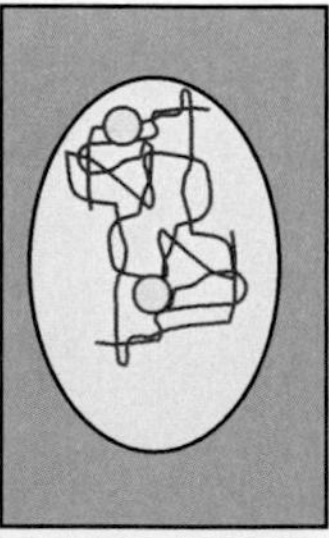
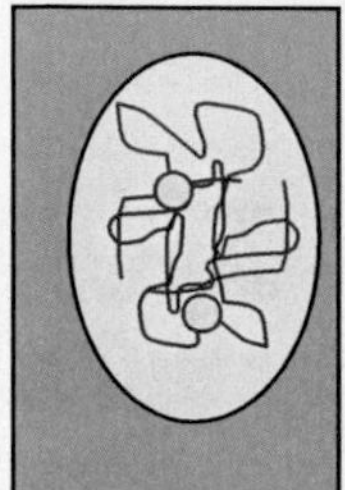
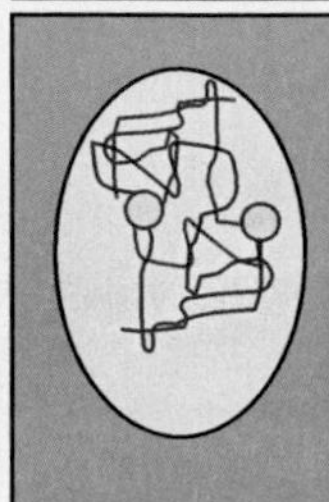

- Four cells from one original cell, each with one chromosome from each homologous pair.
- These are haploid cells.
- One or more may now undergo differentiation into gametes.
- In spermatogenesis all four differentiate into sperms.
- In oogenesis only one differentiates into a secondary oocyte.

Crossing Over

Crossing Over

This process may occur in prophase 1. Chromatids within the homologous pair may touch, break and re-join in a different way. This means parts of the maternal and paternal chromosomes swap over and this mixes alleles causing variety.

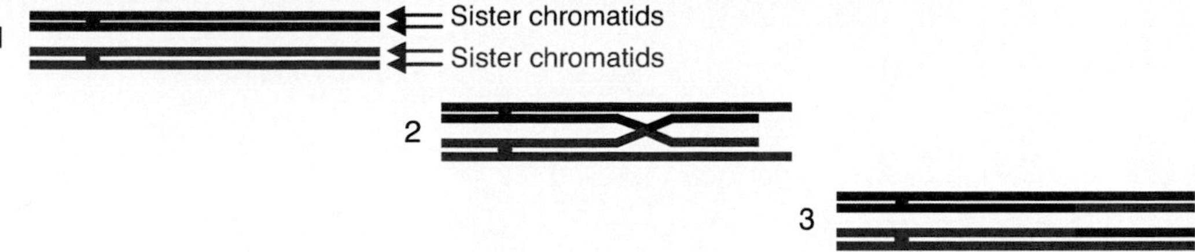
1
Sister chromatids
Sister chromatids
2
3

Non-disjunction

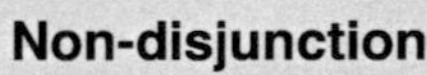
Non-disjunction

Normally at meiosis the cell shown below would split into four cells.

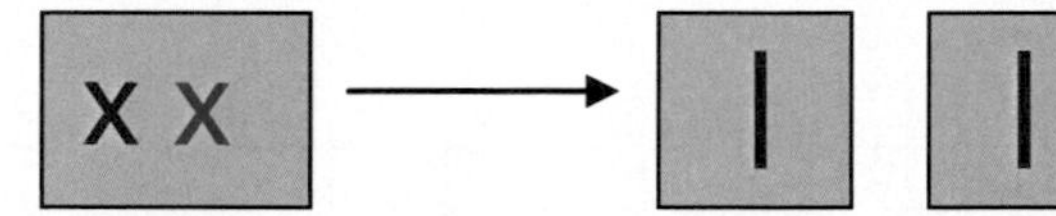
X X

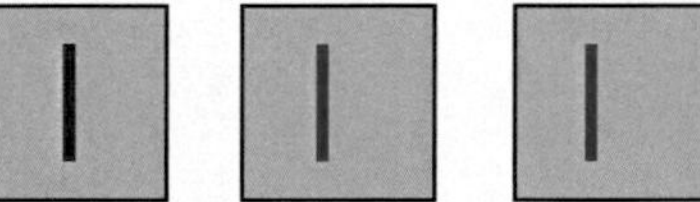

Non-disjunction is when separation of chromosomes fails to occur. This can happen at either the first or the second division.

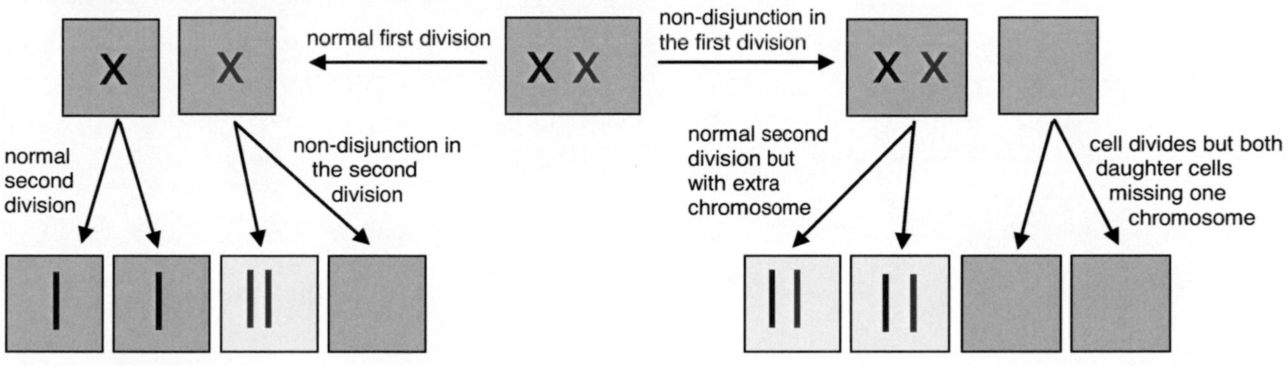
normal first division
X X
non-disjunction in the first division
X X
normal second division
non-disjunction in the second division
normal second division but with extra chromosome
cell divides but both daughter cells missing one chromosome

If a yellow gamete is fertilised, then the zygote will have one extra chromosome.
An example in humans is Down syndrome where the extra chromosome is number 21.
This is called trisomy 21.

Karyotyping

Karyotyping

Pair of chromosomes showing matching banding pattern.

Karyotyping is arranging the chromosomes in pairs according to their size and structure.

Key facts

- Used in pre-natal diagnosis of chromosome abnormalities;
- Fetal cells are collected using amniocentesis or chorionic villus sampling;
- Observing major changes in chromosome structure due to mutations such as translocation or duplication;
- Observing changes in chromosome number as in Down syndrome.

Karyotyping is performed using cells collected by chorionic villus sampling (CVS) or amniocentesis, for prenatal diagnosis of chromosome abnormalities.

Revision Meiosis	This exercise only revises the first part of meiosis as the second part is very similar to mitosis on page 20.

Drawing	Name of stage	Key points
	Early Prophase I	1. Supercoiling of DNA. 2.
	Later Prophase I	1. 2.
		1. 2. 3.
		1. 2. 3.
	Telophase I	1. Chromosomes uncoil. 2. 3.

How many chromosomes are there in each body cell of a person with Down syndrome?

What is karyotyping?

What is the purpose of karyotyping?

State two ways cells are collected for karyotyping?

Theoretical Genetics

Theoretical Genetics

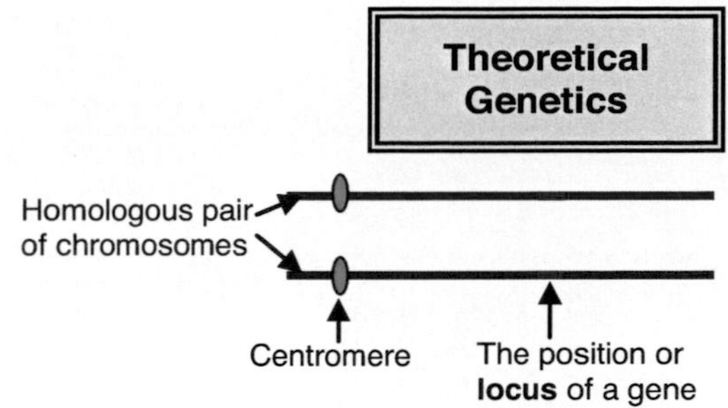

Homologous pair of chromosomes
Centromere
The position or **locus** of a gene

- The definitions are critical and really must be learnt or you will not be able to understand genetics problems or write good answers. Go to page 62.
- Remember that alleles are (nearly) always in pairs because chromosomes are in pairs and so the alleles occupy the pair of gene loci.

Codominance Multiple Alleles

Codominance and Multiple Alleles

- Codominance simply means that both alleles have an effect on the phenotype, ie the phenotype is some form of mixture of the two characteristics.
- Do NOT describe them as both being dominant.

Usually within a population there are many alleles of a gene and this is logically called multiple alleles. However any one individual can only have two of these alleles because it has only one pair of loci for any given gene.

Some genes have more than two alleles. This is called multiple alleles.

The example you have to know is the ABO blood grouping. Here there are three alleles – I^A, I^B, and i. This is an unusual case though because they also show codominance – alleles I^A and I^B are codominant. This results in four different phenotypes or blood groups.

Genotypes	Phenotype or blood group
I^AI^A, I^Ai	A
I^BI^B, I^Bi	B
I^AI^B	AB
ii	O

Sex Linkage

Sex Linkage

These are genes found on the X chromosome. The female sex chromosomes are XX and the male sex chromosomes are XY. The commonest mistake with these problems is that students forget that the Y chromosome does not carry an allele. A simple way of avoiding this mistake is to write the symbol Y^-. Writing $^-$ next to the Y will prevent you from writing an allele there.

Some genes are present on the X chromosome and absent from the shorter Y chromosome.

These are called sex linked or X-linked genes.

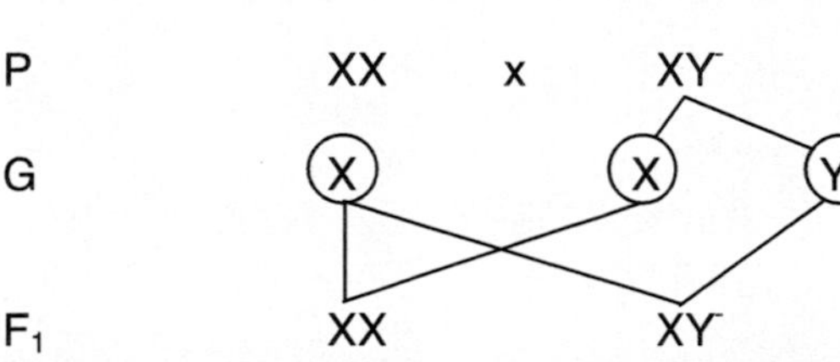

P
XX
x
XY^-
G
X
X
Y^-
F_1
XX
XY^-

Females can be heterozygous or homozygous with respect to sex linked genes.

The sex ratio is always 1:1

A female carrier must be heterozygous as one X chromosome has the dominant allele and the other has the recessive allele. X^AX^a

Males produce X sperm and Y sperm and therefore determine the sex of the offspring.

The term 'carrier' can be applied to any individual that is heterozygous for a recessive characteristic.

Colour-blindness and haemophilia are examples of sex linked characteristics.

Genetics Problems

Genetics Problems

Key points for answering genetics problems

- ALWAYS choose a letter to represent a gene where the upper and lower cases are CLEARLY different when on their own. S and s may look different next to each other but when you are quickly writing out a problem you could easily get them muddled when you have separated them into gametes.
- Always set out a genetics answer fully and clearly showing:
    - the parental generation
    - the gametes
    - the first filial generation

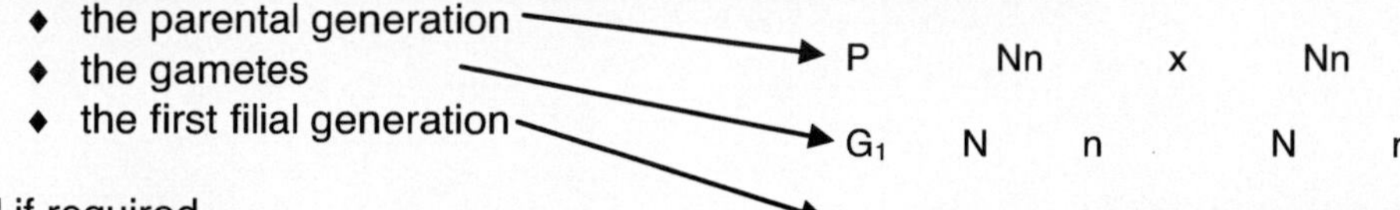

P Nn x Nn
G_1 N n N n
F_1

	N	n
N	NN Normal	Nn Normal
n	Nn Normal	nn Not normal

This is called a **Punnett grid.** Note that it includes both genotypes and phenotypes.

and if required
- the second gametes, G_2
- the second filial generation, F_2.

- A phenotype is expressed in words.
- A genotype is expressed in letters.

Key points for solving genetics problems

- Genetics problems are easy if you know the clues to look for.
- All problems you will be asked to solve fall into four types:
    1. Simple monohybrid cross.
    2. Codominance.
    3. Multiple alleles.
    4. Sex linkage.

Type 2 is easy to recognise because the offspring are some form of mixture of the parents, eg red x white gives pink, or black x white gives black and white speckled. Type 3 will only be on the human ABO blood grouping. Type 4 is less easy to recognise but is often indicated by the frequent use of 'male' and 'female' in the problem and differences between the male and female offspring.

Define dominant allele.	Define recessive allele.
Define genotype.	Define phenotype
Define heterozygous.	Define homozygous.
Define codominant.	Define locus.
Define carrier.	Define sex linkage.
Define test cross.	Which sex chromosome does not carry a sex linked allele?

The female sex chromosomes are .... The male sex chromosomes are ....

Example One – Pure breeding long winged flies are crossed with short winged flies and all the offspring are long winged. Long wings is dominant. When these offspring are crossed with short winged flies approximately one half of the offspring have short wings. Explain fully.

Solution.
We are told long wings is dominant so we can choose letters. Let L = long and l = short. We are also told the long winged flies are pure breeding which means the genotype is homozygous. The genotype must be LL. The short wing parents must be ll as l is recessive.

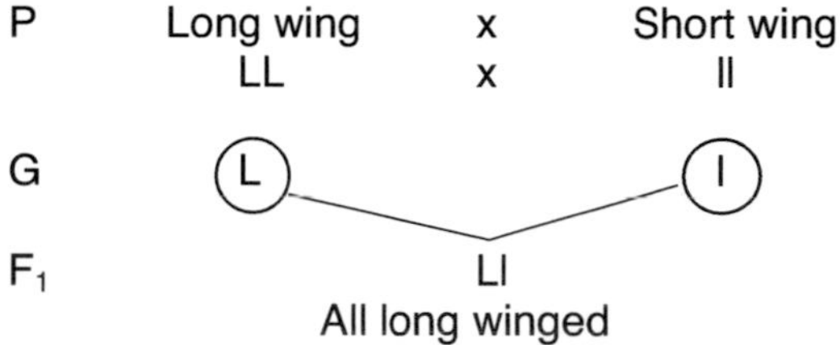

P Long wing x Short wing
LL x ll
G L l
F_1 Ll
All long winged

Notice that on the gametes row we only need to write one L and one l. This is because all the gametes are the same and so there is no need to write more. This saves time in the exam. Now for the second part of the problem. Since we are not crossing offspring amongst themselves we have to start with P again.

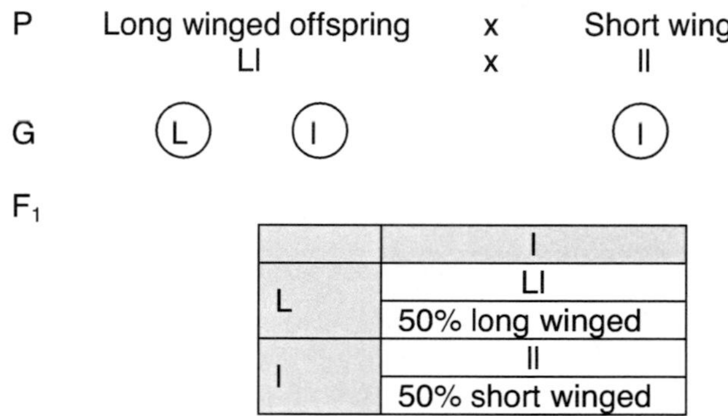

P Long winged offspring x Short wing
Ll x ll
G L l l
F_1

	l
L	Ll 50% long winged
l	ll 50% short winged

In theory we get a 50:50 or 1:1 ratio. In the actual cross we get approximately 50:50 and so, allowing for experimental error, our actual or observed ratio fits our ratio predicted from the Punnett grid above.

Example Two – Claire is blood group A and her husband Clive is blood group O. Celine is blood group AB and her husband David is blood group B. At the hospital Claire and Celine's baby girls were born at the same time but Claire feels the staff accidentally muddled them up. Baby Melissa given to Celine is blood group O. Explain how this could solve the difficulty.

Solution
If the baby is blood group O it's genotype must be ii. Celine is blood group AB and therefore has the genotype I^AI^B so she cannot give an i allele to the baby. Claire is blood group A and so either has the genotype I^AI^A or I^Ai. Clive has to have the genotype ii. This means that the baby must belong to Claire and Clive.

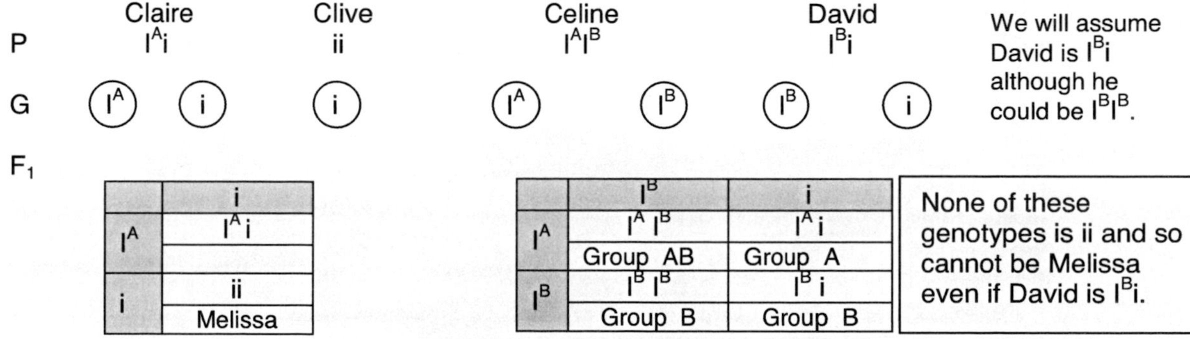

P Claire I^Ai Clive ii Celine I^AI^B David I^Bi
G I^A i i I^A I^B I^B i
We will assume David is I^Bi although he could be I^BI^B.
F_1
None of these genotypes is ii and so cannot be Melissa even if David is I^Bi.

	i
I^A	I^Ai
i	ii Melissa

	I^B	i
I^A	I^AI^B Group AB	I^Ai Group A
I^B	I^BI^B Group B	I^Bi Group B

Example Three – A woman, whose father had haemophilia but whose mother was normal (not a carrier), married a man who also had haemophilia. Determine the phenotypes of their sons and daughters.

Solution
Let H = the normal allele; h = the haemophilia allele.
The woman's father must have had the genotype X^hY^- since he had haemophilia. The woman inherited his X^h chromosome, but her other X chromosome from her mother was normal X^H. Thus the woman had the genotype X^HX^h. Her husband was X^hY^-.

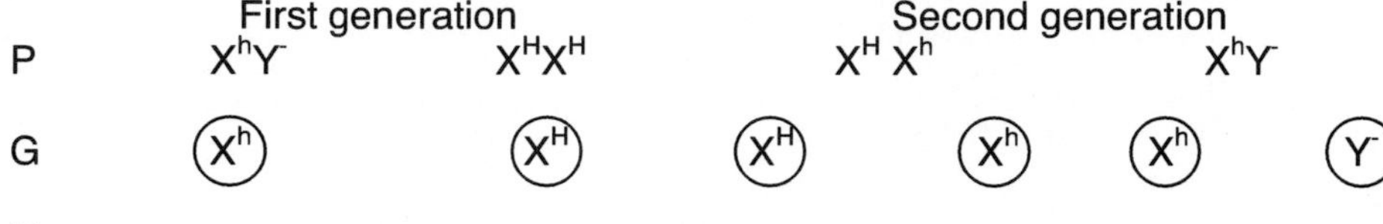

First generation
P
X^hY^-
X^HX^H
Second generation
$X^H X^h$
X^hY^-
G
X^h
X^H
X^H
X^h
X^h
Y^-

F_1

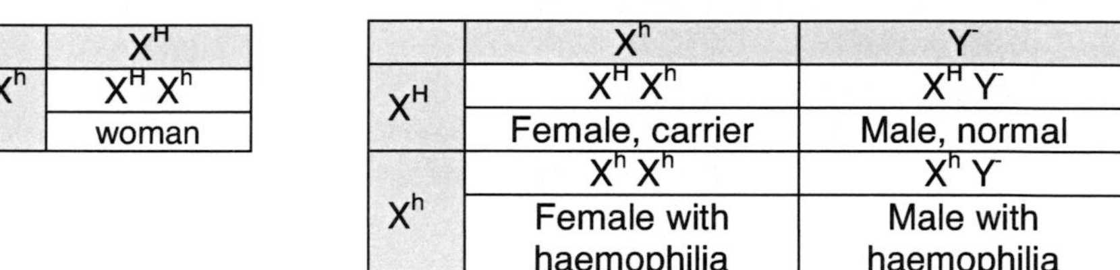

	X^H
X^h	$X^H X^h$ woman

	X^h	Y^-
X^H	$X^H X^h$ Female, carrier	$X^H Y^-$ Male, normal
X^h	$X^h X^h$ Female with haemophilia	$X^h Y^-$ Male with haemophilia

There are several problems for you to try at the end of this chapter.

Pedigree Charts

Pedigree Charts

These have standard symbols.

Normal female Normal male Affected female Affected male

The symbol for a heterozygous individual is rather variable. Sometimes half the square or circle is filled in, sometimes there is a black dot in the middle of the square or circle. The question will have a key, or if <u>you</u> draw it <u>you</u> have to provide a key.

Example

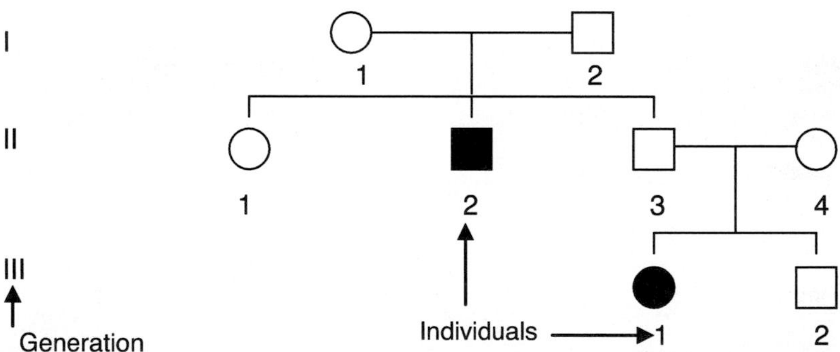

I
1
2
II
1
2
3
4
III
Generation
Individuals
1
2

Some information has deliberately been missed from the above diagram but we can deduce it.
Two common questions are – 1. Is the disorder sex linked? 2. Is the disorder dominant or recessive?
We can answer question 2 first. The disorder has to be recessive since neither individual in generation I has it but II2 does have it. Similarly III1 has it but neither of her parents.
Is it sex linked? Remember that sex linked alleles are only on the X chromosome. If we give the symbol n to the disorder then III1 must be X^nX^n. One X^n must have come from her father making him X^nY. He should show the disorder but he doesn't, and thus from this we can deduce that the gene is not sex linked. A useful hint is that it is often a male that provides the essential clue.

We can now continue to deduce that both I1 and I2 must be heterozygous, and also II3 and II4.
We could now show this in a Punnett grid. Use N for the dominant normal allele and n for the recessive disorder allele.

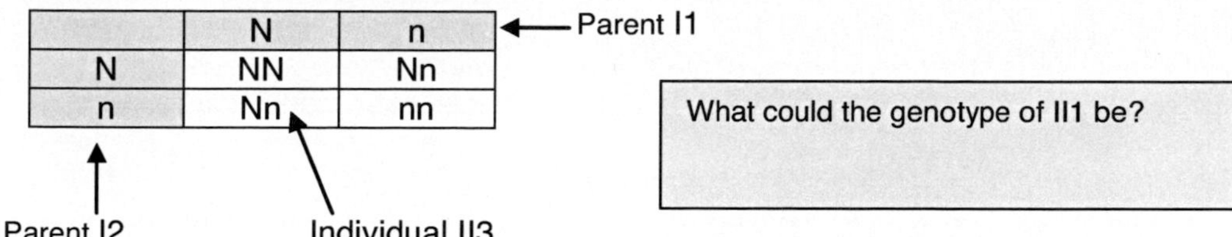

	N	n
N	NN	Nn
n	Nn	nn

Parent I1
Parent I2
Individual II3

What could the genotype of II1 be?

The Test Cross

Test Cross

This is done in order to determine whether a dominant phenotype is homozygous or heterozygous. This is <u>always</u> crossed with the homozygous recessive. If the dominant phenotype is in fact heterozygous we would expect 50% of the offspring to show the recessive phenotype. An example of a test cross is shown below.

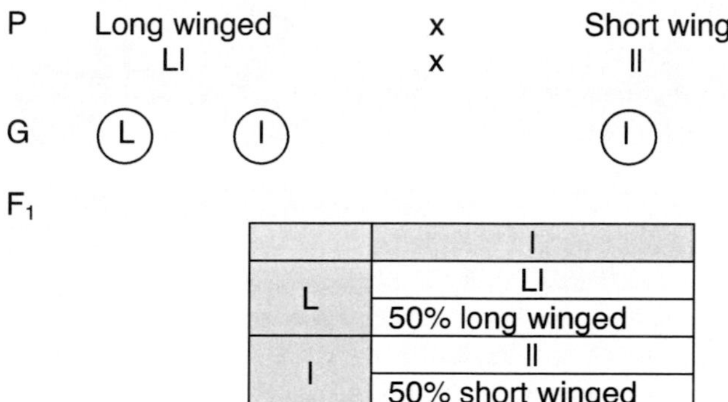

P Long winged x Short wing
Ll x ll

G (L) (l) (l)

F_1

	l
L	Ll 50% long winged
l	ll 50% short winged

The Polymerase Chain Reaction

Polymerase Chain Reaction

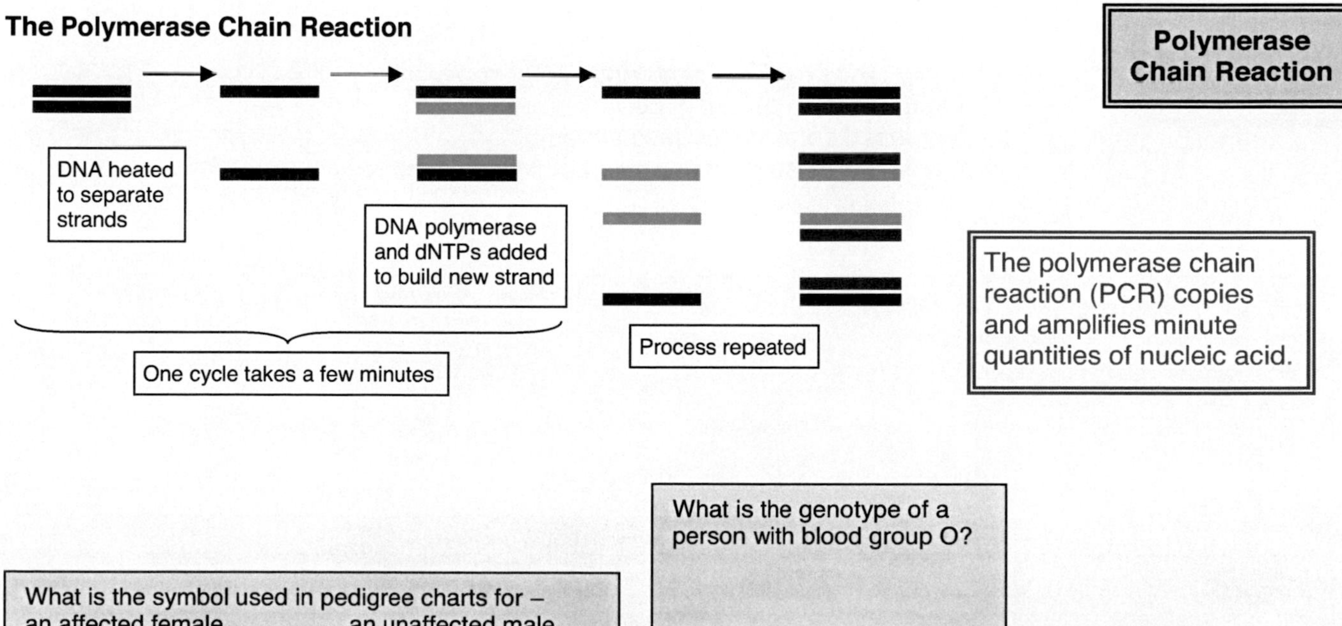

DNA heated to separate strands
DNA polymerase and dNTPs added to build new strand
One cycle takes a few minutes
Process repeated

The polymerase chain reaction (PCR) copies and amplifies minute quantities of nucleic acid.

What is the genotype of a person with blood group O?

What is the symbol used in pedigree charts for –
an affected female an unaffected male

What is the genotype of a person who is a carrier for haemophilia?

DNA Profiling

DNA profiling

Gel electrophoresis involves fragments of DNA moving in an electric field and separating according to their size.

Gel electrophoresis of DNA is used in DNA profiling.

Principles

- Satellite DNA is short sequences of DNA repeated many times;
- It varies between individuals so much that the probability of two individuals being the same is zero;
- PCR may be used to increase the amount of DNA;
- Great care to prevent contamination is required as the PCR will also amplify contaminant DNA;
- DNA is cut up with restriction enzymes (see section Gene Transfer on page 67);
- Gel electrophoresis separates the DNA fragments;
- The banding patterns are compared.

Uses

- Paternity – sometimes a woman is unsure who the father might be, or the man disputes being the father or wants to know if he is the father. DNA profiling from a mouth swab is used.
- Forensic investigations – often tiny samples of DNA can be found such as a drop of blood or saliva, a hair follicle, scrapings under a finger nail, and the DNA can be amplified using the PCR before profiling.

Other uses -

- Family relationships for immigrants;
- Determining if rare birds and other animals being sold as captive bred have actually been captive bred or been stolen from the wild.

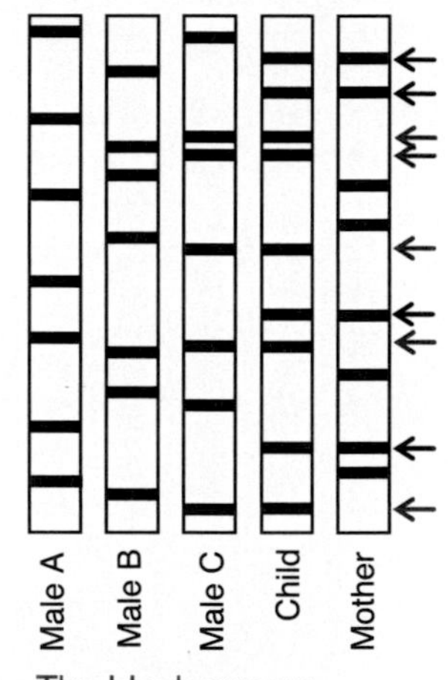

Male A
Male B
Male C
Child
Mother

The black arrows correspond to the mother.
The red arrows show that the father of the child is male C.

An example of how DNA profiling has been used to determine paternity.

Human Genome Project

The Human Genome Project

Outcomes

- Improved knowledge of how human genes function;
- Improved diagnosis of genetic disease;
- Increased potential for gene therapy;
- Increased potential to design drugs to combat genetic malfunctions.

What is gel electrophoresis?

What does the polymerase chain reaction do?

What is a test cross?

What is the genetic principle of the test cross?

Gene Transfer

Key requirements

- The gene we want to transfer;
- A plasmid;
- A host cell – usually a bacterium (eg. *E.coli*) or yeast;
- Two enzymes - a restriction enzyme;
  - DNA ligase.

What is a plasmid?

(See page 13).

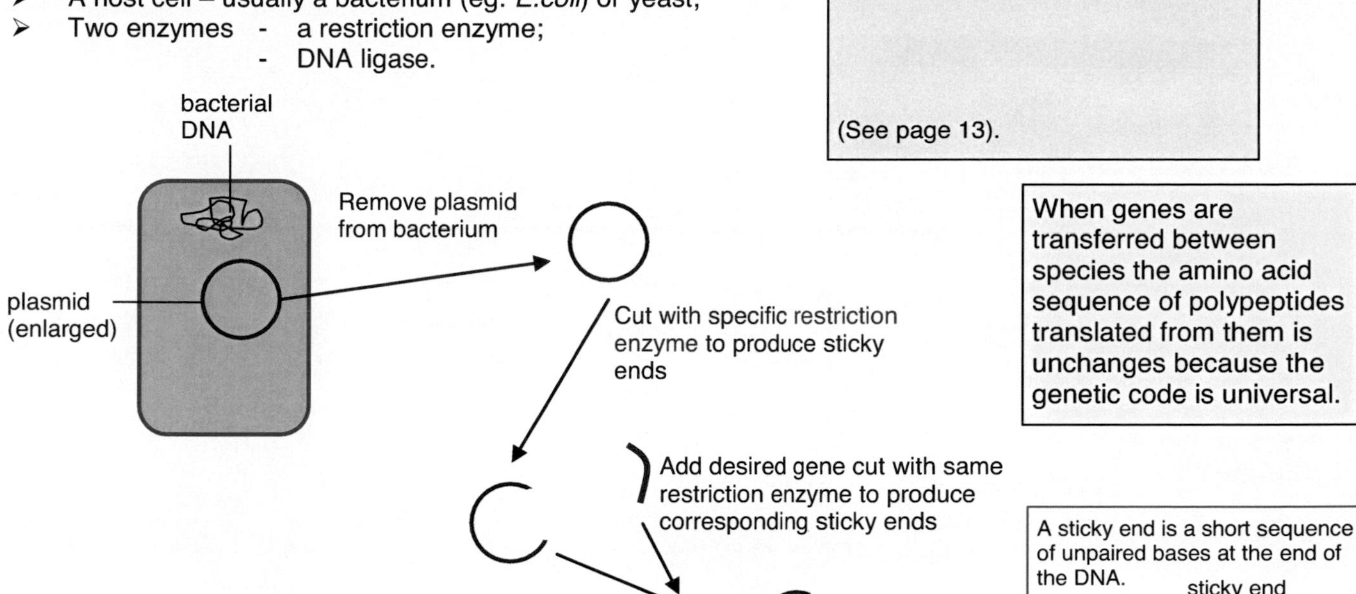

bacterial DNA
plasmid (enlarged)
Remove plasmid from bacterium
Cut with specific restriction enzyme to produce sticky ends
Add desired gene cut with same restriction enzyme to produce corresponding sticky ends

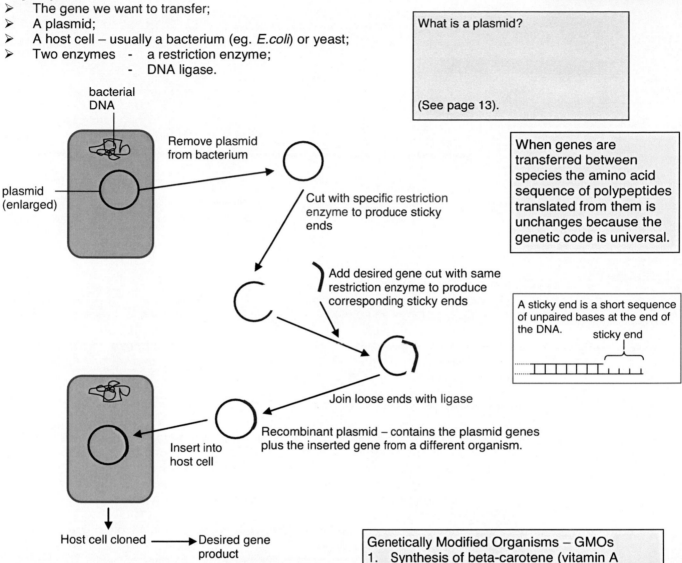

When genes are transferred between species the amino acid sequence of polypeptides translated from them is unchanges because the genetic code is universal.

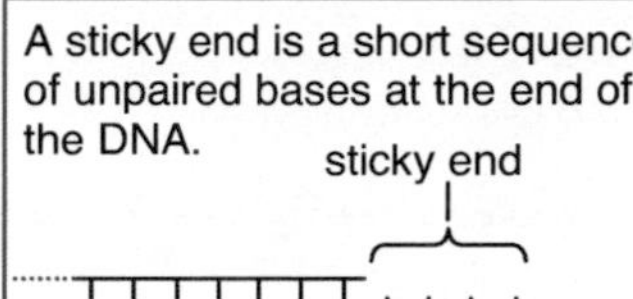

A sticky end is a short sequence of unpaired bases at the end of the DNA.
sticky end

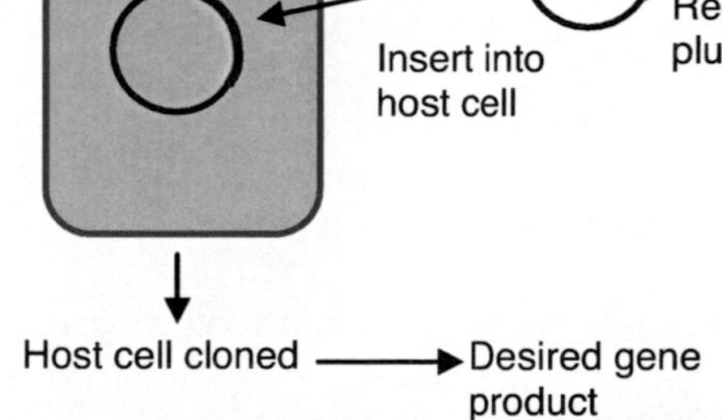

Join loose ends with ligase
Recombinant plasmid – contains the plasmid genes plus the inserted gene from a different organism.
Insert into host cell
Host cell cloned
Desired gene product

Genetically Modified Organisms – GMOs

1. Synthesis of beta-carotene (vitamin A precursor) in rice ('Golden Rice')
2. Synthesis of Bt toxin in cotton (see below).

Points for discussion – Synthesis of Bt toxin in cotton

Benefits

- *Bacillus thuringiensis* is a bacterium that produces a toxin which kills caterpillars that consume the bacteria;
- Bt cotton contains the bacterial gene that codes for the toxin;
- The cotton bollworm is a serious pest in the major cotton growing countries of the world;
- Control by chemicals was expensive, damaging to the environment, damaging to human health;
- Bt cotton has resulted in an enormous reduction in the use of chemical pesticides;
- Insects quickly became resistant to one insecticide requiring a more toxic one or more environmentally damaging one;
- Bt cotton is specifically targeted at insects feeding on the cotton so no other insects are affected;
- Long term monitoring has shown no resistance yet in cotton pest species;
- Cotton yields have increased significantly.

Possible harm

- The gene may spread to other plant species. However all studies so far have shown this has not occurred.
- The gene could however spread easily to wild species of cotton but its use is banned in countries where these wild varieties grow.
- Exposure of soil organisms to Bt toxin leached from dead plant material is potentially harmful but again studies have shown that there is no evidence of this.

Cloning Technique

The Cloning Technique

Define clone.

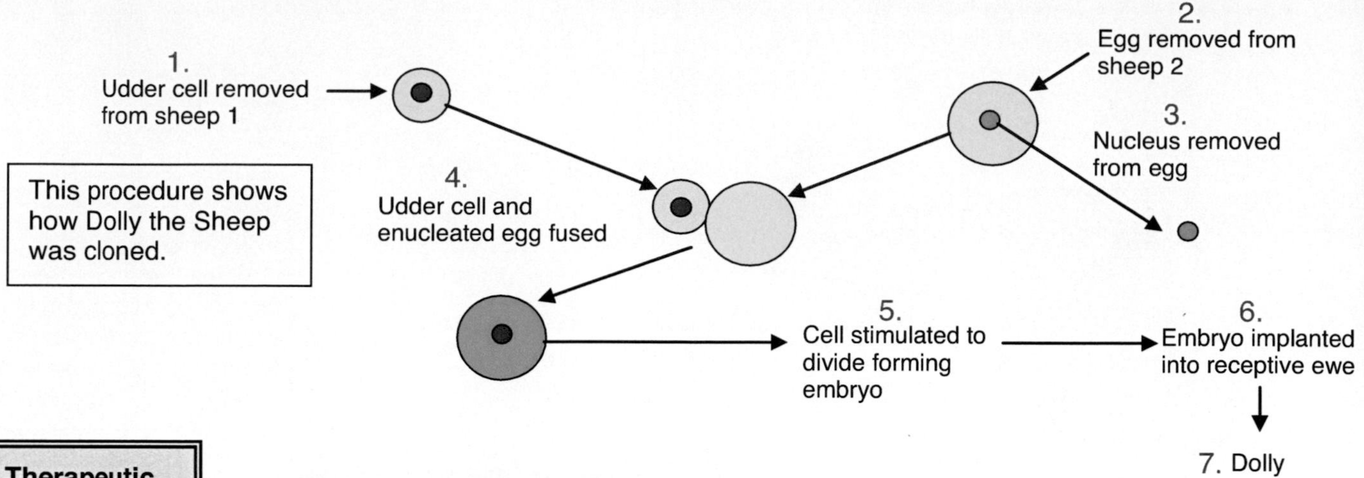
1.
Udder cell removed from sheep 1
This procedure shows how Dolly the Sheep was cloned.
2.
Egg removed from sheep 2
3.
Nucleus removed from egg
4.
Udder cell and enucleated egg fused
5.
Cell stimulated to divide forming embryo
6.
Embryo implanted into receptive ewe
7. Dolly

Therapeutic Cloning

Ethics of Therapeutic Human Cloning

This is the creation of an embryo to supply embryonic stem cells for medical use. The technique is the same as for Dolly – a cell from the adult is removed and the nucleus inserted into an empty egg cell. Over 4 days the cell divides to form a hollow ball of cells, or blastocyst, with an inner cell mass that contains the stem cells. The ball is broken open and the stem cells cultured.

Points for Discussion

For

- The cells grown from stem cells are genetically identical to the adult from whom the original cell was taken and so there are no difficulties with rejection and no need for anti-rejection drugs which can leave the body open to other diseases;
- Stem cells can develop into any type of cell – nerve, blood, heart muscle, brain;
- The potential is to repair damage or failure caused by injury, heart attack, Alzheimer's, Parkinson's, leukaemia;
- An even further potential is that they could develop into a complete organ.

Against

- Requires the formation of an embryo that has to be destroyed;
- If the embryo is not destroyed it would develop into a clone of the adult;
- More research needs to be done on adult stem cells that can develop into the tissue from which they were derived and in some cases other tissues, eg. adult bone marrow stem cells can develop into liver cells;
- Can adult stem cells be reprogrammed to become like embryonic stem cells?
- Very occasionally stem cells can develop into tumour cells.

State the two enzymes used in gene transfer.

What is a recombinant plasmid?

Why does transferring a gene from one organism to another not alter the polypeptide translated from it?

Self-test Quiz on Topic 4

1. A eukaryotic chromosome is composed of
   a. DNA and protein,
   b. DNA and phospholipid,
   c. DNA and RNA,
   d. DNA, sugar, phosphate.

2. Karyotyping is a process whereby
   a. genes are sorted according to size,
   b. genetic abnormalities can be marked on chromosomes,
   c. the number of chromosomes can be counted,
   d. chromosomes are sorted according to size and structure.

3. A gene mutation is
   a. due to non-disjunction,
   b. a change in the number of chromosomes,
   c. a change in the base sequence of DNA,
   d. a failure in the process of meiosis.

4. Which of the following shows a correct sequence of stages of the first division of meiosis?
   a. Prophase I, metaphase I, telophase I, anaphase I.
   b. Prophase I, anaphase I, metaphase I, telophase I.
   c. Prophase I, metaphase I, anaphase I, telophase I.
   d. Prophase I, telophase I, metaphase I, anaphase I.

5. Non-disjunction occurs as a result of
   a. the two parts of meiosis occurring in reverse order,
   b. a failure in the spindle fibre network of microtubules,
   c. genes becoming lost,
   d. a failure in the process of cytokinesis.

6. The polymerase chain reaction is a process that
   a. repeatedly copies DNA,
   b. repeatedly copies polypeptides,
   c. increases the length of a DNA molecule,
   d. forms mRNA from DNA.

7. A clone could be
   a. a group of cells produced by mitosis,
   b. a group of cells produced by meiosis,
   c. the offspring produced by sexual reproduction,
   d. a group of cells having different chromosome numbers.

8. During meiosis crossing over occurs during
   a. anaphase.
   b. metaphase.
   c. interphase.
   d. prophase.

9. The genome can be defined as
   a. the number of homozygous genes in a cell,
   b. all the genetic information of a cell or organism,
   c. all of the genes on one chromosome,
   d. all of the genes on the sex chromosomes.

10. Which is the correct statement for sickle cell anaemia?
    a. GAG has mutated to GTG causing glutamic acid to be replaced by valine;
    b. GAG has mutated to GTG causing valine to be replaced by glutamic acid;
    c. GTG has mutated to GAG causing glutamic acid to be replaced by valine;;
    d. GTG has mutated to GAG causing valine to be replaced by glutamic acid.

11. Gel electrophoresis is used in
    a. karyotyping;
    b. DNA profiling;
    c. meiosis;
    d. forming a Punnett grid.

12. With sex-linked (X-linked) genes
    a. both males and females are carriers;
    b. only males are affected;
    c. only females are carriers;
    d. only twins are affected.

13. Down syndrome is
    a. an example of a trisomy;
    b. a result of non-disjunction in the sex chromosomes;
    c. due to a gene mutation;
    d. an example of karyotyping.

14. A haploid cell is one in which
    a. only one of each pair of chromosomes is present;
    b. there are 23 pairs of chromosomes;
    c. the sex chromosomes are missing;
    d. there is no nucleus.

15. Sickle cell anaemia is
    a. a human genetic disease caused by an extra chromosome 21;
    b. a genetic disease only inherited by a son from his father;
    c. caused by the production of a faulty protein;
    d. due to non-disjunction.

16. The probability that a family of four children born to the same parents consists only of boys is
    a. a quarter;
    b. a half;
    c. an eighth;
    d. a sixteenth,

17. A mother of a child is blood group A and the father is blood group B. The child could have blood group
    a. A;
    b. B;
    c. A or B;
    d. A, B, AB, or O.

18. Huntingdons disease is caused by a dominant allele that is not sex linked. If the father has one copy of the allele and the mother no copies, what is the probability that their second child will have the allele?
    a. An eighth;
    b. A quarter;
    c. A half;
    d. Zero.

19. The picture on the right shows a number of DNA profiles. Which male is the father of the child?
   a. Male A.
   b. Male B.
   c. Male C.
   d. Male D.

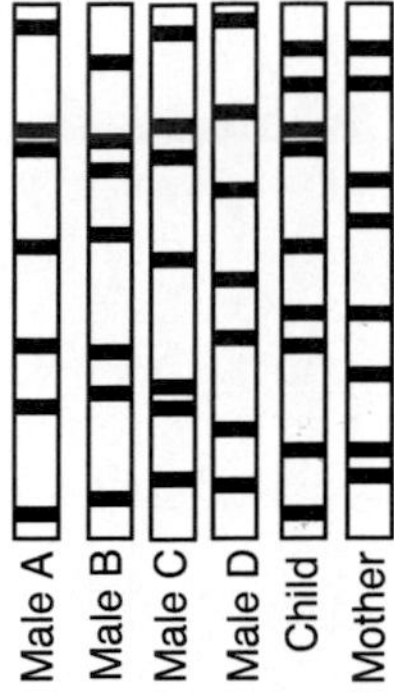
Male A
Male B
Male C
Male D
Child
Mother

20. Sickle cell anaemia is caused by
   a. a dominant gene mutation;
   b. a chromosome mutation;
   c. a base substitution mutation;
   d. a sex linked gene.

21. Two chromosomes that carry the same genes but not necessarily the same alleles are called
   a. homozygous chromosomes;
   b. homologous chromosomes;
   c. sex chromosomes;
   d. codominant chromosomes.

22. A woman has one recessive sex linked haemophilia allele and one normal allele. Which of the following statements is true?
   a. She is a carrier for the haemophilia allele.
   b. She will develop haemophilia.
   c. The probability of passing the haemophilia allele to her sons is 100%.
   d. All of her daughters will have the same genotype as herself.

23. A bacterial gene could work in a plant cell because
   a. bacteria are prokaryotes;
   b. the bacterial chromosome is circular and so are plant plasmids;
   c. bacterial cells and plant cells have the same enzymes for DNA replication;
   d. the genetic code is universal.

24. A restriction enzyme is one that
   a. joins two fragments of DNA together;
   b. prevents the replication of DNA;
   c. cuts DNA;
   d. is synthesised by plasmids.

25. A man has a sex linked recessive allele. His wife does not. What is the probability that their second son will also have the sex linked recessive allele?
   a. 100%.
   b. 75%.
   c. 25%.
   d. 0%.

26. A woman is homozygous for a recessive allele found on chromosome 20. Her husband is heterozygous. The probability that she will have a son who is also heterozygous is
   a. 50%.
   b. 0%.
   c. 25%.
   d. 75%.

Genetics Problems

(Answers to these questions are given in Appendix 6 on pages 233 - 235).

Many of the organisms used are imaginary to make a change from all the ones on mice, rabbits and fruit flies. Treat the genetics in the normal way though.

1. Two black female mice were crossed with a grey male. In several litters female A produced 19 black and 18 grey young. Female B produced 25 black young.
   What can you deduce about the nature of black and grey fur colour in mice, and what are the genotypes of the parents?

2. Two yellow Bandycoots were thought by their keeper to be homozygous for coat colour. When they were mated all the babies were yellow. However when these offspring were later mated amongst themselves. The F_2 generation, some of these offspring were orange. This meant that one of the grandparents was heterozygous.
   How would you find out which grandparent was heterozygous?

3. In the Giant Boring beetle (*Coleopsis yawnii*) green eyes are dominant over blue. A blue-eyed beetle, both of whose parents had green eyes, was mated with a green-eyed beetle. They have one baby beetle which is blue-eyed. Deduce the genotypes of all these five individuals? If they have another baby beetle could it be green-eyed, and if so determine its genotype.

4. Once upon a time a Quoll with luminous eyes met a Quoll with blue eyes. Shortly afterwards several little Quolls were born and they all had luminous eyes. Deduce the genotypes of the parents and the offspring.
   Later on in life the little Quolls grew up and all but one met luminous eyed Quolls. All their babies had luminous eyes. The one lonely Quoll however met a beautiful blue-eyed Quoll and some of their babies had blue eyes. Deduce the genotypes of the lonely Quoll, his beautiful mate, and their babies.

5. In humans the ability to taste phenylthiourea depends on the presence of a dominant allele. The gene is not sex linked.
   a. Construct a pedigree chart to show a homozygous taster man and a non-taster woman and their two children.
   b. One of these children marries a person of the same genotype for this gene. Construct a pedigree chart to show this and their three children. Each child has a different genotype.

6. Grandpa has blood group O. His first child, Horace, married a group O woman and they had two children, Belinda and Bertha, who were both group B.
   Grandpa's second child was group A, but the third child in the family, Clint, was group O. Grandpa thought it wise to tell his children before they studied this revision guide that the third child had been adopted.
   a. Deduce Granny's genotype showing all your reasoning.
   b. Why did Grandpa decide to say that Clint was adopted?

7. Web feet is a sex linked characteristic in Dingbats. Female Dingbats are XX and males XY. A webbed male is crossed with a homozygous normal female and the baby Dingbat is a female with normal feet.
   Deduce whether the web allele is dominant or recessive.
   If their next baby is a male determine whether it will have web or normal feet.

Topic 5

Ecology and Evolution

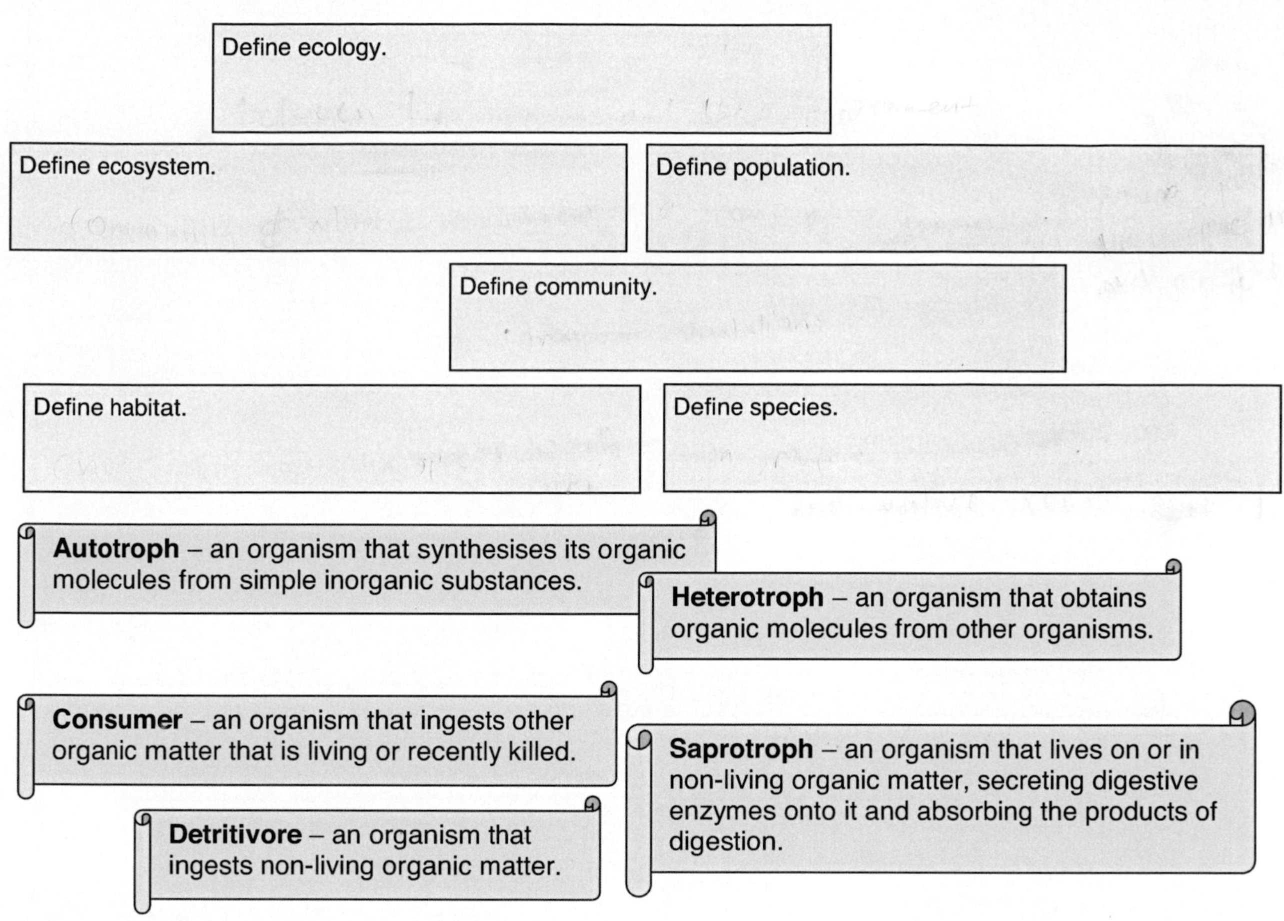

Define ecology.
Define ecosystem.
Define population.
Define community.
Define habitat.
Define species.
Autotroph – an organism that synthesises its organic molecules from simple inorganic substances.
Heterotroph – an organism that obtains organic molecules from other organisms.
Consumer – an organism that ingests other organic matter that is living or recently killed.
Saprotroph – an organism that lives on or in non-living organic matter, secreting digestive enzymes onto it and absorbing the products of digestion.
Detritivore – an organism that ingests non-living organic matter.

Trophic Levels and Food Chains

Trophic Levels and Food Chains

The three major trophic levels are usually represented in a chain or pyramid.

Producer ⟶ Primary consumer ⟶ Secondary consumer

Secondary consumers and above are grouped as higher consumers.
Primary consumers are also called herbivores and higher consumers are all carnivores.
Note the direction of the arrows – always in the direction of the energy flow.

Define trophic level.

- You need to know 3 examples of food chains with at least 4 organisms in each. Only one example is given as it is better to use organisms that you may be familiar with from your own environment. Avoid chains with humans and domestic animals.
- (corn – chicken – human – man-eating tiger would be a poor example.)
- Each chain should include a producer.
- Named organisms at species or genus level should be used.
- Common species names can be used instead of binomial names.
- General names such as 'tree' or 'fish' should not be used.

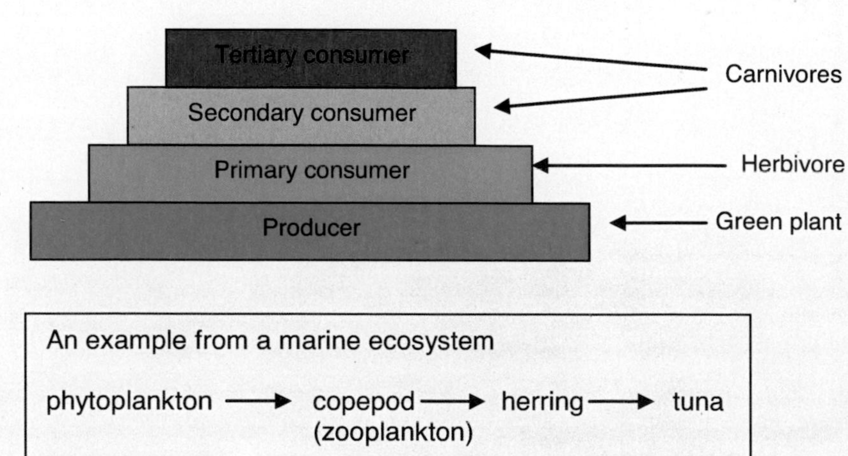

Tertiary consumer
Secondary consumer
Primary consumer
Producer
Carnivores
Herbivore
Green plant
An example from a marine ecosystem
phytoplankton ⟶ copepod (zooplankton) ⟶ herring ⟶ tuna

Food Webs

Food Webs

Key points

- A food web is a series of interlinking food chains.
- An omnivore is an animal that is both a herbivore and a carnivore.
- Omnivores and carnivores can change their trophic level depending on what they are eating.

Look at the food web below.

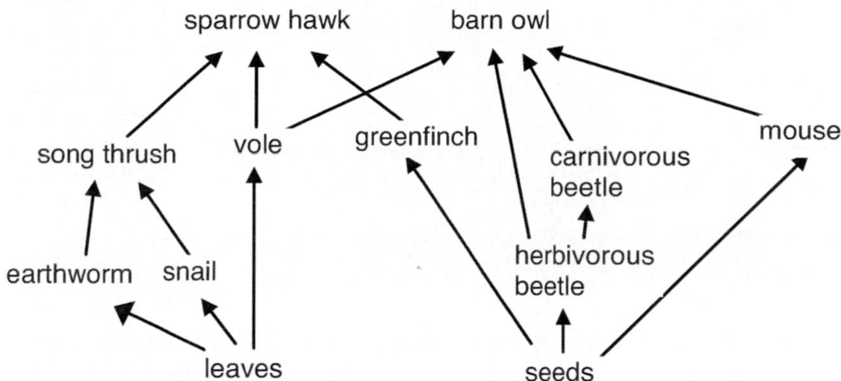

sparrow hawk
barn owl
song thrush
vole
greenfinch
carnivorous beetle
mouse
earthworm
snail
herbivorous beetle
leaves
seeds

Deduce the trophic level of:
1. The snail. ____________
2. The carnivorous beetle. ____________
3. The mouse. ____________
4. The sparrow hawk eating the vole. ____________
5. The sparrow hawk eating the song thrush. ____________
6. The barn owl eating the herbivorous beetle. ____________
7. The barn owl eating the carnivorous beetle. ____________

Energy Flow

Energy Flow

The following diagram illustrates energy flow and losses in a food chain.

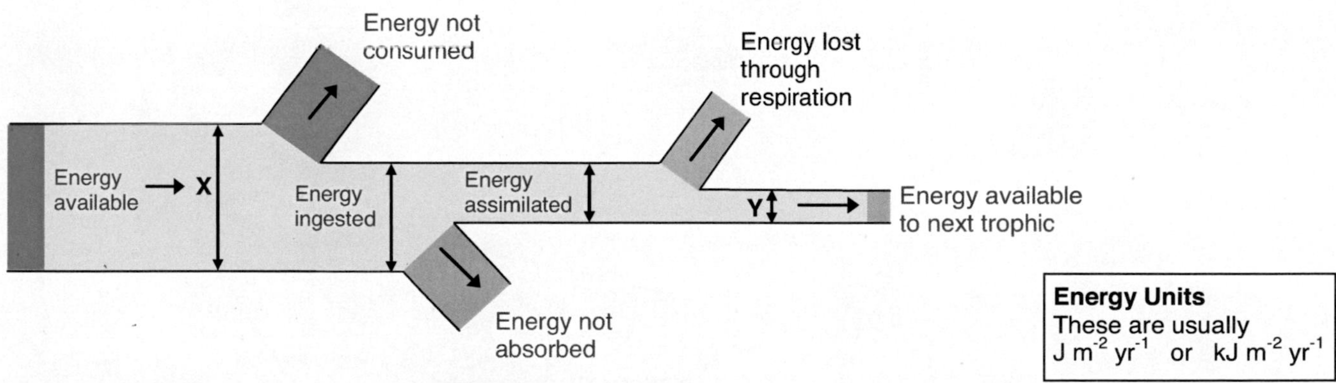

Energy not consumed
Energy lost through respiration
Energy available
X
Energy ingested
Energy assimilated
Y
Energy available to next trophic
Energy not absorbed

Energy Units
These are usually
$J\ m^{-2}\ yr^{-1}$ or $kJ\ m^{-2}\ yr^{-1}$

We can use the snail ----- song thrush link in the web above to illustrate this. The energy available is all the leaves in the place where the snail lives. ■ But it will not eat all of the leaves. ■ After digesting and absorbing some of the leaf material it has eaten some will pass out of its gut as faeces. ■ The snail moves around and therefore uses up some of the energy it has consumed. ■ The remainder of the energy is used for growth. This is what is available to the song thrush. ■

Efficiency of energy flow
In the diagram above the amount of energy available at the start of the trophic level is X. The amount available to the next trophic level is Y. Therefore the efficiency, best calculated as a percentage, is $\frac{Y}{X} \times 100$

The efficiency of energy transfer from one trophic level to the next one is never 100% - commonly 10 – 20%.

Pyramid of Energy

Pyramid of Energy

The above diagram easily translates into an energy pyramid.

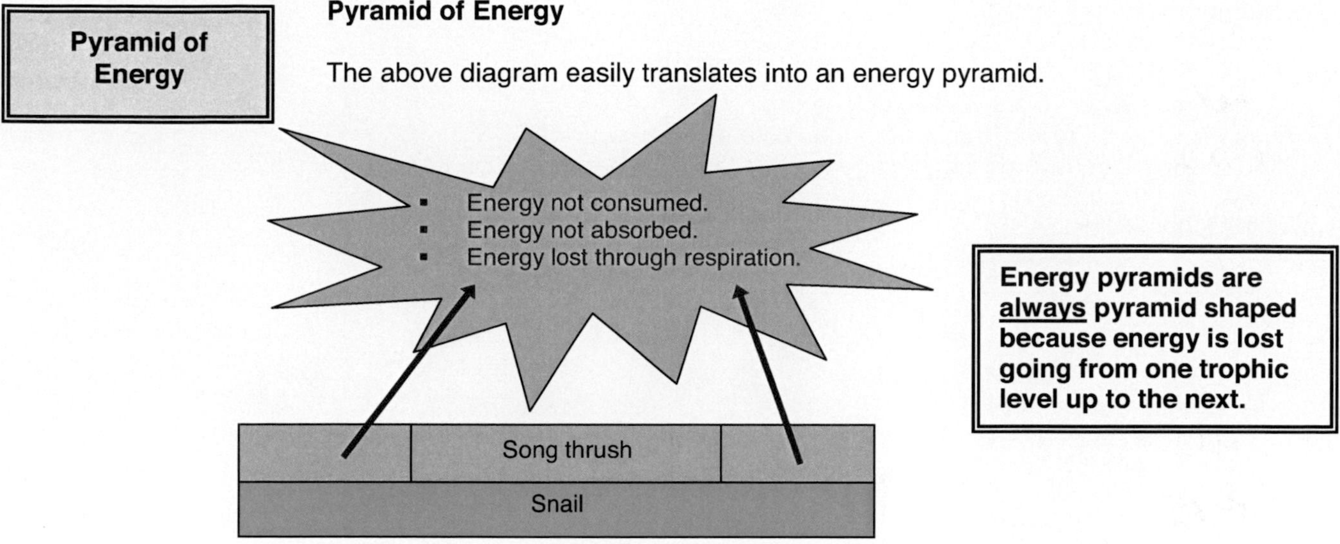

Energy not consumed.
Energy not absorbed.
Energy lost through respiration.
Song thrush
Snail

Energy pyramids are always pyramid shaped because energy is lost going from one trophic level up to the next.

The blue boxes represent the energy lost going from one end of the energy flow diagram (previous page) to the other. We can apply exactly the same principles with the song thrush ---- sparrow hawk link.

Energy, Nutrients and Ecosystems

Energy, Nutrients and Ecosystems

Key points

- Energy enters an ecosystem as light energy trapped by photosynthesis.
- All this trapped light energy is eventually converted to heat energy and this leaves the ecosystem and radiates into space.
- Nutrients are recycled.

Refer back to the energy flow diagram on the previous page. All of the leaf material not eaten by the snails will either be eaten by something else or die and be decomposed ('eaten') by bacteria and fungi. Similarly the waste material from the snail will be decomposed. This principle applies to every organism in the ecosystem.

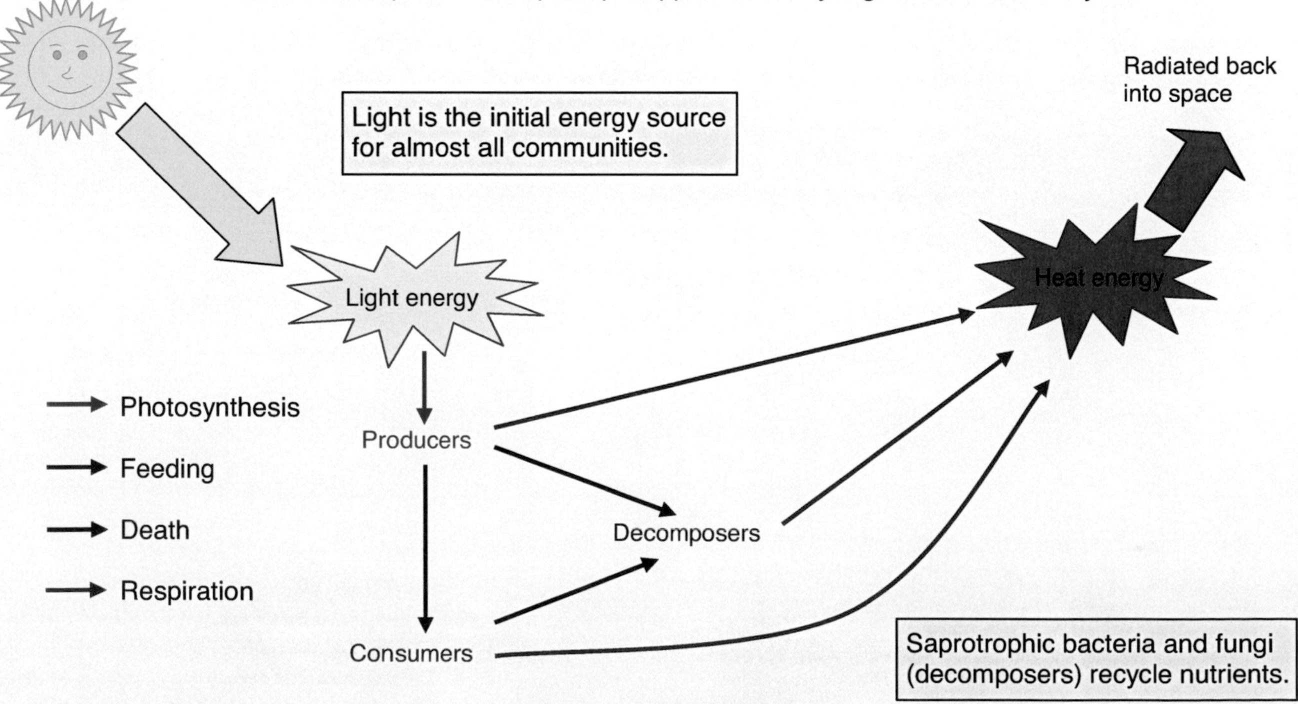

Light is the initial energy source for almost all communities.
Radiated back into space
Heat energy
Light energy
Photosynthesis
Feeding
Death
Respiration
Producers
Decomposers
Consumers
Saprotrophic bacteria and fungi (decomposers) recycle nutrients.

Distinguish between autotrophs and heterotrophs.

List the three main trophic levels in the correct order.

In a food chain in which direction do the arrows point?

Distinguish between detritivores, saprotrophs and consumers.

Carbon Cycle

The Carbon Cycle

Below is a "Carbon Cycle Do-it-Yourself" kit. The green boxes with double lines are stages and the boxes with single lines are processes that link the stages. Rearrange them to form the cycle so that no arrows cross. The best way to do this is to copy the boxes onto a sheet of paper and then cut them out.
Set it out like a clock with 'Carbon dioxide in the atmosphere' at 12 o'clock and go clockwise. It really is very simple if you think logically. The first step would be to ask yourself what happens to this carbon dioxide first and continue from there. Do the 5 stages first and then add the processes on the arrows. You must use all the processes boxes.

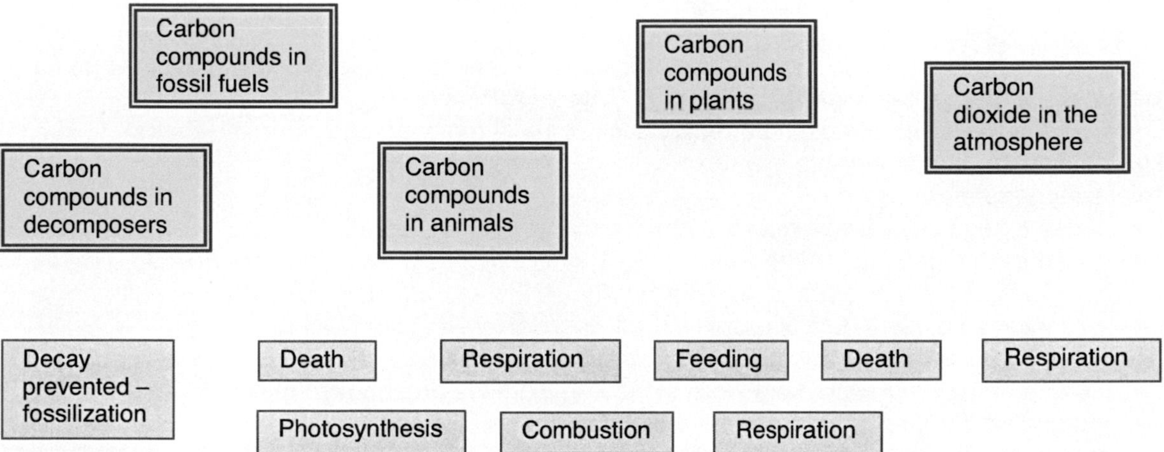

Carbon compounds in fossil fuels
Carbon compounds in plants
Carbon dioxide in the atmosphere
Carbon compounds in decomposers
Carbon compounds in animals
Decay prevented – fossilization
Death
Respiration
Feeding
Death
Respiration
Photosynthesis
Combustion
Respiration

A completed cycle is given in Appendix 7 on page 240.

The Greenhouse Effect

The Greenhouse Effect

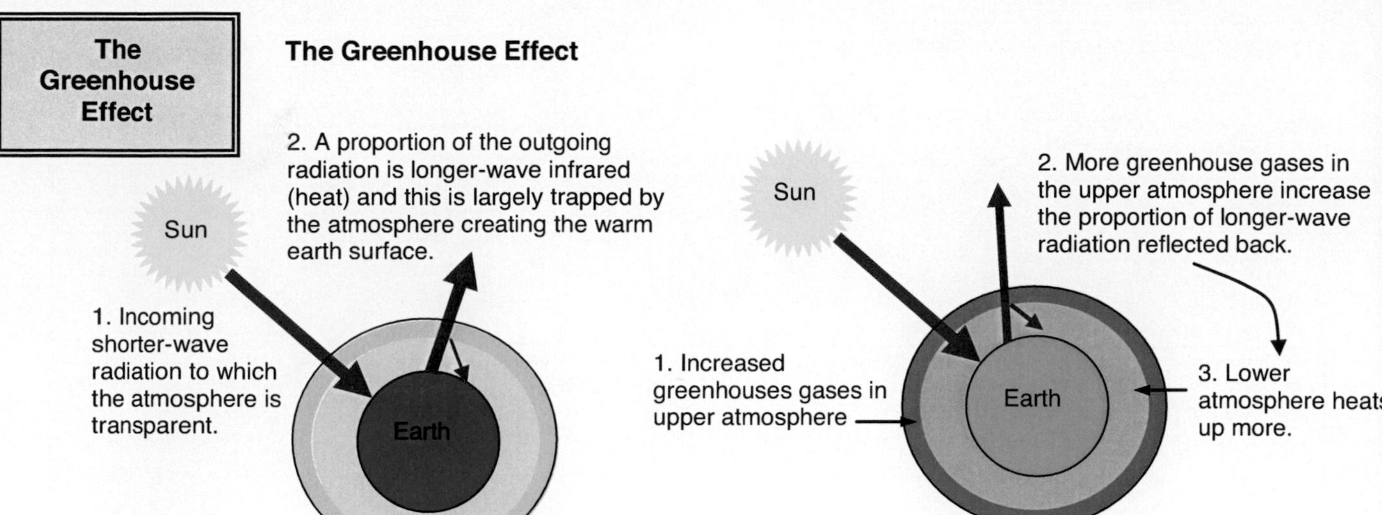

2. A proportion of the outgoing radiation is longer-wave infrared (heat) and this is largely trapped by the atmosphere creating the warm earth surface.
Sun
1. Incoming shorter-wave radiation to which the atmosphere is transparent.
Earth
Sun
2. More greenhouse gases in the upper atmosphere increase the proportion of longer-wave radiation reflected back.
1. Increased greenhouses gases in upper atmosphere
Earth
3. Lower atmosphere heats up more.

Key Points

- The greenhouse effect is a natural phenomenon and has helped to create a warm atmosphere that allowed evolution of life on the planet.
- Greenhouse gases include carbon dioxide, methane, nitrogen oxides and water vapour.
- Carbon dioxide levels have been rising due to increasing use of fossil fuels in power stations and motor vehicles.
- Analysis of air bubbles trapped in ice in Antarctica showed carbon dioxide levels remained fairly constant from 500BC to 1880.

Date	Carbon dioxide concentration /ppm	% increase from 1880
1880	270	
1958	315	16.7
2000	360	33.3
2004	375	38.9
2006	382	41.5
2008	386	42.9
2010	388	43.7

Data from the Mauna Loa monitoring station in Hawaii. (ppm = parts per million) Try this web site - http://www.esrl.noaa.gov/gmd/ccgg/trends/

- Methane levels have risen due to rice and cattle farming - paddy fields and cattle release methane – and also melting of permafrost.
- The gases in the upper atmosphere reflect back some of the heat rising from the Earth.
- This causes the atmosphere to heat up.
- This rising temperature can -
  - cause a rise in sea levels due to thermal expansion of the oceans;
  - cause the ice caps to melt releasing huge quantities of fresh water into the oceans. This may
    - affect the flow of the ocean currents, which in turn affects global weather patterns.
    - cause a rise in sea levels which will flood lower lying land.
  - affect global weather patterns directly by affecting rainfall and air currents;
  - increase evaporation so more water vapour to increase greenhouse effect;
  - enhance plant growth where plants have adequate water and minerals;
  - melt permafrost causing release of trapped methane.

Reversing the Trend

- Reduce the consumption of fossil fuels by using alternative energy sources – wind, solar, hydroelectric, geothermal, waste incineration, burning biomass, hydrogen fuel cells.
- Vehicles using biofuels made from ethanol or plant oils (biodiesel). Arguments against this are –
  - it is not cost effective since energy from fossil fuels is required to manufacture the biofuel;
  - land used for food crops could be changed to fuel crops leading to food shortages;
  - more rainforest is cleared for fuel crops.
- Plant hardwood trees to lock up carbon dioxide.
- Carbon capture and storage (CCS).

The Precautionary Principle

> If the effects of a human-induced change would be very large, perhaps catastrophic, those responsible for the change must prove that it will **not** do harm before proceeding, rather than those who are concerned about the change having to prove that it **will** do harm in order to prevent the change going ahead.

The Precautionary Principle

Evaluating The Precautionary Principle with Respect to Global Warming

Evaluating The Precautionary Principle

Key points

- Do we care about global warming or is it too far in the future for us to worry about?
- Do we rely on future technologies to solve the problem at a later date?
- Is it really happening? Scientists are arguing on both sides of the fence.
- Is enough effort being put in to collect data and do we know enough to act?
- Regardless of the answers to these questions if we do nothing the result could be catastrophic for the biosphere and thus the Precautionary Principle <u>should</u> be applied.

However -

- Is all the data collected being made available for scrutiny or is 'unfavourable' data being hidden?
- Are 'organisations' with a vested interest in not implementing the Precautionary Principle influencing how the data is used?
- What is the goal? The Kyoto Protocol attempts to set limits to the rise in greenhouses gases from industrialised countries but not all nations signed the treaty.
- Does the goal reflect the Precautionary Principle?
- Is it appropriate? Scientists argue that it is far too small to be really effective.
- Is the goal achievable and who is responsible for reaching it – Governments, individuals or both? Indications are that nations that signed up are falling far short of the target.
- How can the conflict between the goal and the needs of developing nations – China and India in particular - be resolved?
- Will economies be harmed and thus lead to human suffering?
- How can the conflict between the goal and the desire for large corporations in the developed countries to make profits for their shareholders be resolved?
- Will implementation of actions to reduce greenhouse gases have a negative effect elsewhere, eg destroying rainforest to plant crops for biofuels; changing from food crops to fuel crops.

Arctic Ecosystems

Arctic Ecosystems

Key points

- Predictions of global warming are that the largest temperature rises could be in higher latitudes;
- Average winter temperatures have increased by 3 - 4^{0}C in the last 50 years;
- If arctic soils start to thaw then decomposition of organic matter could release even more carbon dioxide and methane;
- If the ice sheets decrease in size then more sea is exposed which absorbs rather than reflects heat leading to even more rapid warming and more ice melting – a positive feedback process;
- Melting ice leads to an increase in sea levels;
- Melting ice alters the salinity which affects ocean currents and weather patterns;
- Reduced sea ice leads to increased shipping and increased pollution;
- Vegetation zones will move along with resulting changes in animal populations and invasion by alien species;
- Reduction in sea ice forces polar bears to swim further and reduces their hunting and breeding success.
- Changes in sea ice and vegetation affect how indigenous populations use their environment.

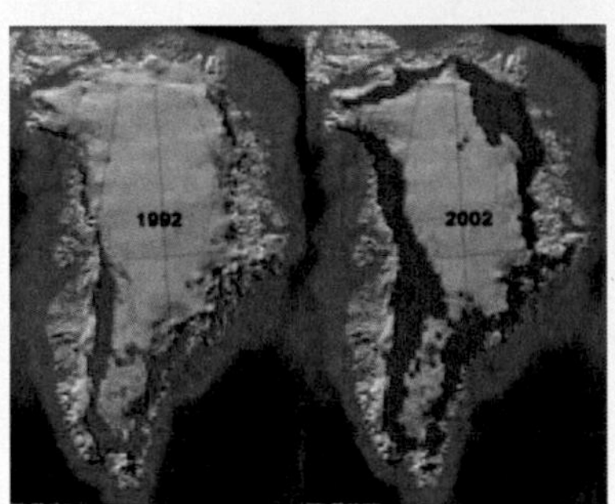
1992
2002
Changes in the Greenland ice sheet.

Populations

Sigmoid Growth Curve

Populations

Key points
- A population may increase in size due to natality (birth) and immigration from other populations;
- A population may decrease in size due to mortality (death) and emigration to other populations.

The Sigmoid Growth Curve

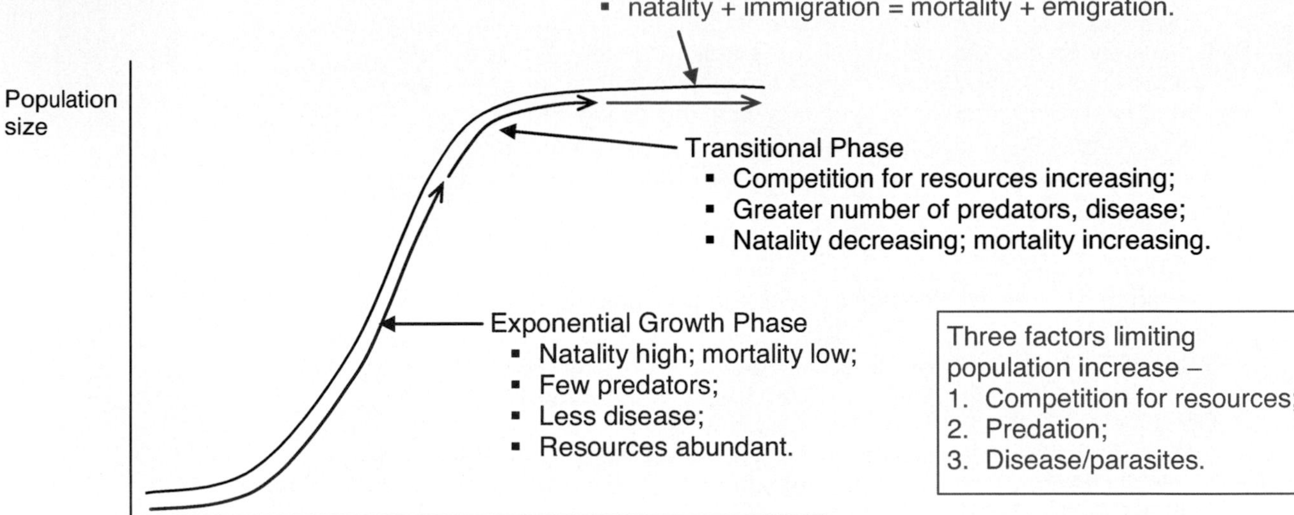

Plateau Phase
▪ natality + immigration = mortality + emigration.
Population size
Transitional Phase
▪ Competition for resources increasing;
▪ Greater number of predators, disease;
▪ Natality decreasing; mortality increasing.
Exponential Growth Phase
▪ Natality high; mortality low;
▪ Few predators;
▪ Less disease;
▪ Resources abundant.
Time

Three factors limiting population increase –
1. Competition for resources;
2. Predation;
3. Disease/parasites.

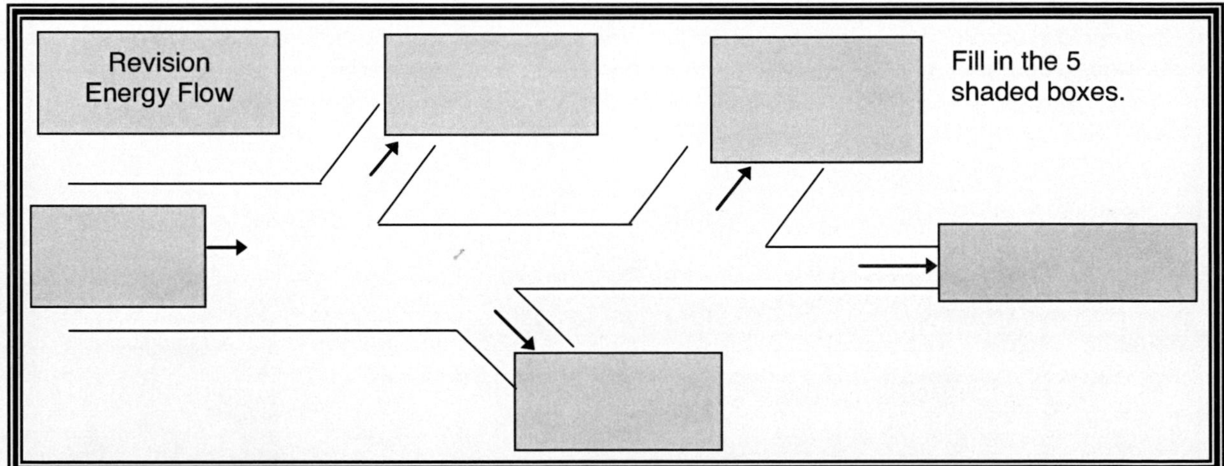

Revision Energy Flow
Fill in the 5 shaded boxes.

Why is a pyramid of energy always pyramid shaped?

List three greenhouse gases.

Complete the sentence.
Energy usually enters an ecosystem as ______________

energy and leaves as ________________ energy, but

nutrients are __________________ within the ecosystem.

Outline the Precautionary Principle.

Describe three effects of global warming on the arctic ecosystem.

Evolution

Define evolution.

Evolution

Evidence for Evolution

1. Fossils

- The fossil remains of extinct species provide evidence that species are continuously evolving;
- Older rocks contain simpler organisms and species that are no longer living;
- Younger rocks contain species that resemble those that are alive today;
- It is not a perfect record of the evolution of species, but it does show that changes in species have taken place in the past.

The first fossil is simply a print of a shell in mud which has hardened. In the other two the organism has been replaced with hard minerals.

2. Selective breeding of domesticated animals -

- Breeds have been produced for food production, working, pets, sport.
- Humans have selected a particular feature and used these animals to breed from;
- Offspring which showed an increase in this feature were bred from and the process repeated.
- Dogs – Chinese dog (food), sheep dog (working), dachshund (pet), greyhound (sport).
- Cattle – Jersey (milk), Aberdeen Angus (beef).

3. Homologous structures - have the same origin but now have different functions.

- Example - the pentadactyl limb;
- So called because it typically has five digits;
- Found in all four classes of terrestrial vertebrates – amphibians, reptiles, birds and mammals.

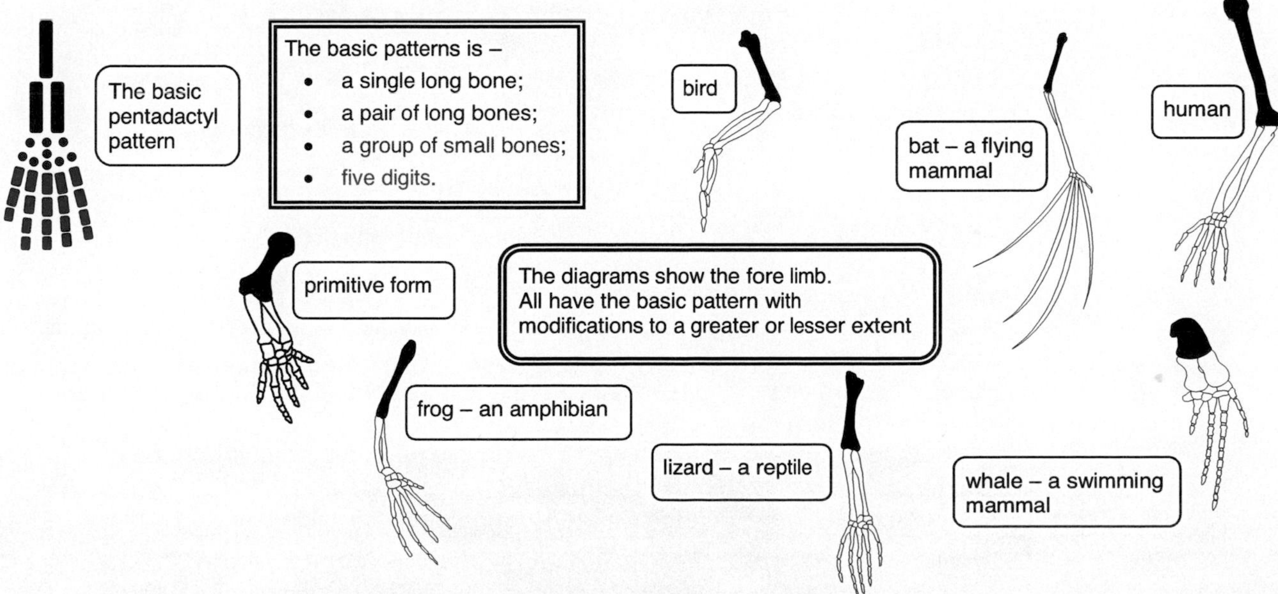
The basic pentadactyl pattern
The basic patterns is –
a single long bone;
a pair of long bones;
a group of small bones;
five digits.
bird
bat – a flying mammal
human
primitive form
The diagrams show the fore limb.
All have the basic pattern with modifications to a greater or lesser extent
frog – an amphibian
lizard – a reptile
whale – a swimming mammal

Natural Selection

Evolution by Natural Selection

Key Steps

The Darwin - Wallace principle of evolution by natural selection.

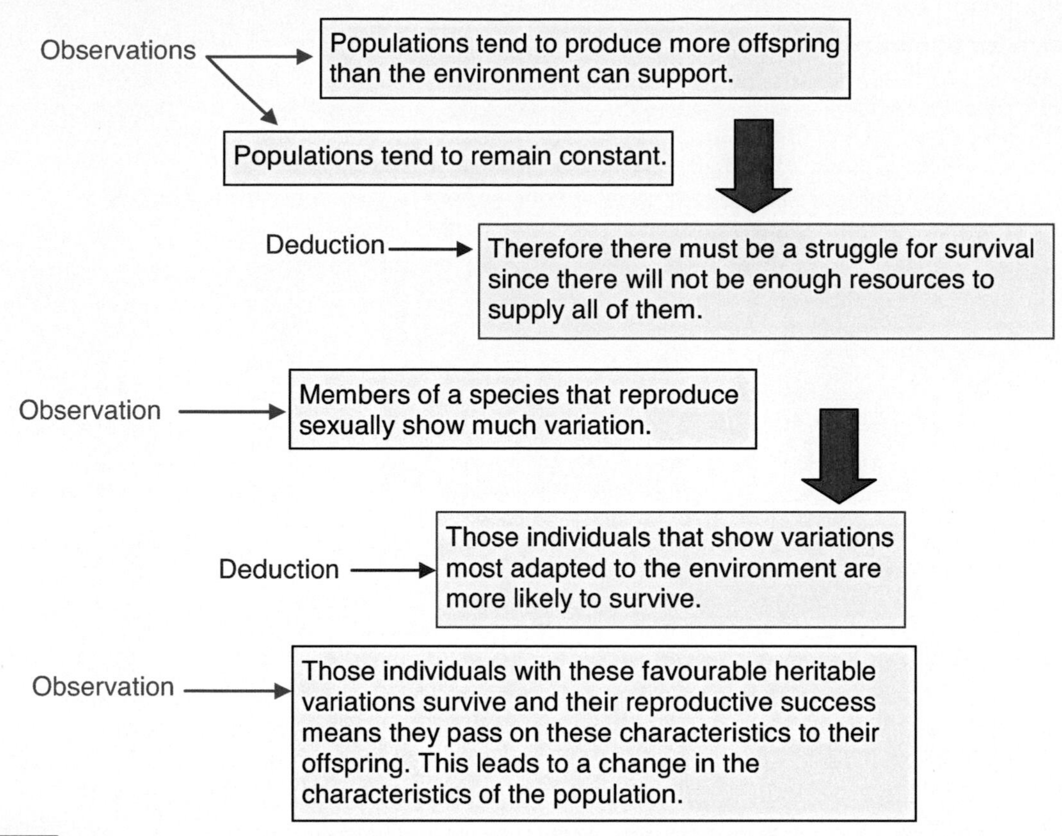

Observations
Populations tend to produce more offspring than the environment can support.
Populations tend to remain constant.
Deduction
Therefore there must be a struggle for survival since there will not be enough resources to supply all of them.
Observation
Members of a species that reproduce sexually show much variation.
Deduction
Those individuals that show variations most adapted to the environment are more likely to survive.
Observation
Those individuals with these favourable heritable variations survive and their reproductive success means they pass on these characteristics to their offspring. This leads to a change in the characteristics of the population.

Environmental Change

Evolution in Response to Environmental Change

Example 1 – Multiple antibiotic resistance in bacteria.

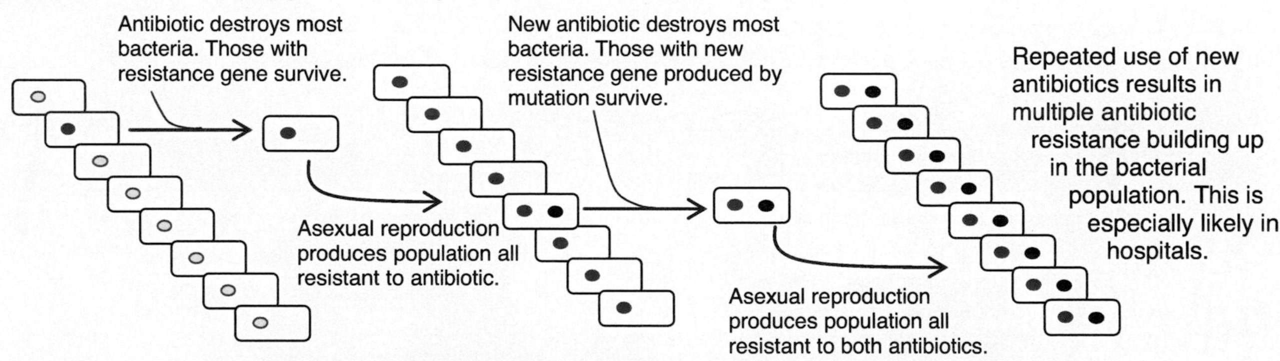

Antibiotic destroys most bacteria. Those with resistance gene survive.
Asexual reproduction produces population all resistant to antibiotic.
New antibiotic destroys most bacteria. Those with new resistance gene produced by mutation survive.
Asexual reproduction produces population all resistant to both antibiotics.
Repeated use of new antibiotics results in multiple antibiotic resistance building up in the bacterial population. This is especially likely in hospitals.

Example 2 – Metal tolerance in plants

- Waste heaps from metal ore mining and processing leave waste heaps with toxic concentrations of metal ions that kill most plants.
- Seeds of some plants (eg the grass *Agrostis*) may contain genes that produce tolerance to these metal ions.
- All seeds germinating on these waste heaps die apart from those with the resistance genes.
- These grow and pass on their resistance genes to their offspring.

Sexual Reproduction Promotes Variation

Sexual Reproduction and Variation

Key facts

- ➢ In meiosis there is random alignment of bivalents – see below.
- ➢ In meiosis there is crossing over which mixes maternal and paternal genes. (Refer back to page 59).
- ➢ Fertilisation between gametes is random. (Look at the Punnett grid on page 62).

How Random Alignment produces variety.

Variety in the gametes is produced by how the bivalents line up on the equator in metaphase 1.
Consider two pairs of chromosomes, A and its homologue a, and B and its homologue b. Look at the box on the right. If the bivalents line up on the equator in the way shown, gametes with chromosome combinations AB and ab form.

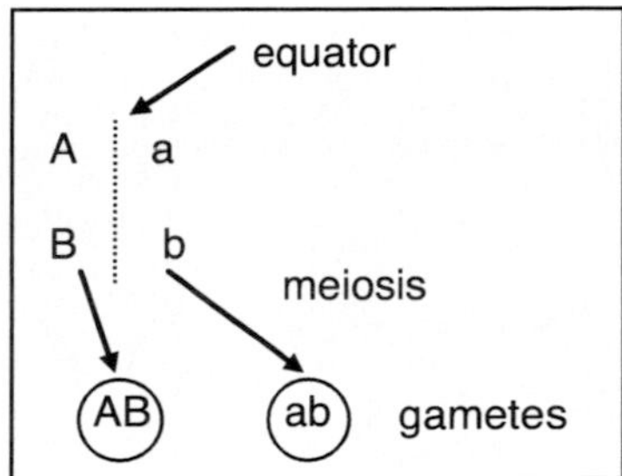
equator
A
a
B
b
meiosis
AB
ab
gametes

Now look what happens if the pairs lined up differently. This time we get gametes with chromosome combinations Ab and aB.

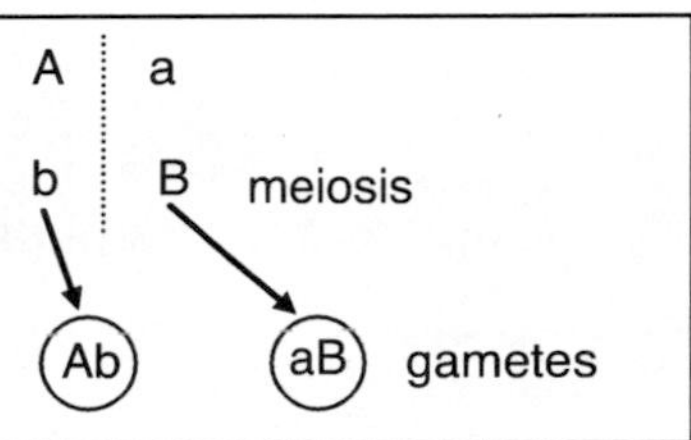
A
a
b
B
meiosis
Ab
aB
gametes

Thus we have produced variety as this individual can produce 4 different types of gamete simply as a result of the way the bivalents line up on the equator.

You may be interested to know that the number of genetically different sperms or eggs that a human could (in theory) produce in this way is 8,388,608.

The Hierarchy of Taxa

Hierarchy of Taxa

One way to remember this is –
King
Philip
Classified
Over
Fifty
Green
Spiders

Kingdom
Phylum
Class
Order
Family
Genus
Species

Taxonomic rank	Plant example	Animal example
Kingdom	Plantae	Animalia
Phylum	Angiospermaphyta	Chordata
Class	Dicotyledonaea	Mammalia
Order	Ranales	Primates
Family	Ranunculacae	Hominidae
Genus	*Ranunculus*	*Homo*
Species	*acris*	*sapiens*
Common name	Meadow buttercup	Human

The Binomial System

Binomial System

Each organism has two Latin names, its genus and species.

It is typed in italics but when hand-written it is underlined

Homo sapiens = modern humans.

The genus starts with a capital letter

The species starts with a small letter

Other examples –

Lumbricus terrestris = earthworm
Turdus merula = English blackbird
Panthera leo = lion
Panthera tigris = tiger

Plant Phyla

Plant Phyla

Group	Structural Features
Bryophyta Mosses and Liverworts	No roots or cuticle; Rhizoids similar to root hairs; Mosses with simple leaf-like structures; Liverworts have flattened shape called a thallus; Spores produced in capsules.
Filicinophyta Ferns	Roots; Leaves in fronds; Cuticle on leaves; Can form small trees, but not woody; Spores produced in structures called sporangia.
Coniferophyta Conifers	Shrubs to very large trees; Roots, stems, leaves; Woody stems and roots; Produce seeds.
Angiospermophyta Flowering plants	Highly variable in structure – tiny herbaceous to large trees; Roots, stems, leaves, flowers; Can form woody tissue; Some parasitic; Produce seeds.

Animal Phyla

Animal Phyla

Group	Structural Features
Porifera Sponges	No special shape; Lack tissues and organs; Collection of cells of different types organised into pores, canals and chambers.
Cnidaria Jellyfish and sea anemones	Two cell layers; Radial symmetry; Two forms – medusa and polyp; Tentacles with stinging cells (nematoblasts).
Platyhelminthes Flatworms	Flat and unsegmented; Bilaterally symmetric; Rudimentary head; Mouth but no anus.
Annelida Segmented worms	Segmented body; Bilaterally symmetric; Bristles (chaetae); Mouth and anus.
Mollusca Snails, slugs, squids,	Soft, flexible body with no obvious segmentation; Head, muscular foot and visceral hump; Many with a single or double shell.
Arthropoda Crabs, spiders, scorpions, centipedes, insects	Segmented; Bilaterally symmetric; Hard, chitinous exoskeleton; Jointed appendages.

Dichotomous Key

A Dichotomous Key

Key feature

➢ Dichotomous means two, therefore each step is a pair of statements, and the number to the right directs you to the next pair.

Example.

1 Leaf with smooth margin. ———— 2
  Leaf with toothed margin. ———— 15
2 Lateral veins branch off midrib in pairs. ———— 3
  Lateral veins branch alternately left and right. ———— 7
3 Tip of leaf blade pointed where midrib extends into it. ———— pear
  Tip of leaf blade rounded. ———— 10

Self-test Quiz on Topic 5

1. Food chains generally start with
   a. herbivores,
   b. green plants,
   c. carnivores,
   d. decomposers.

2. In an ecosystem
   a. energy is recycled,
   b. pyramids of energy always start with herbivores at the base,
   c. there are always three trophic levels,
   d. elements are recycled.

3. In an ecosystem which of the following is true?
   a. Respiration is part of the carbon cycle but photosynthesis is not.
   b. Green plants do not depend on decomposers.
   c. Green plants are affected by abiotic factors.
   d. Energy loss at each trophic level limits the number of trophic levels in a food chain to three.

4. A community can be defined as
   a. a group of populations living with each other in an area,
   b. a group of organisms that can interbreed,
   c. the habitat in which the organisms are found,
   d. a group of populations living and interacting with the abiotic environment.

5. Which of the following statements is true.
   a. The trophic level of an organism is the height above ground where it is found.
   b. The transfer of energy from one trophic level to the next is never 100% efficient.
   c. There are always more herbivores in a food chain than carnivores.
   d. A food web always contains at least 10 organisms.

6. Which of the following graphs represents a sigmoid growth curve?

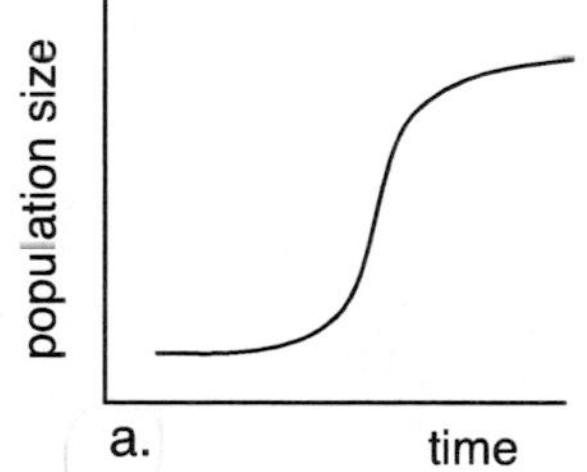

population size
time

a.

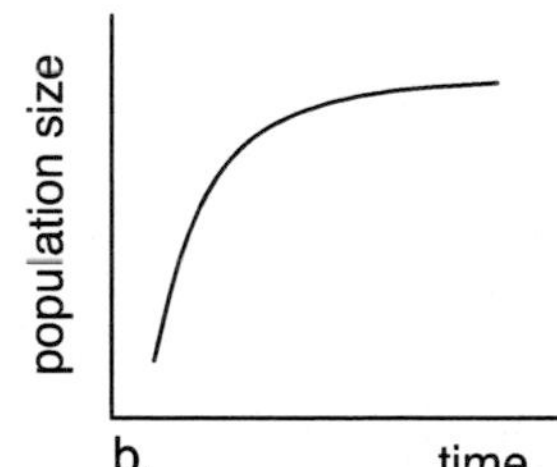

population size
time

b.

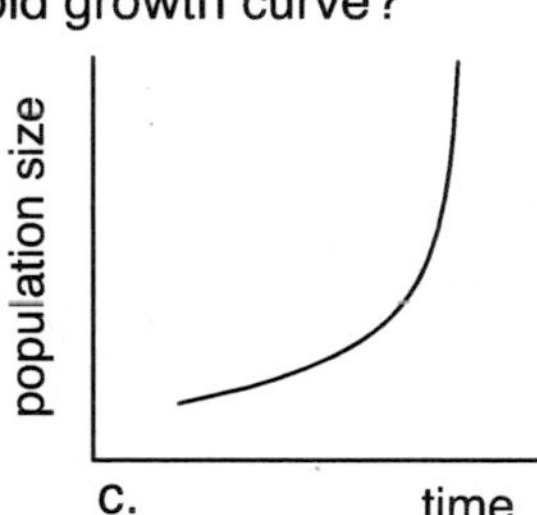

population size
time

c.

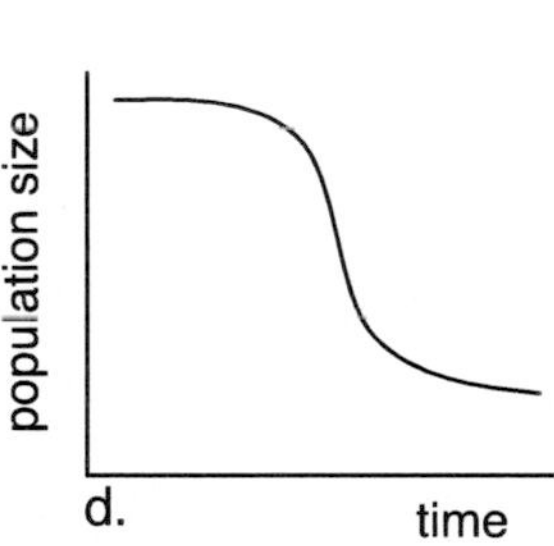

population size
time

d.

7. Populations evolve because
   a. individuals in the population show variation;
   b. natural selection removes those genetic combinations that are unfavourable;
   c. selection pressure brings about favourable mutations;
   d. species that reproduce sexually have more variation in their genome.

8. The initial source of energy for most communities is
   a. light energy,
   b. chemical energy,
   c. green plants,
   d. producers.

9. Decomposers are
   a. saprotrophic fungi and bacteria,
   b. producers,
   c. piles of dead plant and animal material,
   d. detritivores.

10. Use the key to identify the leaf.

1	leaf margin even	2
	leaf margin wavy	oak
2	veins branch off central vein in pairs	5
	veins branch off alternately left and right	3
3	tip of leaf blade with extended point	lilac
	tip of leaf blade without extended point	4
4	leaf margin smooth	beech
	leaf margin toothed	rose

a.	oak
b.	lilac
c.	beech
d.	rose

11. Which of the following is a correct sequence for the hierarchy of taxa?
    a. Phylum, class, genus, family.
    b. Phylum, family, order, genus.
    c. Class, order, genus, species.
    d. Class, phylum, genus, species.

12. Which of the following is the correct definition of evolution?
    a. A change in the heritable characteristics of a population.
    b. An increase in the mutation rate of a population.
    c. A high level of selection pressure on a population.
    d. The selection of a specific desirable characteristic in an individual.

13. The greenhouse effect is due to
    a. the accumulation of glass dust in the atmosphere,
    b. an increase in the heat output of the sun,
    c. a decrease in the proportion of solar energy radiated back into space from the earth's atmosphere,
    d. an increase in heat output due to the rise in human population.

14. A food web is
    a. a complex food chain,
    b. food chains that include decomposers,
    c. all of the producers in a community,
    d. a group of interlinking food chains.

15. A pyramid of energy is always pyramid shaped because
    a. there are always more consumers than producers,
    b. energy is lost between one trophic level and the next one up,
    c. most food chains start with light energy from the sun,
    d. carnivores consume more energy finding food than herbivores.

16. In a sigmoid growth curve the order of the phases over time is
    a. exponential growth phase, transitional phase, plateau phase,
    b. exponential growth phase, plateau phase, transitional phase,
    c. transitional phase, exponential growth phase, plateau phase,
    d. plateau phase, exponential growth phase, transitional phase.

17. Which of the following factors is least likely to bring about a reduction in global warming
    a. consuming only food grown in the country of origin;
    b. increased use of renewable energy sources;
    c. using natural gas rather than oil as a source of energy;
    d. recycling organic waste materials as a manure.

18. Which of the following are greenhouse gases?
    a. water, methane, carbon dixide, hydrogen.
    b. nitrogen oxide, carbon dioxide, oxygen.
    c. methane, carbon dixide, nitrogen oxide.
    d. nitrogen oxide, water, methane, oxygen.

19. In the binomial system of classification
    a. all organisms are divided into two groups;
    b. all organisms have two names representing the genus and the species;
    c. all organisms have two names representing the family and the species;
    d. organisms are always arranged in pairs.

20. Sexual reproduction can promote variation in a species by
    a. random alignment of chromosomes at metaphase I of meiosis;
    b. repeated mitotic divisions of the embryo cells,
    c. meiosis in the embryo cells;
    d. cloning of the gametes.

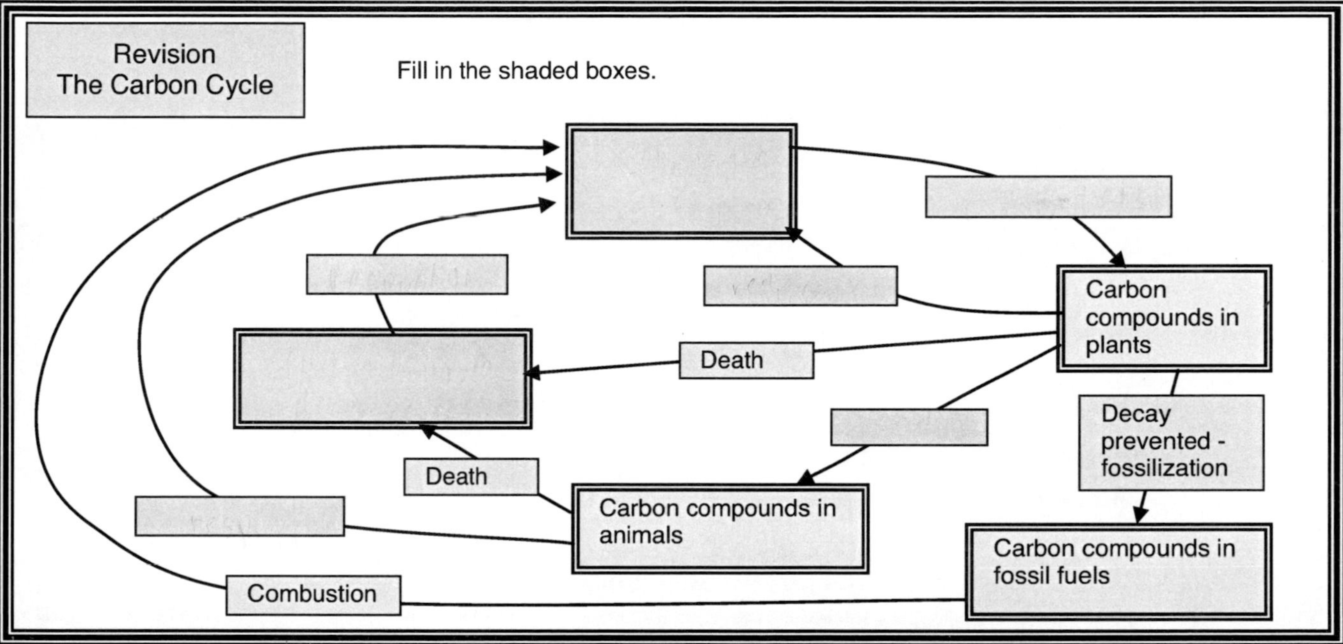
Revision
The Carbon Cycle
Fill in the shaded boxes.
Carbon compounds in plants
Death
Death
Decay prevented - fossilization
Carbon compounds in animals
Carbon compounds in fossil fuels
Combustion

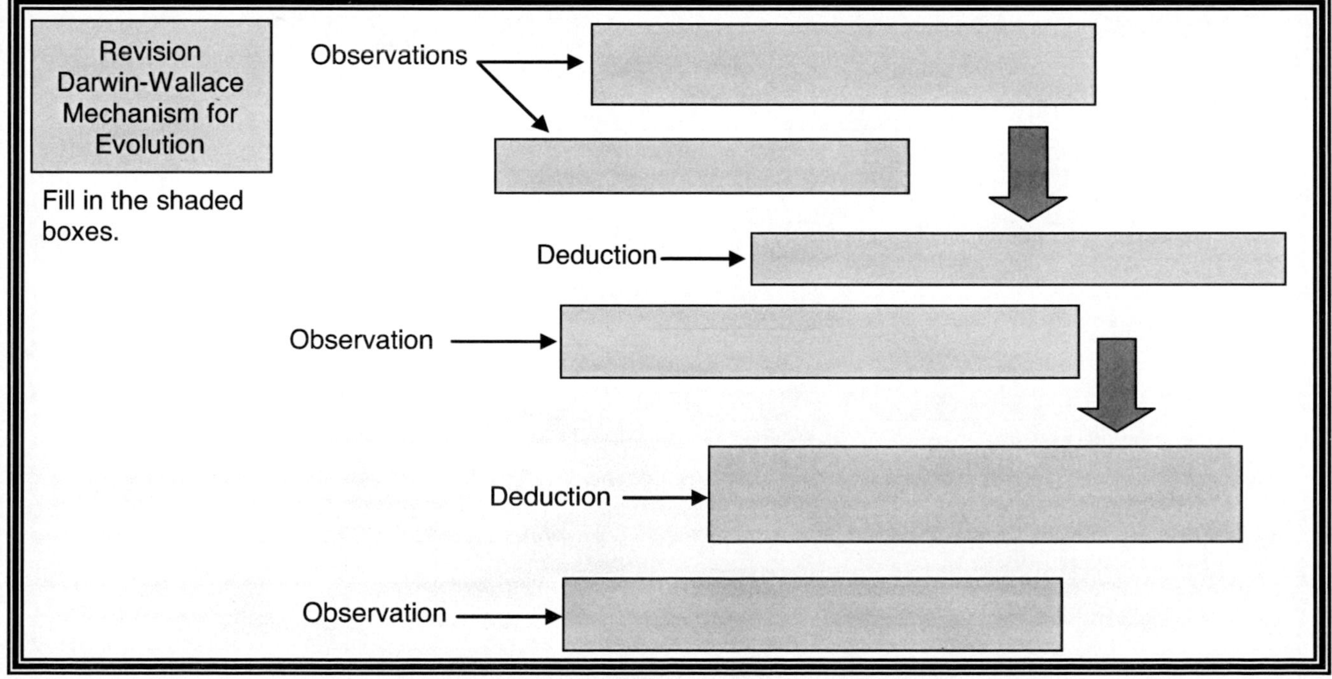
Revision
Darwin-Wallace Mechanism for Evolution
Fill in the shaded boxes.
Observations
Deduction
Observation
Deduction
Observation

Topic 6

Human Health and Physiology

Digestion

Digestion

Key points

- Large molecules cannot pass through the wall of the villus.
- Large molecules, especially proteins, can stimulate an antibody response.
- Large molecules need to be broken down into their constituent units in order to be reassembled in the way the body wants.
- The reactions are too slow at body temperature without enzymes.

Enzymes

Enzymes

Enzyme group	Example	Source	Substrate	Products	Optimum pH
Carbohydrase	Amylase	Salivary gland	Starch	Maltose	7.2
Protease	Pepsin	Stomach wall	Protein	Peptides	2
Lipase	Pancreatic lipase	Pancreas	Lipid	Glycerol Fatty acids	8

Regions of the Gut

Regions of the Gut

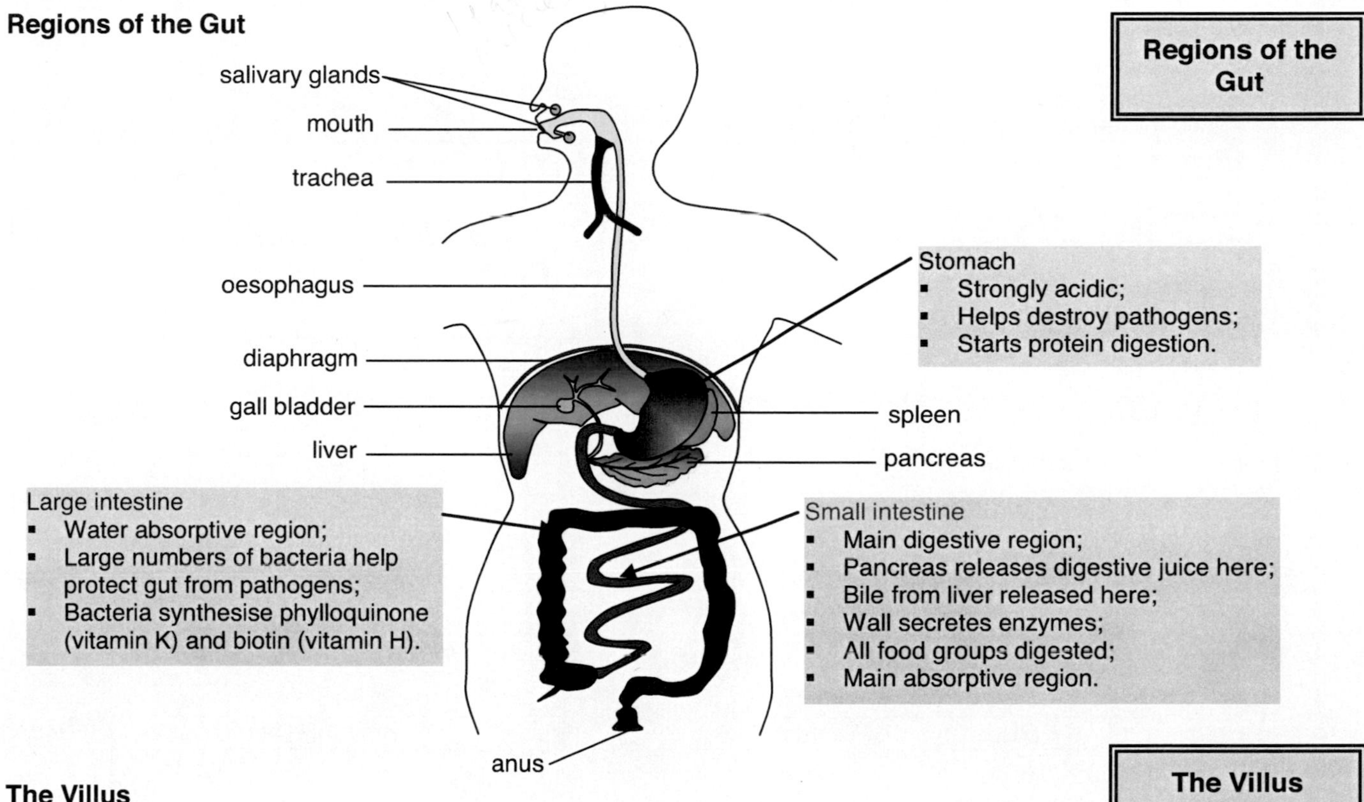
salivary glands
mouth
trachea
oesophagus
diaphragm
gall bladder
liver
spleen
pancreas
anus
Stomach
▪ Strongly acidic;
▪ Helps destroy pathogens;
▪ Starts protein digestion.
Large intestine
▪ Water absorptive region;
▪ Large numbers of bacteria help protect gut from pathogens;
▪ Bacteria synthesise phylloquinone (vitamin K) and biotin (vitamin H).
Small intestine
▪ Main digestive region;
▪ Pancreas releases digestive juice here;
▪ Bile from liver released here;
▪ Wall secretes enzymes;
▪ All food groups digested;
▪ Main absorptive region.

The Villus

The Villus

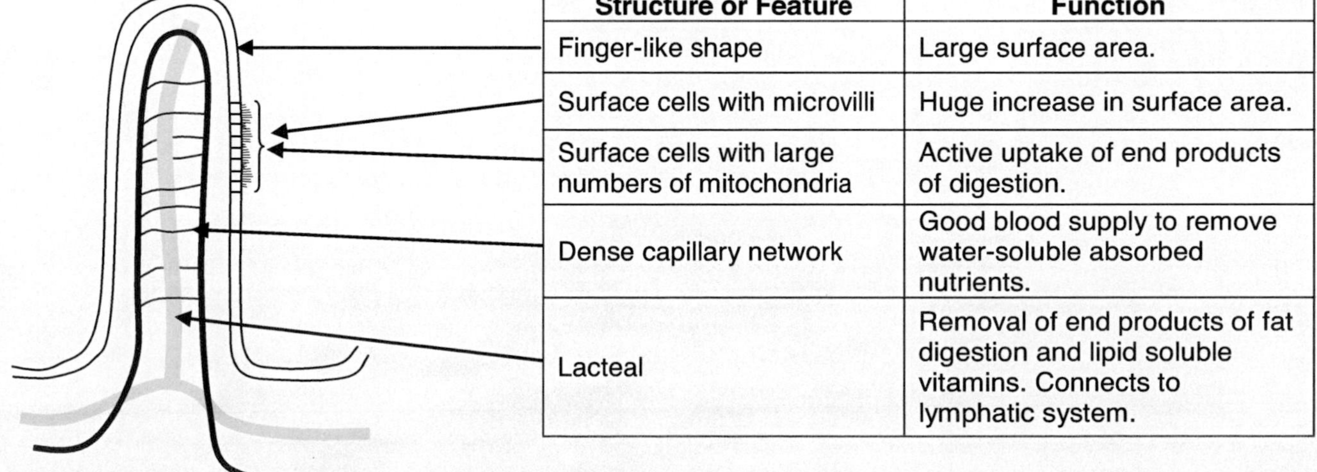

Structure or Feature	Function
Finger-like shape	Large surface area.
Surface cells with microvilli	Huge increase in surface area.
Surface cells with large numbers of mitochondria	Active uptake of end products of digestion.
Dense capillary network	Good blood supply to remove water-soluble absorbed nutrients.
Lacteal	Removal of end products of fat digestion and lipid soluble vitamins. Connects to lymphatic system.

Absorption and Assimilation

Absorption	Assimilation
Movement of the end products of digestion from the gut into the blood stream or lymphatic system.	Use by the body of these absorbed substances either to release energy or to build new cells.

Revision Digestion

Complete the following tables by filling in the missing words on the lines or in the boxes

Enzymes

Enzyme group	Example	Source	Substrate	Products	Optimum pH
Carbohydrase		Salivary gland	Starch		
Protease			Protein	Peptides	
Lipase			Lipid	and	

Regions of the Gut

Stomach	Small intestine	Large intestine
Strongly ___________	Main digestive region	___________ absorptive region
Helps destroy ________________	______________ releases digestive juice here	Large numbers of ___________ help protect gut from pathogens
Starts _______________ digestion	________ from __________ released here	Bacteria synthesise phylloquinone (vitamin K) and biotin (vitamin H)
	Wall secretes ____________	
	All food groups digested	
	Main absorptive region	

The Villus

Structure or Feature	Function
Finger-like shape	
Surface cells with microvilli	
	Active uptake of end products of digestion
Dense capillary network	
	Removal of end products of fat digestion and lipid soluble vitamins

List four reasons for digestion

The Transport System

The Heart

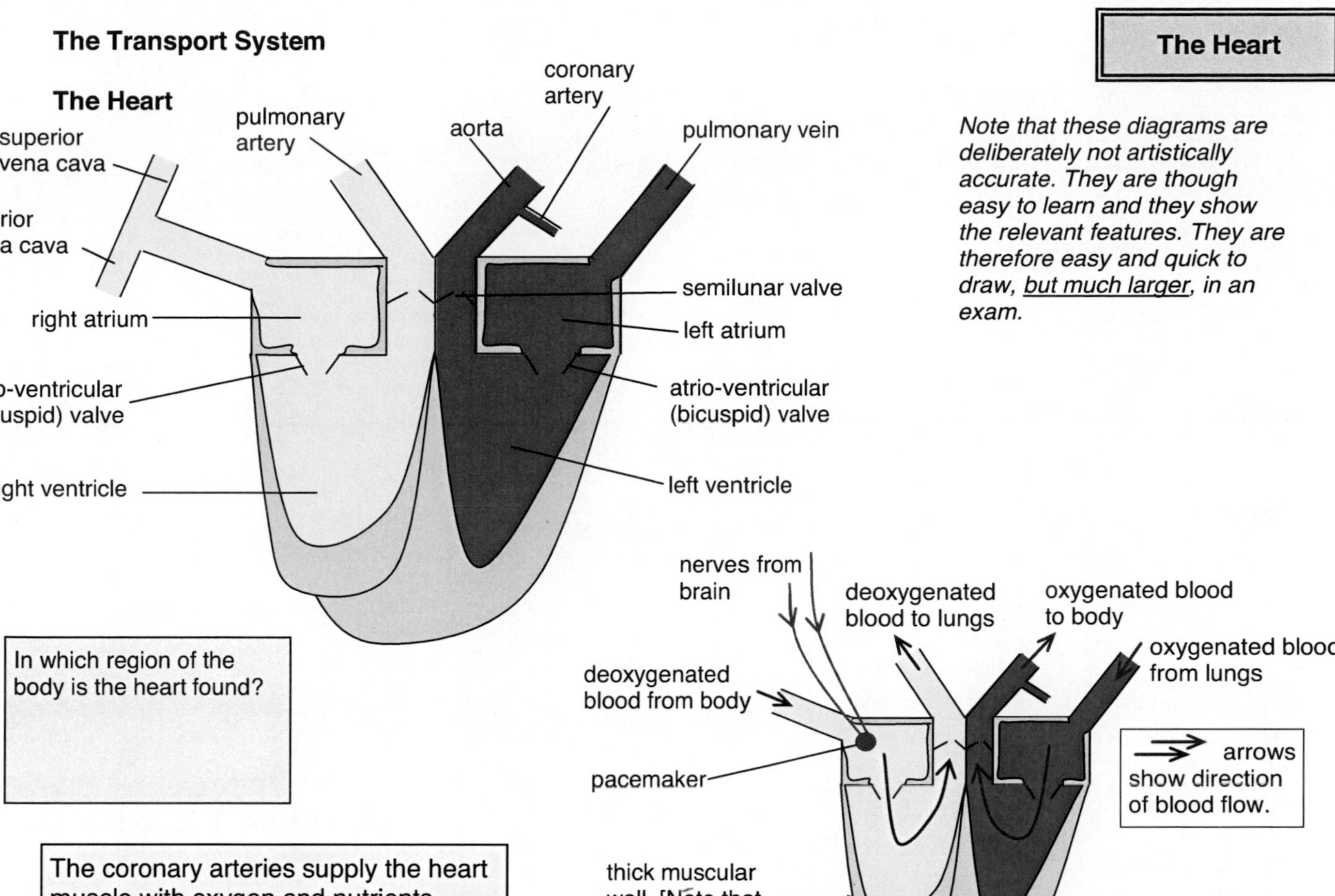

superior vena cava
inferior vena cava
pulmonary artery
aorta
coronary artery
pulmonary vein
semilunar valve
right atrium
left atrium
atrio-ventricular (tricuspid) valve
atrio-ventricular (bicuspid) valve
right ventricle
left ventricle
nerves from brain
deoxygenated blood to lungs
oxygenated blood to body
oxygenated blood from lungs
deoxygenated blood from body
pacemaker
arrows show direction of blood flow.
thick muscular wall. [Note that the wall of the left ventricle is thicker].
right
left

The Heart

Note that these diagrams are deliberately not artistically accurate. They are though easy to learn and they show the relevant features. They are therefore easy and quick to draw, <u>but much larger</u>, in an exam.

In which region of the body is the heart found?

The coronary arteries supply the heart muscle with oxygen and nutrients.

Key points

- Left atrium collects oxygenated blood from pulmonary vein.
- Right atrium collects deoxygenated blood from vena cava.
- Atria pump blood into ventricles.
- Ventricles contract to pump blood out of heart into arteries.
- Right ventricle pumps deoxygenated blood to lungs via pulmonary artery.
- Left ventricle pumps oxygenated blood to body (apart from lungs) via aorta.
- Left ventricle pumps blood under higher pressure than right ventricle.
- When ventricles contract blood pressure closes atrio-ventricular valves.
- When ventricles relax blood pressure due to backflow closes semilunar valves.
- Coronary arteries carry oxygenated blood to the heart muscle.

What is the function of the valves in the heart?

Control of the Heartbeat

Control of Heartbeat

Key points

- Heart muscle can contract of its own accord. This property of is called **myogenic**.
- The pacemaker is a small patch of special muscle tissue on the wall of the right atrium near the point where the vena cava enters.
- The pacemaker releases an electrical impulse approximately 70 times per minute.
- The electrical impulse causes the heart muscle to contract.
- Involuntary nerves from the cardiac control centre in the medulla of the brain are attached to the pacemaker.
- Impulses down the cardiac depressor nerve cause the heart rate to slow down, eg during sleep.
- Impulses down the cardiac accelerator nerve cause the heart rate to speed up, eg during exercise.
- The hormone adrenalin from the adrenal gland stimulates the pacemaker causing the heart rate to speed up.

Blood Vessels

➢ The Blood Vessels

	Structure	Function
Arteries	Thick muscular wall	Withstand high pressure; Contracts to increase blood pressure.
	Elastic fibres	Stretched by pulse and when contract help to maintain steady blood flow.
	Collagen fibres	Tough inelastic fibres protect and prevent the wall from being over stretched.
	Endothelium	Smooth lining.
Capillaries	Wall of single layer of flattened cells	Reduced distance for diffusion between blood and tissues.
	Narrow lumen	Increased surface area.
	No muscle, elastic or fibrous tissue; Gaps between cells	Facilitate diffusion as substances only have to pass through the basement membrane.
Veins	Endothelium	Smooth lining.
	Large lumen	Reduces resistance to flow.
	Collagen fibres	Protection.
	Valves	Prevent backflow when pressure very low.
	Thin walls	Allows vein to be squashed between muscle blocks which pumps blood.

Transverse section of artery

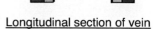

basement membrane

Longitudinal section of capillary

flow

Longitudinal section of vein

Blood is composed of –
- Plasma;
- Erythrocytes (red cells);
- Leucocytes (white cells) –
  - Phagocytes,
  - Lymphocytes;
- Platelets.

Transported by the blood –
- Nutrients;
- Oxygen;
- Carbon dioxide;
- Hormones;
- Antibodies;
- Urea;
- Heat

Revision The Heart

Label the diagram below in the places indicated.
Add arrows to show the direction of blood flow.

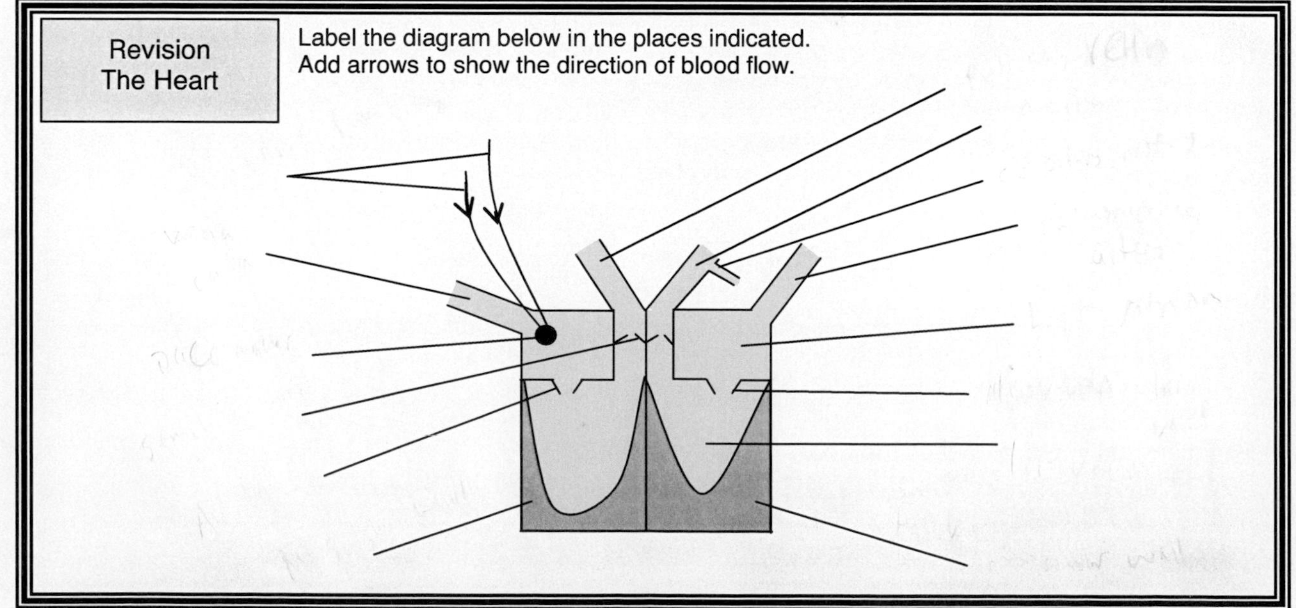

State two ways the rate of heartbeat can be increased.

List the components of blood.

List 7 things transported by the blood.

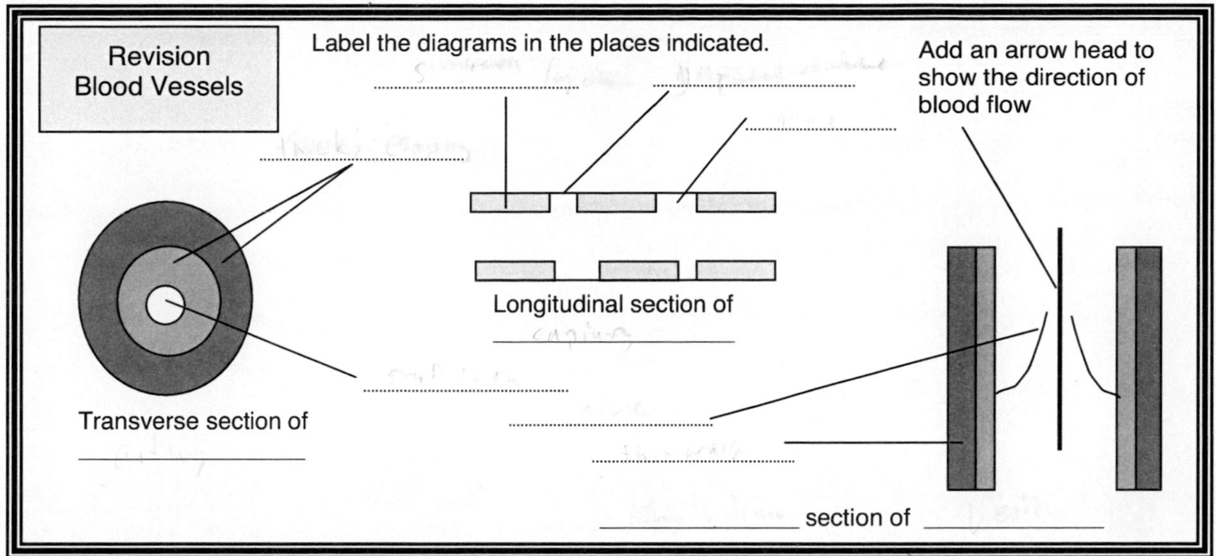

Revision
Blood Vessels
Label the diagrams in the places indicated.
Add an arrow head to show the direction of blood flow
Longitudinal section of
Transverse section of
section of

Defence Against Infectious Disease

Define pathogen.

Defence

Antibiotics

Antibiotics – why they are effective against bacteria and not viruses.

Key points

- Act against specific chemicals or chemical pathways in prokaryotes;
- Hence do not affect eukaryotic cells;
- Viruses are intra-cellular parasites using the host cell chemical pathways;
- Hence any drugs used against viruses would damage the host cell.

Surface Barriers

Surface Barriers

Key points - Skin

- Dead waterproof surface layer.
- Tough, elastic.
- Oily secretion (sebum) from sebaceous gland in hair follicle controls fungal and bacterial growth and stops skin cracking.
- Dry – discourages growth of pathogens.
- Surface layer continually shed which removes pathogens.

Key points – Mucous Membranes

- In air passages traps pathogens, swept up to throat and swallowed;
- In vagina, acidic (due to bacterial action) to prevent growth of pathogens.

Phagocytic Leucocytes

Phagocytic Leucocytes

Key points

- Phagocytes destroy pathogens in blood and tissue fluid;
- They ingest pathogens and destroy them with enzymes from lysosomes;
- They can push their way through capillary walls into tissue fluid. This is especially important for controlling infection from cuts and scratches.

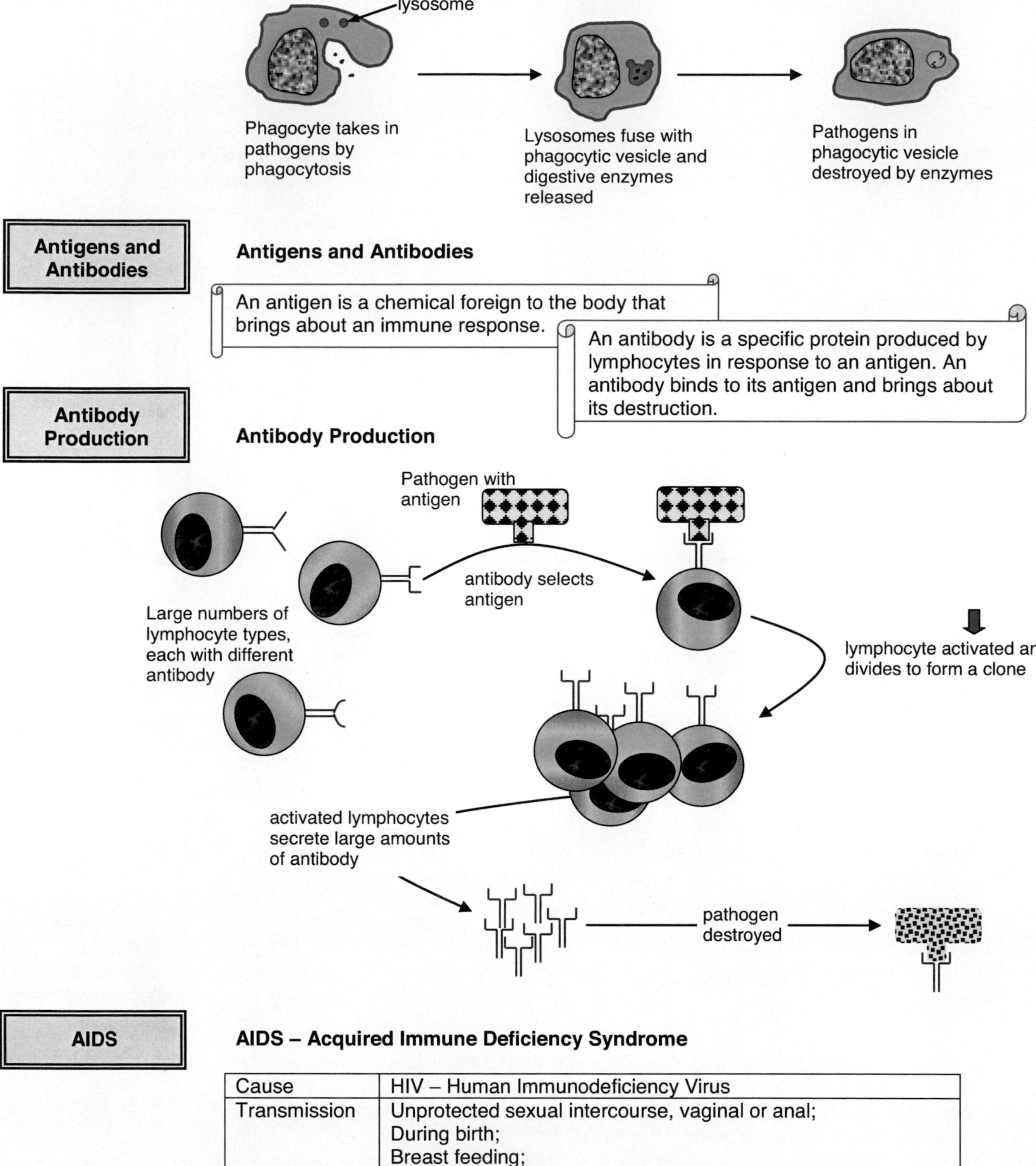
lysosome
Phagocyte takes in pathogens by phagocytosis
Lysosomes fuse with phagocytic vesicle and digestive enzymes released
Pathogens in phagocytic vesicle destroyed by enzymes
Pathogen with antigen
antibody selects antigen
Large numbers of lymphocyte types, each with different antibody
lymphocyte activated and divides to form a clone
activated lymphocytes secrete large amounts of antibody
pathogen destroyed

Antigens and Antibodies

Antigens and Antibodies

An antigen is a chemical foreign to the body that brings about an immune response.

An antibody is a specific protein produced by lymphocytes in response to an antigen. An antibody binds to its antigen and brings about its destruction.

Antibody Production

Antibody Production

AIDS

AIDS – Acquired Immune Deficiency Syndrome

Cause	HIV – Human Immunodeficiency Virus
Transmission	Unprotected sexual intercourse, vaginal or anal; During birth; Breast feeding; Blood transfusion; Contaminated needles. Across placenta but this is rare.
Social implications	Breakdown of family structure. Huge drain on medical resources. Huge loss of workforce.

The vast majority of cases at the moment are in Africa, with up to 50% of the population in some places infected with HIV. However the disease is spreading rapidly in Asia. Drugs are available which help to control the effect of the virus in the body, but these are expensive and people in less economically developed countries cannot afford them. The drug companies that developed them are under pressure to allow such countries to manufacture their own, or buy in, cheaper copies of the drugs. Individual families may lose income and be unable to buy food and clothing. If large numbers of the workforce are affected and unable to work then the overall economy of the country can be affected as they may have a reduction in products that they export to earn currency.

HIV and the Immune System

Key points

- The activation of the lymphocytes (See ⬇ on the diagram on the previous page) requires another type of white blood cell called a Helper cell.
- HIV destroys these Helper cells;
- The lymphocytes cannot divide to form a clone of antibody producing cells;
- Antibodies are not produced and the pathogen survives to cause an infection;
- Infections begin to accumulate in the body – the lungs are especially vunerable.

Revision Blood Vessels

Fill in the 6 shaded boxes.

	Structure	Function
	Thick muscular wall	
Arteries		Stretched by pulse and when contract help to maintain steady blood flow.
	Collagen fibres	Tough inelastic fibres protect and prevent the wall from being over stretched.
Capillaries	Wall of single layer of flattened cells	
	Gaps between cells	
	Large lumen	
Veins	Collagen fibres	Protection
	Valves	

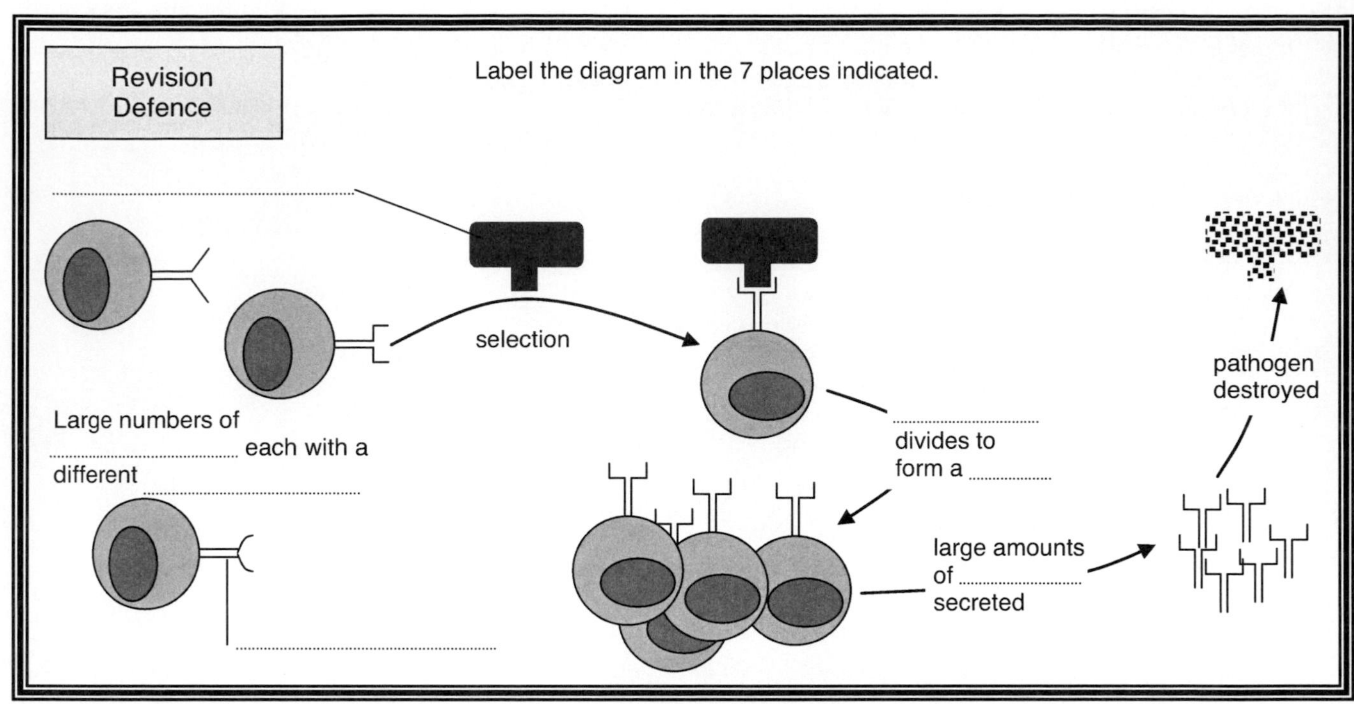
Revision
Defence
Label the diagram in the 7 places indicated.
selection
pathogen
destroyed
Large numbers of
.... each with a
different
divides to
form a
large amounts
of
secreted

Draw a phagocytic leukocyte engulfing bacteria.

Distinguish between an antigen and an antibody.

How do mucous membranes act as a barrier?

List three key features about skin as a protective barrier.

List four ways HIV can be transmitted.

Which cells does HIV destroy?

Why does this cause AIDS?

Gas Exchange

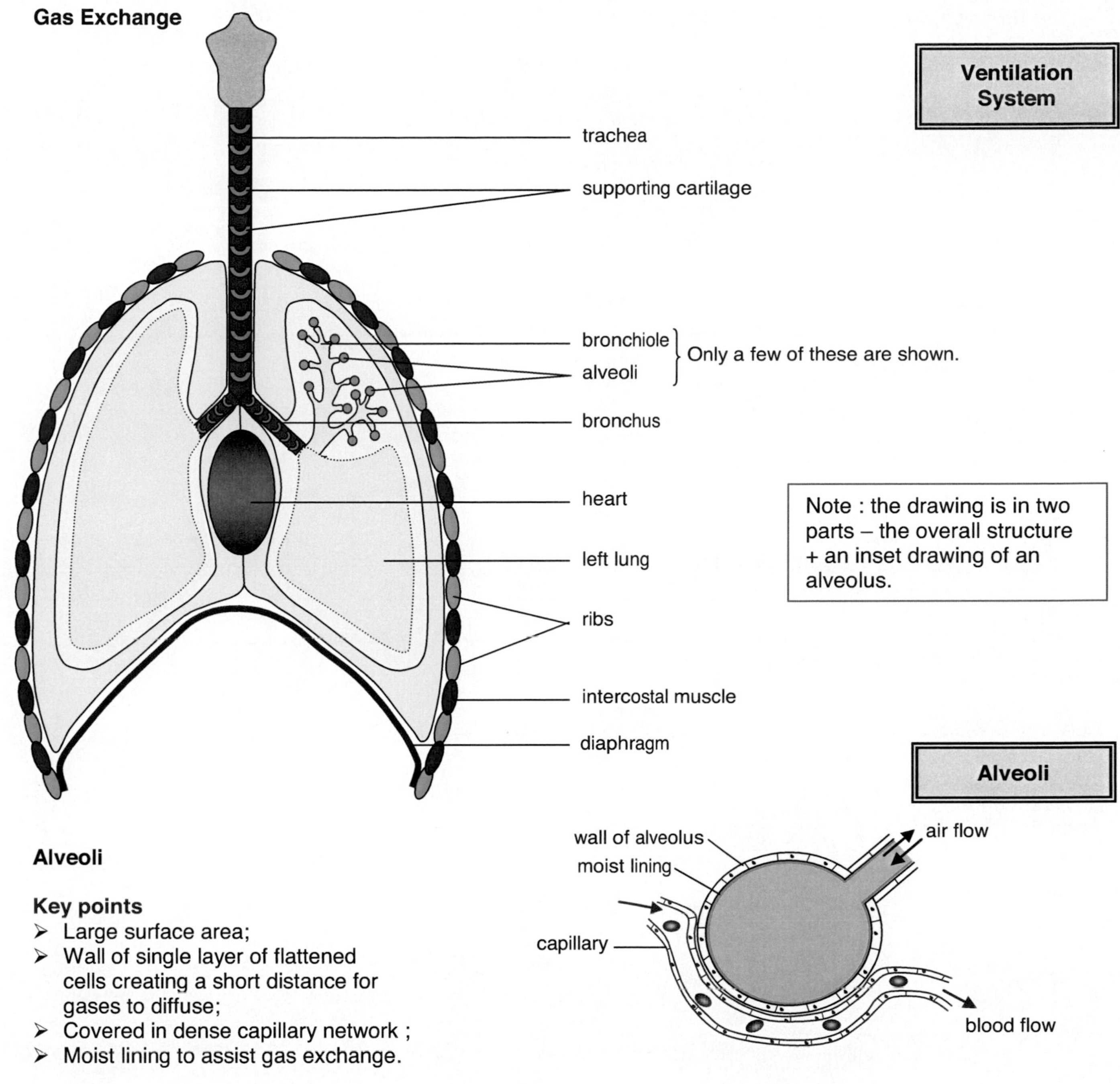
Ventilation System
trachea
supporting cartilage
bronchiole
alveoli
Only a few of these are shown.
bronchus
heart
left lung
ribs
intercostal muscle
diaphragm
Note : the drawing is in two parts – the overall structure + an inset drawing of an alveolus.
Alveoli
wall of alveolus
moist lining
air flow
capillary
blood flow

Alveoli

Key points

- Large surface area;
- Wall of single layer of flattened cells creating a short distance for gases to diffuse;
- Covered in dense capillary network ;
- Moist lining to assist gas exchange.

Ventilation	Breathing air in and out of the lungs.
Gas exchange	In lungs – diffusion of oxygen from alveoli into blood. – diffusion of carbon dioxide from blood into alveoli.
Cell respiration	The chemical breakdown of sugar in cells, with the use of enzymes, to release energy.

Ventilation

Mechanism of Ventilation

Principles

- The thoracic cavity is a sealed box.
- Atmospheric pressure is effectively constant.
- If the volume of the thoracic cavity increases the pressure decreases.
- Atmospheric pressure forces air into the lungs.
- If the volume of the thoracic cavity decreases the pressure increases.
- Air is forced out of the lungs.

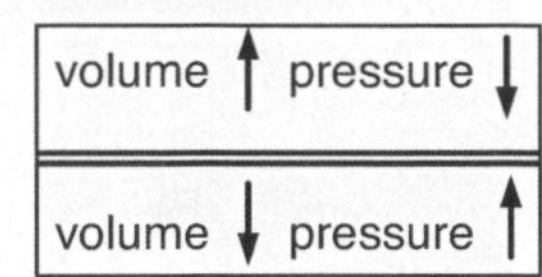
volume ↑ pressure ↓
volume ↓ pressure ↑

External intercostal muscles	Attached to the rib cage. When contract rib cage moves up <u>and</u> out. Volume increases; pressure decreases → breathe in. Internal intercostal muscles relaxed.
Internal intercostal muscles	Attached to the rib cage. When contract rib cage moves down <u>and</u> in. Volume decreases; pressure increases → breathe out. External intercostal muscles relaxed.
Diaphragm	Dome shaped structure separating thoracic cavity from abdominal cavity. When radial muscle contracts dome flattens. Volume increases; pressure decreases → breathe in.
Abdominal muscles	Abdominal muscles contract and push diaphragm back to dome shape. Volume decreases; pressure increases → breathe out. Diaphragm muscle relaxed.

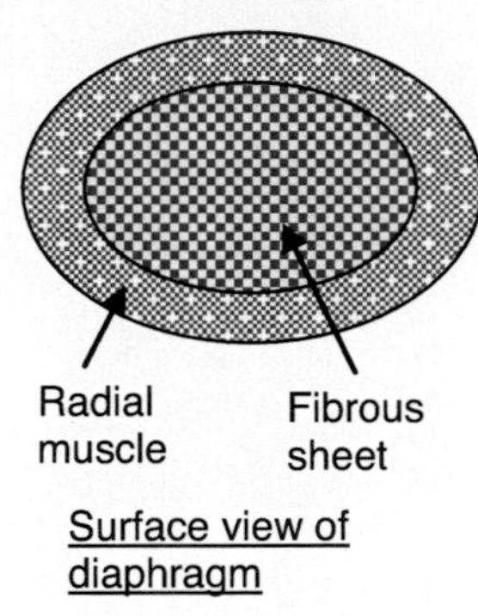
Radial muscle
Fibrous sheet

Surface view of diaphragm

Need for Ventilation

Need for Ventilation

Key points

- Efficient gas exchange depends upon high concentration gradient;
- As oxygen diffuses into blood / carbon dioxide diffuses out of blood, concentration gradients decrease;
- Ventilation brings in fresh oxygen and removes carbon dioxide, which maintains concentration gradient;
- Steep diffusion gradient allows for rapid diffusion of gases.

Distinguish between ventilation, gas exchange and respiration.

Where are the intercostal muscles found?

What type of muscle is found in the diaphragm?

List the four parts of the air passages in the lungs in order.

List four features of alveoli that help gas exchange.

What happens to the thorax pressure when the volume increases?

The Nervous System

The Nervous System

The nervous system consists of -

- Central nervous system (CNS);
- Peripheral nerves.

It is composed of specialised cells called neurons that carry electrical impulses rapidly.

Nerve impulses are conducted –

- from receptors to the CNS by sensory neurons;
- within the CNS by relay neurons;
- from the CNS to effectors by motor neurons.

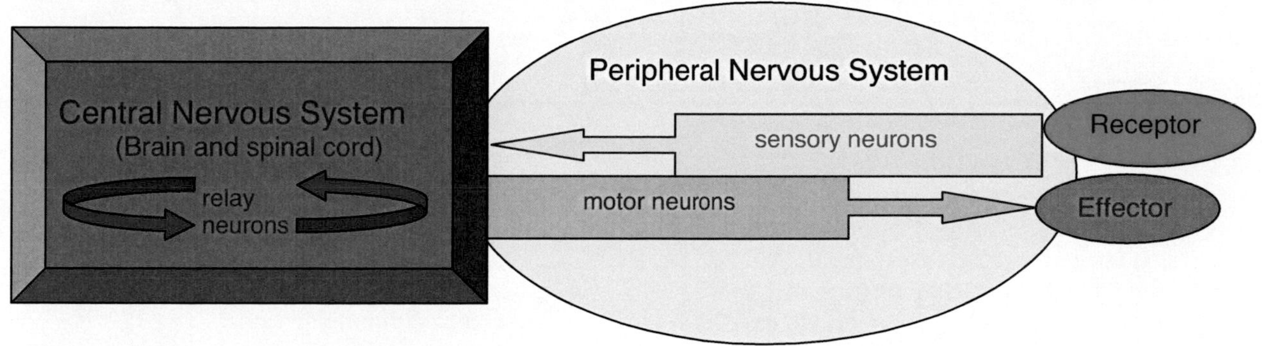

Central Nervous System
(Brain and spinal cord)
relay neurons
Peripheral Nervous System
sensory neurons
motor neurons
Receptor
Effector

The Nerve Impulse

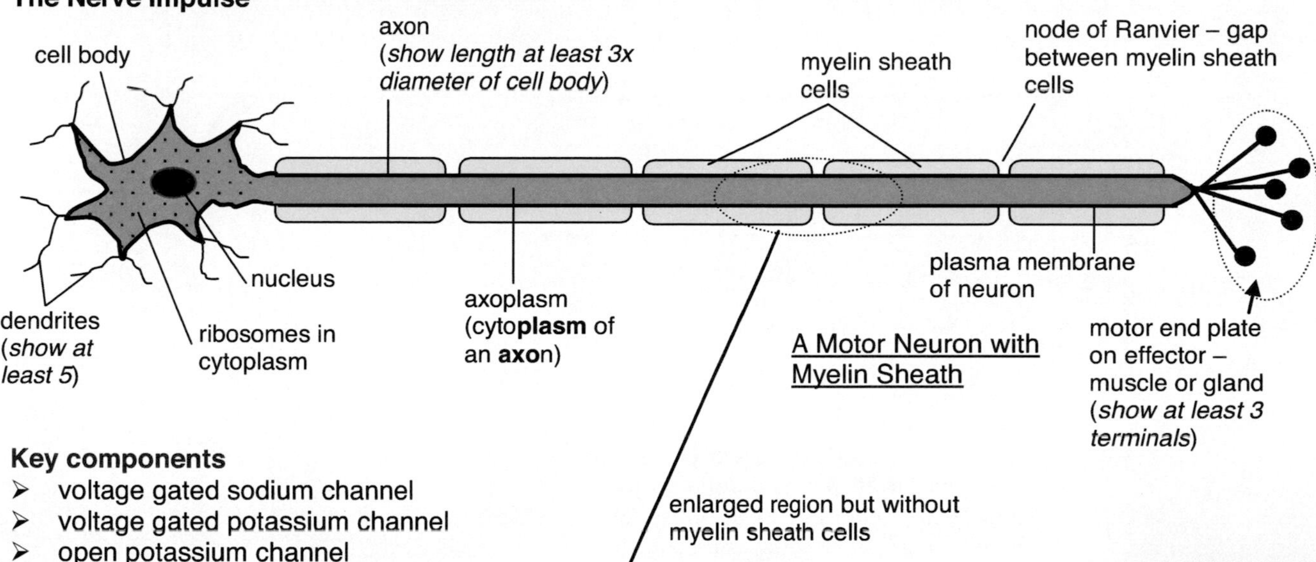

cell body
axon (*show length at least 3x diameter of cell body*)
myelin sheath cells
node of Ranvier – gap between myelin sheath cells
nucleus
dendrites (*show at least 5*)
ribosomes in cytoplasm
axoplasm (cyto**plasm** of an **axo**n)
plasma membrane of neuron
A Motor Neuron with Myelin Sheath
motor end plate on effector – muscle or gland (*show at least 3 terminals*)
enlarged region but without myelin sheath cells

Key components

- voltage gated sodium channel
- voltage gated potassium channel
- open potassium channel
- linked sodium – potassium pump

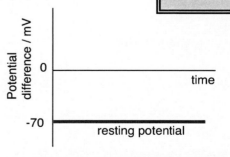

Resting Potential

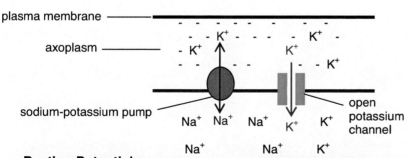

plasma membrane

axoplasm

sodium-potassium pump

open potassium channel

K^+ Na^+

Potential difference / mV

0

-70

time

resting potential

Resting Potential

Key points

- The sodium-potassium pump brings potassium ions into the axoplasm and removes sodium ions (in the ratio $2K^+ : 3Na^+$); ⟷
- Potassium ions diffuse down a concentration gradient out of the axoplasm through an open ion channel; ⟶
- Negative ions (proteins) in the axoplasm cannot diffuse out.

Define resting potential.

Action Potential

Action Potential

Define action potential.

Key point
Consists of two parts -
1. Depolarisation;
2. Recovery.

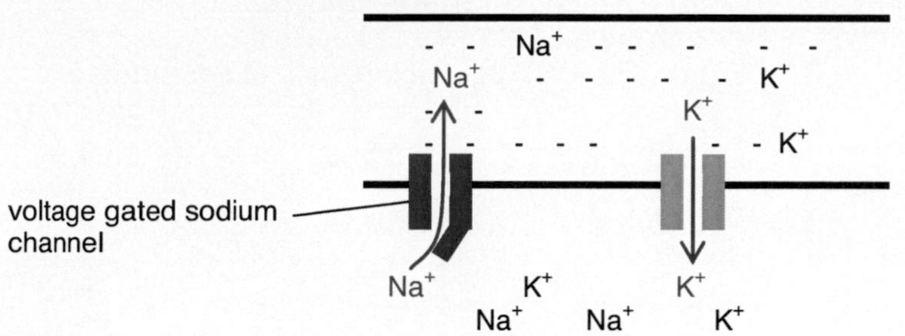
Na+
Na+
K+
K+
K+
voltage gated sodium channel
Na+
K+
K+
Na+
Na+
K+

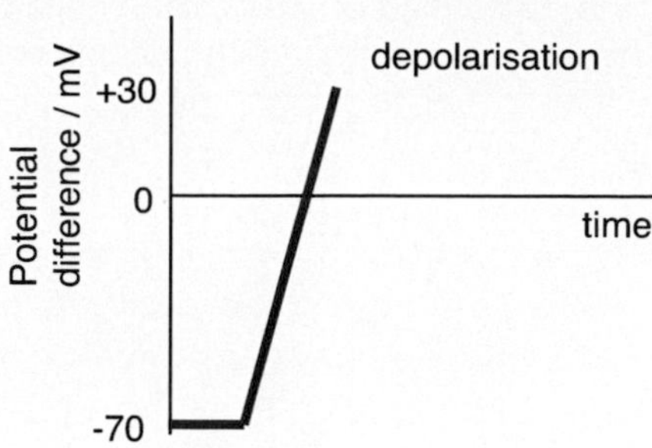
Potential difference / mV
+30
0
-70
depolarisation
time

1. Depolarisation

Key points
- A stimulus causes voltage gated sodium channels to open;
- A few sodium ions diffuse into the axoplasm down a diffusion gradient;
- This causes the potential difference rapidly to reverse – <u>depolarisation</u>.

2. Recovery

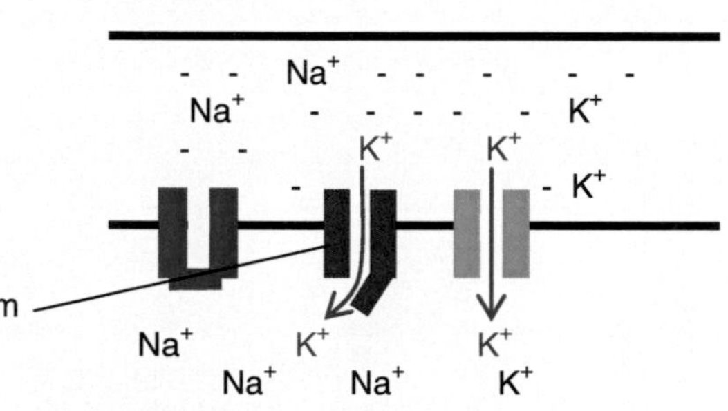
Na+
Na+
K+
K+
K+
K+
voltage gated potassium channel
Na+
K+
K+
Na+
Na+
K+

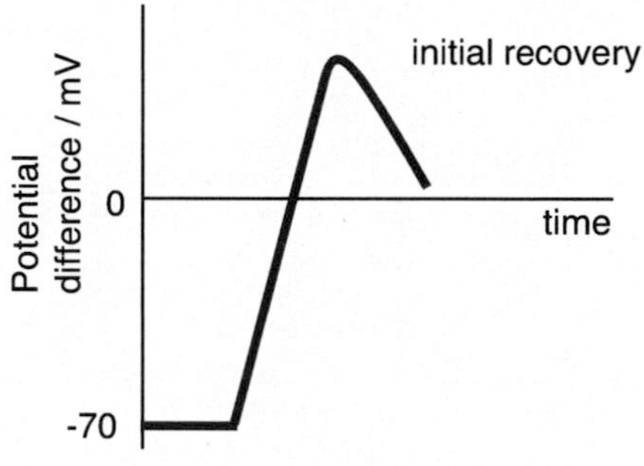
Potential difference / mV
0
-70
initial recovery
time

Initial recovery
Key points
- Voltage gated sodium channels close;
- Voltage gated potassium channels open;
- Increased flow of potassium ions diffusing down the concentration gradient;

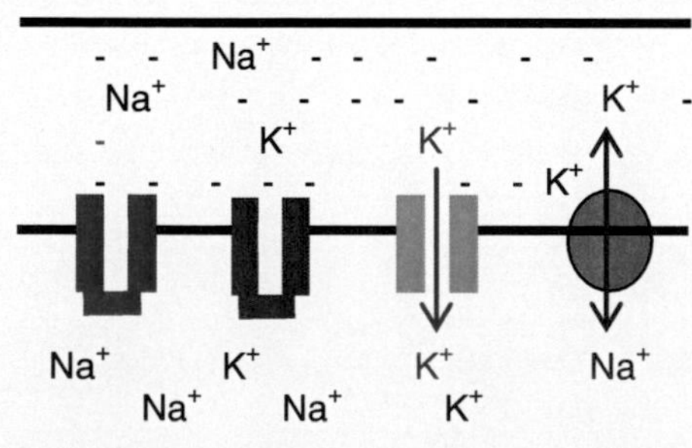
Na+
Na+
K+
K+
K+
K+
Na+
K+
K+
Na+
Na+
Na+
K+

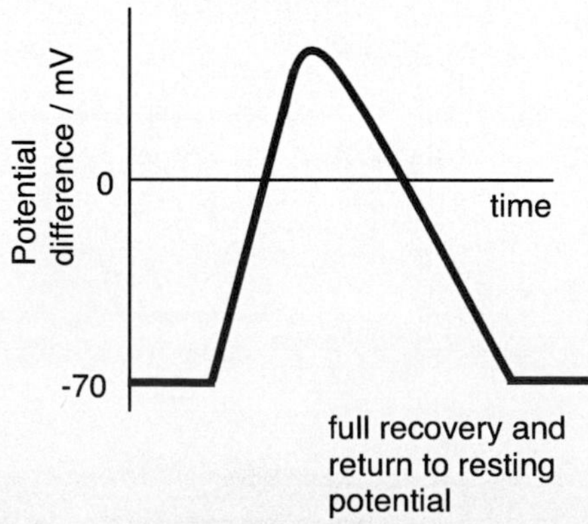
Potential difference / mV
0
-70
time
full recovery and return to resting potential

Full recovery and return to resting potential
Key points
- All voltage gated channels closed;
- Sodium-potassium pump removing sodium ions from axoplasm;
- Diffusion of potassium ions through open channel.

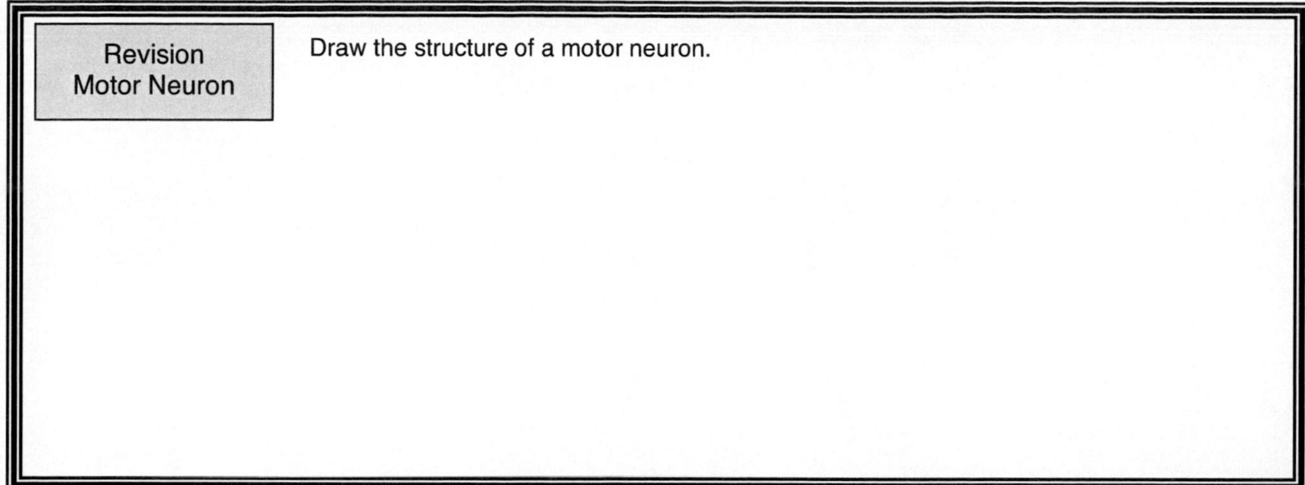
Revision
Motor Neuron
Draw the structure of a motor neuron.

The Synapse

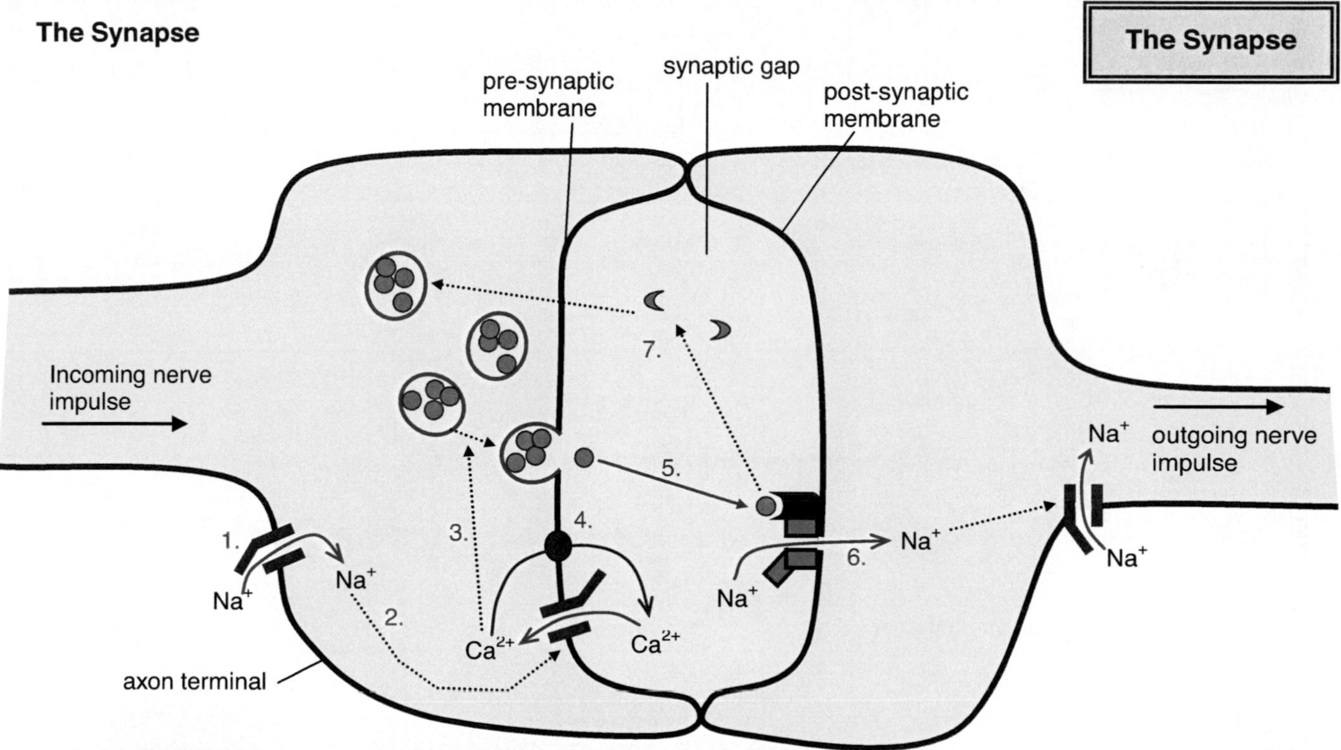
The Synapse
synaptic gap
pre-synaptic membrane
post-synaptic membrane
Incoming nerve impulse
7.
5.
4.
3.
1.
Na+
Na+
2.
Ca2+
Ca2+
axon terminal
Na+
6.
Na+
Na+
outgoing nerve impulse
Na+

Key components

- Voltage gated sodium channels on axon terminal;
- Voltage gated calcium channels on pre-synaptic membrane;
- Vesicles of neurotransmitter;
- Neurotransmitter receptors on post-synaptic membrane;
- Chemical gated sodium channels on post-synaptic membrane;
- Calcium pump.

Sequence of events

1. Sodium ions enter the axoplasm of the axon terminal through voltage gated sodium ion channels when the action potential arrives at the axon terminal.
2. This opens the voltage gated calcium ion channels allowing Ca^{2+} to diffuse into the axon terminal from the synaptic gap.
3. The influx of calcium ions causes vesicles of neurotransmitter to move to the pre-synaptic membrane and burst.
4. The calcium ions are removed by an active pump.
5. Neurotransmitter diffuses across the synaptic gap and binds to a specific receptor on the post-synaptic membrane.
6. This opens the chemical gated channel allowing an influx of sodium ions into the post-synaptic neuron, which causes depolarisation triggering a post-synaptic impulse.
7. The neurotransmitter is removed and taken up through the pre-synaptic membrane and re-synthesised into neurotransmitter. Some neurotransmitters are broken down by an enzyme in the synaptic gap before uptake.

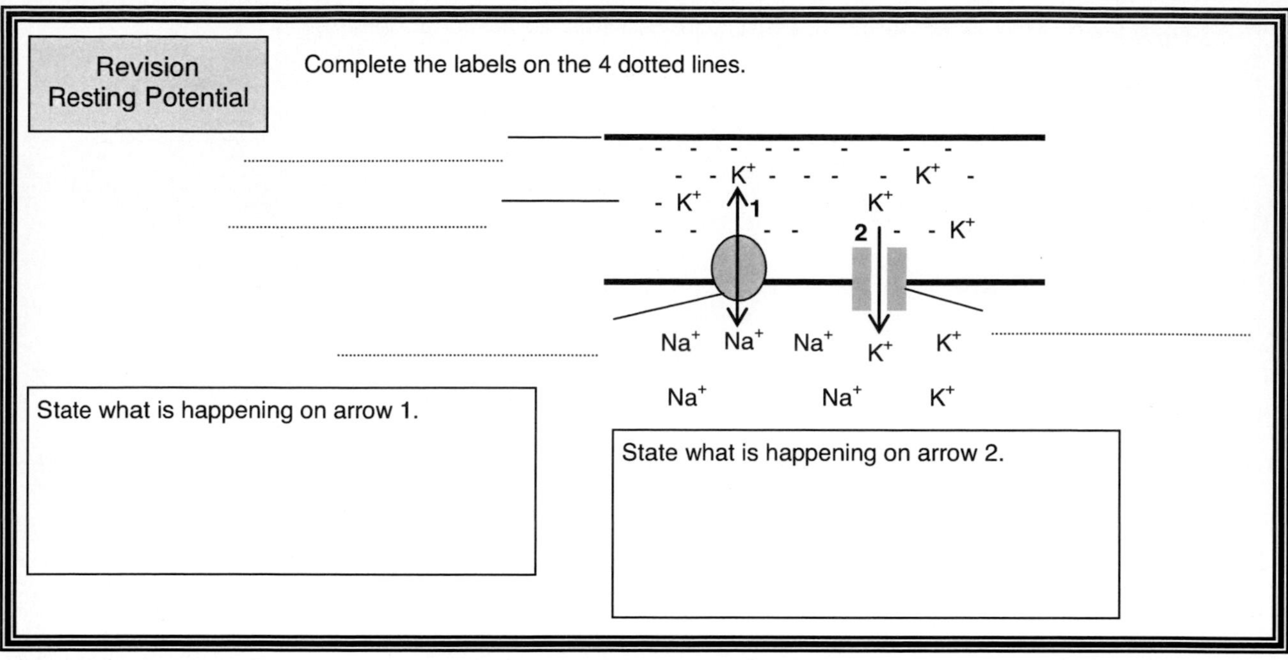
Revision
Resting Potential
Complete the labels on the 4 dotted lines.
K+
K+
K+
K+
K+
1
2
Na+
Na+
Na+
K+
K+
Na+
Na+
K+
State what is happening on arrow 1.
State what is happening on arrow 2.

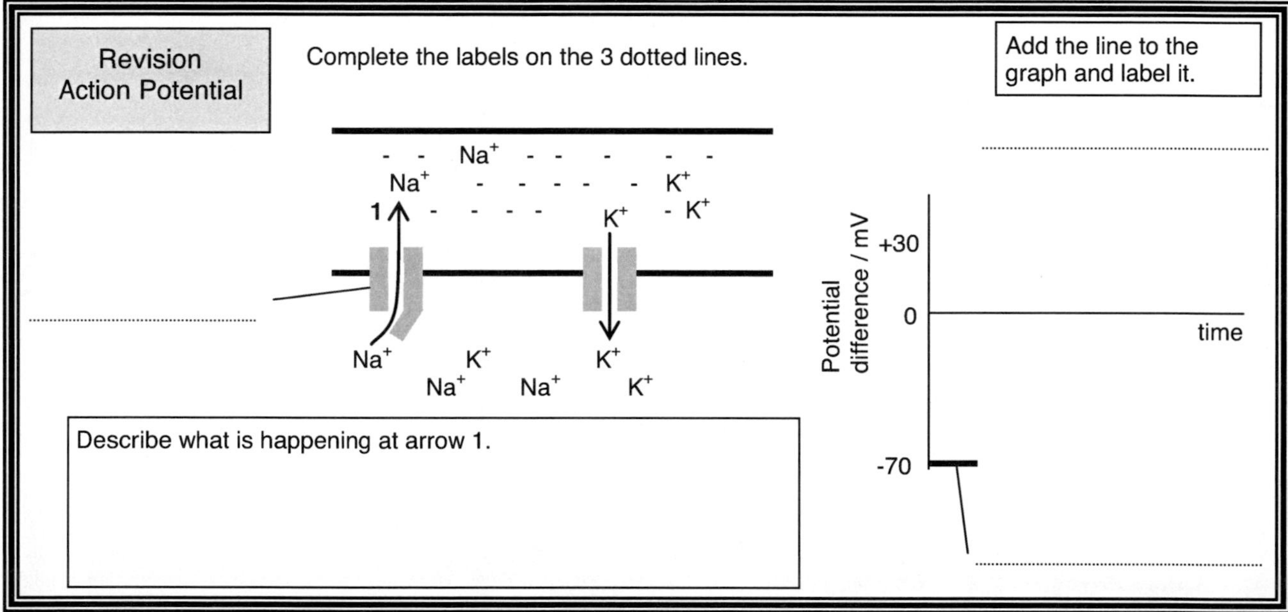
Revision
Action Potential
Complete the labels on the 3 dotted lines.
Add the line to the graph and label it.
Na+
Na+
1
K+
K+
K+
Na+
K+
K+
Na+
Na+
K+
Potential difference / mV
+30
0
time
-70
Describe what is happening at arrow 1.

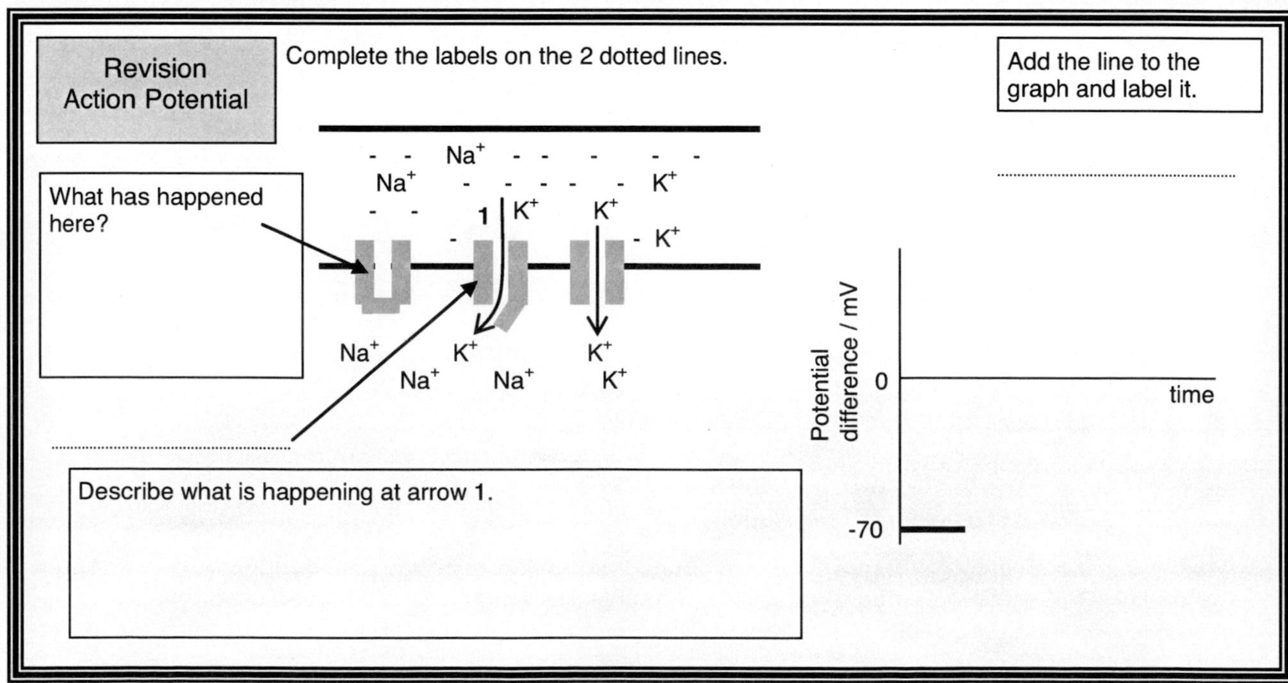
Revision
Action Potential
Complete the labels on the 2 dotted lines.
Add the line to the graph and label it.
What has happened here?
Na+
Na+
1
K+
K+
K+
K+
Na+
K+
K+
Na+
Na+
K+
Potential difference / mV
0
time
-70
Describe what is happening at arrow 1.

Revision Action Potential

Complete the label on the dotted line.

Add the line to the graph and label it.

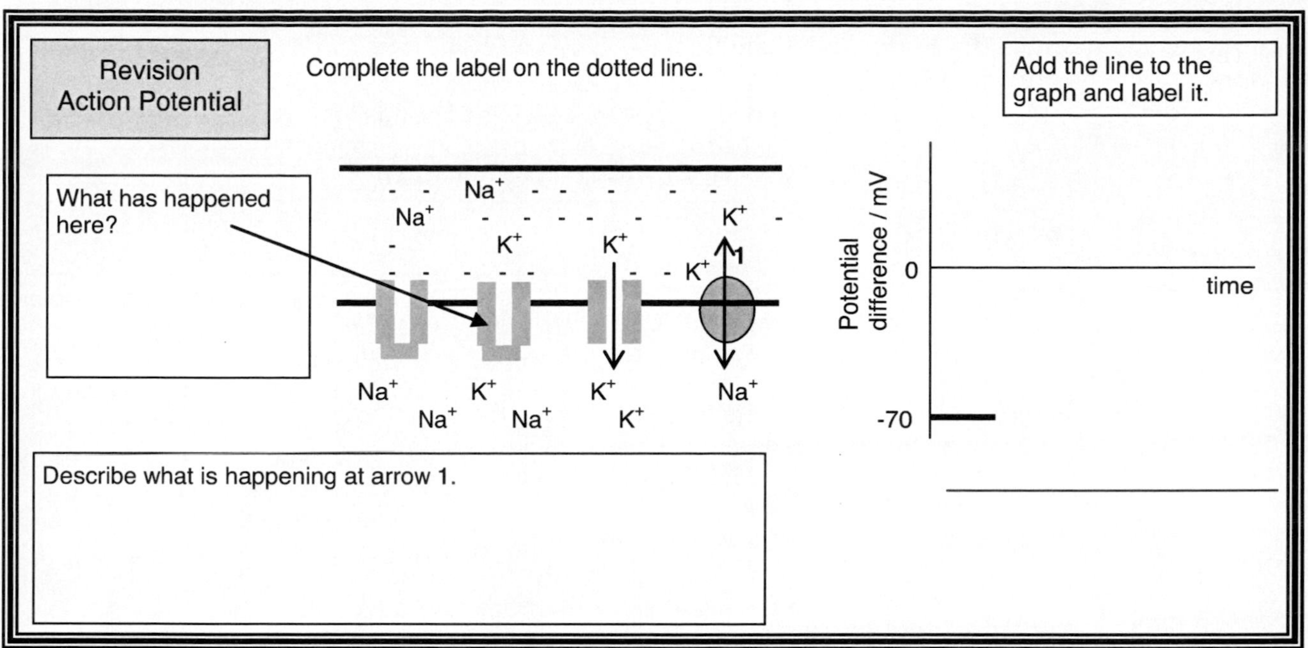
What has happened here?
Na$^+$
Na$^+$
K$^+$
K$^+$
K$^+$
K$^+$
1
Na$^+$
K$^+$
K$^+$
Na$^+$
Na$^+$
Na$^+$
K$^+$
Potential difference / mV
0
time
-70

Describe what is happening at arrow 1.

Revision Synapse

Complete the labels on the 9 dotted lines.

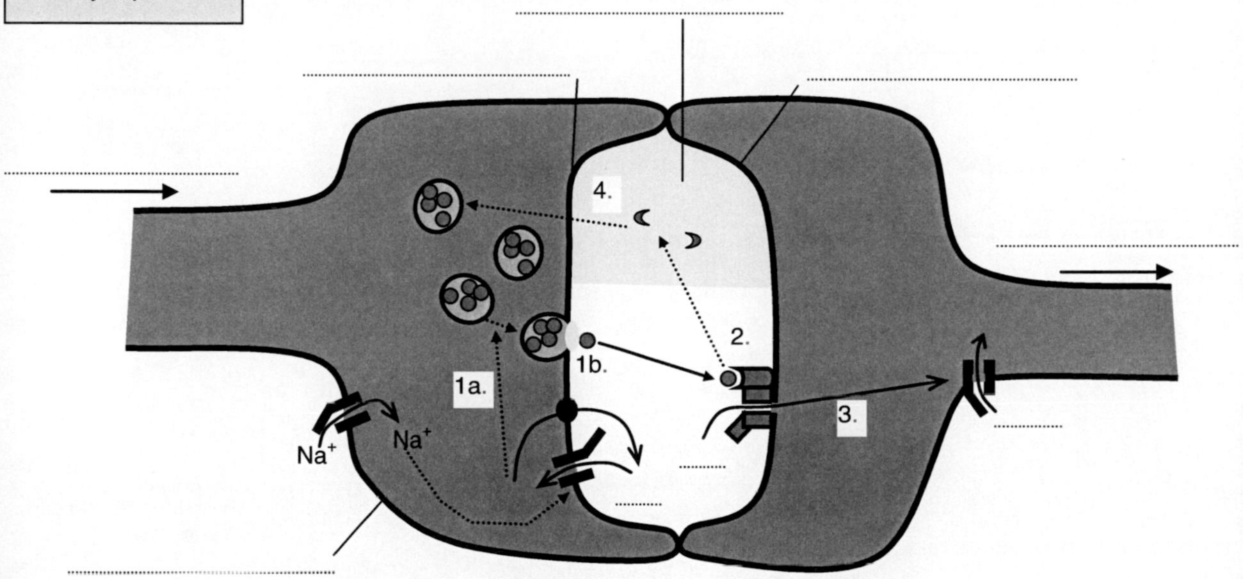

4.

2.

1b.

1a.

3.

Na$^+$

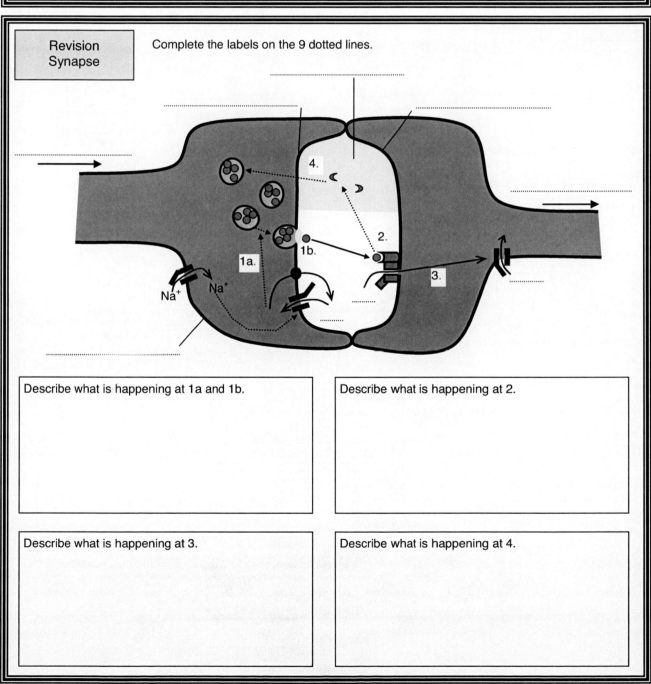

Na$^+$

Describe what is happening at 1a and 1b.

Describe what is happening at 2.

Describe what is happening at 3.

Describe what is happening at 4.

Endocrine System

The Endocrine System

The endocrine system consists of glands that secrete hormones directly into the blood stream and which are transported by the blood.

Homeostasis

Homeostasis

Homeostasis is maintaining the internal environment –
- blood pH,
- carbon dioxide concentration,
- blood glucose concentration,
- body temperature,
- water balance,

between narrow limits.

Principles

- Receptor or sensor monitors level of variable;
- Co-ordinating centre regulates level of variable;
- Effectors bring about the changes directed by the co-ordinating centre;
- The endocrine and nervous systems are both involved in homeostasis.

Negative Feedback

Negative Feedback

Principle

- When a variable deviates from the norm the result of the effector mechanisms is to return the variable back to the norm.

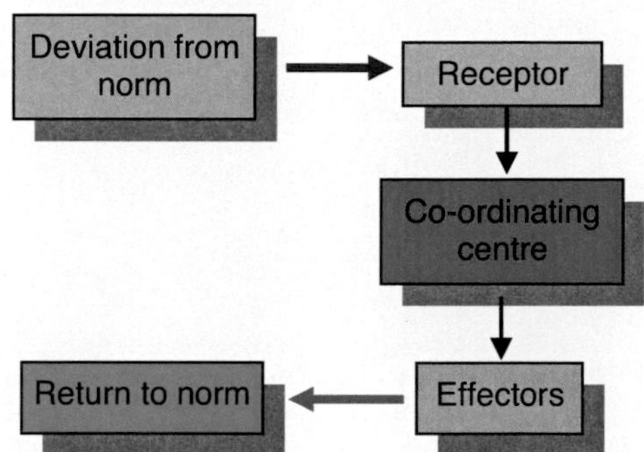

Deviation from norm
Receptor
Co-ordinating centre
Effectors
Return to norm

Temperature Regulation

Temperature Regulation

Key points

- Blood temperature is monitored by the hypothalamus, a region of the brain.
- The hypothalamus also receives information from temperature receptors in the skin.
- Nerve impulses are sent from the hypothalamus to co-ordinate the processes.

Skin

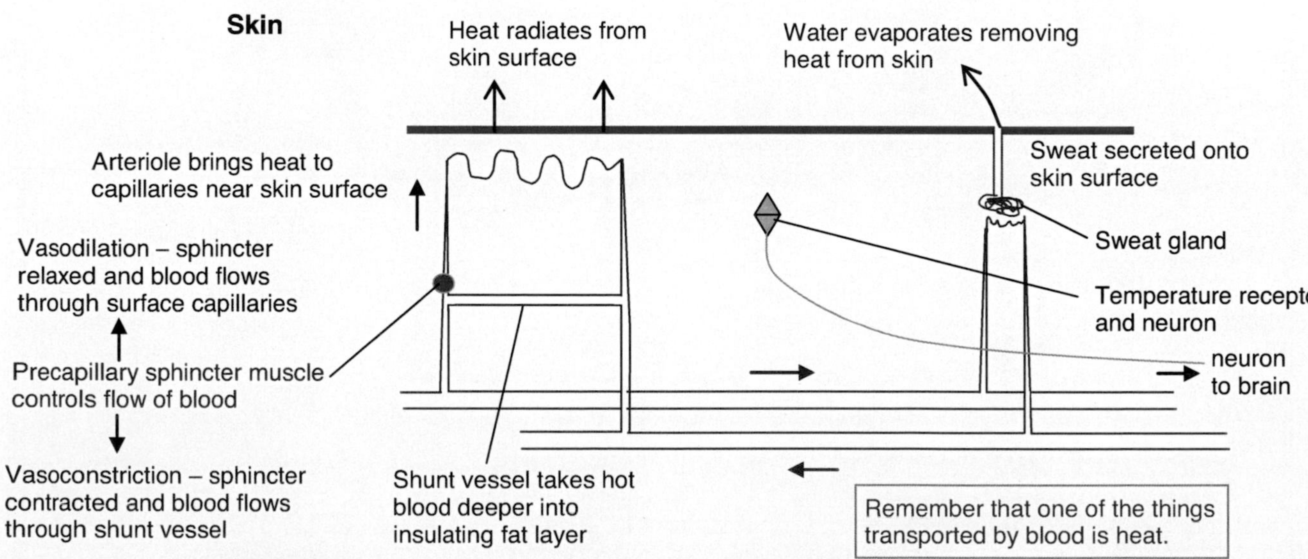

Heat radiates from skin surface
Water evaporates removing heat from skin
Arteriole brings heat to capillaries near skin surface
Sweat secreted onto skin surface
Sweat gland
Vasodilation – sphincter relaxed and blood flows through surface capillaries
Temperature receptor and neuron
Precapillary sphincter muscle controls flow of blood
neuron to brain
Vasoconstriction – sphincter contracted and blood flows through shunt vessel
Shunt vessel takes hot blood deeper into insulating fat layer

Remember that one of the things transported by blood is heat.

Shivering

Key points

- Shivering is when the muscles undergo tiny contractions.
- Muscle contraction requires energy from ATP and this has to be made via respiration;
- Respiration produces heat which warms the blood.

Control of Blood Glucose

Control of Blood Glucose

Change in blood sugar level detected by islet cells in pancreas

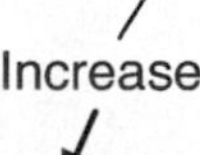

Increase	Decrease
Beta cells in pancreas secrete insulin	Alpha cells in pancreas secrete glucagon
Blood glucose lowered by – 1. Increased uptake into cells. 2. Increased conversion to glycogen in muscles and liver. 3. Increased conversion to fat. 4. Increased rate of respiration.	Blood glucose raised by – 1. Increased breakdown of liver glycogen. 2. Synthesis of glucose from fats and amino acids.

Tip – You are studying the **IB** course - Insulin --- **B**eta cells.

Warning – take care not to confuse glycogen and glucagon. Glucag**on** is the horm**one**.

Diabetes

Diabetes

Key facts

- Diabetes is failure to control blood glucose level leading to abnormally high levels of glucose in the blood (hyperglycaemia);
- The kidney threshold* is exceeded and glucose is excreted;
- Urine volume increases causing thirst;
- Muscle tissue is broken down leading to weight loss;
- Vision can be seriously damaged (retinopathy);
- Kidney failure may occur.

* When the kidney first filters the blood glucose is found in this filtrate. However it is normally all reabsorbed back into the blood. The threshold is the maximum level of glucose in the filtrate that can all be reabsorbed.

Type I (Early Onset or Juvenile) diabetes

- Usually starts early in life, often very suddenly;
- Due to loss of insulin secreting cells in the pancreas;
- Controlled by testing level of blood sugar and then injecting an appropriate quantity of insulin;
- Control has to continue throughout life;
- Potential for stem cell therapy.

Type II (Late Onset) diabetes

- Comes on gradually, usually in late middle age;
- Often associated with long term overweight;
- Persistant over-eating of sugary foods causes high levels of plasma insulin;
- This reduces the sensitivity of the insulin target cells;
- Often controlled by reducing carbohydrate intake which allows the target cells to recover.

List the three types of neuron. Which one is found in the CNS?

State what the endocrine system consists of.

List 5 factors which are under homeostatic control.

Name the region of the brain that monitors blood temperature.

State the two components of the nervous system.

▪

▪

State why shivering can raise blood temperature.

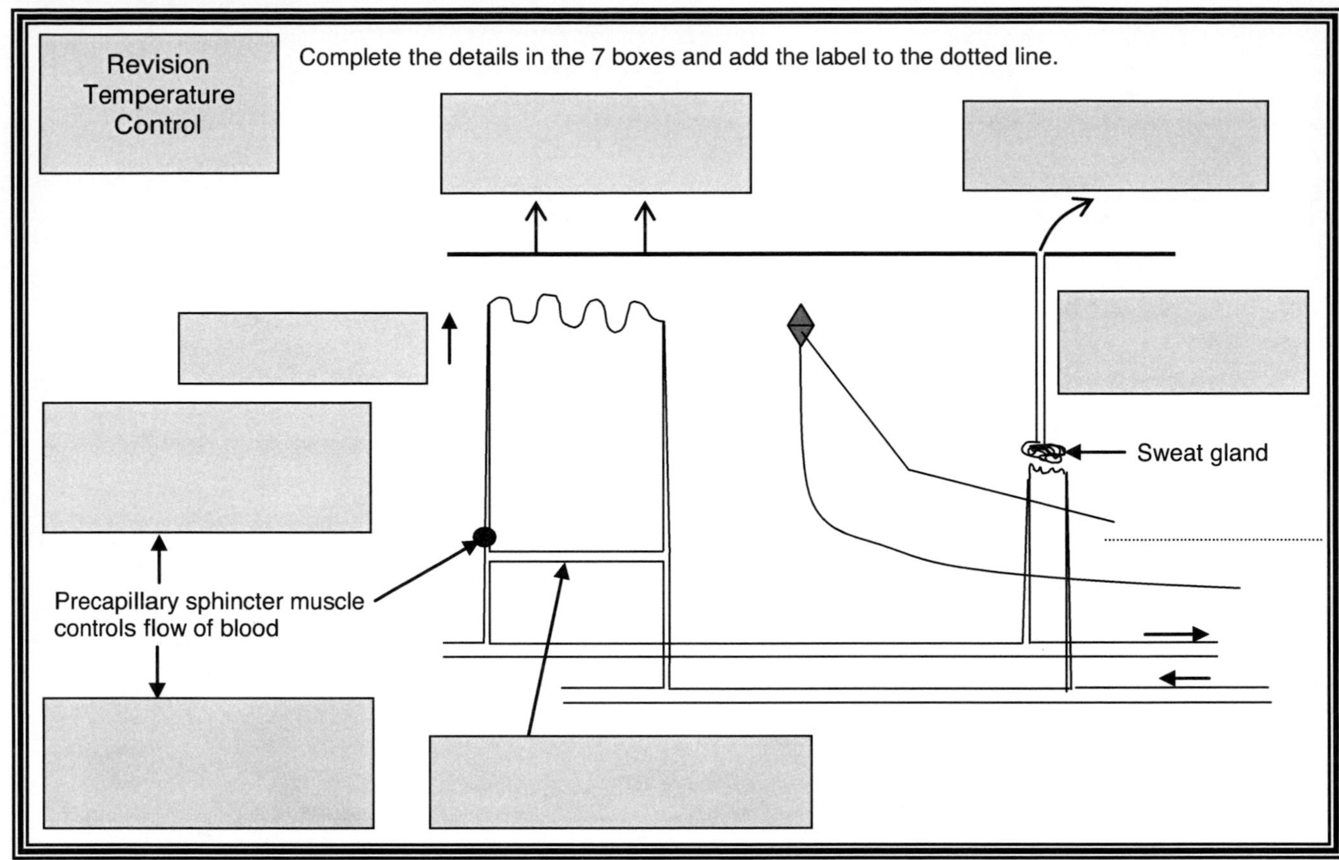
Revision Temperature Control
Complete the details in the 7 boxes and add the label to the dotted line.
Sweat gland
Precapillary sphincter muscle controls flow of blood

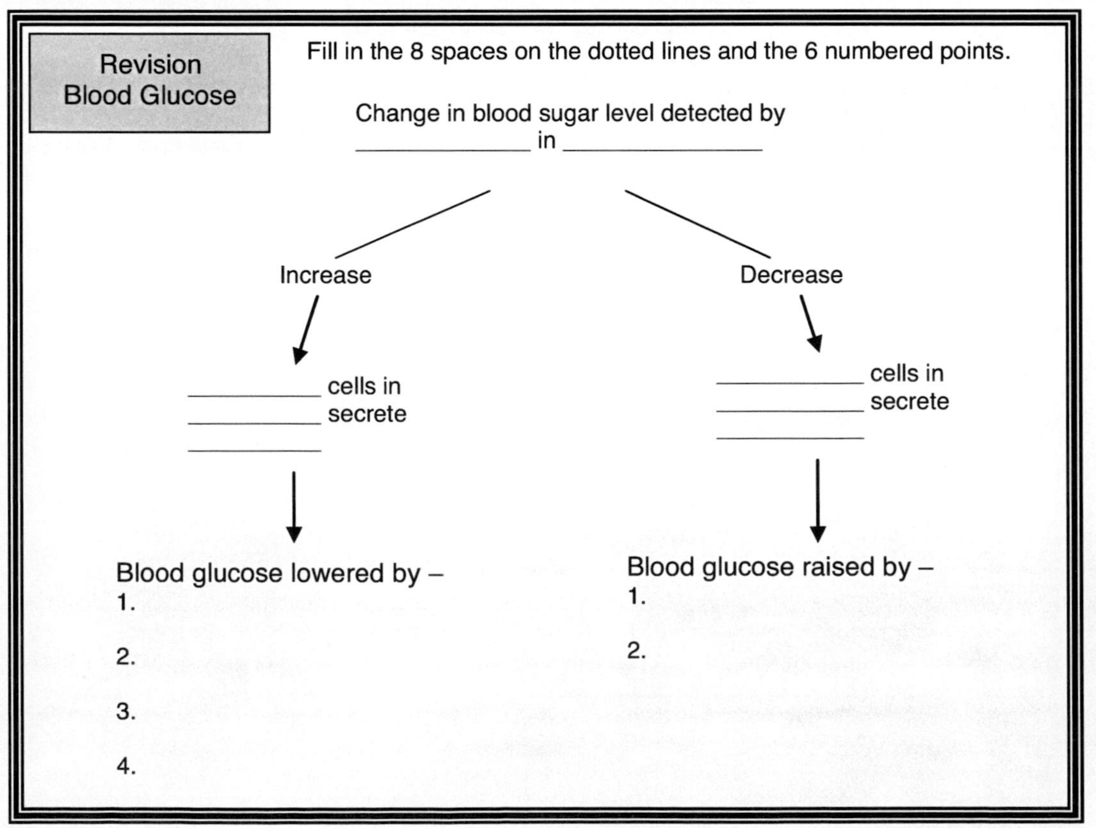
Revision Blood Glucose
Fill in the 8 spaces on the dotted lines and the 6 numbered points.
Change in blood sugar level detected by ______________ in ________________
Increase
Decrease
__________ cells in __________ secrete __________
__________ cells in __________ secrete __________
Blood glucose lowered by –
1.
2.
3.
4.
Blood glucose raised by –
1.
2.

What happens to the pressure in the thorax if the external intercostal muscles contract?	What happens to the pressure in the thorax if the diaphragm muscles contract?
What is the principle of negative feedback?	Name the pancreatic cells that release glucagon.
	Which two types of neuron make up the peripheral nervous system?

Revision Breathing

Fill in the missing words.

External intercostal muscles	Attached to the rib cage. When contract rib cage moves __________ and __________. Volume ____________________________; Pressure ____________________________ → breathe ___________.
Internal intercostal muscles	Attached to the rib cage. When contract rib cage moves __________ and __________. Volume ____________________________; Pressure ____________________________ → breathe ___________.
Diaphragm	Dome shaped structure separating thoracic cavity from abdominal cavity. When __________ muscles contracts dome _____________. Volume ____________________________; Pressure ____________________________ → breathe ___________.
Abdominal muscles	When __________ muscles of diaphragm relax abdominal muscles ___________ and push diaphragm back to dome shape. Volume ____________________________; Pressure ____________________________ → breathe ___________.

Revision Diabetes

Fill in the15 blank spaces.

Type I (Early Onset or Juvenile) diabetes

- Usually starts......................................in life, often very suddenly;
- Due to loss of .... secreting cells in the.. ;
- Controlled by testing .... and then .... an appropriate quantity of .... ;
- Control has to continue .... ;

Type II (Late Onset) diabetes

- Comes on .... , usually in late middle age;
- Often associated with long term .... ;
- Persistant over-eating of sugary foods causes.................................... levels of.. ;
- This.................................... the sensitivity of the.. cells;
- Often controlled by .... which allows the .... to recover.

Reproductive Systems (including urinary system)

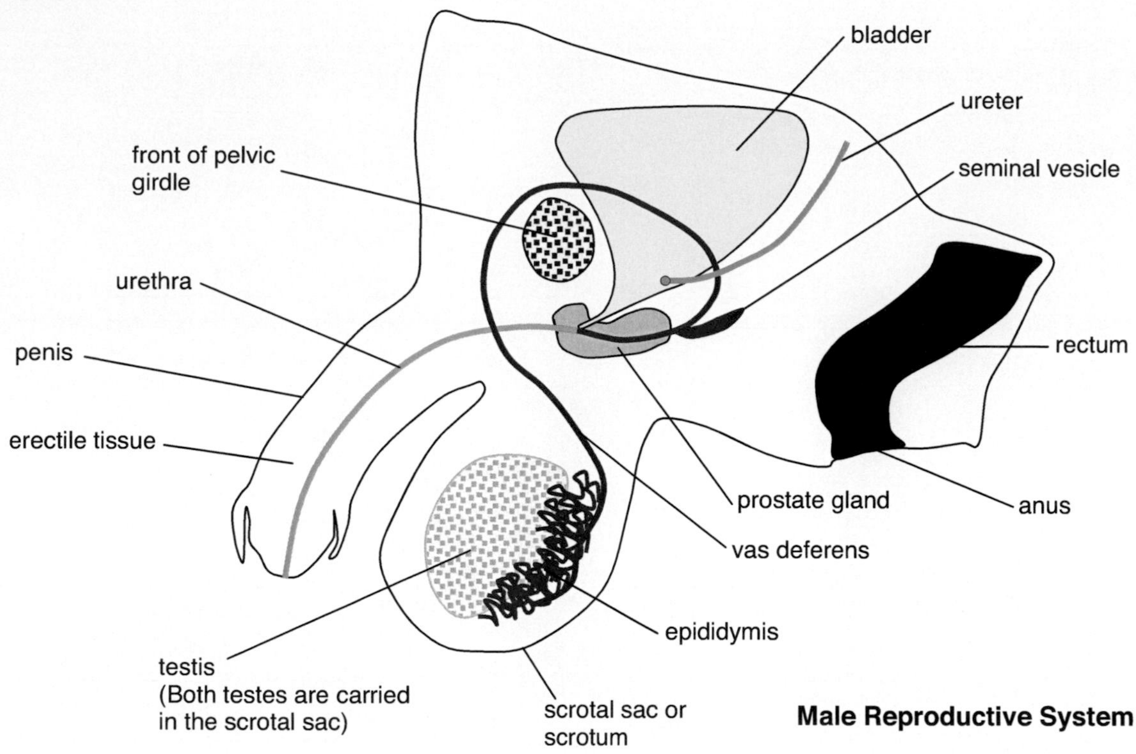
bladder
ureter
front of pelvic girdle
seminal vesicle
urethra
penis
rectum
erectile tissue
prostate gland
anus
vas deferens
epididymis
testis
(Both testes are carried in the scrotal sac)
scrotal sac or scrotum

Male Reproductive System

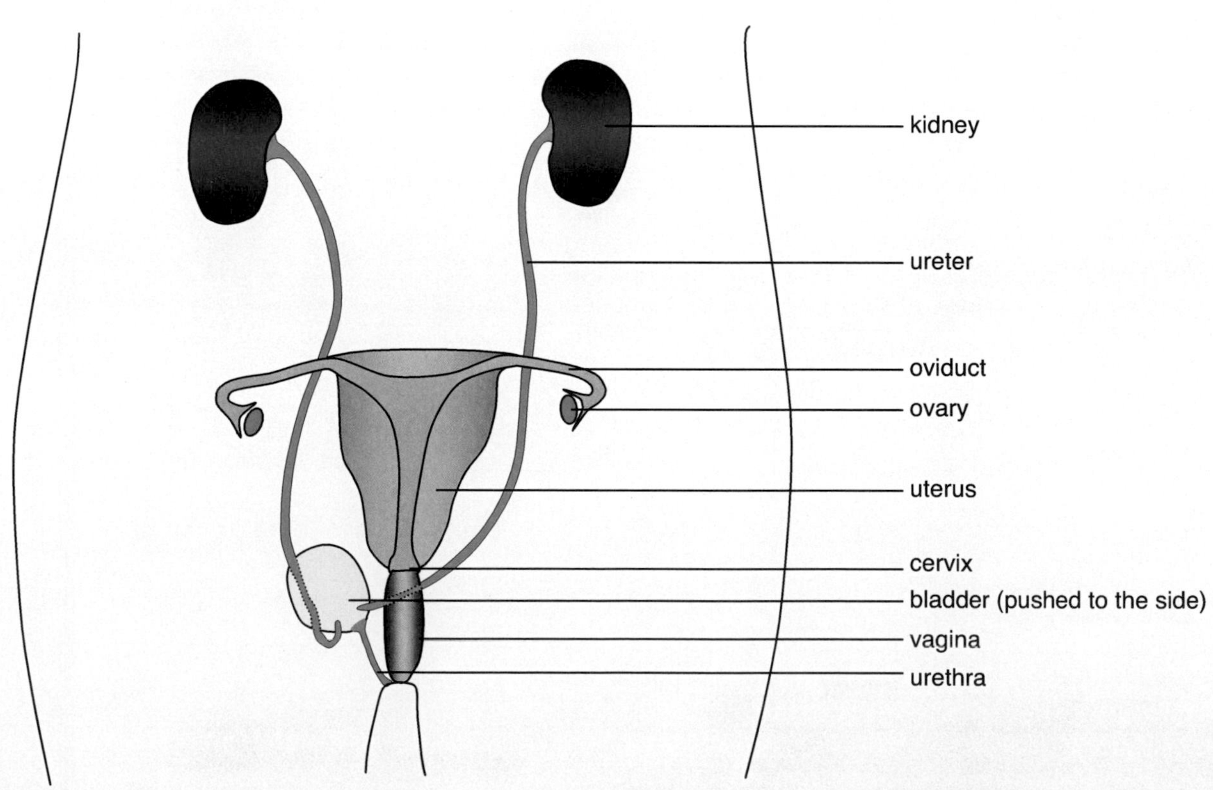
kidney
ureter
oviduct
ovary
uterus
cervix
bladder (pushed to the side)
vagina
urethra

Female Reproductive System

Reproductive Hormones

Hormone	Function	
	Boys	Girls
Testosterone	• Pre-natal development of genitalia; • Development of secondary sexual characteristics; • Maintains the sex drive.	
Estrogen		• Pre-natal development of genitalia; • Development of secondary sexual characteristics.
Follicle stimulating hormone (FSH)		• Causes one or more follicles in the ovaries to mature; • Stimulates secretion of estrogen.
Luteinising hormone (LH)		• Stimulates secretion of estrogen; • Stimulates ovulation; • Stimulates conversion of empty follicle into corpus luteum and secretion of progesterone.
Estrogen		• Initiates repair of uterus lining; • Positive feedback on LH to trigger ovulation.
Progesterone		• Completes repair of uterus lining; • Negative feedback on pituitary to block release of FSH; • Maintains uterus lining in early part of pregnancy.

Revision Male Reproductive System

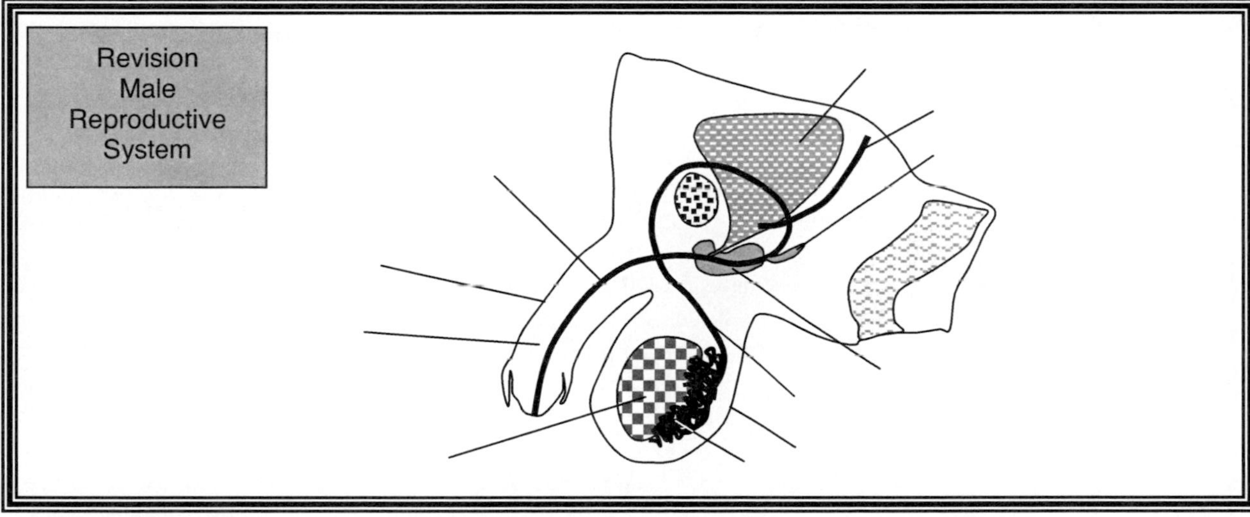

Revision Female Reproductive System

Label the structures indicated.

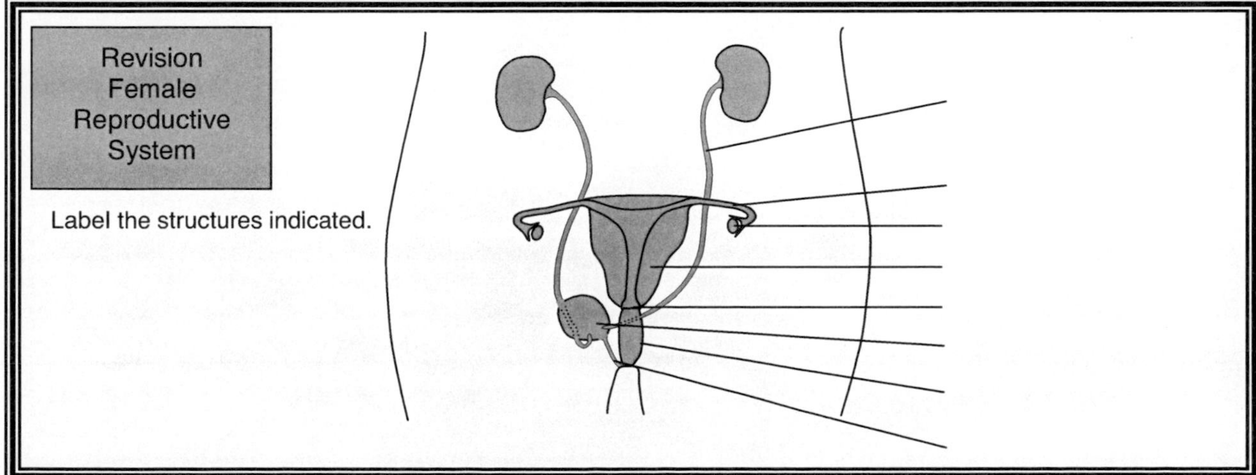

Hormones in the Menstrual Cycle

Interactions of Hormones in the Menstrual Cycle.

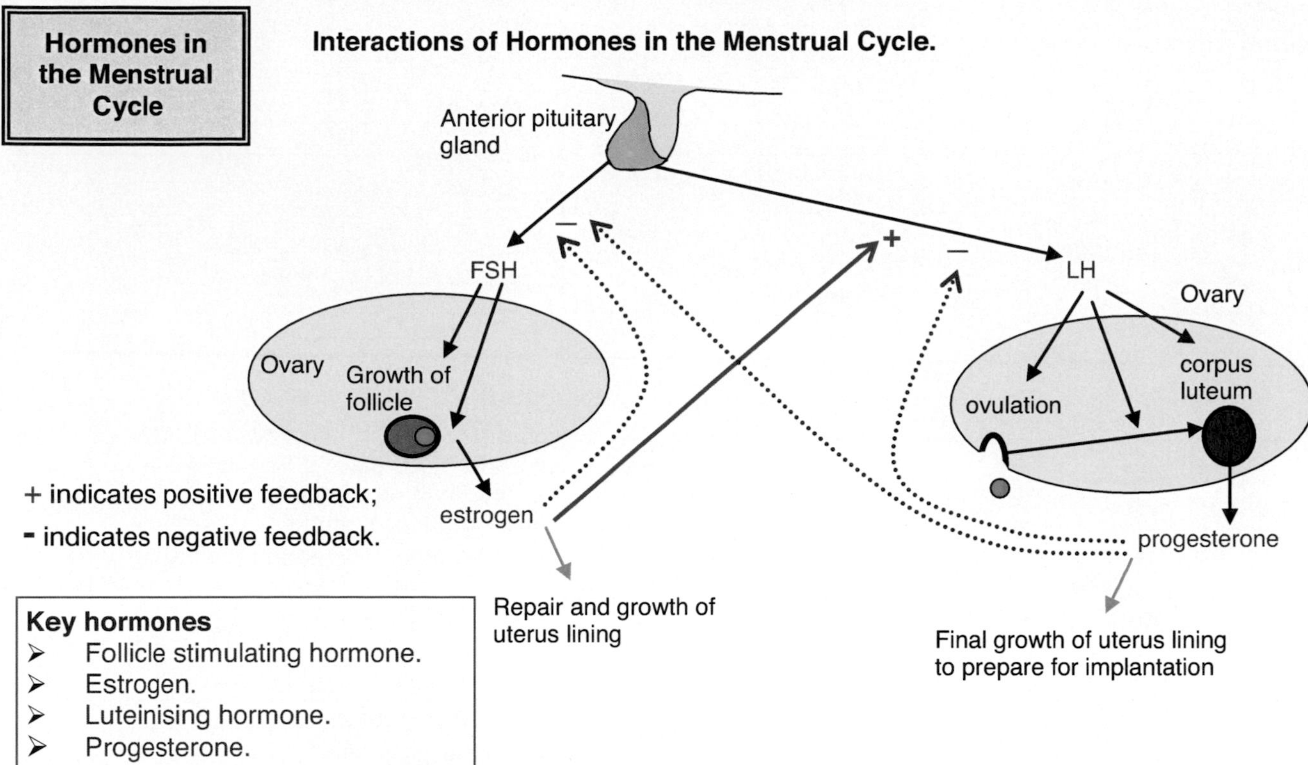
Anterior pituitary gland
FSH
LH
+
–
–
Ovary
Growth of follicle
estrogen
Repair and growth of uterus lining
Ovary
ovulation
corpus luteum
progesterone
Final growth of uterus lining to prepare for implantation
+ indicates positive feedback;
- indicates negative feedback.

Key hormones
- Follicle stimulating hormone.
- Estrogen.
- Luteinising hormone.
- Progesterone.

Note – the number of bullet points corresponds to the number of arrows from each hormone on the diagram above.

Link these steps to both the diagram above and to the levels of hormones on the graphs below.

Key steps
- FSH released from anterior pituitary.
  - stimulates growth of follicle;
  - stimulates secretion of estrogen.
- Estrogen released from follicle cells.
  - stimulates repair and growth of endometrium (uterus lining);
  - negative feedback on pituitary to block FSH release;
  - nearing middle of cycle it reaches a critical level which causes a positive feedback on pituitary to release LH.
- LH released from anterior pituitary.
  - stimulates ovulation;
  - stimulates conversion of empty follicle to corpus luteum;
  - stimulates secretion of estrogen and progesterone by corpus luteum.
- Progesterone released from corpus luteum.
  - stimulates final growth of uterus lining;
  - negative feedback on pituitary blocking FSH;
  - negative feedback on pituitary blocking LH.

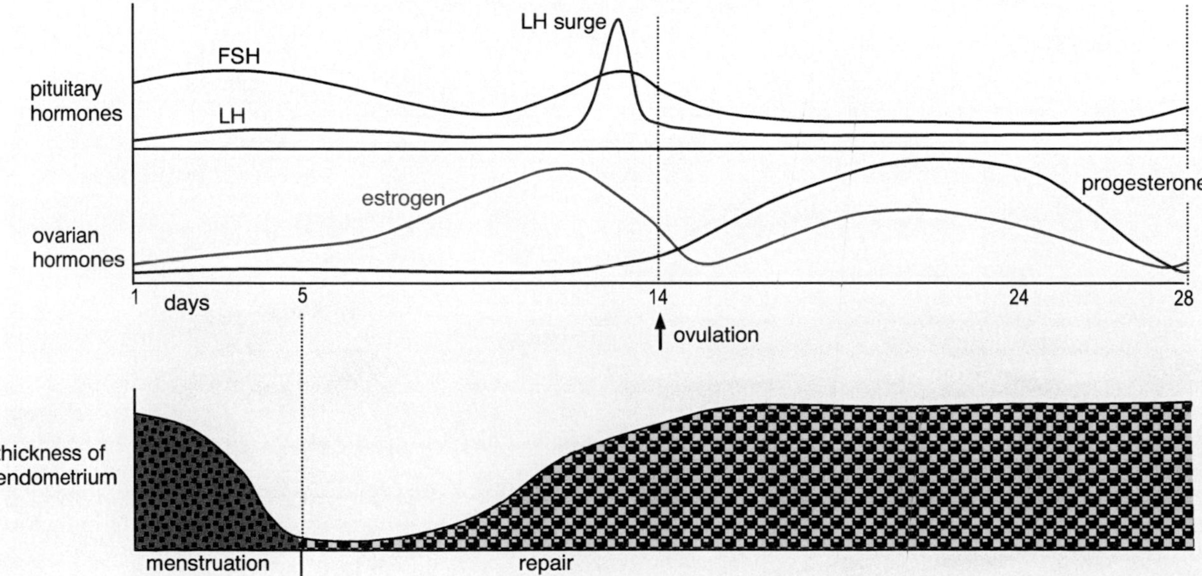
LH surge
FSH
pituitary hormones
LH
estrogen
progesterone
ovarian hormones
1
days
5
14
24
28
ovulation
thickness of endometrium
menstruation
repair

In Vitro Fertilisation – IVF

Key Steps

- FSH is injected into the woman in order to induce development of several follicles in the ovaries;
- Eggs from mature follicles are removed several days later by a tube inserted via the vagina;
- The eggs are transferred to a dish of warmed physiological saline and the sperms from the man added;
- After a few days incubation the embryos are examined for any signs of abnormalities;
- If necessary a more detailed genetic check can be carried out by karyotyping and/or gene probes;
- Hormonal treatment prepares the mother's uterus;
- Selected embryos are then inserted into the mother's uterus.

Ethical Issues of IVF

Positive

- May allow a childless couple to have a child;
- Screening and selection prevents genetic abnormalities from being passed on;

Negative

- More embryos than are used are produced so some die;
- If more than one selected embryo implants then multiple births can affect health of the children. (Improved techniques mean chances of a successful implantation are now much higher. Fertility treatment clinics are now being encouraged to insert only one embryo)
- Inherited forms of infertility could be passed on to children;
- May lead to abuse by selecting embryos other than for avoiding genetic abnormalities, eg choosing a girl or boy, or for producing identical twins.

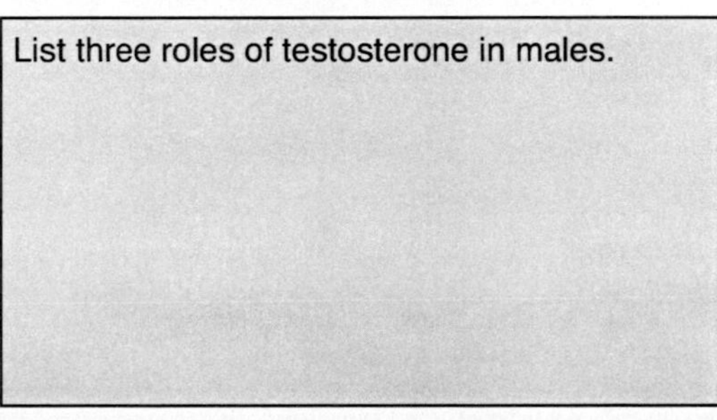
List three roles of testosterone in males.

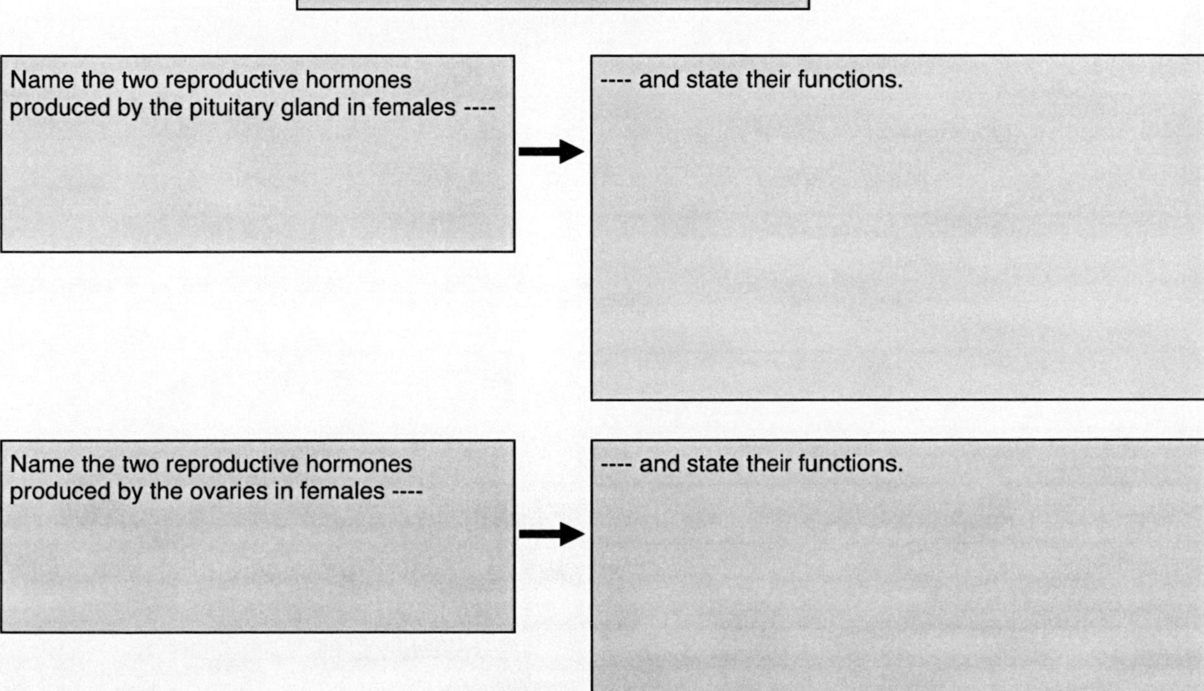
Name the two reproductive hormones produced by the pituitary gland in females ----
---- and state their functions.
Name the two reproductive hormones produced by the ovaries in females ----
---- and state their functions.

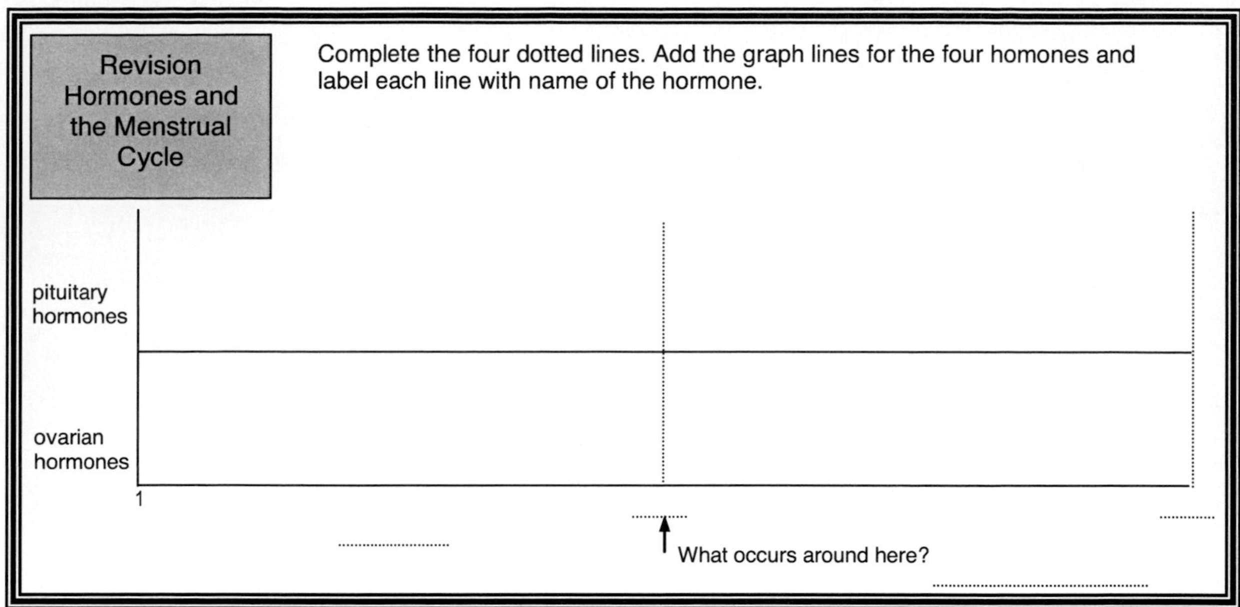
Revision Hormones and the Menstrual Cycle
Complete the four dotted lines. Add the graph lines for the four homones and label each line with name of the hormone.
pituitary hormones
ovarian hormones
1
What occurs around here?

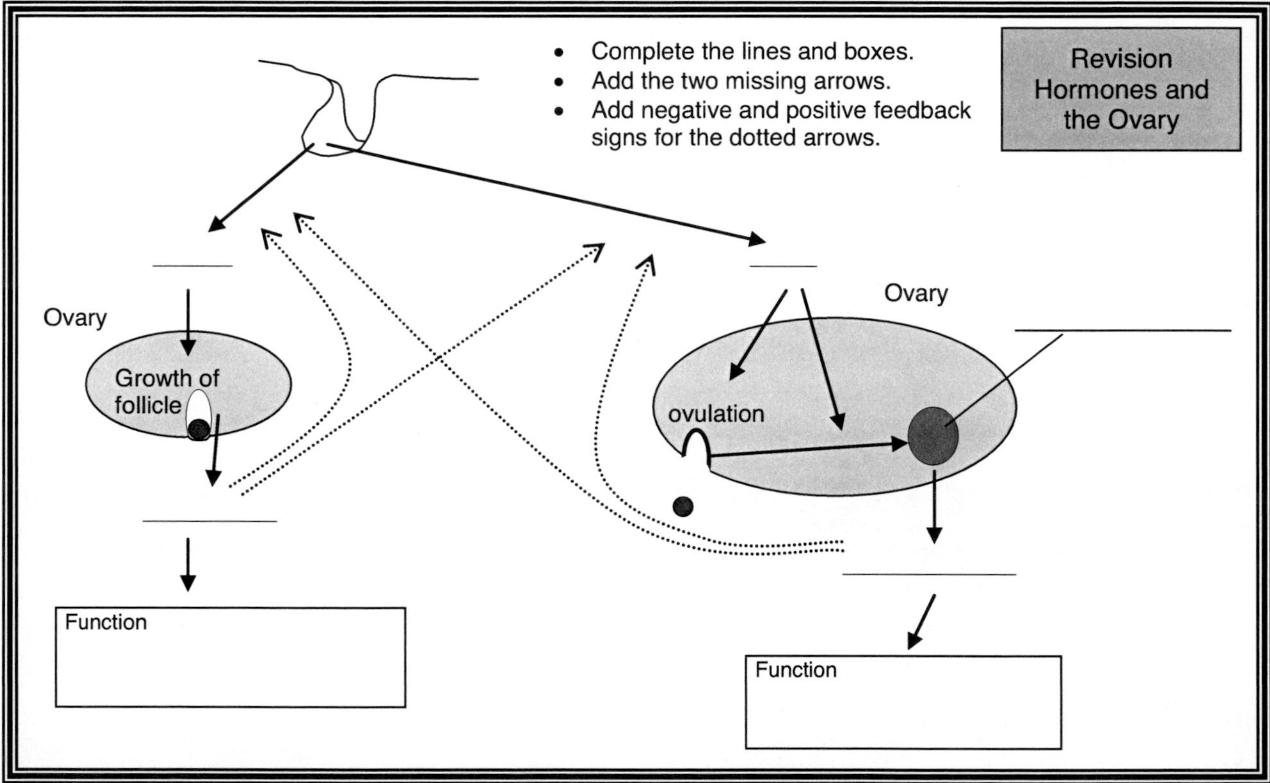
Complete the lines and boxes.
Add the two missing arrows.
Add negative and positive feedback signs for the dotted arrows.
Revision Hormones and the Ovary
Ovary
Growth of follicle
Ovary
ovulation
Function
Function

List the key steps in the process of IVF.

State two positive and two negative ethical issues relating to IVF.

Self-test Quiz on Topic 6

1. Which of the following is the correct sequence for the gut structures?
   a. Mouth, stomach, oesophagus, small intestine, large intestine.
   b. Mouth, oesophagus, stomach, large intestine, small intestine.
   c. Mouth, oesophagus, stomach, small intestine, large intestine.
   d. Mouth, stomach, small intestine, large intestine, oesophagus.

2. Digestion is necessary because
   a. large food molecules cannot be absorbed through the intestine wall,
   b. this makes the food more nutritious,
   c. it changes the pH so the food molecules can be absorbed,
   d. only large food molecules can be taken up by phagocytosis.

3. The finger-like shape of a villus is so that
   a. the surface area is increased for absorption,
   b. it is able to move food along the intestine,
   c. it protects the absorptive surface of the intestine,
   d. it helps to break up the large pieces of food.

4. Assimilation is
   a. absorption of digested food,
   b. use of absorbed food by the body,
   c. removal of undigested food from the body,
   d. absorption of gases through the alveoli.

5. Which line in the table below shows correctly the type of blood in the vessel?

	Coronary artery	Pulmonary artery	Vena cava	Pulmonary vein
a.	oxygenated	oxygenated	deoxygenated	deoxygenated
b.	oxygenated	deoxygenated	oxygenated	deoxygenated
c.	deoxygenated	oxygenated	deoxygenated	deoxygenated
d.	oxygenated	deoxygenated	deoxygenated	oxygenated

6. Which line in the table below shows correctly the description for the blood vessels?

	Artery	Capillary	Vein
a.	Large lumen	Thin layer of muscle	Valves
b.	Thin layer of muscle	Valves	Large lumen
c.	Thick layer of muscle	Wall one cell thick	Valves
d.	Thick layer of muscle	Valves	Thin layer of muscle

7. Which of the following statements is <u>not</u> correct?
   a. When the ventricles contract the semilunar valves are opened.
   b. When the atria contract the atrio-ventricular valves are opened.
   c. When the atria contract the semilunar valves are closed.
   d. When the ventricles contract the atrio-ventricular valves are opened.

8. Myogenic means
   a. the heart is able to change the rate at which it beats,
   b. the heart muscle is able to contract of its own accord,
   c. the heart rate is regulated at all times by the brain,
   d. heart muscle is unaffected by nerve impulses.

9. The hormone that affects heart rate is
   a. testosterone,
   b. oxytocin,
   c. insulin,
   d. adrenalin.

10. The pacemaker is
   a. the region of the heart that regulates the rate of the heart beat,
   b. the region of the brain that regulates the rate of the heart beat,
   c. the region of the brain that regulates the rate of breathing,
   d. the nerves from the brain that affect the heart rate,

11. Which of the following statements is correct?
   a. Antibodies are proteins made by erythrocytes.
   b. Antigens are molecules made by leucocytes.
   c. Antibodies are proteins that can destroy antigens.
   d. Antigens are proteins that can destroy antibodies.

12. A pathogen may be defined as
   a. a form of vaccine that is used to stimulate a defence response,
   b. a type of white blood cell that fights infection,
   c. an organism or virus that causes disease,
   d. a bacterial population on or in the body.

13. Which of the following is a correct statement about phagocytic leucocytes?
   a. They produce antibodies.
   b. They ingest dead cells and pathogens.
   c. They transport carbon dioxide in the blood stream.
   d. They have lost their nucleus.

14. Which of the following is <u>not</u> a correct statement about lymphocytes?
   a. They recognise an antigen.
   b. They produce only one particular type of antibody,
   c. They possess a nucleus.
   d. They divide to form a clone of cells producing different types of antibody.

15. Which of the following is <u>not</u> a characteristic of alveoli.
   a. They have thin muscular walls to aid breathing.
   b. They have a moist lining.
   c. The walls are only one cell thick.
   d. They are covered in a dense network of capillaries.

16. Which of the lines in the following table correctly describes the column headings?

	Ventilation	Gas exchange	Cell respiration
a.	Release of energy from glucose.	Taking air into the lungs via the tracheae.	Transfer of carbon dioxide from blood to air.
b.	The process of breathing.	Transfer of oxygen from air to blood.	Release of energy from glucose.
c.	Exchange of gases between air and blood.	The process of breathing.	Breakdown of glucose to carbon dioxide.
d.	Taking air into the lungs via the tracheae.	Exchange of gases between air and blood.	The process of breathing.

17. Which of the lines in the following table correctly relates to the column headings?

	Breathing in		Breathing out	
	Diaphragm	Internal Intercostal muscles	External Intercostal muscles	Abdominal muscles
a.	Relaxed	Relaxed	Contracted	Contracted
b.	Contracted	Contracted	Relaxed	Relaxed
c.	Relaxed	Contracted	Relaxed	Contracted
d.	Contracted	Relaxed	Relaxed	Contracted

18. Ventilation is necessary because it
    a. regulates water vapour loss from the body,
    b. exercises the intercostal muscles,
    c. prevents the diaphragm from sticking to the rib cage,
    d. maintains concentration gradients of gases in the alveoli.

19. Homeostasis can be described as
    a. maintaining a constant internal environment,
    b. blood clotting,
    c. maintaining a steady breathing rate,
    d. maintaining a constant weight.

20. Negative feedback can be describes as
    a. a mechanism that corrects a change in the level of a variable,
    b. ejection of the contents of the stomach through the mouth,
    c. changing the level of a variable to suit the demands of the body,
    d. monitoring the level of a variable.

21. Nerve cells are also called
    a. erythrocytes,
    b. neurons,
    c. leucocytes,
    d. platelets.

22. Which of the following statements is correct?
    a. Insulin is produced by alpha pancreatic islet cells and lowers blood glucose levels.
    b. Reduced blood glucose levels stimulate release of glycogen from alpha pancreatic islet cells.
    c. Raised blood glucose levels stimulate release of insulin from beta pancreatic islet cells.
    d. A rise in blood temperature stimulates release of glucagon which stimulates sweating.

23. Which of the following statements is <u>not</u> correct?
    a. Estrogen is produced by girls and testosterone produced by boys.
    b. Progesterone has a negative feedback effect on the pituitary gland.
    c. Progesterone is produced by the ovaries,
    d. The ovary produces luteinising hormone.

24. Which of the following hormones has a sharp rise approximately in the middle of the menstrual cycle?
    a. Progesterone.
    b. Testosterone.
    c. Luteinising hormone.
    d. Estrogen.

25. During the resting potential
    a. K^+ diffuses out of the axon.
    b. K^+ is actively transported out of the axon.
    c. Na^+ is actively transported into the axon.
    d. the potential difference is slightly positive.

26. Depolarisation occurs because
    a. active transport of ions stops,
    b. Na^+ is actively transported into the axon,
    c. Na^+ is diffuses into the axon,
    d. the voltage gated K^+ channels open.

27. The axon membrane becomes repolarised because
    a. the voltage gated K^+ channels open allowing more K^+ to enter the axoplasm,
    b. the voltage gated Na^+ channels open allowing more Na^+ to leave the axoplasm,
    c. Na^+ is actively transported out of the axon,
    d. Na^+ and K^+ are actively transported out of the axon.

28. During synaptic transmission of an impulse
    a. the incoming impulse causes neurotransmitter to be released from the post synaptic membrane,
    b. neurotransmitter is bound to the post synaptic membrane receptors and the chemical gated Na^+ channels are open,
    c. the incomomg impulse causes neurotransmitter to be released from the post synaptic membrane receptors and broken down in the synaptic gap,
    d. neurotransmitter released into the synaptic gap is taken up through the post synaptic membrane.

29. Nerve impulses from the brain to the heart
    a regulate the opening and closing of the valves,
    b alter the rate at which the heart beats,
    c cause the coronary artery to contract,
    d prevent adrenalin from decreasing the heart rate.

Topic 7

Nucleic Acids and Proteins

DNA Structure

DNA Structure

Key points

- Cytosine and thymine are pyrimidines – they all have a **y**;
- Adenine and guanine are purines;
- Hydrogen bonds between the bases - A T has two
  - G C has three (**Gee Cee** Thr**ee**)
- The sugar – phosphate chains form anti-parallel strands;

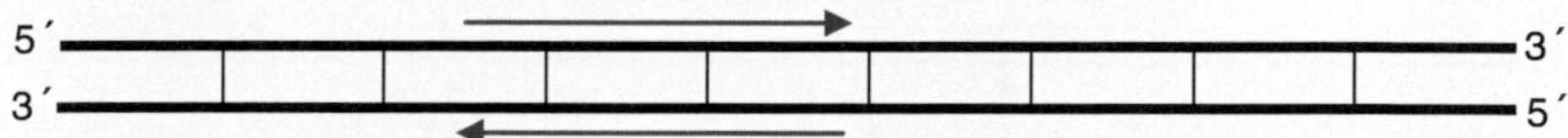

5′
3′
3′
5′

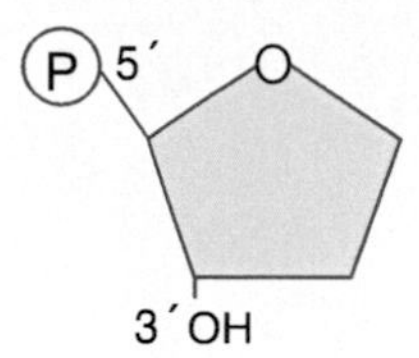

P
5′
3′OH

- The sugars are linked by phosphate groups attached to carbons 3 and 5 of the sugar. (This happens with both ribose and deoxyribose).
- This is called a 3' – 5' linkage.
- 3' means carbon 3 of the sugar contains a hydroxyl group and is the 'free' end.
- Similarly 5' means carbon 5 of the sugar has a phosphate attached and nothing more. It is the other 'free' end.

Eukaryotic genes can contain introns and exons. (See page 122).

Nucleosome

Nucleosome

Key points

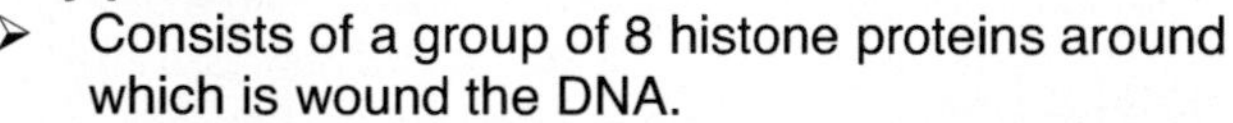
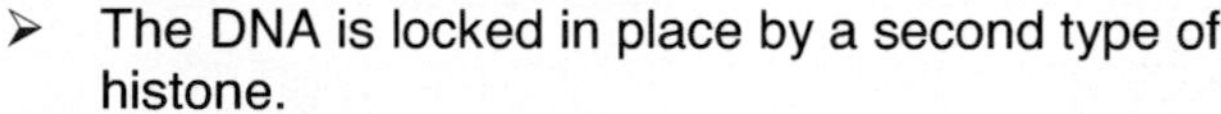

- Consists of a group of 8 histone proteins around which is wound the DNA.
- The DNA is locked in place by a second type of histone.

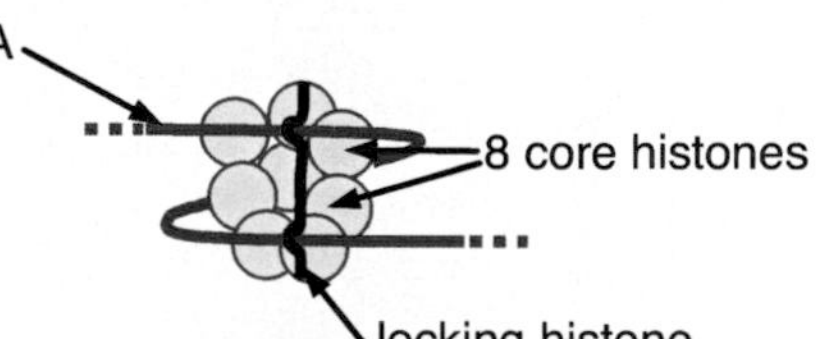

DNA
8 core histones
locking histone

Nucleosomes help to supercoil the chromosomes and help to regulate transcription.

Types of DNA

Types of Nuclear DNA

Nuclear DNA can be divided into two types -

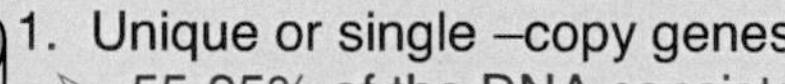

1. Unique or single –copy genes
   - 55-95% of the DNA consists of sequences called genes that have only a single copy.
   - These code for the functional polypeptides used by the cell or body, eg
     - structural proteins;
     - transport proteins;
     - enzymes;
     - hormones.

2. Highly repetitive sequences (satellite DNA)
   - 5-45% of the DNA;
   - 5 to 300 base pairs long;
   - Repeated either a moderate number of times or maybe up to 10^5 times in a genome, eg in the guinea pig the sequence CCCTAA is repeated 10,000 times at the centromere region and this may be important in attaching the microtubule;
   - Location of these sequences shows no apparent pattern;
   - Function generally unclear.
   - Used in DNA profiling. (See page 66).

DNA Replication in Prokaryotes

DNA replication occurs in a 5' – 3' direction.

In eukaryotic chromosomes replication starts at many points.

Enzyme	Function
Helicase	• Unwinds the DNA at the replication fork; • Breaks the hydrogen bonds between the bases.
DNA polymerase III	• Adds deoxynucleoside triphosphates to the 3' end.
RNA primase	• Adds nucleoside triphosphates on the lagging strand to form an RNA primer.
DNA polymerase I	• Removes the RNA primer; • Replaces it using deoxynucleoside triphosphates.
DNA ligase	• Joins the Okazaki fragments together.

Okazaki fragments are short lengths of new single stranded DNA made on the lagging strand. **Deoxynucleoside triphosphates** are the building blocks of DNA. Information about them is given on the next page.

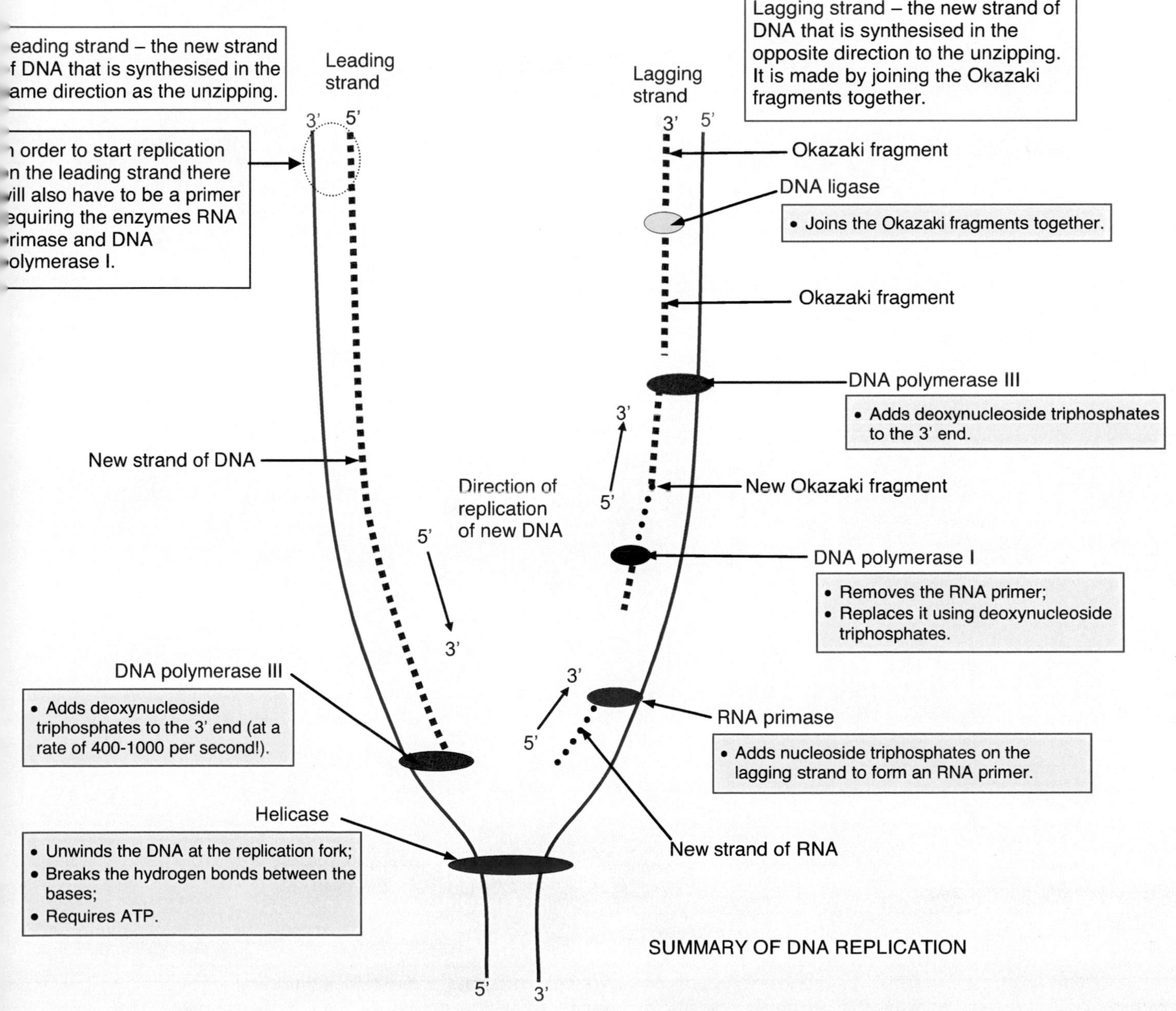
eading strand – the new strand f DNA that is synthesised in the ame direction as the unzipping.
Leading strand
Lagging strand
Lagging strand – the new strand of DNA that is synthesised in the opposite direction to the unzipping. It is made by joining the Okazaki fragments together.
3'
5'
3'
5'
n order to start replication n the leading strand there vill also have to be a primer equiring the enzymes RNA rimase and DNA olymerase I.
Okazaki fragment
DNA ligase
• Joins the Okazaki fragments together.
Okazaki fragment
DNA polymerase III
• Adds deoxynucleoside triphosphates to the 3' end.
New strand of DNA
Direction of replication of new DNA
New Okazaki fragment
DNA polymerase I
• Removes the RNA primer;
• Replaces it using deoxynucleoside triphosphates.
DNA polymerase III
• Adds deoxynucleoside triphosphates to the 3' end (at a rate of 400-1000 per second!).
RNA primase
• Adds nucleoside triphosphates on the lagging strand to form an RNA primer.
Helicase
• Unwinds the DNA at the replication fork;
• Breaks the hydrogen bonds between the bases;
• Requires ATP.
New strand of RNA
5'
3'

SUMMARY OF DNA REPLICATION

Deoxynucleoside triphosphates

Deoxynucleoside triphosphates

You will remember that a nucleotide consists of deoxyribose + base + phosphate.

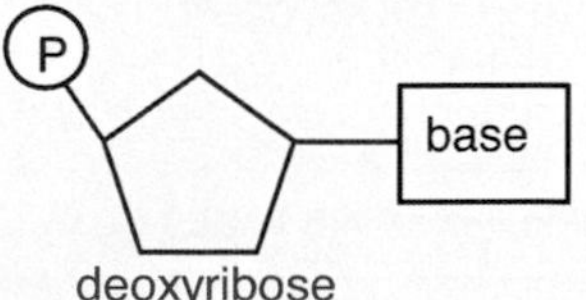

P
base
deoxyribose

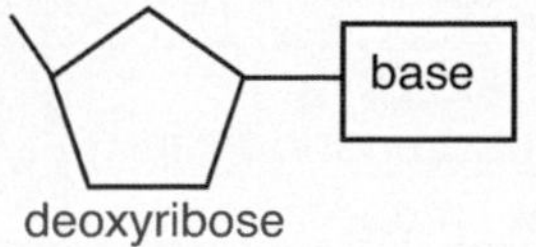

base
deoxyribose

A deoxynucleoside is just deoxyribose + base.

Thus a deoxynucleoside triphosphate is a deoxynucleoside with three phosphates.

The standard abbreviation for a deoxynucleoside triphosphate is dNTP and for a nucleoside triphosphate (ribose instead of deoxyribose) is NTP.

dNTPs are used to synthesise DNA;

NTPs are used to synthesise RNA.

When this molecule is added to the chain the two end phosphate groups are chopped off. The sequence is shown below.

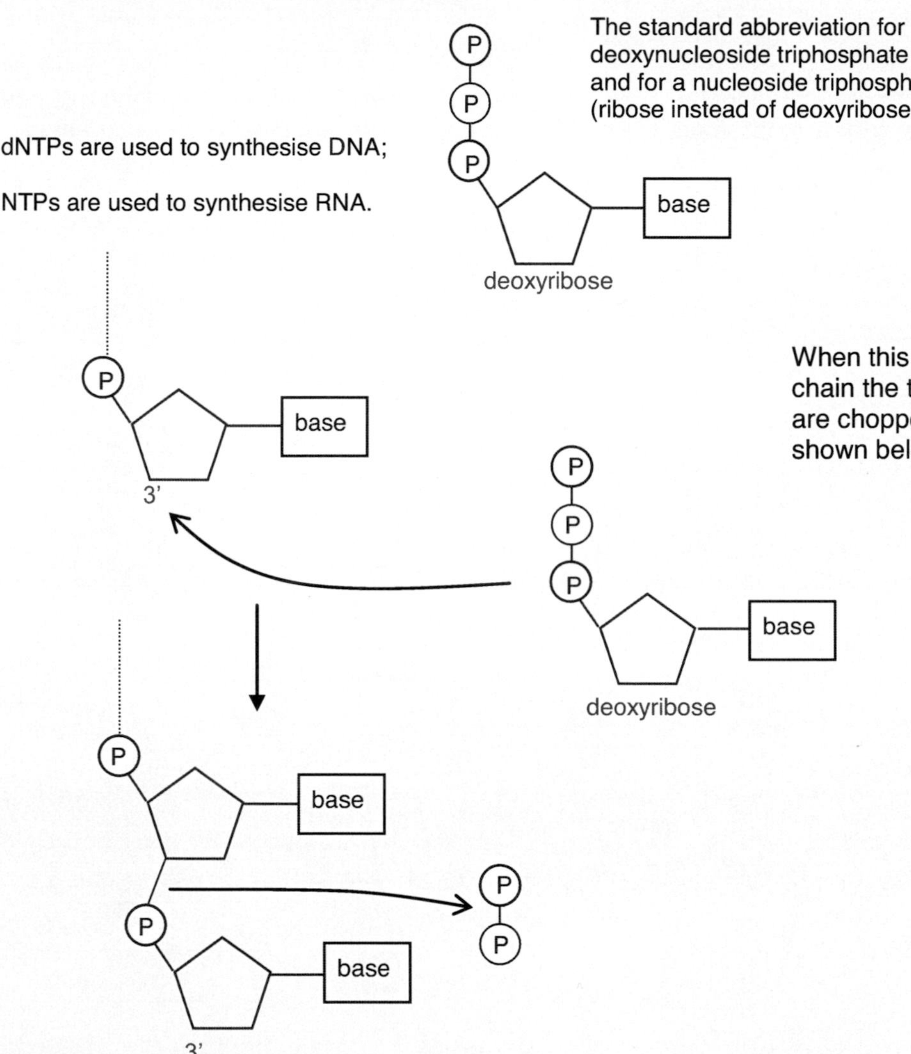

P
P
P
base
deoxyribose
P
base
3'
P
P
P
base
deoxyribose
P
base
P
base
3'
P
P

State the components of a nucleosome.

State the two functions of a nucleosome.

In which direction does DNA replication occur?

How many enzymes are required for DNA replication?

What are the names of the two strands of DNA during replication?

What is the name of the building blocks for DNA?	What is the name of the building blocks for RNA?	What is the name of the short fragments of new DNA on the lagging strand?

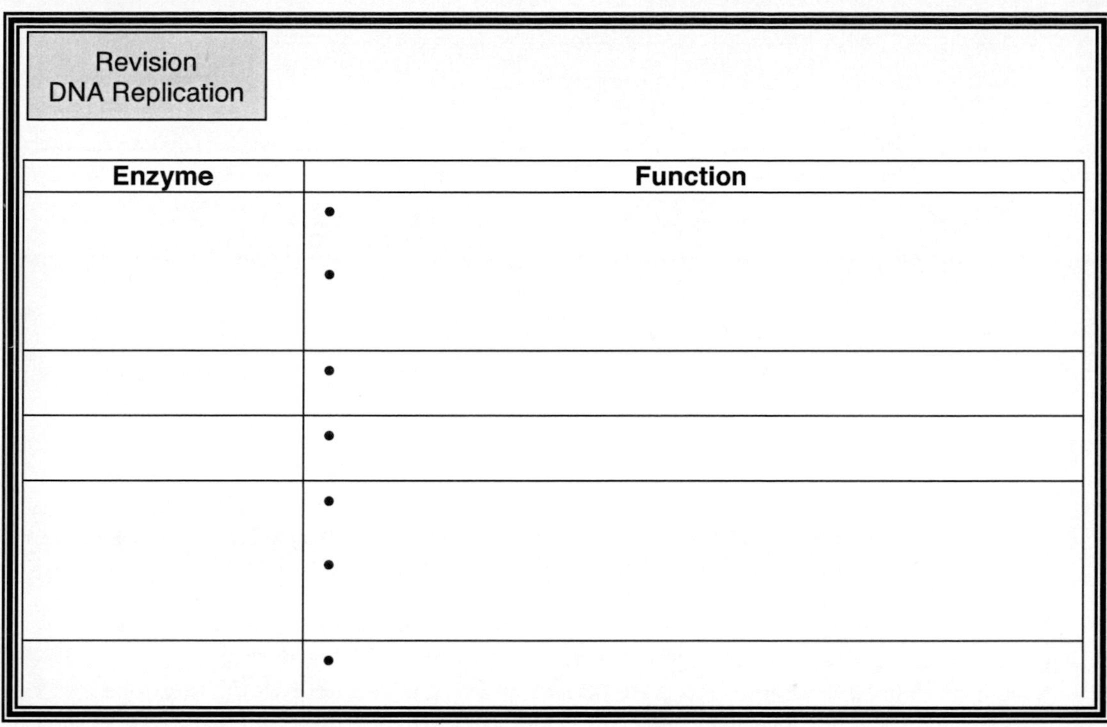

Revision
DNA Replication

Enzyme	Function
	• •
	•
	•
	• •
	•

Revision
DNA Replication

Label on the lines and complete the small boxes with numbers to show the direction of the strands. Put arrow heads on the two purple lines to show the direction of replication.

_______ strand

_______ strand

_______ fragment

____

This enzyme is joining two DNA fragments

Direction of replication of new DNA

____

This enzyme is adding dNTPs

New strand of DNA

____

This enzyme is replacing RNA nucleotides using dNTPS

____

This enzyme is adding dNTPs

____

This enzyme is unwinding the parent DNA and breaking the hydrogen bonds

____

This enzyme is adding NTPs

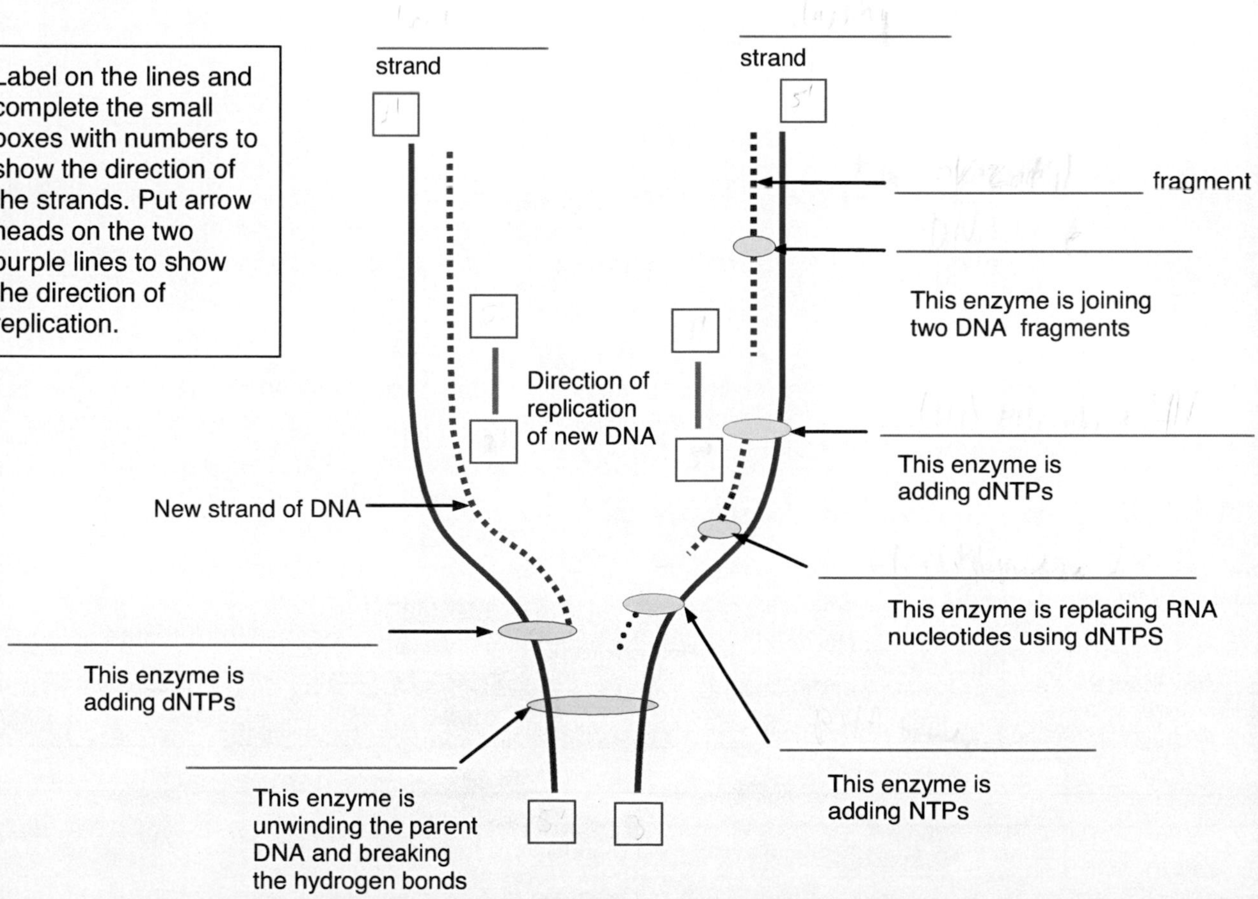

Transcription

Transcription in Prokaryotes

This is the formation of a molecule of messenger RNA (mRNA) from a DNA template in the nucleus.

Transcription is carried out in a 5' – 3' direction.

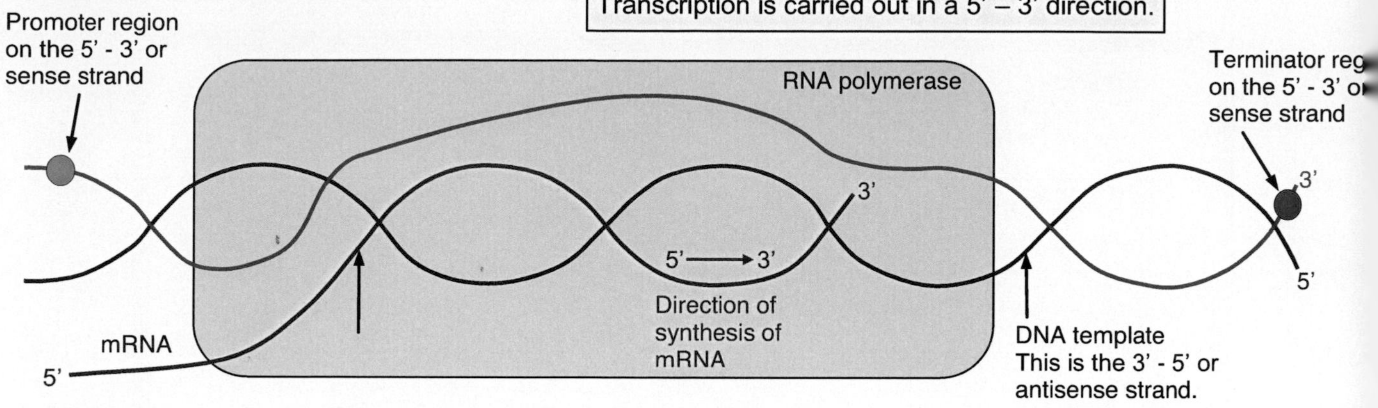

Promoter region on the 5' - 3' or sense strand

RNA polymerase

Terminator reg[ion] on the 5' - 3' o[r] sense strand

3'

5' ⟶ 3'

Direction of synthesis of mRNA

mRNA

5'

3'

5'

DNA template
This is the 3' - 5' or antisense strand.

Sense and Antisense

Key points

- **DNA template** – only one side of the DNA double helix is a **gene**. This is called the **sense strand.** The other side is the complementary sequence of bases. It is called the **antisense strand** and is transcribed into RNA by RNA polymerase. The sense strand has the same sequence of bases as the mRNA but with T not U.

Remember – the an**t**isense strand is **t**ranscribed.

- **Promoter region** – a specific sequence of DNA bases at the start of a gene to which RNA polymerase binds. It is found on the sense strand.

- **RNA polymerase** – this enzyme adds nucleoside triphosphates (NTPs) using base pairing to the DNA template. It can only bind to the DNA in the presence of special proteins made by genes elsewhere in the genome.

- As the RNA polymerase moves forward it unwinds and separates the DNA strands at the front and joins and rewinds them at the back. In the diagram above the RNA polymerase is moving from left to right.

- As the RNA is synthesised it separates from the DNA .

- **Terminator region** – a specific sequence of DNA bases marking the end of the transcription process. RNA polymerase breaks free and the mRNA strand is released. Like the promoter region it is found on the sense strand.

- **Gene regulation** –
  - post-transcriptional modification of RNA. See introns and exons below.
  - other genes, sometimes on different chromosomes, that produce proteins that block the binding of RNA polymerase to the promoter region and prevent transcription.

Introns and Exons

Introns and Exons
Post-transcriptional Modification of RNA

Key points

- Much eukaryotic DNA is transcribed into primary mRNA.
- Primary mRNA contains sequences (introns) that are not translated into part of the protein.
- Introns are removed.
- Exons make up the mature mRNA.
- This takes place in the nucleus.

These names come from –
Introns are intervening RNA; Exons are expressed.

Eukaryotic RNA needs the removal of introns to form mature mRNA.

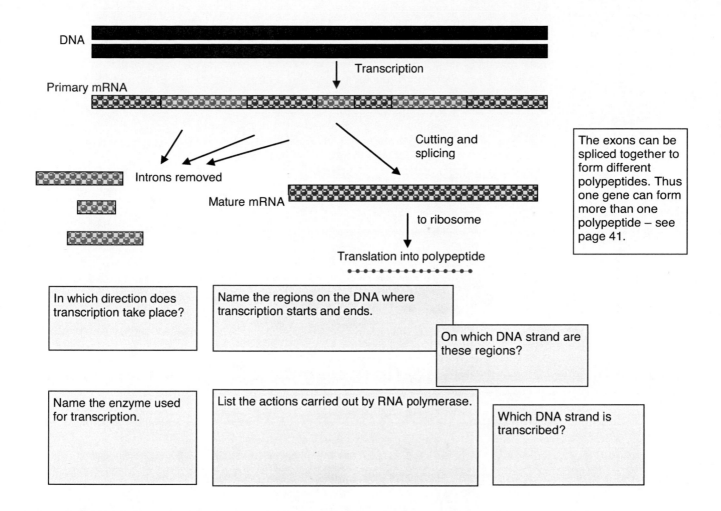

DNA

Transcription

Primary mRNA

Cutting and splicing

Introns removed

Mature mRNA

to ribosome

Translation into polypeptide

The exons can be spliced together to form different polypeptides. Thus one gene can form more than one polypeptide – see page 41.

In which direction does transcription take place?

Name the regions on the DNA where transcription starts and ends.

On which DNA strand are these regions?

Name the enzyme used for transcription.

List the actions carried out by RNA polymerase.

Which DNA strand is transcribed?

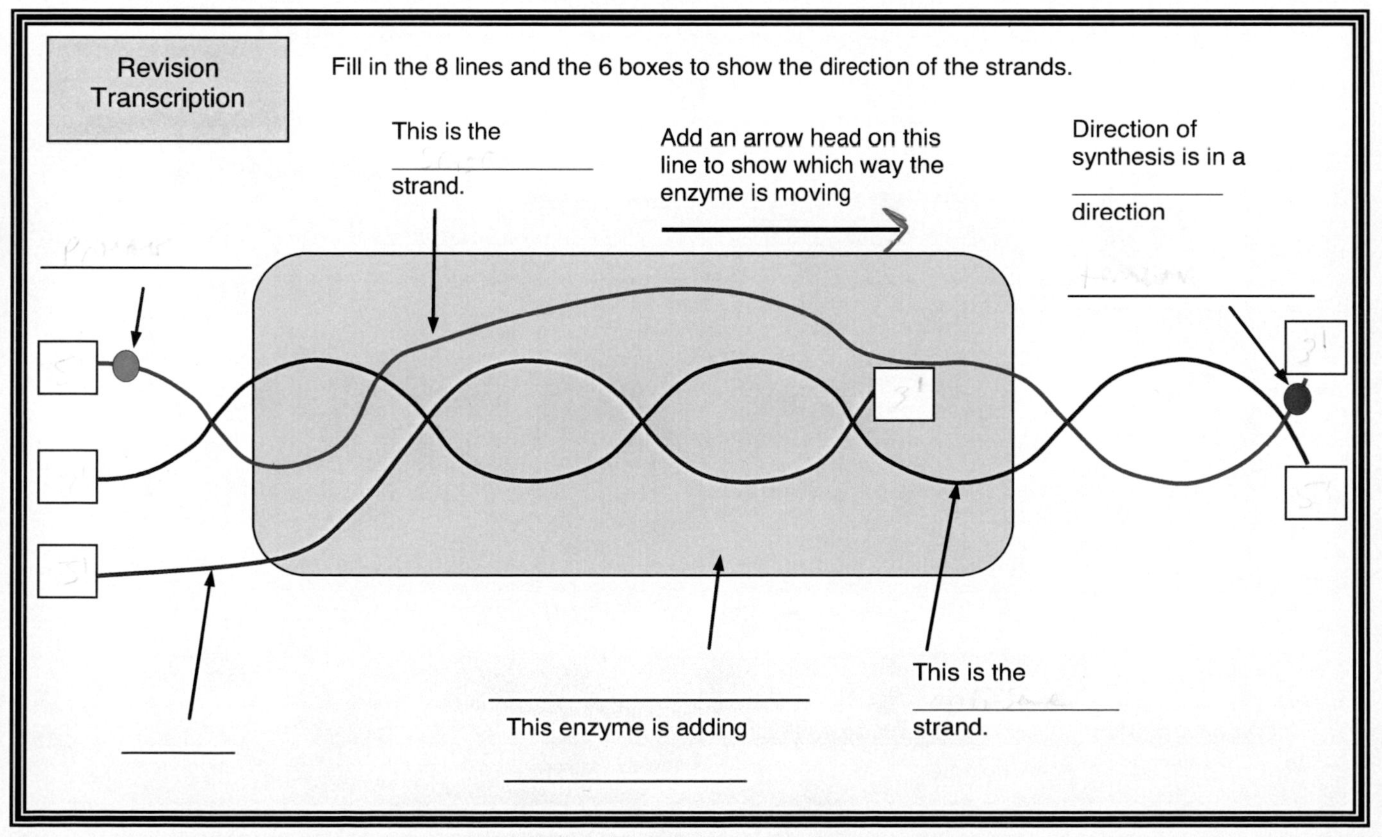

Revision Transcription
Fill in the 8 lines and the 6 boxes to show the direction of the strands.
This is the
strand.
Add an arrow head on this line to show which way the enzyme is moving
Direction of synthesis is in a
direction
This enzyme is adding
This is the
strand.

tRNA

tRNA

Key points

- There are 61 codons (excluding the three stop codons).
- Therefore there are 61 anticodons.
- Therefore there are 61 different types of tRNA.
- All tRNA molecules have the same basic shape.
- The amino acid is joined at the CCA terminal of the 3' end.
- Adding the amino acid requires energy from ATP and a specific enzyme.

UAC ← Anticodon

Hydrogen bonding forms double stranded RNA

5'

C
C
A

3'

Simple representation of a tRNA molecule

Active site

UAC

Enzyme

C
C
A

R group

Amino acid joined here using ATP

Active site of enzyme recognises -

- Specific anticodon.
- Specific amino acid due to its R group.
- CCA terminal at the 3' end.

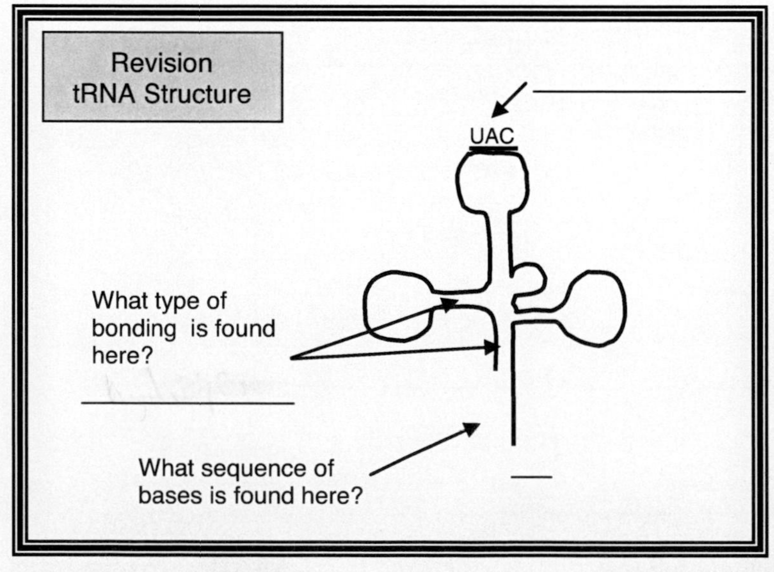
Revision
tRNA Structure
UAC
What type of bonding is found here?
What sequence of bases is found here?

Ribosome Structure

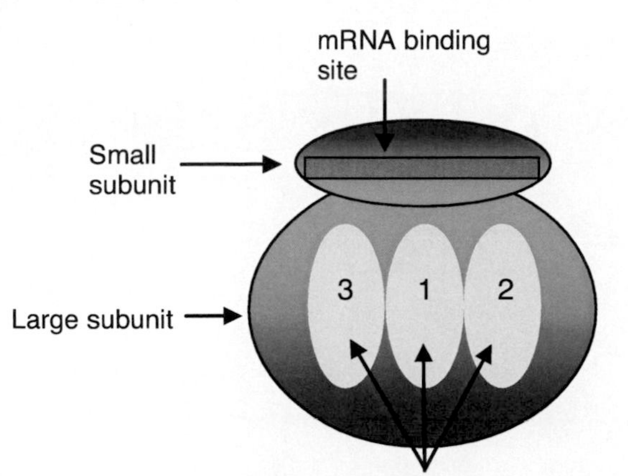

mRNA binding site
Small subunit
Large subunit
3
1
2

tRNA binding sites.
You do not need to know their names so we can simply number them in the order in which they are used.

Ribosome Structure

- Ribosomes are composed of ribosomal RNA (rRNA) and protein.
- There are two subunits.
- The small one binds to mRNA.
- The large one has three binding sites for tRNA.
- They are manufactured in the nucleolus within the nucleus.

Translation

Translation

Translation consists of –
1. Initiation;
2. Elongation;
3. Translocation;
4. Termination.

Translation occurs in a 5' – 3' direction.

1. Initiation

Initiation for all polypeptides takes place in the cytoplasm which is where the ribosomal subunits are.

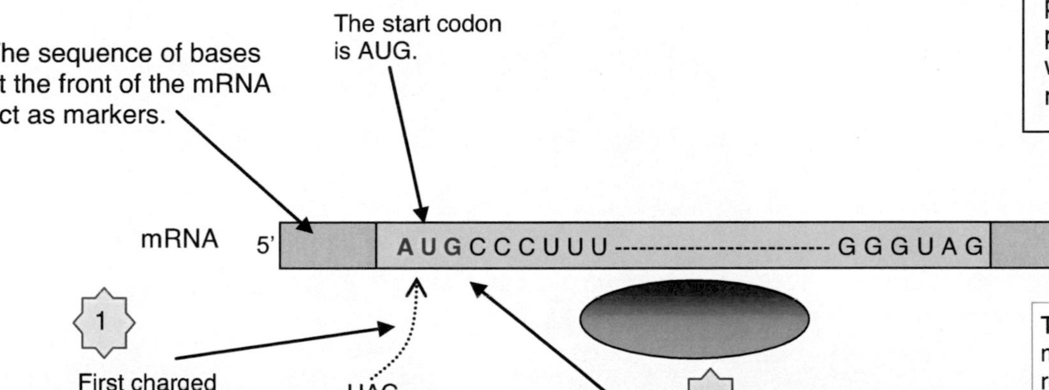

The sequence of bases at the front of the mRNA act as markers.
The start codon is AUG.
mRNA
5'
A U G C C C U U U ------------------------- G G G U A G
3'
1
UAC
AA
Amino acid attached to tRNA
2

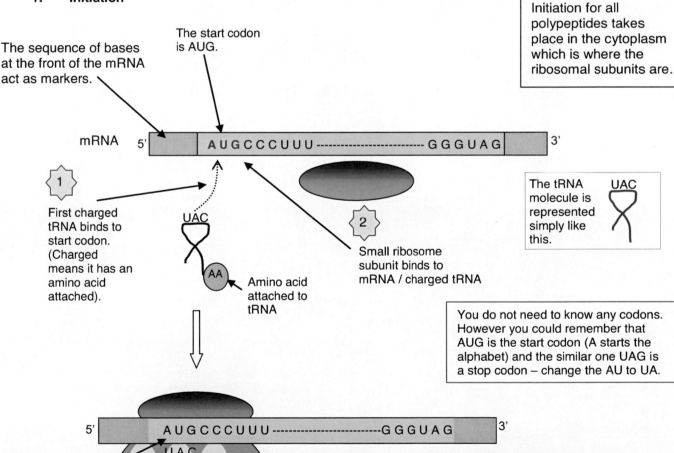

First charged tRNA binds to start codon. (Charged means it has an amino acid attached).

Small ribosome subunit binds to mRNA / charged tRNA

The tRNA molecule is represented simply like this. UAC

You do not need to know any codons. However you could remember that AUG is the start codon (A starts the alphabet) and the similar one UAG is a stop codon – change the AU to UA.

5' A U G C C C U U U -------------------------G G G U A G 3'

UAC

AA

Base pairing by hydrogen bonding.

3 Large ribosome subunit attaches so that the first charged tRNA is in binding site 1.

Initiation complex

Tip: Use simple codons such as CCC or AAA – much easier to base pair and less likely to make mistakes. Always, though, include adenine A so you can show it pairs with uracil U. Five codons as shown is sufficient.

2. Elongation

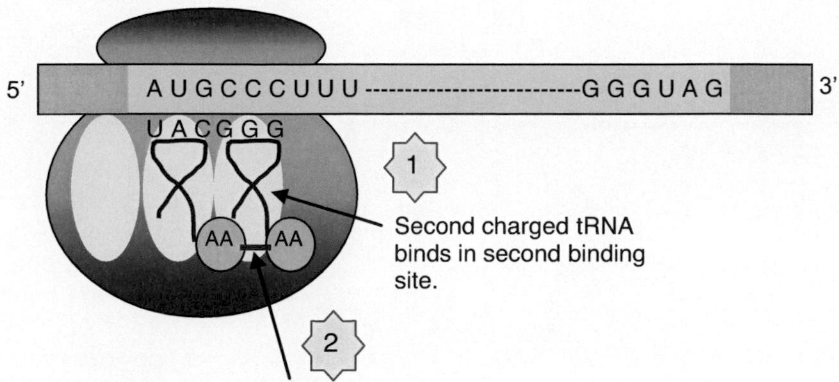
5'
AUGCCCUUU---------------------------GGGUAG
3'
UACGGG
AA
AA
1
Second charged tRNA binds in second binding site.
2

Peptide bond formed between the two amino acids.

If the polypeptide is destined for export it needs to be synthesised on the rER. The first part of the polypeptide is a signal that causes the ribosome to bind to the rER. As the polypeptide is sythesised it is passed through a protein channel in the rER.

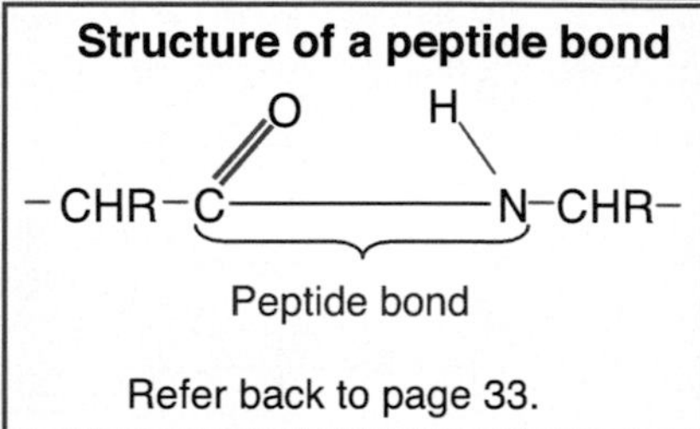
Structure of a peptide bond
O
H
−CHR−C——N−CHR−
Peptide bond
Refer back to page 33.

3. Translocation

3 The mRNA is moved along one codon and thus the ribosome has moved one codon in a 5' – 3' direction.

5' AUGCCCUUU---------------------------GGGUAG 3'

UAC GGG AA AA

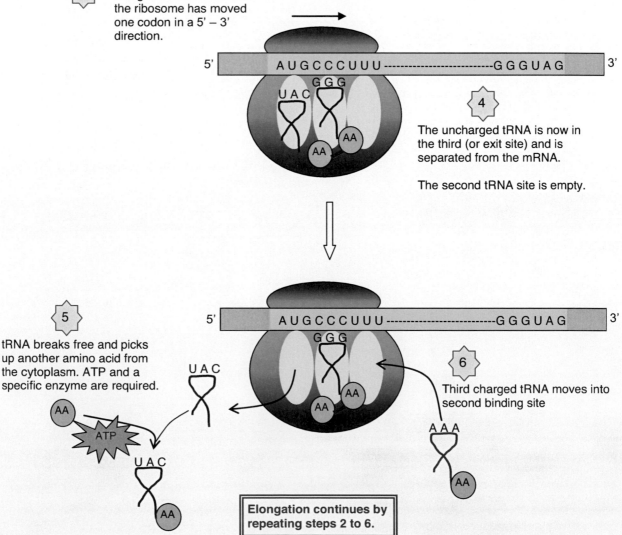

4 The uncharged tRNA is now in the third (or exit site) and is separated from the mRNA.

The second tRNA site is empty.

5' AUGCCCUUU---------------------------GGGUAG 3'

GGG AA AA

5 tRNA breaks free and picks up another amino acid from the cytoplasm. ATP and a specific enzyme are required.

UAC

AA ATP

UAC AA

6 Third charged tRNA moves into second binding site

AAA AA

Elongation continues by repeating steps 2 to 6.

4. Termination

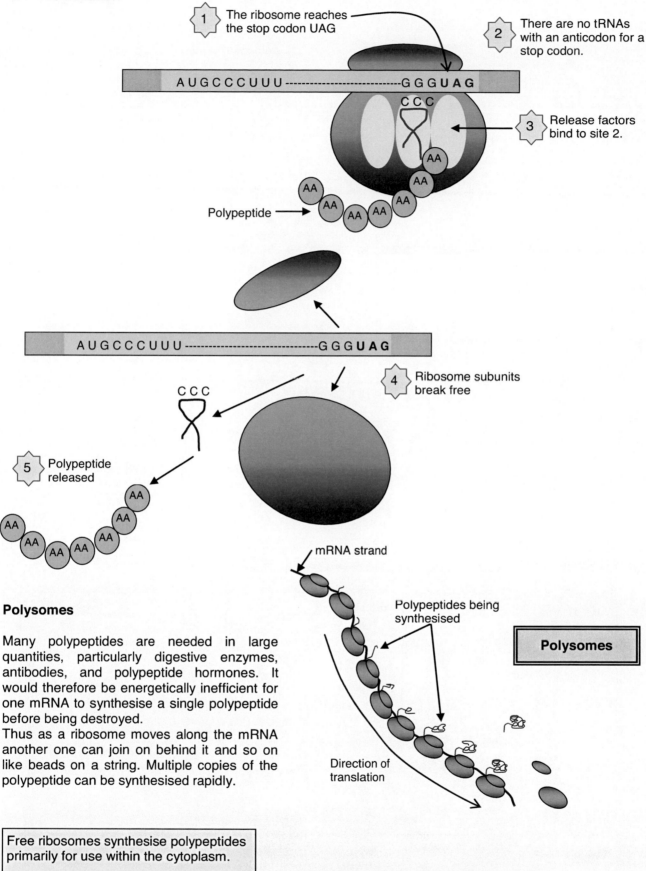

1 The ribosome reaches the stop codon UAG

2 There are no tRNAs with an anticodon for a stop codon.

AUGCCCUUU --------------------------- GGG**UAG**

CCC

3 Release factors bind to site 2.

AA AA AA AA AA AA AA AA

Polypeptide

AUGCCCUUU ------------------------------- GGG**UAG**

CCC

4 Ribosome subunits break free

5 Polypeptide released

AA AA AA AA AA AA AA

Polysomes

Many polypeptides are needed in large quantities, particularly digestive enzymes, antibodies, and polypeptide hormones. It would therefore be energetically inefficient for one mRNA to synthesise a single polypeptide before being destroyed.
Thus as a ribosome moves along the mRNA another one can join on behind it and so on like beads on a string. Multiple copies of the polypeptide can be synthesised rapidly.

mRNA strand

Polypeptides being synthesised

Direction of translation

Polysomes

Free ribosomes synthesise polypeptides primarily for use within the cytoplasm.

Ribosomes bound to ER synthesise polypeptides primarily for secretion or lysosomes.

State the 5'-3' sequence of bases on the tRNA where the amino acid binds.

List the four stages of translation.	State what happens during the first stage of translation.	State what happens at the last stage of translation.

Distinguish between the role of free ribosomes and those bound to endoplasmic reticulum.	What is a polysome?

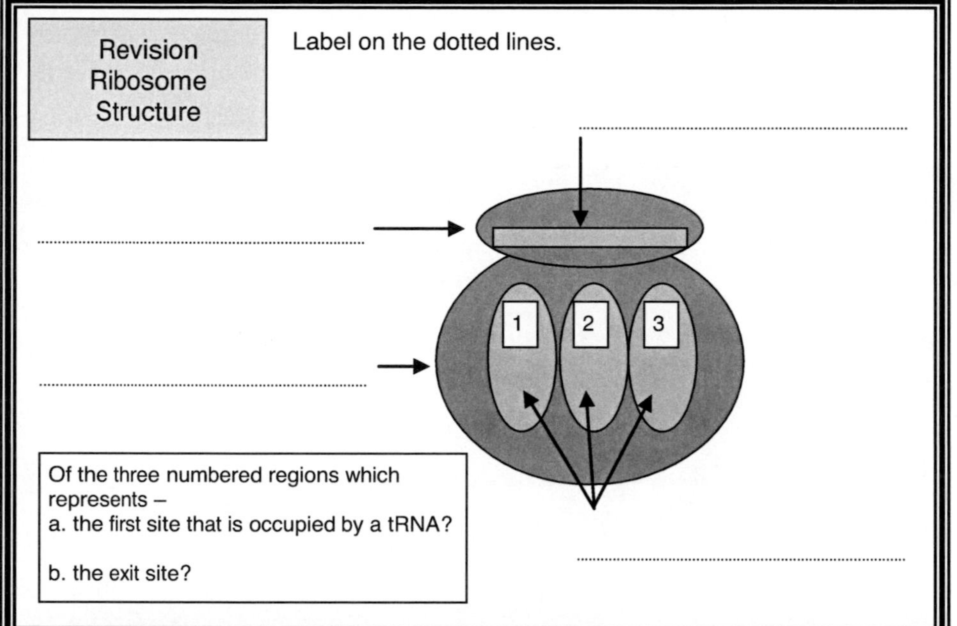

Revision Ribosome Structure
Label on the dotted lines.
1
2
3
Of the three numbered regions which represents –
a. the first site that is occupied by a tRNA?
b. the exit site?

How many anticodons are there?

Draw the structure of a peptide bond.

What two molecules are required to join an amino acid to its tRNA?

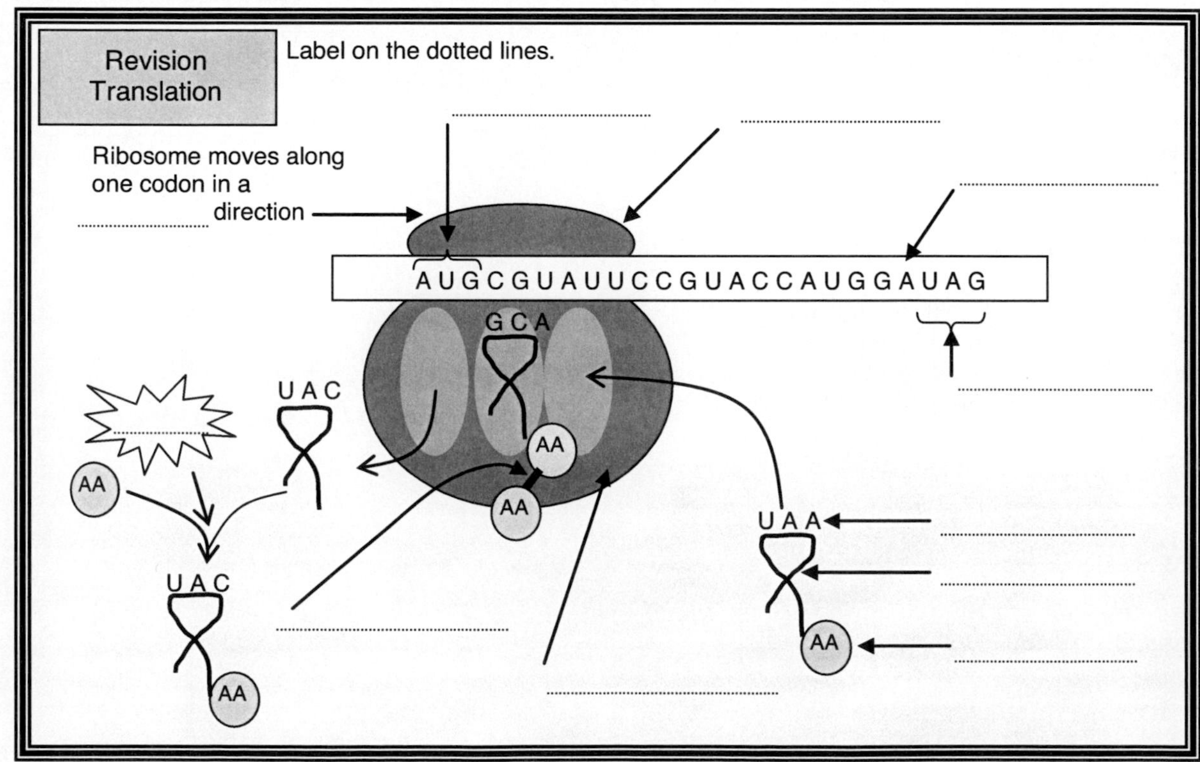

Revision Translation
Label on the dotted lines.
Ribosome moves along one codon in a .... direction
AUGCGUAUUCCGUACCAUGGAUAG
GCA
UAC
AA
UAC
AA
AA
AA
UAA
AA

Levels of Protein Structure

Protein Structure

Level	Characteristics	Bonding involved
Primary	Linear sequence of amino acids	Covalent – peptide bonds
Secondary	Alpha helix / Beta-pleated sheet	Hydrogen bonding between amino acids some distance apart in the linear sequence C N | | N—H ·········0 =C | | C C
Tertiary	Folding into a three-dimensional shape Beta-pleated sheet Alpha helix This folding creates pockets which form the active site in enzymes or binding sites for other molecules, or the binding site in active transport proteins.	Covalent – disulfide bridges Weak links including – • Hydrogen bonds, • Ionic bonds, • Mutual attraction between non-polar groups.
Quaternary	Two or more polypeptide chains linked together. This can also create pockets as with tertiary structure.	Covalent – disulfide bridges Weak links including – • Hydrogen bonds, • Ionic bonds, • Mutual attraction between non-polar groups.

Conjugated Proteins

Sometimes tertiary and quaternary level proteins have a non-protein group (the prosthetic group) attached. This is called a **conjugated protein**. In myoglobin and haemoglobin for example the prosthetic group is haem. The glycoproteins in membranes are also conjugated proteins, the non-protein group being the carbohydrate.

Fibrous and Globular Proteins

Fibrous and Globular Proteins

Fibrous proteins	Globular proteins
Mainly secondary structure	Tertiary or quaternary structure
Keratin in hair Collagen in tendons	Enzymes Antibodies (Immunoglobulins)

Polar and Non-polar R Groups of Amino Acids

Polar and Non-polar R Groups

Recall amino acid structure (page 29)

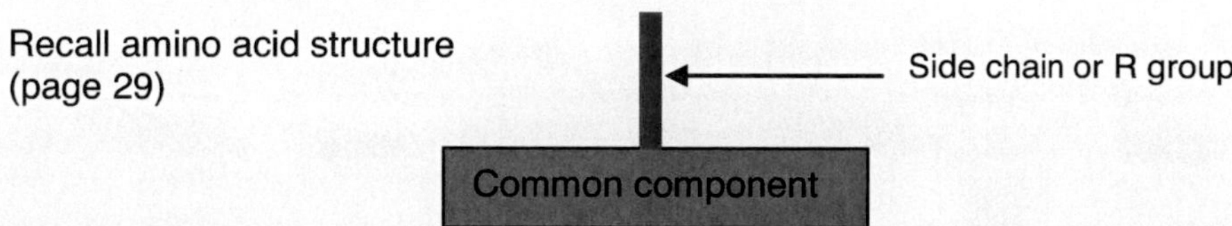
Side chain or R group
Common component

Some of these side chains are polar and some are non-polar. These play an essential role in protein function. Here are three examples.

1. **Integral membrane proteins.**
These are anchored in place by having hydrophobic, or non-polar R groups positioned in contact with the hydrophobic core of the membrane. The projecting regions must have polar R groups.

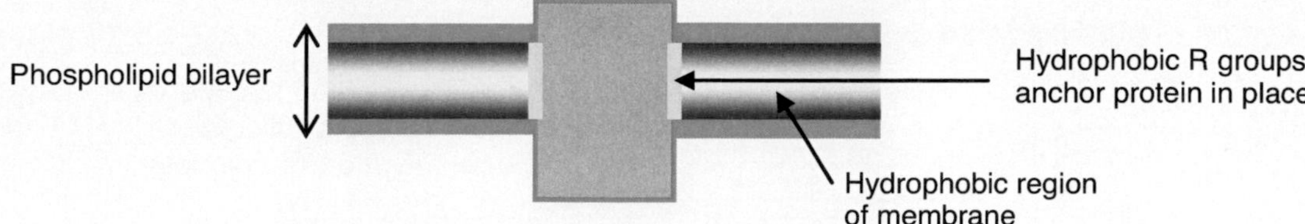

Phospholipid bilayer
Hydrophobic R groups anchor protein in place
Hydrophobic region of membrane

2. **Hydrophilic ion channels in membranes.**

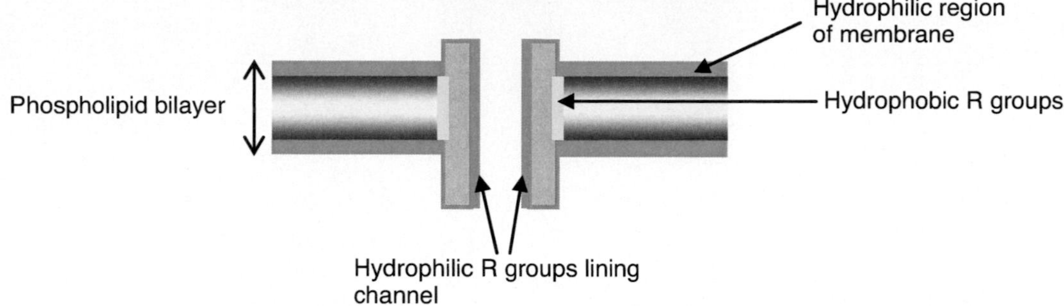

Hydrophilic region of membrane
Phospholipid bilayer
Hydrophobic R groups
Hydrophilic R groups lining channel

3. **The active site of an enzyme must allow the substrate to bind.**

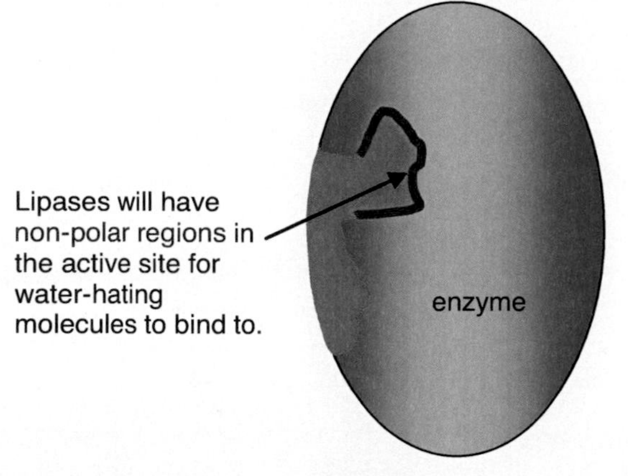

Lipases will have non-polar regions in the active site for water-hating molecules to bind to.
enzyme

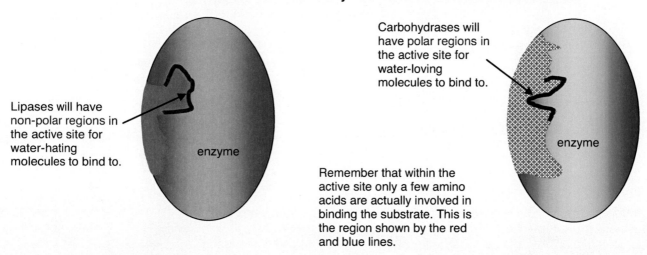

Carbohydrases will have polar regions in the active site for water-loving molecules to bind to.

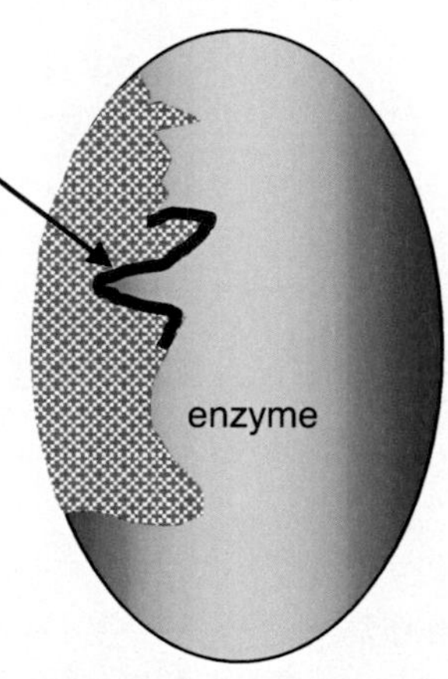

enzyme

Remember that within the active site only a few amino acids are actually involved in binding the substrate. This is the region shown by the red and blue lines.

What do the terms polar and non-polar mean?	What is a conjugated protein?	List the bonds used in the tertiary structure of a protein.

What are the two types of folding found in the secondary structure of proteins?	State two examples of – Fibrous proteins	Globular proteins

Functions of Proteins

Functions of Proteins

Function	Protein
Defence of body.	**Immunoglobulins** are antibodies.
Transports of substances between regions of the cell.	**Tubulin** forms microtubules within cytoplasm.
Contractile force for muscle contraction	**Actin** forms microfilaments in cells. Bundles form actin filaments in muscle.
Water balance maintenance	**Albumin** is one of many plasma proteins that has an important role in controlling the water potential of the blood and in buffering.
Enzymes for catalysis	**Ribulose bisphosphate carboxylase** is one of hundreds of enzymes that catalyse the metabolic processes within organisms. RuBP catalyses the addition of carbon dioxide to ribulose bisphosphate in the light independent reaction of photosynthesis.
Structural support	**Collagen.** This is found in artery walls and tendons.
Hormones	**Insulin; HCG** (glycoprotein**)**
Transport in the blood.	**Haemoglobin** transports oxygen within the blood.

Induced Fit Model of Enzyme Action

Induced Fit Model of Enzyme Action

Key points

- In many enzymes the shape of the active site only corresponds to the shape of the substrate when the substrate binds;
- This prevents possible but undesirable substrates from binding;
- The active site is flexible;
- This allows a group of related molecules that have similar shapes to be able to bind, eg peptidases;
- It reduces the number of different types of enzyme that are required.

- As the substrate binds to the enzyme it causes the shape of the active site to change to fit the shape of the substrate.
- Only the substrates for that enzyme can do this.
- It allows one enzyme to catalyse reactions with different but similarly shaped substrates.

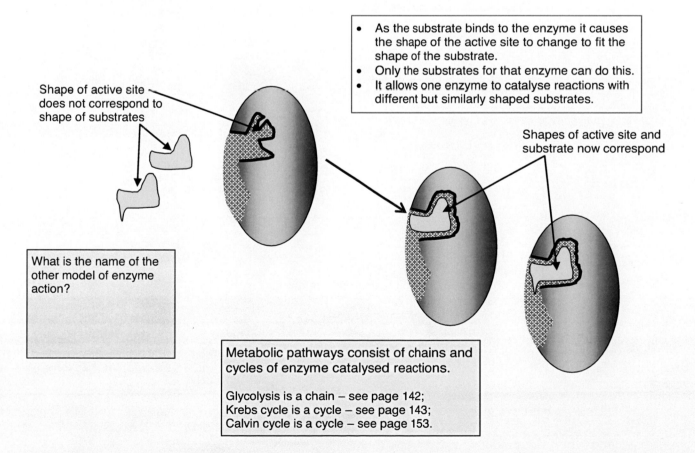

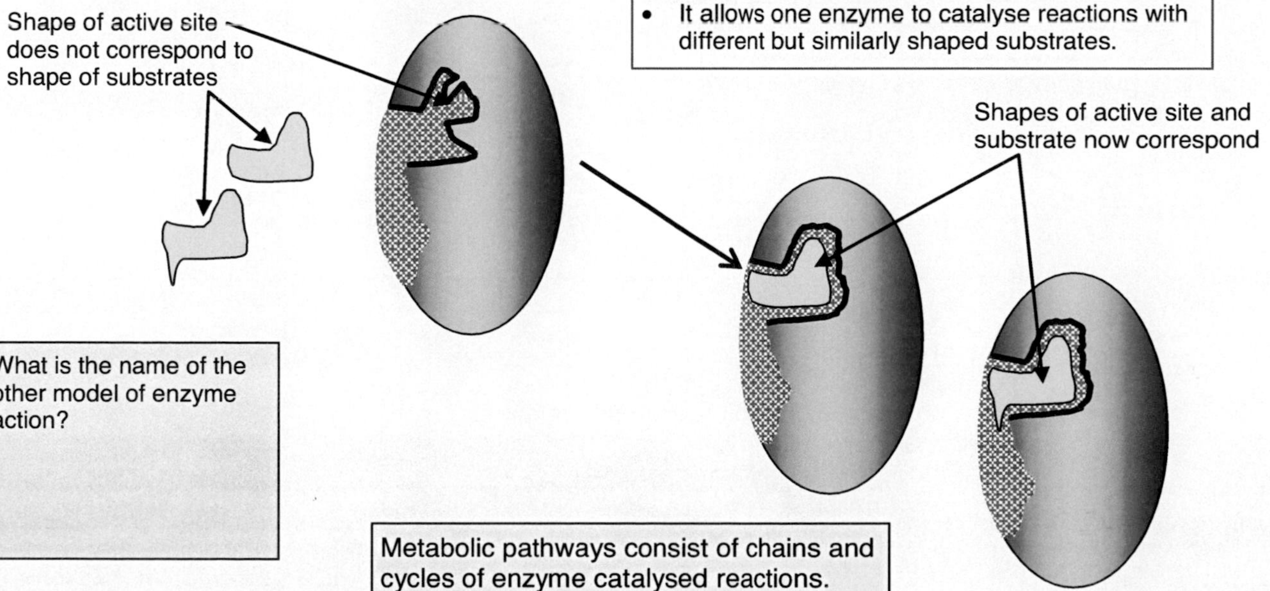

Shape of active site does not correspond to shape of substrates

Shapes of active site and substrate now correspond

What is the name of the other model of enzyme action?

Metabolic pathways consist of chains and cycles of enzyme catalysed reactions.

Glycolysis is a chain – see page 142;
Krebs cycle is a cycle – see page 143;
Calvin cycle is a cycle – see page 153.

Activation Energy

Activation Energy

Key points

- ➢ In order for a chemical reaction to start it usually requires an input of energy.
- ➢ This is called the activation energy. (You might perhaps have done a practical using Benedicts reagent to test for sugar. This requires an input of heat energy).
- ➢ The function of enzymes is to lower the activation energy so that the reaction takes place at physiological temperatures, generally between 0 and 40°C.
- ➢ Remember –
  - enzyme binds to substrate(s) to form an enzyme-substrate complex;
  - reaction occurs resulting in an enzyme-product(s) complex;
  - product(s) released from enzyme.

E + S → ES → EP → E + P

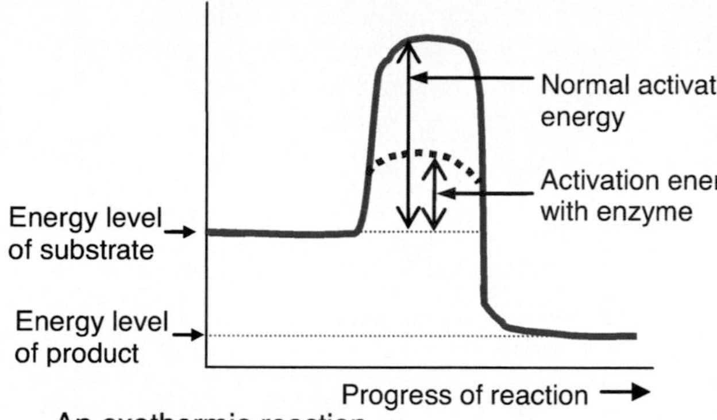
Normal activation energy
Activation energy with enzyme
Energy level of substrate
Energy level of product
Progress of reaction

An exothermic reaction

Exothermic – energy is given out. Note that the energy level of the product is lower than that of the substrate.

Inhibition

Inhibition of Enzymes

1. Competitive

Key point

- ➢ Substrate and inhibitor have similar shapes and compete for the active site.

An example is shown in green.

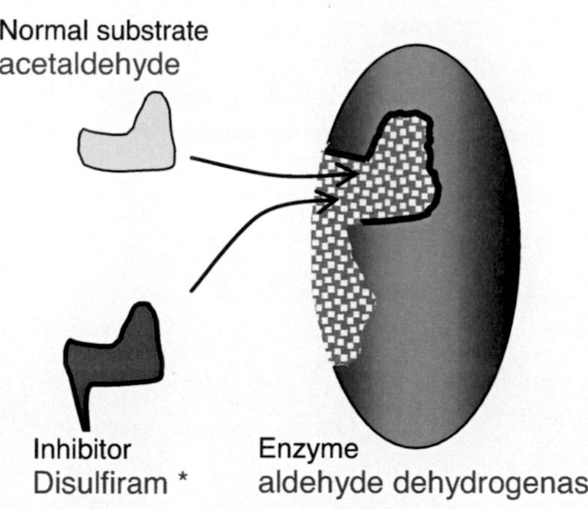
Normal substrate
acetaldehyde
Inhibitor
Disulfiram *
Enzyme
aldehyde dehydrogenase

How many active sites does an enzyme normally have?

2. Non-competitive

Key points

- ➢ Inhibitor has its own binding site.
- ➢ Substrate and inhibitor do not compete for the active site.
- ➢ Binding of the inhibitor causes a conformational change in the active site, ie changes its shape, preventing binding of substrate.

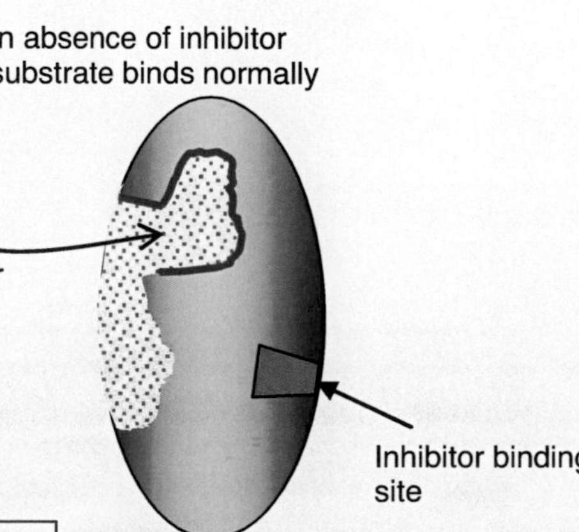
In absence of inhibitor substrate binds normally
Inhibitor binding site

* In the liver the metabolic pathway is -
ethanol → acetaldehyde —*aldehyde dehydrogenase*→ acetate
Disulfiram is a drug used to help recovering alcoholics. Acetaldehyde is not broken down in the liver and its accumulation in the blood causes severe headache and nausea.

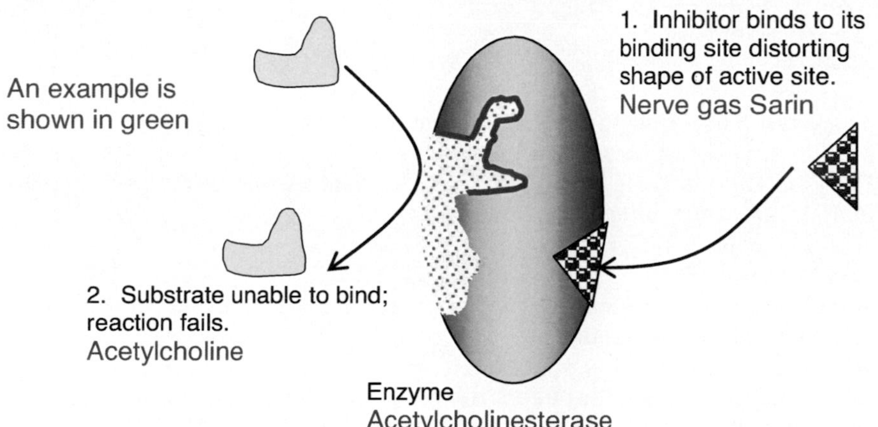
An example is
shown in green
1. Inhibitor binds to its
binding site distorting
shape of active site.
Nerve gas Sarin
2. Substrate unable to bind;
reaction fails.
Acetylcholine
Enzyme
Acetylcholinesterase

Graphical Representation of Inhibition

Graphical Representation of Inhibition

Graph showing the effect of a fixed concentration of inhibitor on the rate of a reaction when substrate concentration changes.

At higher substrate concentrations the relative amount of competitive inhibitor becomes so low it has no effect.

Since the non-competitive inhibitor binds to a different site it will always reduce the rate of reaction.

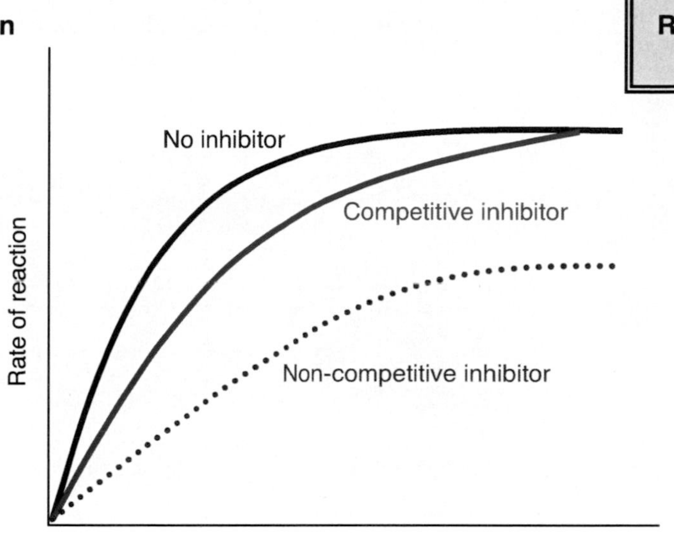
No inhibitor
Competitive inhibitor
Non-competitive inhibitor
Rate of reaction
Substrate concentration

What does an enzyme do to activation energy?

In an exothermic reaction is the energy level of the substrate higher or lower than the energy level of the product?

List four functions of proteins, excluding membrane proteins.

Revision Activation Energy

Complete and label the graph. There are 4 labels plus the axes.

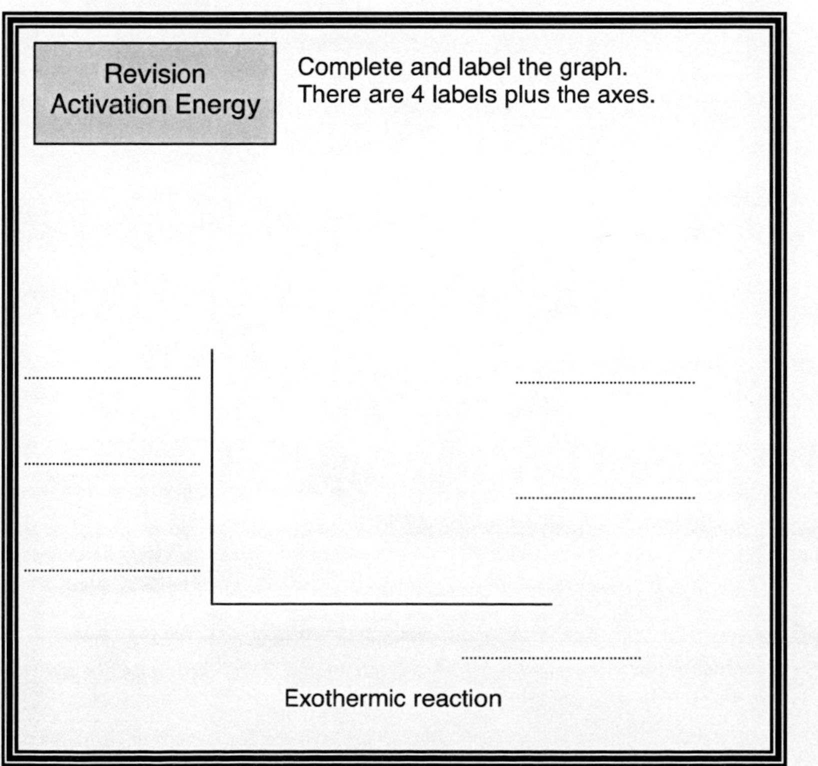
Exothermic reaction

Allostery

Allostery

The example of non-competitive inhibition above (Sarin gas) is harmful, but in the body many examples exist where the property is used to regulate metabolic pathways. Enzymes that behave in this way are called **allosteric enzymes**. Instead of the term inhibitor the term **effector** is used.

Key points

- Quaternary level structure of the enzyme (refer back to page 129);
- At least two subunits;
- One subunit has the substrate active site;
- Other subunit has the effector binding site called the allosteric site.
- There may be more than one allosteric site.
- The effector may be an activator or an inhibitor of the enzyme.
- The enzyme alternates between the active form that reacts with the substrate and the inactive form that does not.
- The allosteric activator stabilises the active form.
- The allosteric inhibitor stabilises the inactive form.

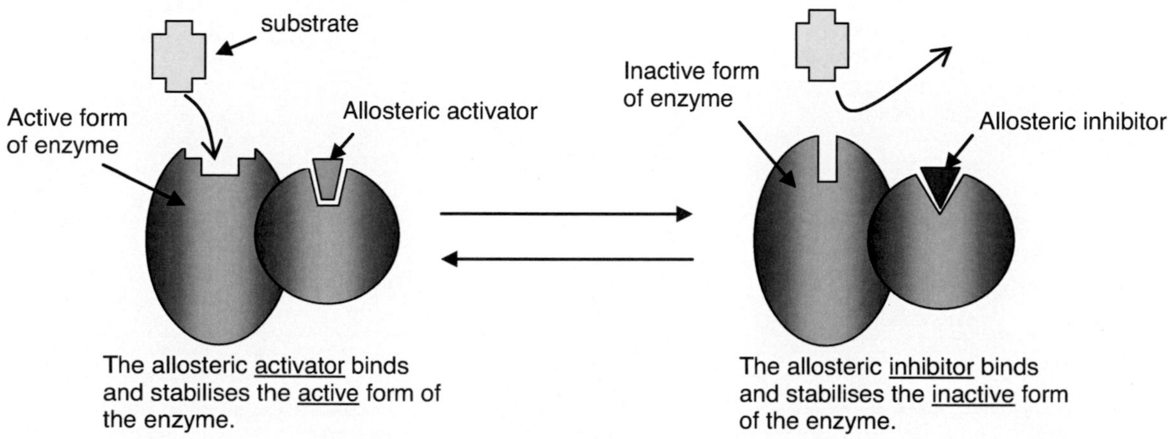
substrate
Active form of enzyme
Allosteric activator
Inactive form of enzyme
Allosteric inhibitor
The allosteric activator binds and stabilises the active form of the enzyme.
The allosteric inhibitor binds and stabilises the inactive form of the enzyme.

How then does this work to regulate a metabolic pathway? Phosphorylase is an enzyme in muscle that removes a glucose phosphate from the end of glycogen at the start of glycolysis. Remember that glycolysis is the first stage in producing ATP from glucose. If the muscle is resting it does not need much ATP and hence the relative concentration of ATP will be high. On the other hand if it is active then it will be using up ATP and the relative concentration of AMP (adenosine monophosphate) will be high. It therefore makes sense to regulate this key enzyme so that glycogen is not broken down unnecessarily and wasted. ATP and AMP act as the allosteric effectors.

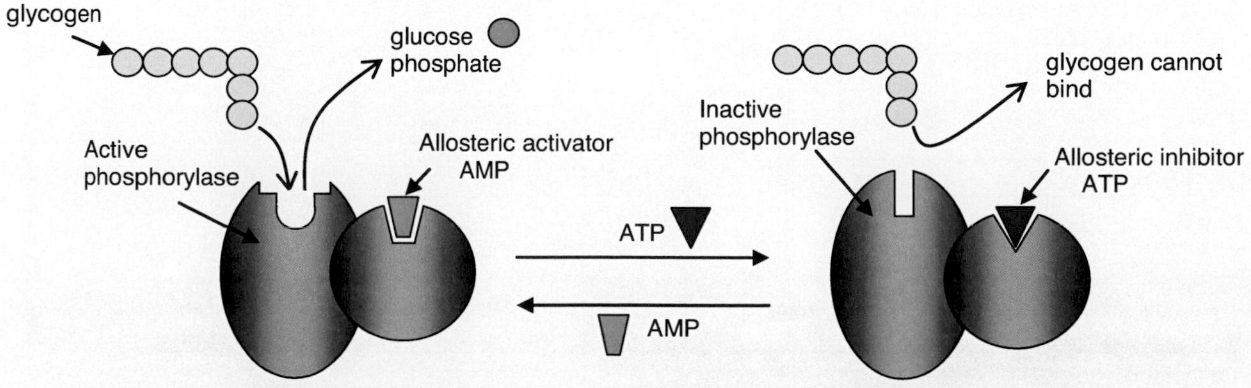
glycogen
glucose phosphate
Active phosphorylase
Allosteric activator AMP
ATP
AMP
Inactive phosphorylase
glycogen cannot bind
Allosteric inhibitor ATP

Distinguish between a competitive inhibitor and a non-competitive inhibitor.

State an example of -

enzyme	substrate	competitive inhibitor
enzyme	substrate	non-competitive inhibitor.

Is allostery a form of competitive or non-competitive inhibition?

Name the two binding sites in an allosteric enzyme.

Revision
Protein Structure

Complete on the dotted lines.

Level	Characteristics	Bonding involved
Primary	....	....
Secondary	a. .... b.	....
Tertiary	....	Covalent – .... Weak links including – ....
Quaternary	....	Covalent .... Weak links including – ....

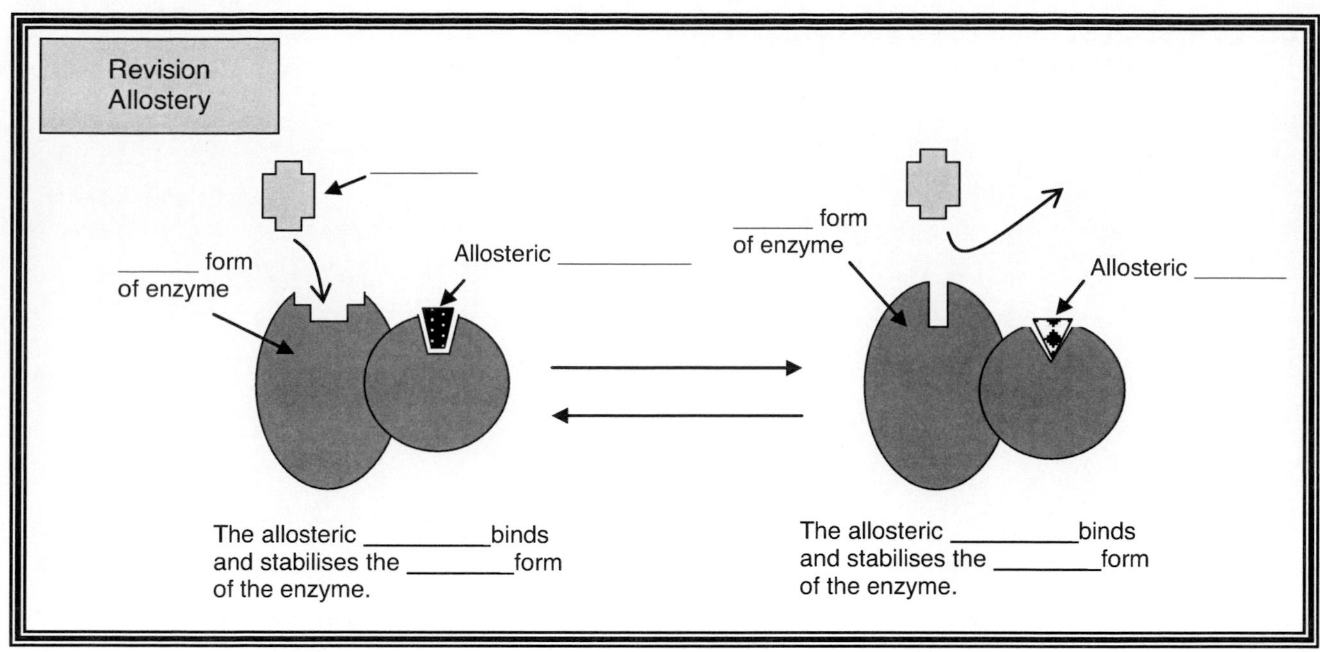
Revision
Allostery
______ form
of enzyme
Allosteric __________
______ form
of enzyme
Allosteric _______
The allosteric __________binds
and stabilises the ________form
of the enzyme.
The allosteric __________binds
and stabilises the ________form
of the enzyme.

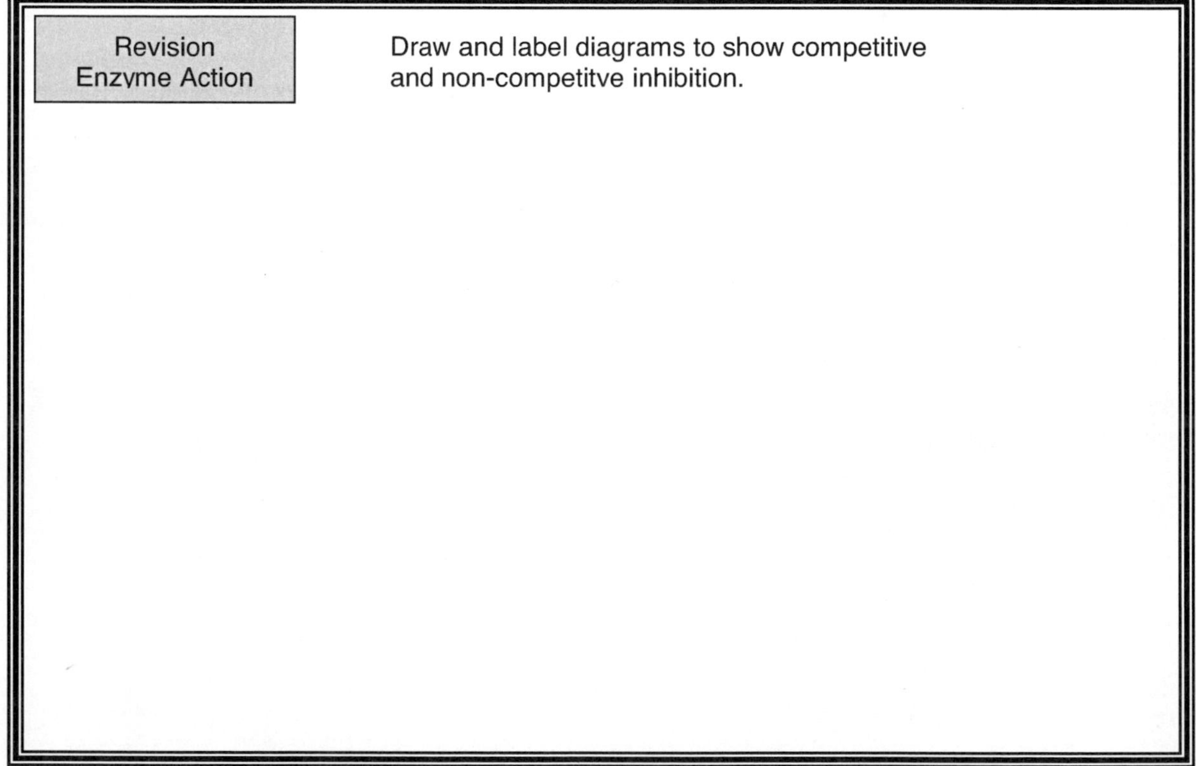
Revision
Enzyme Action
Draw and label diagrams to show competitive
and non-competitve inhibition.

Self-test Quiz on Topic 7

1. A nucleosome consists of
   a. DNA and RNA,
   b. DNA and phospholipid,
   c. DNA and 8 histone proteins,
   d. DNA and 9 histone proteins.

2. DNA replication occurs in a
   a. 5' – 3' direction,
   b. 3' – 5' direction,
   c. 3' – 3' direction,
   d. 5' – 5' direction.

3. DNA contains four types of base. Which of the following is correct?
   a. Thymine and adenine are purines.
   b. Guanine and cytosine are pyrimidines.
   c. Cytosine and thymine are pyrimidines.
   d. Cytosine and thymine are purines.

4. In the eukaryotic chromosome replication is initiated
   a. at the 5' end only,
   b. at the 3' end only,
   c. at many points within the chromosome,
   d. next to the centromere.

5. Which of the following statements about tRNA is correct?
   a. It contains the bases A, C, T and G;
   b. The anticodon is found at the 3' CCA end.
   c. The amino acid binds at the 5' CCA end.
   d. The amino acid binds at the 3' CCA end.

6. During transcription which enzymes are needed?
   a. RNA polymerase only,
   b. RNA polymerase and helicase,
   c. RNA polymerase and DNA polymerase I,
   d. RNA polymerase, DNA polymerase III and DNA ligase.

7. With respect to translation, which of the following statements is <u>not</u> correct?
   a. tRNA binds to mRNA at binding sites in the ribosome.
   b. An AAA codon binds to a TTT anticodon.
   c. There are 64 codons.
   d. An amino acid is joined to its tRNA using ATP as an energy source.

8. The formation of mature mRNA from the initial RNA transcript requires
   a. the removal of introns,
   b. the removal of exons,
   c. the splicing together of introns and exons,
   d. the addition of histones.

9. Which of the following statements about proteins is <u>not</u> correct?
   a. Fibrous and globular proteins always have tertiary structure.
   b. A conjugated protein may have either tertiary or quaternary structure.
   c. Tertiary structure proteins usually contain disulfide bridges.
   d. The alpha helix and beta-pleated sheet are both components of secondary structure.

10. Which of the following statements about enzymes is <u>not</u> correct?
   a. An enzyme will have either tertiary or quaternary level structure.
   b. The active site of an enzyme does not always correspond to the shape of the substrate.
   c. An enzyme may have more than one binding site.
   d. In an enzyme catalysed reaction the activation energy is usually raised.

11. Allostery occurs in cells. It can be described as
   a. inhibition of an enzyme due to a non-substrate molecule binding in the active site,
   b. a lowering of activation energy to allow the reaction to proceed faster,
   c. regulation of enzyme activity by the binding of a non-substrate molecule,
   d. competitive inhibition of the enzyme by a product formed later in the metabolic pathway.

12. Which of the following diagrams represents a peptide bond?

a. 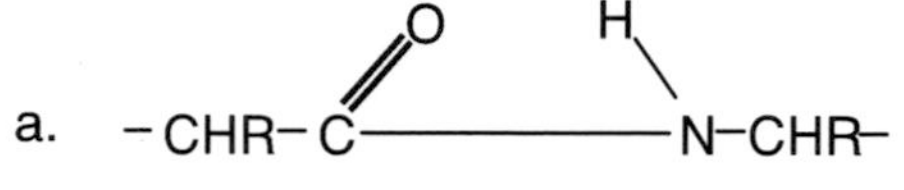
O
H
−CHR−C
N−CHR−

b. 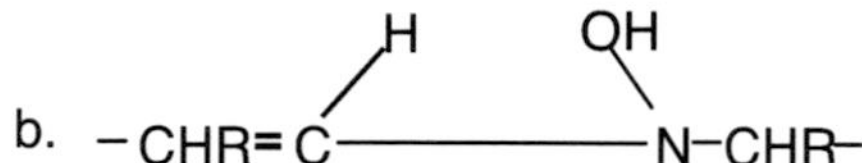
H
OH
−CHR=C
N−CHR−

c. 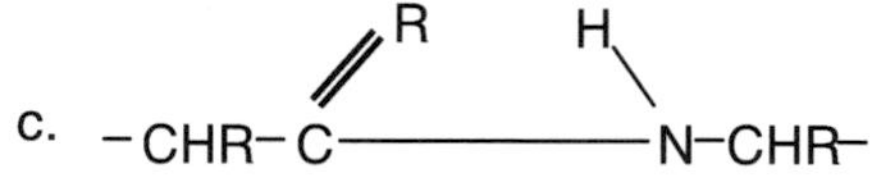
R
H
−CHR−C
N−CHR−

d. NH H
−CHR−C N−CHR−

13. In the table below which line represents the correct function for the listed enzymes? (NTPs = nucleoside triphosphates; dNTPs = deoxynucleoside triphosphates)

	DNA polymerase I	RNA primase	DNA ligase	DNA polymerase III
a.	Joins dNTPs to the leading strand only.	Adds an RNA sequence at the end of Okasaki fragments.	Joins two Okasaki fragments together.	Uses dNTPs on both leading and lagging strands.
b.	Replaces nucleotides on the lagging strand using dNTPs.	Adds an RNA sequence on the lagging strand.	Joins two Okasaki fragments together.	Uses dNTPs on both leading and lagging strands.
c.	Joins dNTPs on both leading and lagging strands.	Joins two Okasaki fragments together.	Adds an RNA sequence at the end of Okasaki fragments.	Replaces NTPs on the lagging strand with dNTPs.
d.	Joins dNTPs on both leading and lagging strands.	Joins NTPs to the leading strand only.	Adds an RNA sequence on the lagging strand.	Joins two Okasaki fragments together.

14. In a molecule of DNA the sense strand is
   a. the strand that is transcribed,
   b. the strand containing the base uracil,
   c. the strand that has the same adenine, guanine and cytosine base sequence as mRNA,
   d. the strand used to make tRNA molecules.

15. In the process of transcription promoter and terminator base sequences are required. Which statement about them is correct?
    a. They are both found on the sense strand of DNA.
    b. They are both found on the antisense strand of DNA.
    c. They are both found on the 5' – 3' strand of mRNA.
    d. The promoter is found on the DNA and the terminator on the mRNA.

16. Which of the following statements about activation energy is correct?
    a. In an exothermic reaction the energy level of the products is higher than that of the substrate.
    b. Activation energy is the heat released from an exothermic reaction.
    c. Enzymes can only catalyse a reaction if the activation energy is lower than the energy level of the substrate.
    d. In an exothermic reaction the energy level of the substrate is higher than that of the products.

17. A nucleotide consists of
    a. a sugar, a base and two phosphates.
    b. a sugar, a base and one phosphate.
    c. a sugar and a base.
    d. a sugar and a phosphate.

18. Transcription occurs in a
    a. 5' – 3' direction;
    b. 3' – 5' direction;
    c. 3' – 3' direction;
    d. 5' – 5' direction.

19. The function of nucleosomes is to
    a. help regulate translation;
    b. help regulate translation and to supercoil the chromosomes;
    c. help regulate DNA replication;
    d. help regulate transcription and to supercoil the chromosomes.

20. The formation of mature mRNA from the primary transcript occurs
    a. in the cytoplasm;
    b. in the nucleoplasm;
    c. on the rER;
    d. at free ribosomes in the cytoplasm.

21. In the induced fit model of substrate binding
    a. the enzyme induces a change in the shape of the substrate;
    b. the substrate induces a change in the shape of the enzyme;
    c. both substrate and enzyme change shape;
    d. the binding of the substrate prevents the enzyme from catalysing the reaction.

22. A polysome is
    a. a linear sequence of amino acids;
    b. a linear sequence of nucleotides;
    c. a group of ribosomes on an mRNA molecule;
    d. groups of histone proteins on DNA.

23. In a strand of DNA the nucleotides are joined by a
    a. 3' – 3' linkage.
    b. 5' – 5' linkage.
    c. 3' – 6' linkage.
    d. 3' – 5' linkage.

Topic 8

Cell Respiration and Photosynthesis

Oxidation and Reduction

Remember OIL RIG for electrons.
Oxidation **I**s **L**oss of electrons;
Reduction **I**s **G**ain of electrons.

Oxidation is also gain of oxygen or loss of hydrogen;
Reduction is also loss of oxygen or gain of hydrogen.

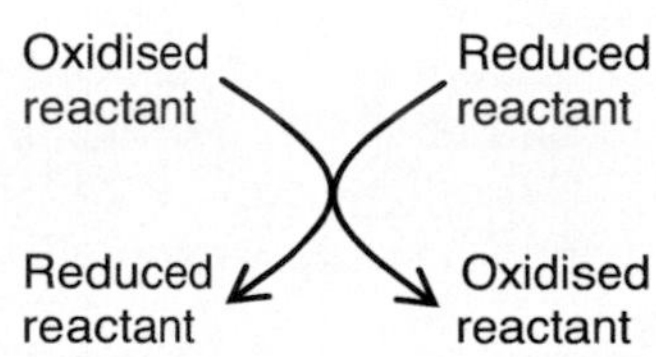

Oxidised reactant
Reduced reactant
Reduced reactant
Oxidised reactant

Oxidation and Reduction

These two reactions always go together as two reactants are involved – as one reactant is oxidised the other is reduced.

Biochemical Pathways

Biochemical Pathways

In biology the biochemical pathways can be much simplified by focusing just on the number of carbon atoms in the molecule. Remember though that the hydrogen and oxygen atoms are still there but are not shown.

This means that in an oxidation or reduction reaction nothing appears to happen as the number of carbon atoms remains the same.

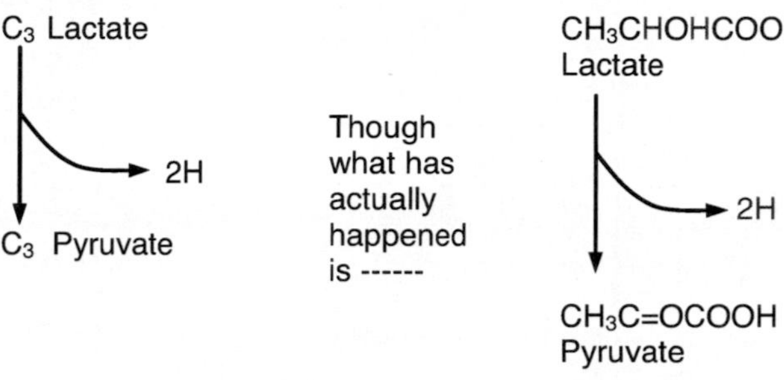

C3 Lactate
2H
C3 Pyruvate
Though what has actually happened is ------
CH3CHOHCOOH
Lactate
2H
CH3C=OCOOH
Pyruvate

The Phosphate Group

Phosphate Group

This occurs frequently in pathways. When it is part of a molecule it is written simply as P, eg glucose phosphate is C_6P; when it is a free phosphate ion it is written as Pi – **P**hosphate **i**on.

Use of the Terms Diphosphate and Bisphosphate.

Diphosphate and Bisphosphate

Both mean that the molecule has two phosphate groups attached to it. Di means the two phosphates are attached to each other; bis means the two phosphates are attached to different parts of the molecule.

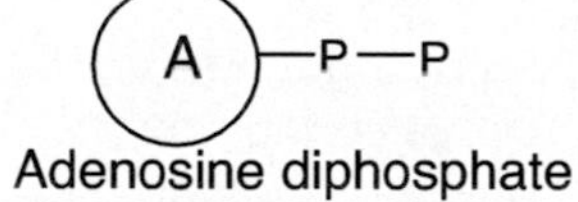

A
P—P

Adenosine diphosphate

P P
C–C–C–C–C–C

Hexose 1, 6-bisphosphate

Hydrogen Carrying Coenzymes

Hydrogen Carrying Coenzymes

There are several reactions where oxidation of the substrate occurs by dehydrogenation. When the hydrogen is removed it is transferred to a hydrogen-carrying coenzyme. Three of these are used.

Oxidised state	Reduced state
NAD^+	$NADH + H^+$
$NADP^+$	$NADPH + H^+$
FAD	$FADH_2$

In all of the pathways given below the biochemistry has been simplified to show only the key stages. Individual steps have been missed out in several places but you do not need to know these.

Glycolysis

Glycolysis

Key points

- Occurs in the cytoplasm;
- Anaerobic, ie. can occur in the absence of oxygen;
- Net energy yield = 2ATP per glucose;
- End product = pyruvate.

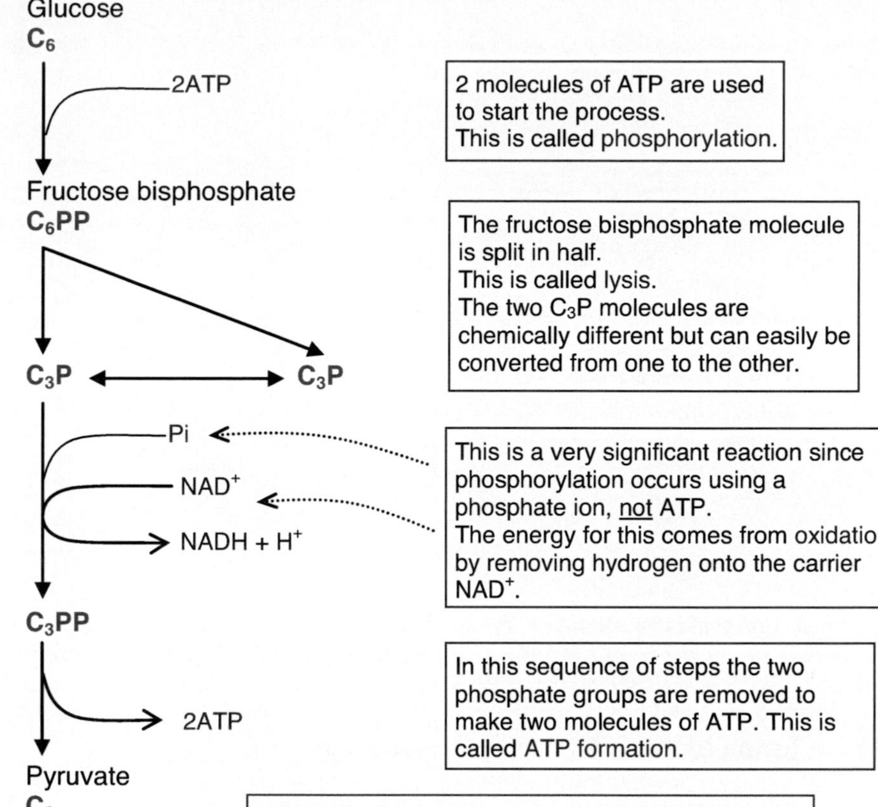

Glucose
C_6
2ATP
2 molecules of ATP are used to start the process. This is called phosphorylation.
Fructose bisphosphate
C_6PP
The fructose bisphosphate molecule is split in half. This is called lysis. The two C_3P molecules are chemically different but can easily be converted from one to the other.
C_3P
C_3P
Pi
NAD^+
$NADH + H^+$
This is a very significant reaction since phosphorylation occurs using a phosphate ion, not ATP. The energy for this comes from oxidation by removing hydrogen onto the carrier NAD^+.
C_3PP
2ATP
In this sequence of steps the two phosphate groups are removed to make two molecules of ATP. This is called ATP formation.
Pyruvate
C_3

Energy Balance

We put 2ATP in at the start and have gained 2ATP so the balance appears to be zero. However we have only used half the glucose molecule – there is still a C_3P from the lysis reaction unused. If this is converted to pyruvate down the same pathway another 2ATP are made creating a net gain of 2ATP.

Mitochondrion Structure

Mitochondrion

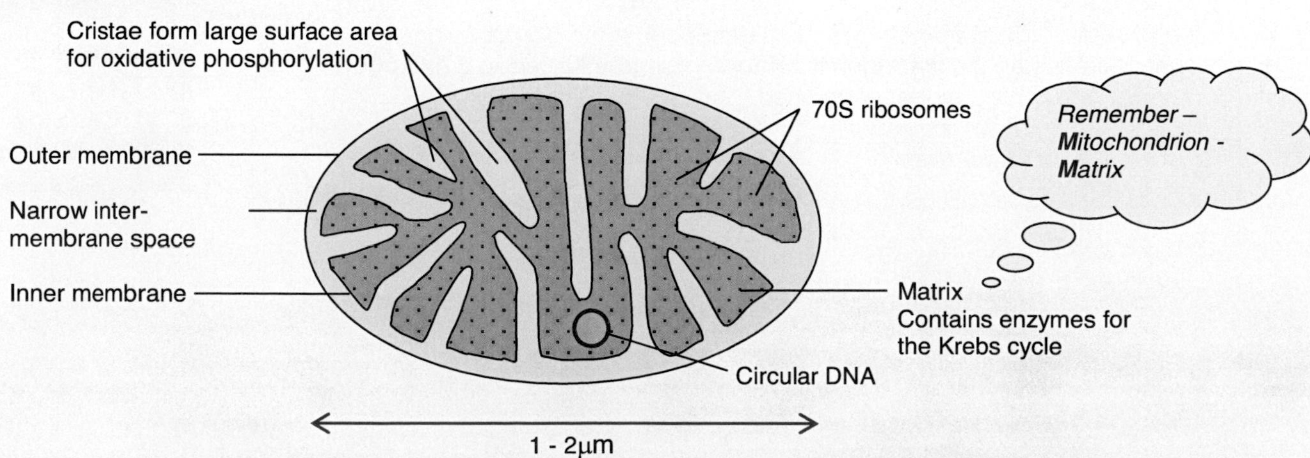

Cristae form large surface area for oxidative phosphorylation
Outer membrane
Narrow inter-membrane space
Inner membrane
70S ribosomes
Remember – Mitochondrion - Matrix
Matrix
Contains enzymes for the Krebs cycle
Circular DNA
1 - 2μm

<u>Structure of the mitochondrion as seen in an electron micrograph.</u> (See page 231).

Aerobic Respiration

Aerobic Respiration

Key points

- Occurs in the mitochondrion;
- Requires oxygen;
- Two stages – link reaction + Krebs cycle;
- Net energy yield = 36 ATP per glucose.

The Link Reaction

Krebs Cycle

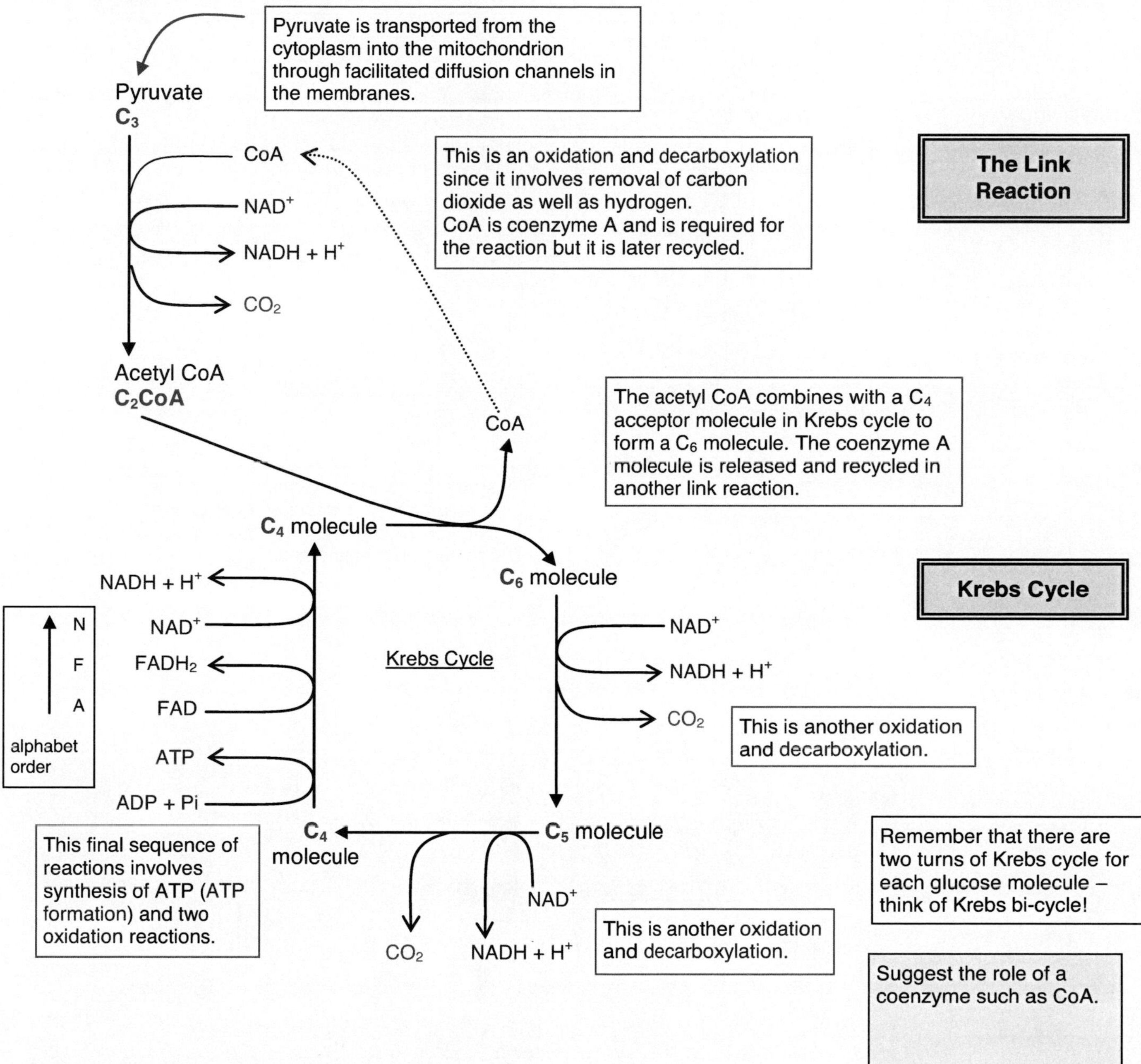

Pyruvate is transported from the cytoplasm into the mitochondrion through facilitated diffusion channels in the membranes.
Pyruvate
C_3
CoA
NAD^+
$NADH + H^+$
CO_2
This is an oxidation and decarboxylation since it involves removal of carbon dioxide as well as hydrogen.
CoA is coenzyme A and is required for the reaction but it is later recycled.
Acetyl CoA
C_2CoA
CoA
The acetyl CoA combines with a C_4 acceptor molecule in Krebs cycle to form a C_6 molecule. The coenzyme A molecule is released and recycled in another link reaction.
C_4 molecule
C_6 molecule
$NADH + H^+$
NAD^+
$FADH_2$
FAD
ATP
ADP + Pi
N
F
A
alphabet order
Krebs Cycle
NAD^+
$NADH + H^+$
CO_2
This is another oxidation and decarboxylation.
C_4 molecule
C_5 molecule
NAD^+
CO_2
$NADH + H^+$
This final sequence of reactions involves synthesis of ATP (ATP formation) and two oxidation reactions.
This is another oxidation and decarboxylation.
Remember that there are two turns of Krebs cycle for each glucose molecule – think of Krebs bi-cycle!

Suggest the role of a coenzyme such as CoA.

The Mitochondrion and Oxidative Phosphorylation

In all the oxidation reactions above the products in Krebs cycle are at progressively lower energy levels. The difference in energy level is partly stored in the electron of the hydrogen, (Remember that a hydrogen atom = H^+ + an electron), and the difference is lost as heat. This electron energy is then released via the electron transport pathway and used to form ATP.

Oxidative Phosphorylation and Chemiosmosis

Key points

- Electrons flow through a sequence of carriers, the electron transport pathway, that include proton pumps;
- At the final pump, cytochrome oxidase, they are added to oxygen and, together with protons from the matrix, form water;
- The energy from the electrons is used to pump protons from the matrix to the inter-membrane space;
- There are three linked proton pumps;
- Protons diffuse from the high concentration in the inter-membrane space back into the matrix via a channel linked to ATP synthase;
- The energy from this proton flow is used to synthesis ATP;
- The narrow inter-membrane space permits the rapid formation of a high proton concentration;
- NADH + H^+ releases its electrons at the first pump thus generating 3 ATP;
- $FADH_2$ releases its electrons at the second pump thus generating only 2 ATP.

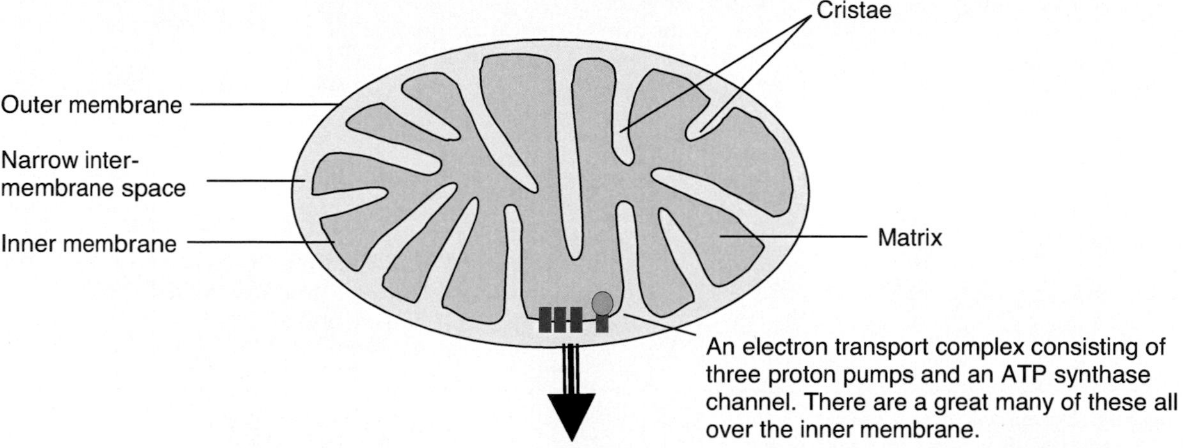
Cristae
Outer membrane
Narrow inter-membrane space
Inner membrane
Matrix
An electron transport complex consisting of three proton pumps and an ATP synthase channel. There are a great many of these all over the inner membrane.

Matrix

NADH + H^+ → NAD^+ + 2H^+ + 2e⁻

½O_2 + 2H^+ + 2e⁻ → H_2O

ADP + Pi → ATP

ATP synthase

first proton pump

inner membrane

inter-membrane space - **narrow**

outer membrane

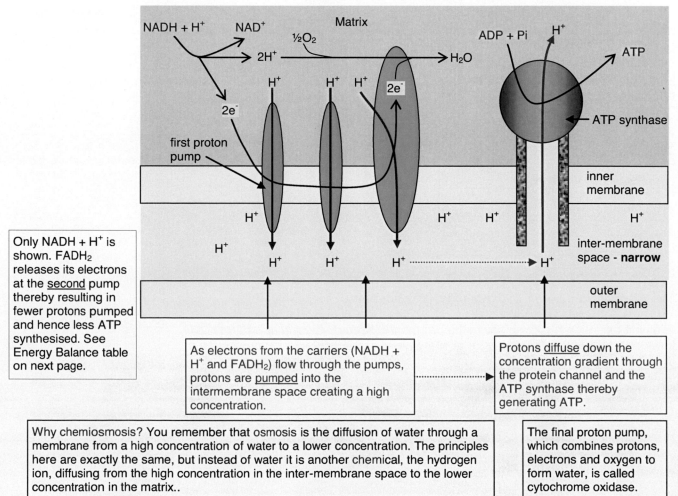

Only NADH + H^+ is shown. $FADH_2$ releases its electrons at the second pump thereby resulting in fewer protons pumped and hence less ATP synthesised. See Energy Balance table on next page.

As electrons from the carriers (NADH + H^+ and $FADH_2$) flow through the pumps, protons are pumped into the intermembrane space creating a high concentration.

Protons diffuse down the concentration gradient through the protein channel and the ATP synthase thereby generating ATP.

Why chemiosmosis? You remember that osmosis is the diffusion of water through a membrane from a high concentration of water to a lower concentration. The principles here are exactly the same, but instead of water it is another chemical, the hydrogen ion, diffusing from the high concentration in the inter-membrane space to the lower concentration in the matrix..

The final proton pump, which combines protons, electrons and oxygen to form water, is called cytochrome oxidase.

Summary

Summary

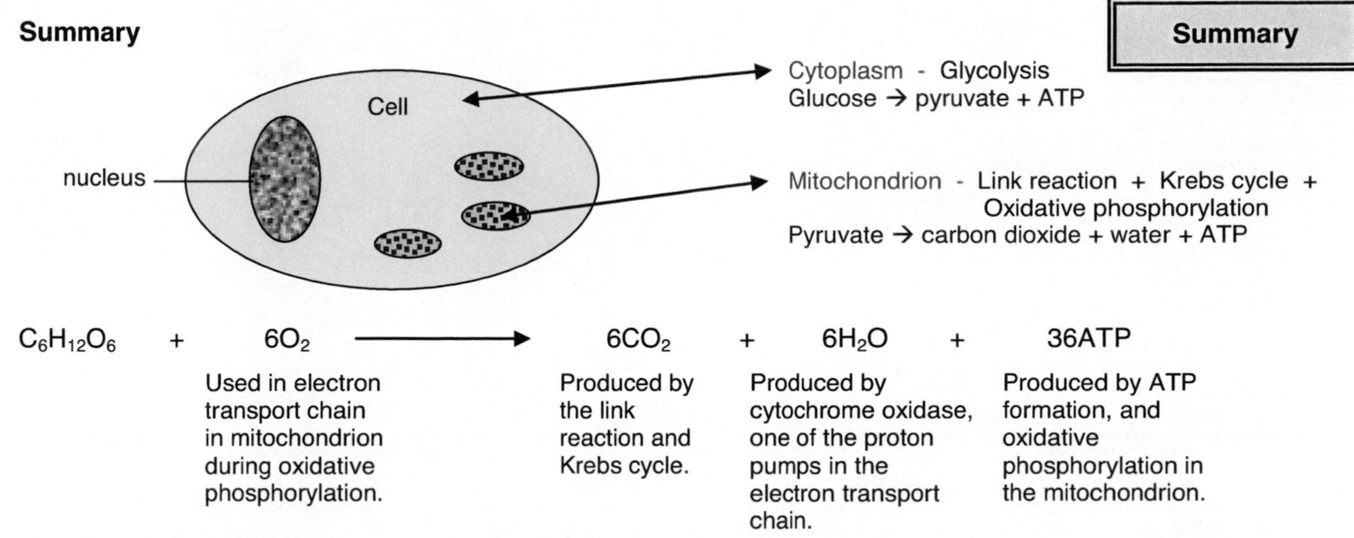
Cell
nucleus
Cytoplasm - Glycolysis
Glucose → pyruvate + ATP
Mitochondrion - Link reaction + Krebs cycle + Oxidative phosphorylation
Pyruvate → carbon dioxide + water + ATP
$C_6H_{12}O_6$ + $6O_2$ → $6CO_2$ + $6H_2O$ + 36ATP
Used in electron transport chain in mitochondrion during oxidative phosphorylation.
Produced by the link reaction and Krebs cycle.
Produced by cytochrome oxidase, one of the proton pumps in the electron transport chain.
Produced by ATP formation, and oxidative phosphorylation in the mitochondrion.

Overall Energy Balance from Respiration of One Glucose Molecule

Energy Balance

Stage		
Glycolysis	2ATP used at start	-2 ATP
	$2NADH + H^+$ If oxygen is present its electrons are transferred across the envelope to form $2FADH_2$ inside the mitochondrion.	4 ATP
	ATP formation	4 ATP
Link reaction	$2NADH + H^+$	6 ATP
Krebs cycle	ATP formation	2 ATP
	$2FADH_2$	4 ATP
	6NADH + H+	18 ATP
	Net Energy Yield	**36 ATP**

The Respiration Equation

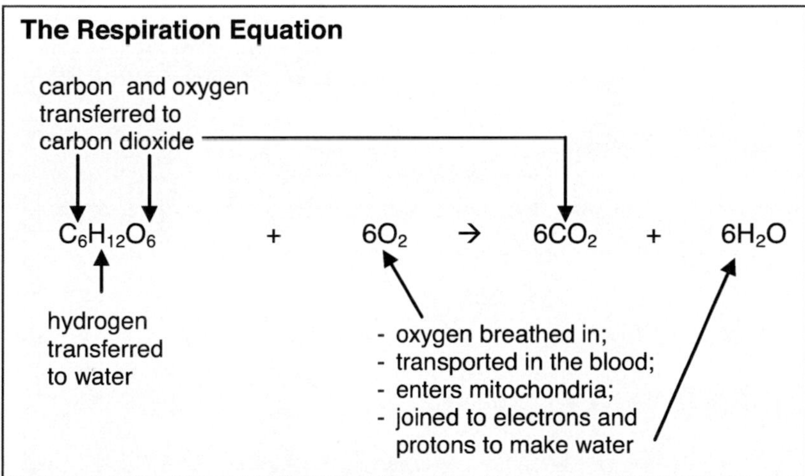
carbon and oxygen transferred to carbon dioxide
$C_6H_{12}O_6$ + $6O_2$ → $6CO_2$ + $6H_2O$
hydrogen transferred to water
- oxygen breathed in;
- transported in the blood;
- enters mitochondria;
- joined to electrons and protons to make water

How many proton pumps are used in oxidative phosphorylation?

How many molecules of ATP can be made by the transfer of electrons from $NADH + H^+$?

What is the reason for the inner mitochondrial membrane being folded?

Name the enzyme in the final step in chemiosmosis.

How many molecules of ATP can be made by the transfer of electrons from $FADH_2$?

What are these folds called?

Is oxidation loss or gain of electrons?	In which part of the cell does glycolysis take place?	In which part of the mitochondrion does the link reaction take place?
In which part of the mitochondrion does Krebs cycle take place?	From 1 molecule of glucose what is the net gain of ATP in glycolysis?	From 1 molecule of glucose how many molecules of $NADH^{+} + H^{+}$ are formed in glycolysis?
Name the type of reaction that splits the fructose/hexose bisphosphate into two 3-carbon compounds.	Name the type of reaction when a phosphate is added to a compound.	Is glycolysis aerobic or anaerobic?

Revision Mitochondrion

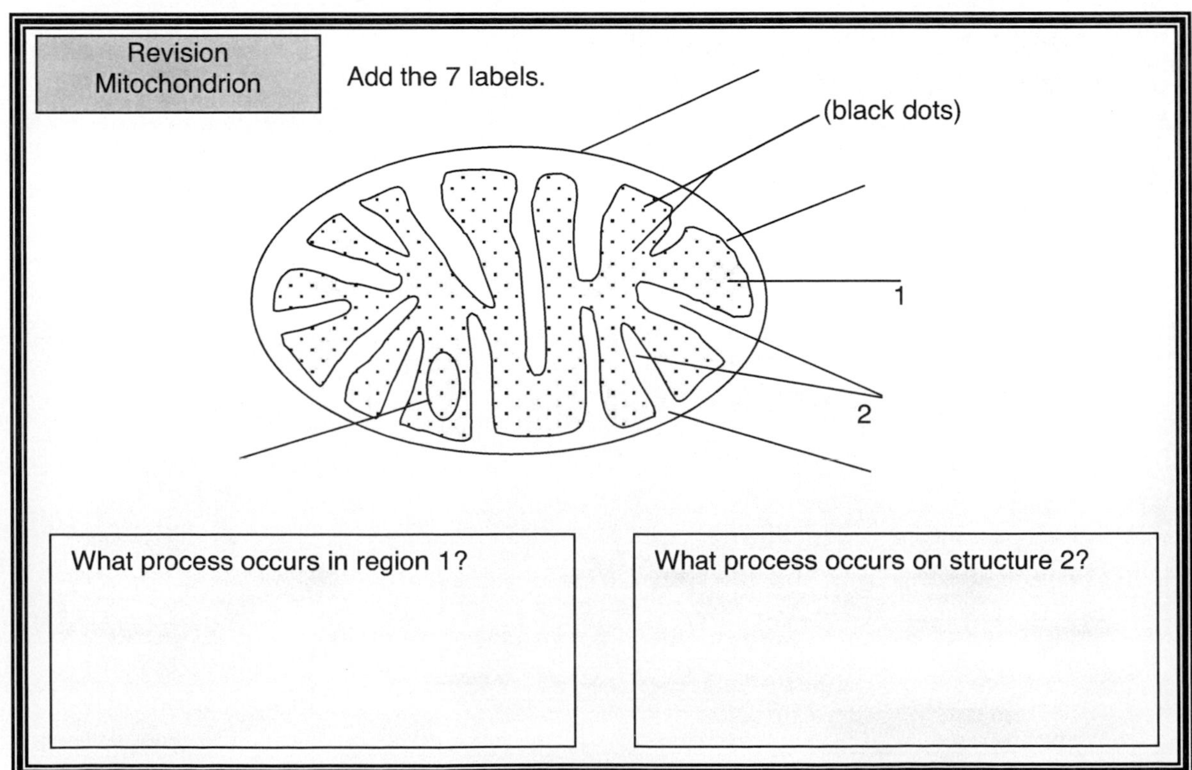
Add the 7 labels.
(black dots)
1
2

What process occurs in region 1?	What process occurs on structure 2?

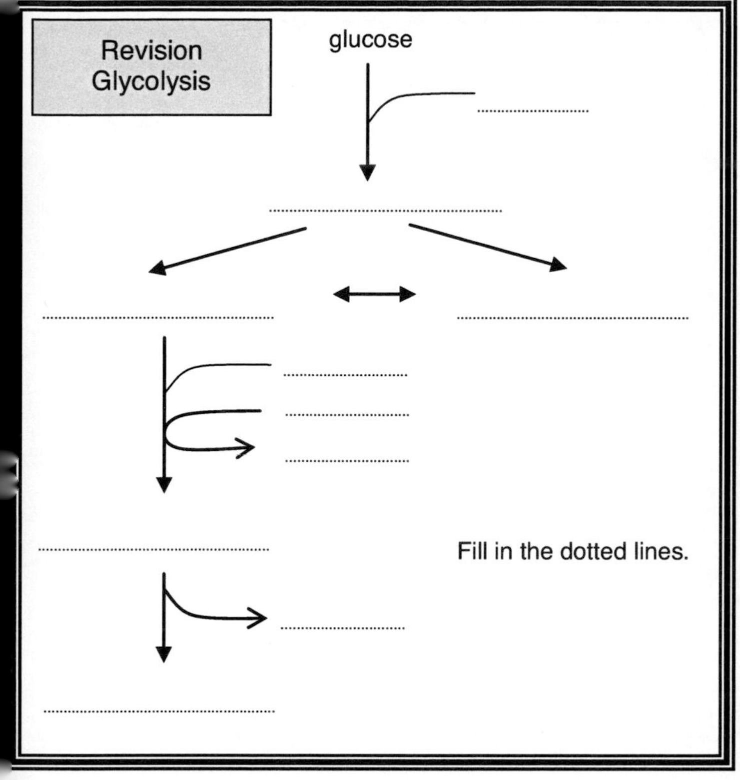
Revision
Glycolysis
glucose
Fill in the dotted lines.

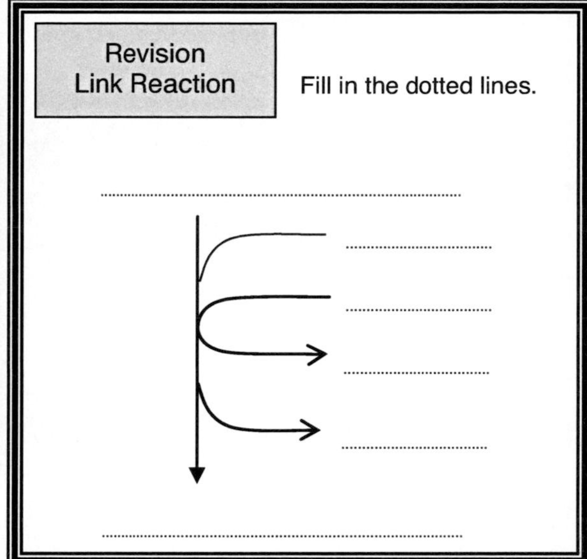
Revision
Link Reaction
Fill in the dotted lines.

Revision
Krebs Cycle

Fill in the dotted lines.

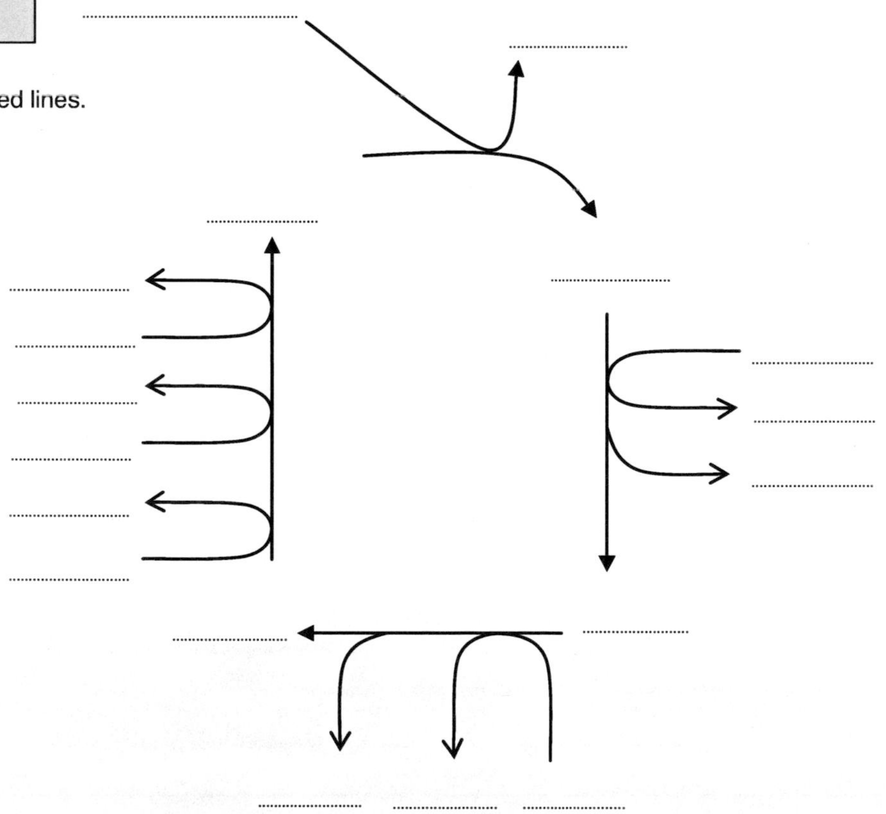

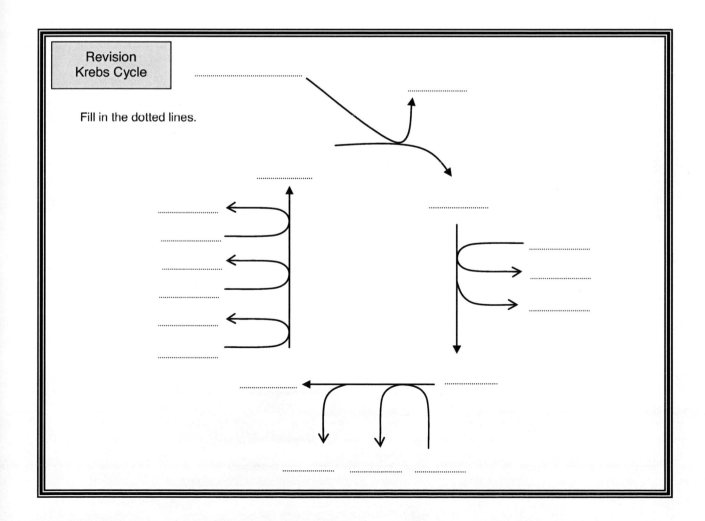

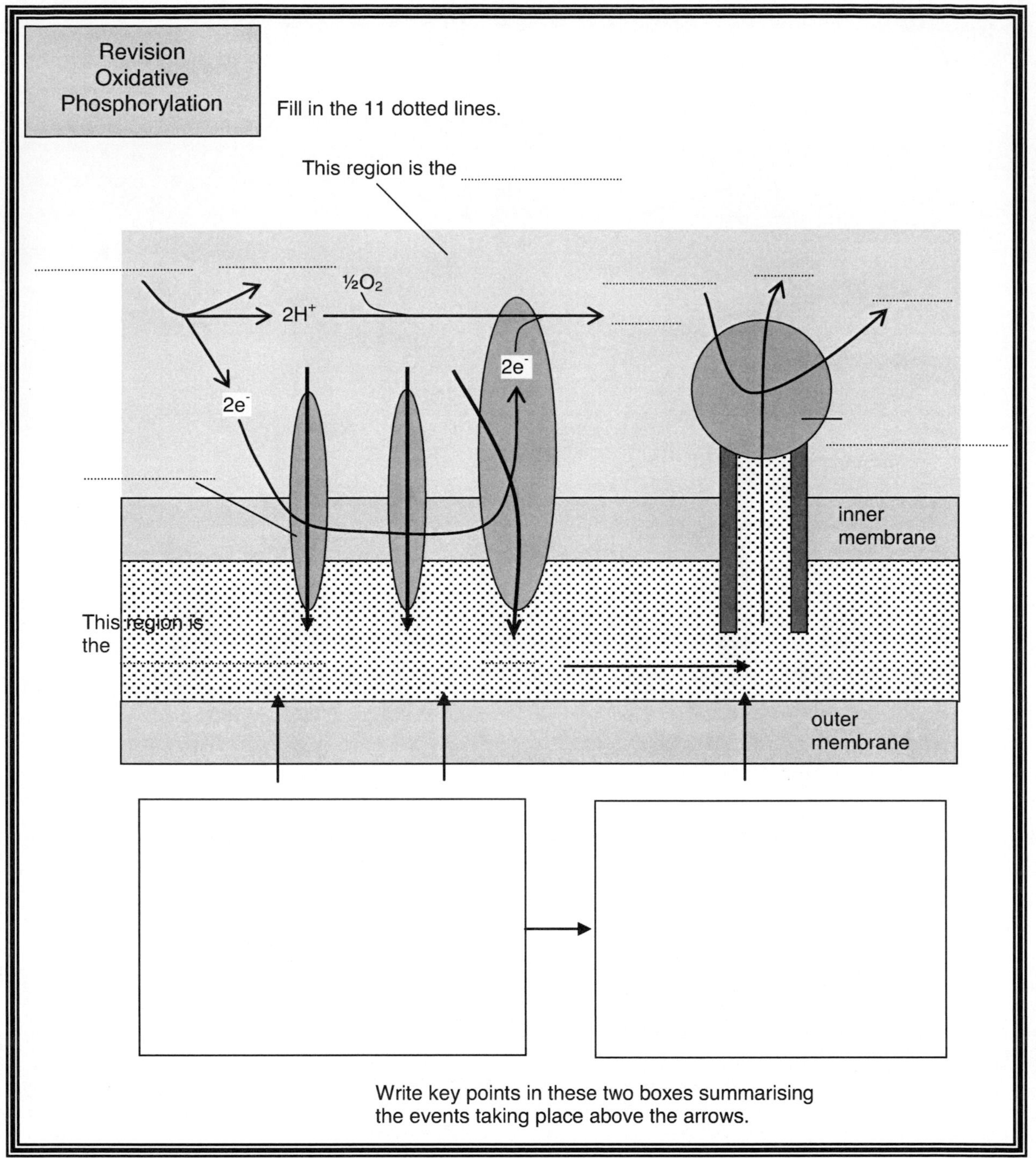
Revision
Oxidative
Phosphorylation
Fill in the 11 dotted lines.
This region is the
½O2
2H+
2e-
2e-
inner
membrane
This region is
the
outer
membrane
Write key points in these two boxes summarising
the events taking place above the arrows.

Photosynthesis

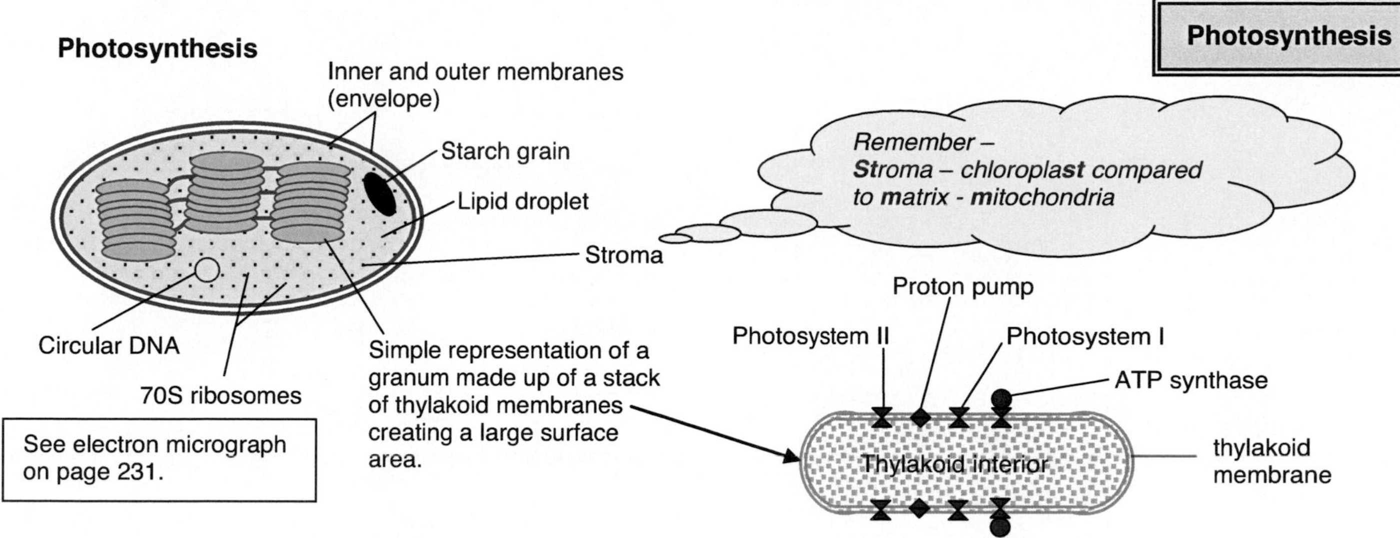
Inner and outer membranes (envelope)
Starch grain
Lipid droplet
Stroma
Circular DNA
70S ribosomes
Simple representation of a granum made up of a stack of thylakoid membranes creating a large surface area.
Remember – Stroma – chloroplast compared to matrix - mitochondria
Proton pump
Photosystem II
Photosystem I
ATP synthase
Thylakoid interior
thylakoid membrane

See electron micrograph on page 231.

Key points

- Chloroplasts have an envelope;
- Thylakoid membranes form stacks called grana;
- These provide a large surface area for light absorption;
- Photosystems I and II contain a mixture of photosynthetic pigments but mainly chlorophyll;
- The photosystems are embedded in the thylakoid membrane;
- Along with the photosystems are molecules for electron transport and proton pumping;
- ATP is generated using the chemiosmotic process – the principle is the same as in mitochondria but the molecules involved are slightly different.

Photosynthesis consists of
- the light dependent reactions, and
- the light independent reactions.

The Light Dependent Reactions

Key points –

- These occur on the thylakoid membranes;
- Photosystem II absorbs light energy (photoactivation);
- This energy is used to promote electrons from chlorophyll to a higher energy level;
- The electrons are replaced in the photosystem by splitting water – photolysis;
- Oxygen gas is released;
- As the electrons fall to a lower energy level along an electron transport chain the energy difference is used to pump protons into the thylakoid interior;
- The protons then diffuse back through ATP synthase, making ATP (photophosphorylation);
- Photosystem I absorbs light energy (photoactivation);;
- This energy is used to promote electrons from chlorophyll to a higher energy level;
- The electron energy may be stored as reducing power in reduced $NADP^+$ for later use in the light independent reaction;
- The electrons may cycle through the electron transport chain again to make more ATP (cyclic photophosphorylation).

Remember that Photosystem II comes before Photosystem I
NADP⁺ is simply NAD⁺ with a phosphate group attached. Remember that Photosynthesis uses NADP⁺.

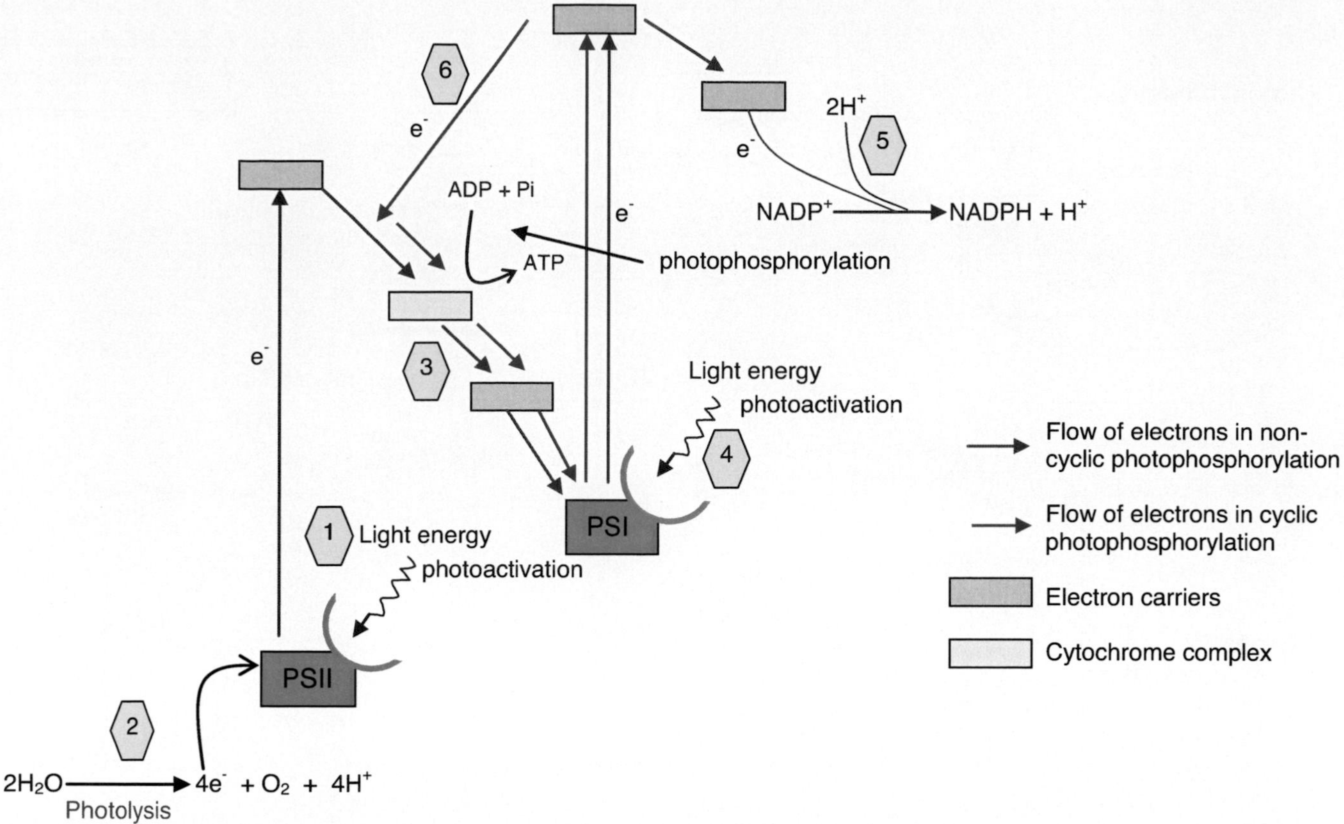
6
e-
ADP + Pi
ATP
e-
2H+
5
e-
NADP+
NADPH + H+
photophosphorylation
e-
3
Light energy
photoactivation
4
PSI
1
Light energy
photoactivation
PSII
2
2H2O
4e- + O2 + 4H+
Photolysis
Flow of electrons in non-cyclic photophosphorylation
Flow of electrons in cyclic photophosphorylation
Electron carriers
Cytochrome complex

Key steps

1. Photosystem II absorbs light energy and electrons are boosted to a higher energy level. This is **photoactivation** of PSII.
2. The electrons lost from PSII are replaced by splitting water – **photolysis**. Oxygen gas is released and the protons can either combine with $NADP^+$ at the end of the pathway or be pumped into the thylakoid interior.
3. The electrons fall in energy level through a series of carriers. One of these is a cytochrome complex which acts as a proton pump. (See non-cyclic photophosphorylation below).
4. The electrons fall into PSI and light energy is absorbed to boost them to an electron carrier. This is **photoactivation** of PSI.
5. The electrons can pass to $NADP^+$ reducing it to NADPH + H^+ with the addition of $2H^+$.
6. Alternatively the electrons can fall back to PSI through the proton pump in a cyclic process that generates ATP. (See cyclic photophosphorylation below).

In which order are the two photosystems with respect to electron flow?

Where are the two photosystems found?

Which photosystem is used in cyclic photophosphorylation?

What is the name of the hydrogen acceptor?

What is photolysis?

What is photoactivation?

The Chloroplast and Photophosphorylation

Photophosphorylation and The Chemiosmotic Theory

This is the synthesis of ATP using the energy from light. The principle is the same as for oxidative phosphorylation in the mitochondria on page 144.

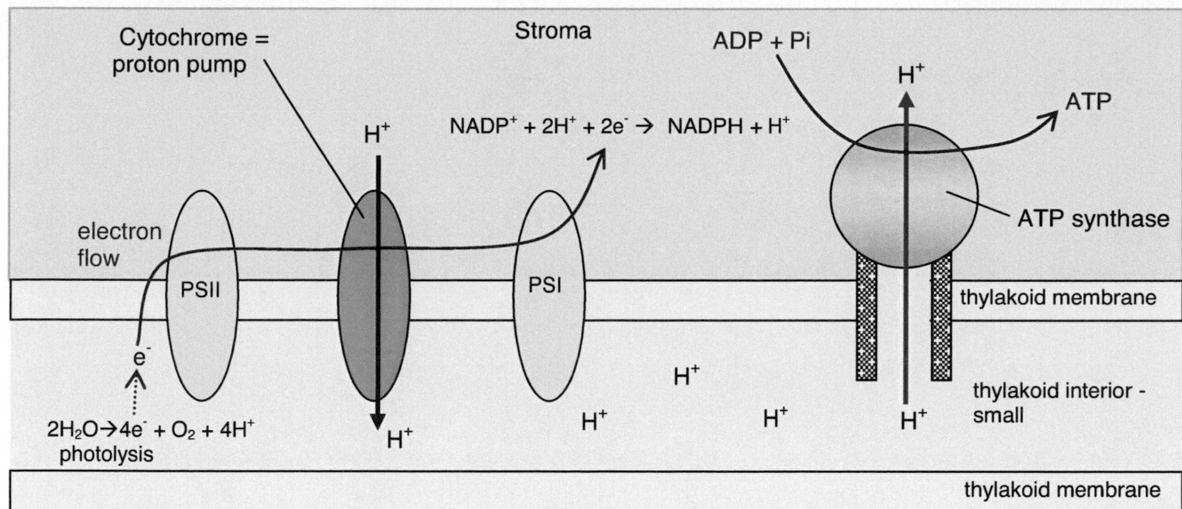

Cytochrome = proton pump
Stroma
ADP + Pi
H^+
ATP
$NADP^+ + 2H^+ + 2e^- \rightarrow NADPH + H^+$
ATP synthase
electron flow
PSII
PSI
thylakoid membrane
e^-
H^+
thylakoid interior - small
$2H_2O \rightarrow 4e^- + O_2 + 4H^+$
photolysis
thylakoid membrane

Key steps

- Electrons flow through the carriers, including photosystems II and I.
- As they pass through the cytochrome complex protons are pumped to the interior of the thylakoid.
- The thylakoid interior is small to increase the concentration of protons.
- The protons then flow back by diffusion down a concentration gradient into the stroma through ATP synthase.
- ATP is generated.

Relate this diagram to the one on the opposite page.

Also note how similar it is to the diagram on page 144.

See note about chemiosmosis at the bottom of page 144.

Difference between the cyclic and non-cyclic pathways -

- With non-cyclic the electrons continue on to join with protons and $NADP^+$ whereas with cyclic they are returned to the chlorophyll in photosystem I.

The cyclic pathway has two advantages.

1. It provides the additional ATP needed to drive the light independent reactions. The Calvin cycle requires more ATP than $NADPH + H^+$. Non-cyclic photophosphorylation gives a ratio of 1:1 so more ATP is needed. Cyclic photophosphorylation provides this additional ATP.
2. It provides ATP that can be used for other processes such as stomatal opening by guard cells.

Summary –

Inputs	- Water
	- Light energy
Products	- Oxygen
	- ATP
	- $NADPH + H^+$

Photosynthesis Spectra

Photosynthesis Spectra

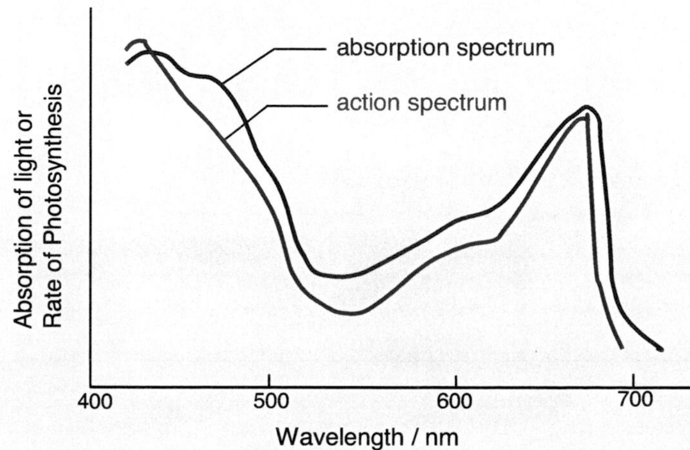

absorption spectrum
action spectrum
Absorption of light or Rate of Photosynthesis
400
500
600
700
Wavelength / nm

An **absorption spectrum** shows how much of a particular wavelength is absorbed by the chloroplast pigments.

An **action spectrum** shows how much photosynthesis takes place at a particular wavelength.

The graph clearly shows the close correlation between the two, indicating that the light energy absorbed is used in the process of photosynthesis.

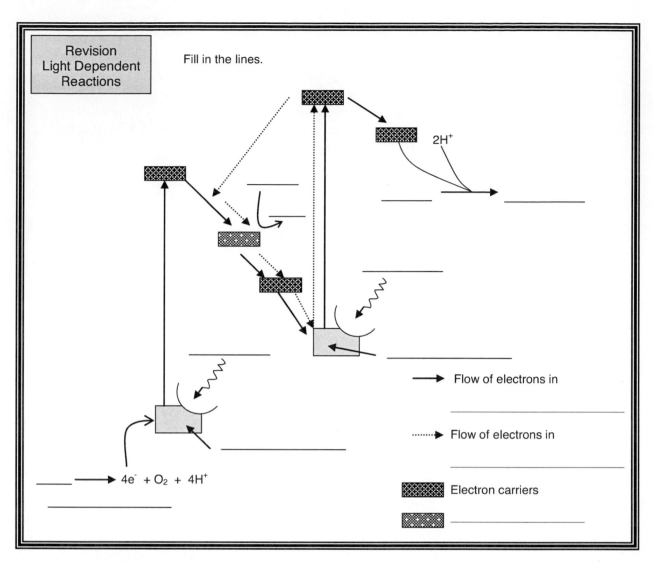

Revision
Light Dependent Reactions

Fill in the lines.

2H⁺

____ → $4e^- + O_2 + 4H^+$

____

→ Flow of electrons in

____

┈▸ Flow of electrons in

____

Electron carriers

____

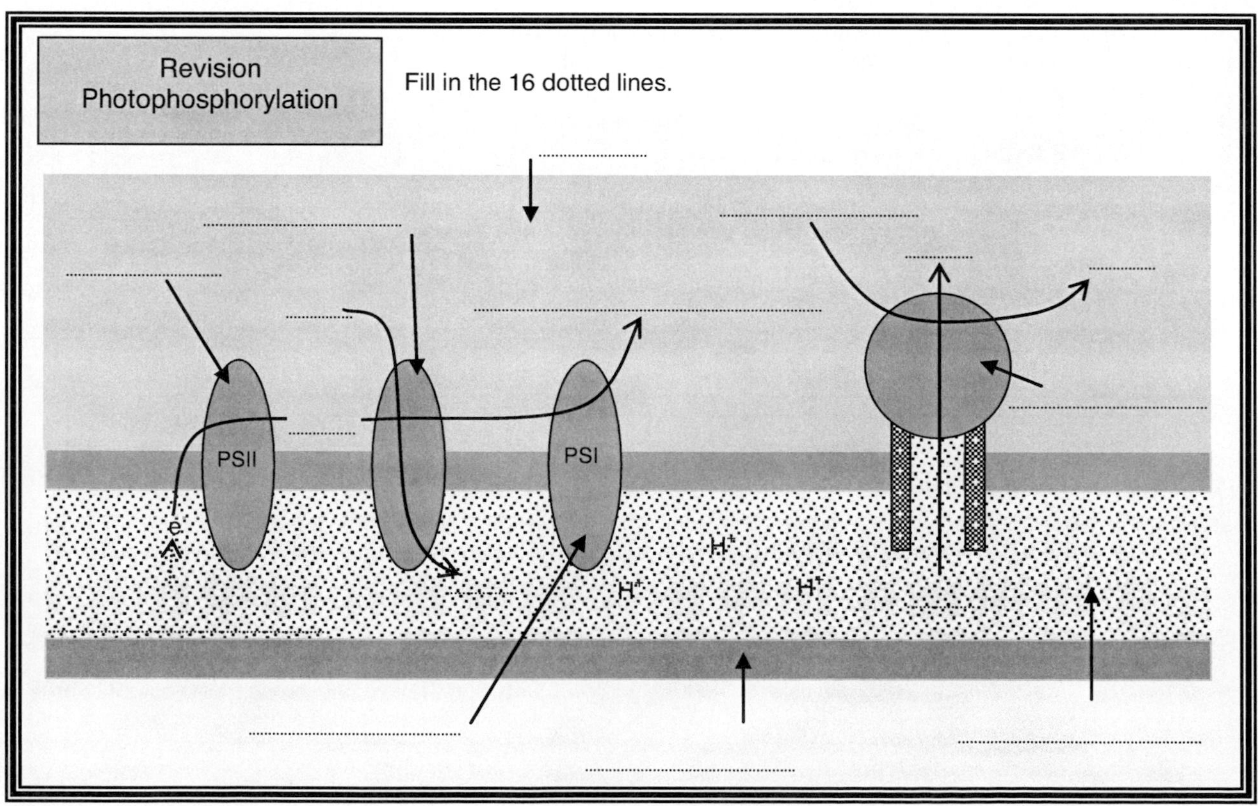

Revision
Photophosphorylation
Fill in the 16 dotted lines.
PSII
PSI
e
H⁺
H⁺
H⁺

The Light Independent Reactions

Key points

- The light independent reactions are driven by the ATP and NADPH + H^+ made in the light dependent reactions. The important point to remember is that both sets of reactions continue at the same time.
- The light independent reactions occur in the stroma.
- It is a cyclic system called the Calvin cycle.

The Light Independent Reactions

Each rotation of the Calvin cycle uses one molecule of carbon dioxide. The diagram below shows three cycles superimposed. This is so that the three molecules of carbon dioxide entering emerge as one 3-carbon compound, triose phosphate.

The Calvin Cycle

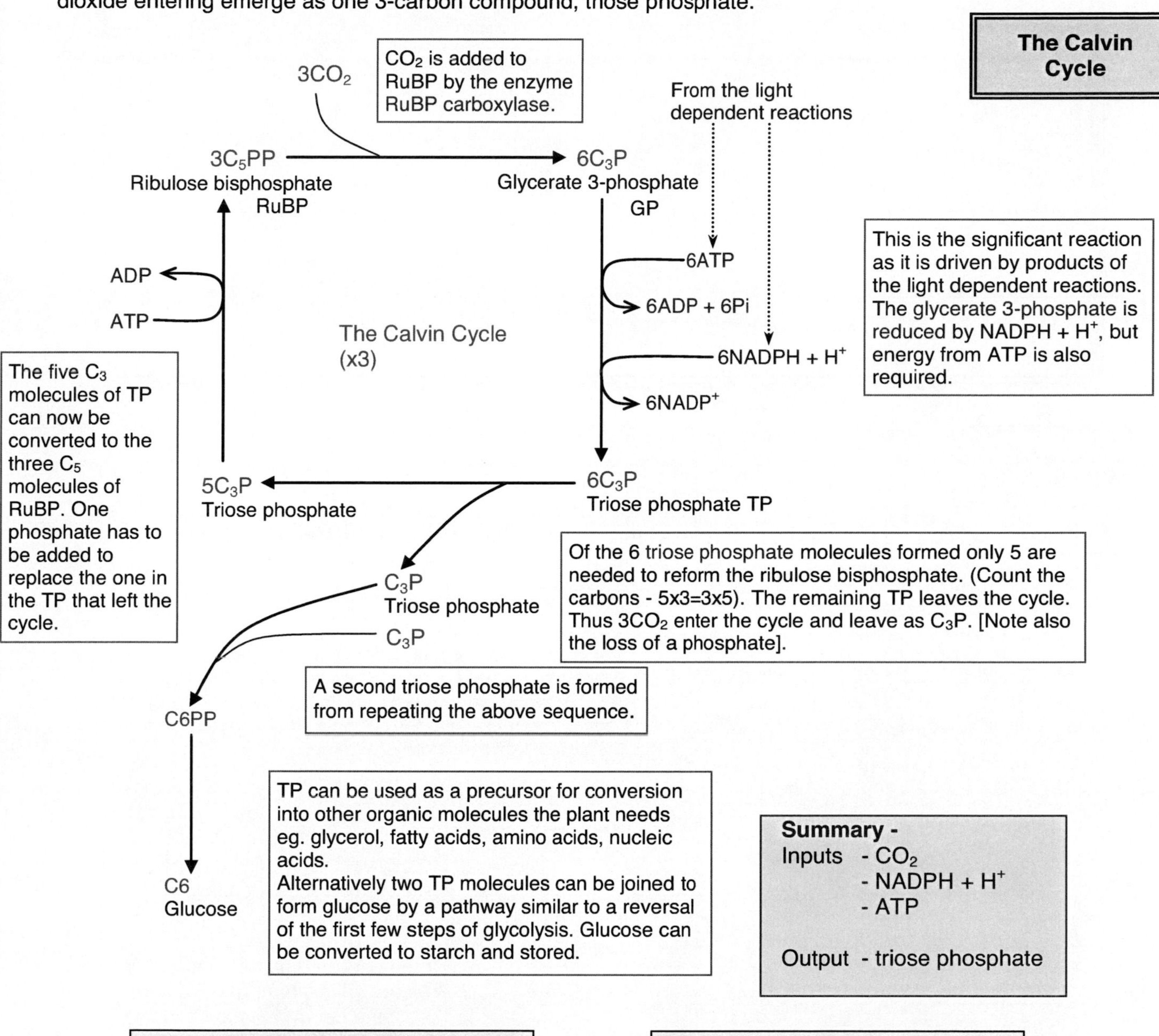

$3CO_2$
CO_2 is added to RuBP by the enzyme RuBP carboxylase.
From the light dependent reactions
$3C_5PP$
Ribulose bisphosphate RuBP
$6C_3P$
Glycerate 3-phosphate GP
6ATP
6ADP + 6Pi
6NADPH + H^+
6NADP$^+$
ADP
ATP
The Calvin Cycle (x3)
This is the significant reaction as it is driven by products of the light dependent reactions. The glycerate 3-phosphate is reduced by NADPH + H^+, but energy from ATP is also required.
The five C_3 molecules of TP can now be converted to the three C_5 molecules of RuBP. One phosphate has to be added to replace the one in the TP that left the cycle.
$5C_3P$
Triose phosphate
$6C_3P$
Triose phosphate TP
C_3P
Triose phosphate
C_3P
Of the 6 triose phosphate molecules formed only 5 are needed to reform the ribulose bisphosphate. (Count the carbons - 5x3=3x5). The remaining TP leaves the cycle. Thus $3CO_2$ enter the cycle and leave as C_3P. [Note also the loss of a phosphate].
A second triose phosphate is formed from repeating the above sequence.
C6PP
C6
Glucose
TP can be used as a precursor for conversion into other organic molecules the plant needs eg. glycerol, fatty acids, amino acids, nucleic acids.
Alternatively two TP molecules can be joined to form glucose by a pathway similar to a reversal of the first few steps of glycolysis. Glucose can be converted to starch and stored.

Summary -
Inputs - CO_2
- NADPH + H^+
- ATP

Output - triose phosphate

In which region of the chloroplast does the Calvin cycle take place?

Name two 'chain' metabolic pathways and two 'ring' metabolic pathways.

In which region of the chloroplast does photophosphorylation take place?

Revision Calvin Cycle

Fill in the dotted lines.

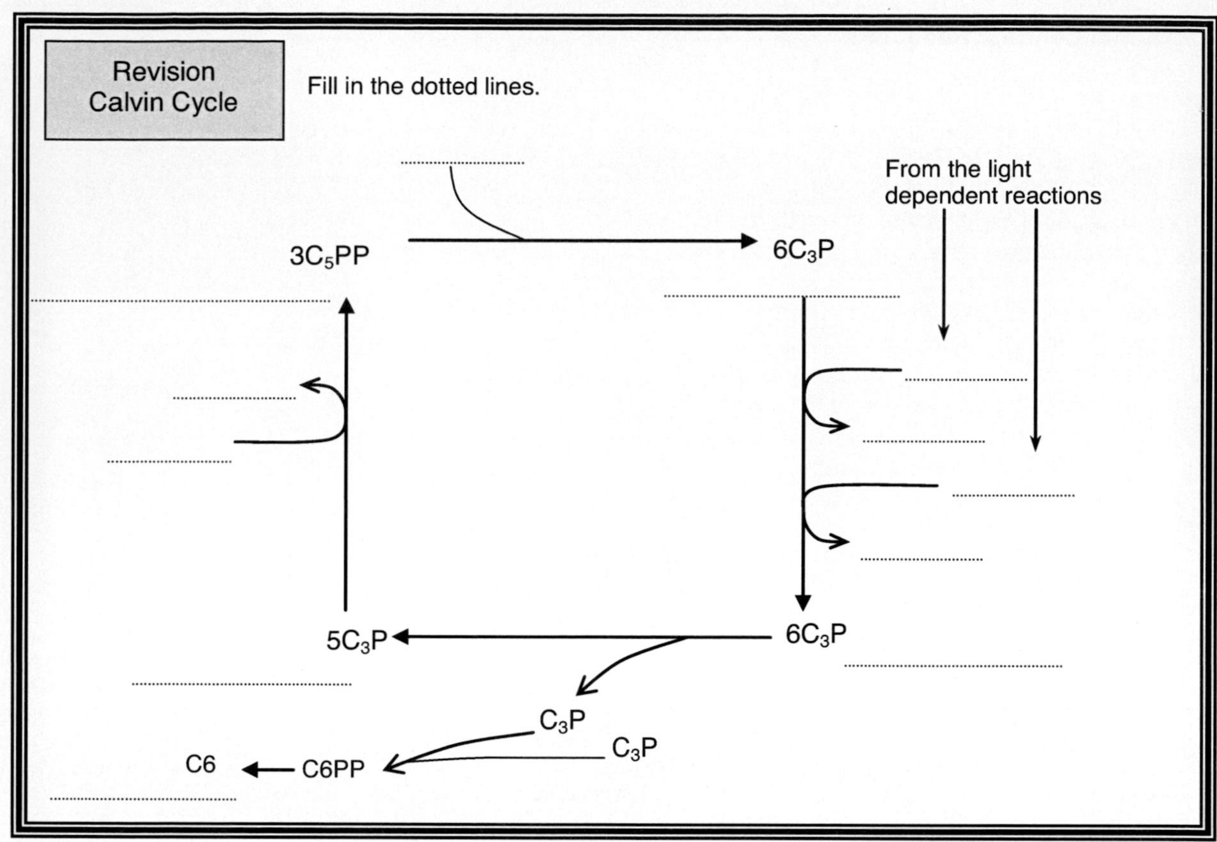

From the light dependent reactions
$3C_5PP$
$6C_3P$
$6C_3P$
$5C_3P$
C_3P
C_3P
C6
C6PP

Limiting Factors

Limiting Factors

Key point

➢ When a chemical process depends on more than one essential condition being favourable, its rate is limited by that factor which is nearest its minimum value.

Imagine a pizza production line.
To make 10 pizzas requires –

10 bases	4 mushrooms
10 tomatoes	20 anchovies
150g grated cheese	18 olives

But suppose you only have 12 olives. This means that you can only make 8 pizzas, so the olives are the limiting factor. Again suppose you have 12 olives but now only 5 tomatoes. Now you can only make 5 pizzas as this time it is the tomato that is the limiting factor.

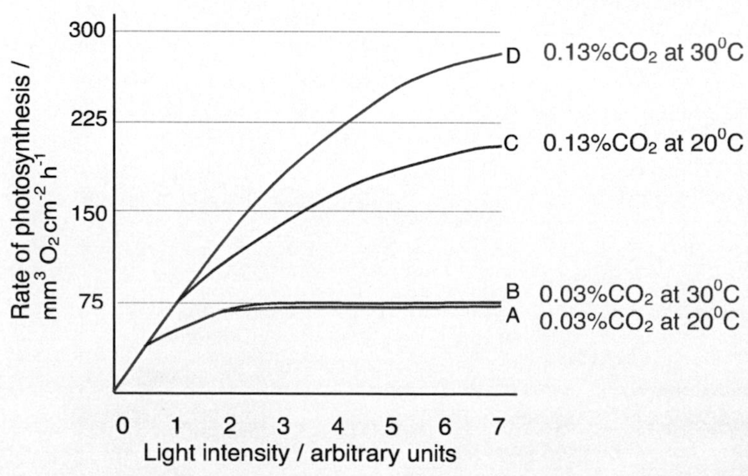

Rate of photosynthesis / $mm^3\ O_2\ cm^{-2}\ h^{-1}$
300
225
150
75
0 1 2 3 4 5 6 7
Light intensity / arbitrary units
D $0.13\%CO_2$ at 30^0C
C $0.13\%CO_2$ at 20^0C
B $0.03\%CO_2$ at 30^0C
A $0.03\%CO_2$ at 20^0C

Curves A and B are identical even though the temperature for B is 10^0C higher. This indicates that temperature is not the limiting factor.

If the carbon dioxide concentration is raised but the temperature kept at 20^0C the curve rises to C, indicating that the limiting factor for A and B was CO_2 concentration.

If the temperature is now raised to 30^0C the curve rises to D, indicating that the limiting factor for curve C was temperature.

Self-test Quiz on Topic 8

1. Oxidation can be described as
   a. loss of oxygen and gain of hydrogen;
   b. gain of oxygen and loss of electrons;
   c. loss of electrons and gain of hydrogen;
   d. gain of electrons and gain of oxygen.

2. In the glycolysis pathway starting with 1 molecule of glucose
   a. 4 molecules of ATP are used,
   b. lysis occurs twice,
   c. 2 molecules of carbon dioxide are produced,
   d. 2 molecules of NAD^+ are reduced.

3. Acetyl Co-A is produced from pyruvate by
   a. reduction and dehydrogenation,
   b. oxidation and decarboxylation,
   c. phosphorylation,
   d. oxidation and condensation.

4. Acetyl Co-A joins Krebs cycle by combining with a
   a. 2-carbon compound,
   b. 4-carbon compound,
   c. 5-carbon compound,
   d. 6-carbon compound.

5. In the process of oxidative phosphorylation in the mitochondrion
   a. both active transport and diffusion of protons takes place,
   b. reduction of NADH + H^+ takes place,
   c. electrons are moved to higher energy levels,
   d. ADP + Pi is formed from ATP.

6. During the light dependent reactions of photosynthesis
   a. ATP is used in the process of cyclic photophosphorylation,
   b. a condensation reaction occurs forming water,
   c. $NADP^+$ is oxidised,
   d. chlorophyll is both oxidised and reduced.

7. During the light independent reactions of photosynthesis
   a. pyruvate combines with ribulose bisphosphate to form glycerate 3-phosphate,
   b. NADPH + H^+ is oxidised during the formation of triose phosphate,
   c. ribulose carboxylase catalyses the formation of ribulose bisphosphate using carbon dioxide,
   d. ATP is produced during the conversion of glycerate 3-phosphate to triose phosphate.

8. Which of the following statements is correct?
   a. Both light dependent and light independent reactions take place in the stroma.
   b. Photophosphorylation occurs in the stroma.
   c. Chemiosmosis occurs on the thylakoid membranes.
   d. The Calvin cycle occurs on the grana.

9. Which of the following statements is correct?
   a. Electrons flow through photosystem I and then photosystem II.
   b. Non-cyclic photophosphorylation involves only photosystem II.
   c. During photolysis water is split to release oxygen as a waste product.
   d. Cyclic photophosphorylation involves photosystems I and II.

10. Which of the following statements is correct?
    a. Photophosphorylation produces ATP.
    b. Photophosphorylation produces ATP and NADPH + H^+.
    c. Photolysis produces ATP.
    d. Six rotations of the Calvin cycle produces one molecule of triose phosphate.

11. Which of the following graphs represents the absorption spectrum for photosynthesis?

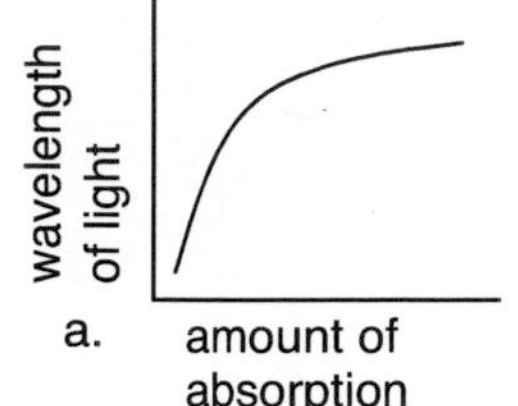
wavelength of light
amount of absorption
a.

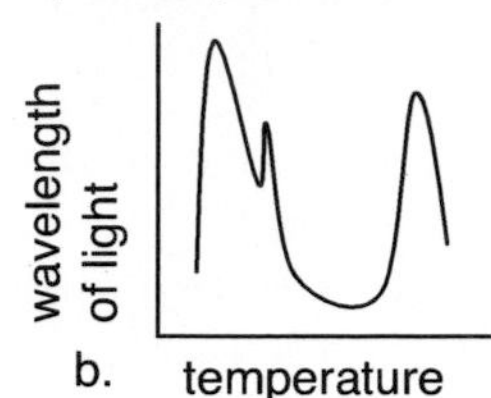
wavelength of light
temperature
b.

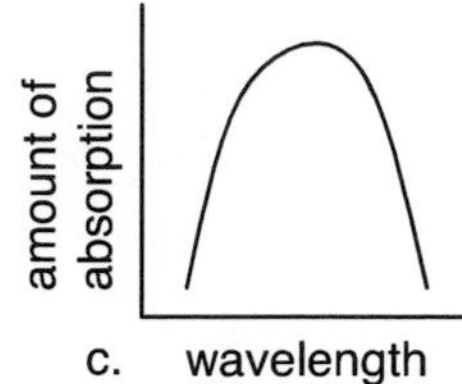
amount of absorption
wavelength of light
c.

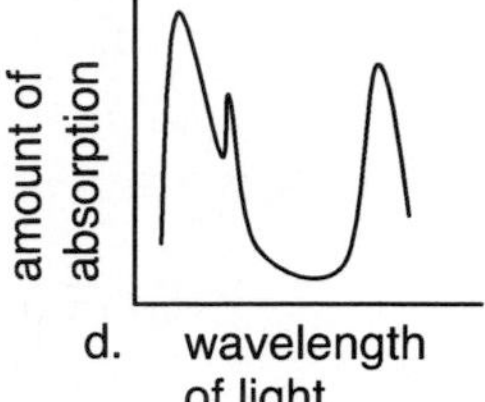
amount of absorption
wavelength of light
d.

12. Which of the following graphs correctly shows that light intensity is acting as a limiting factor for photosynthesis?

a.
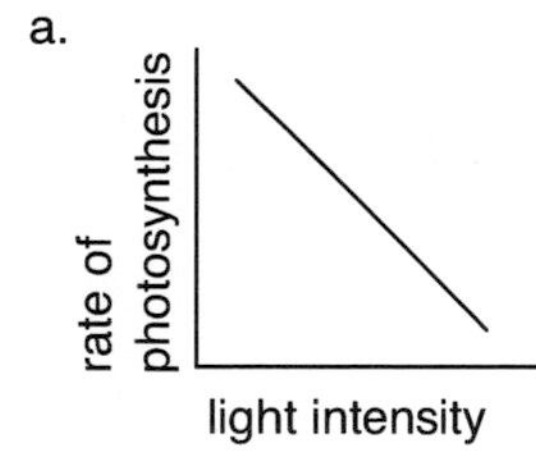
rate of photosynthesis
light intensity

b.
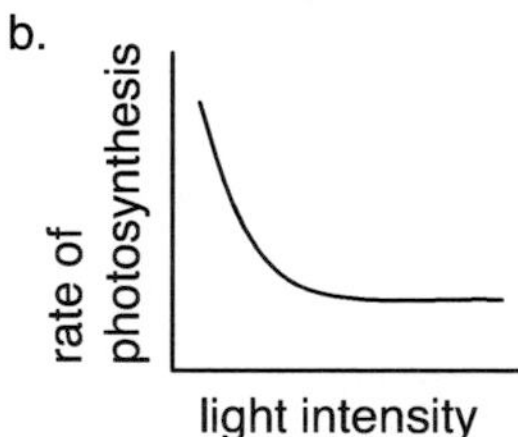
rate of photosynthesis
light intensity

c.
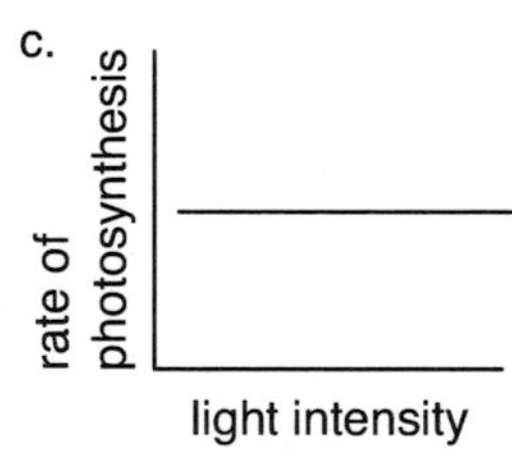
rate of photosynthesis
light intensity

d.
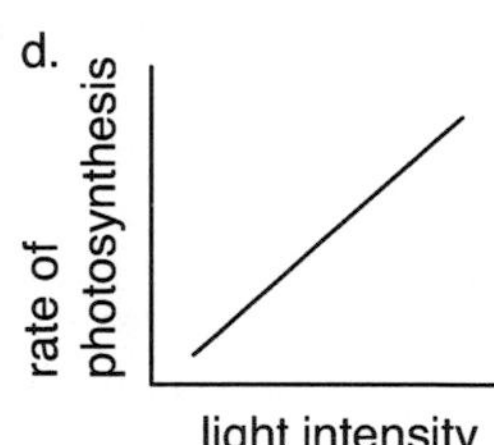
rate of photosynthesis
light intensity

13. Which of the following statements correctly describes a limiting factor?
    a. The optimum temperature at which an enzyme works.
    b. A variable factor that controls the rate of a process and is nearest to its minimum value.
    c. A variable factor in a sequence that functions at the slowest rate.
    d. A factor in a chemical chain that varies in concentration.

Topic 9

Plant Science

Internal Features

Internal Features of a Dicotyledonous Plant Stem

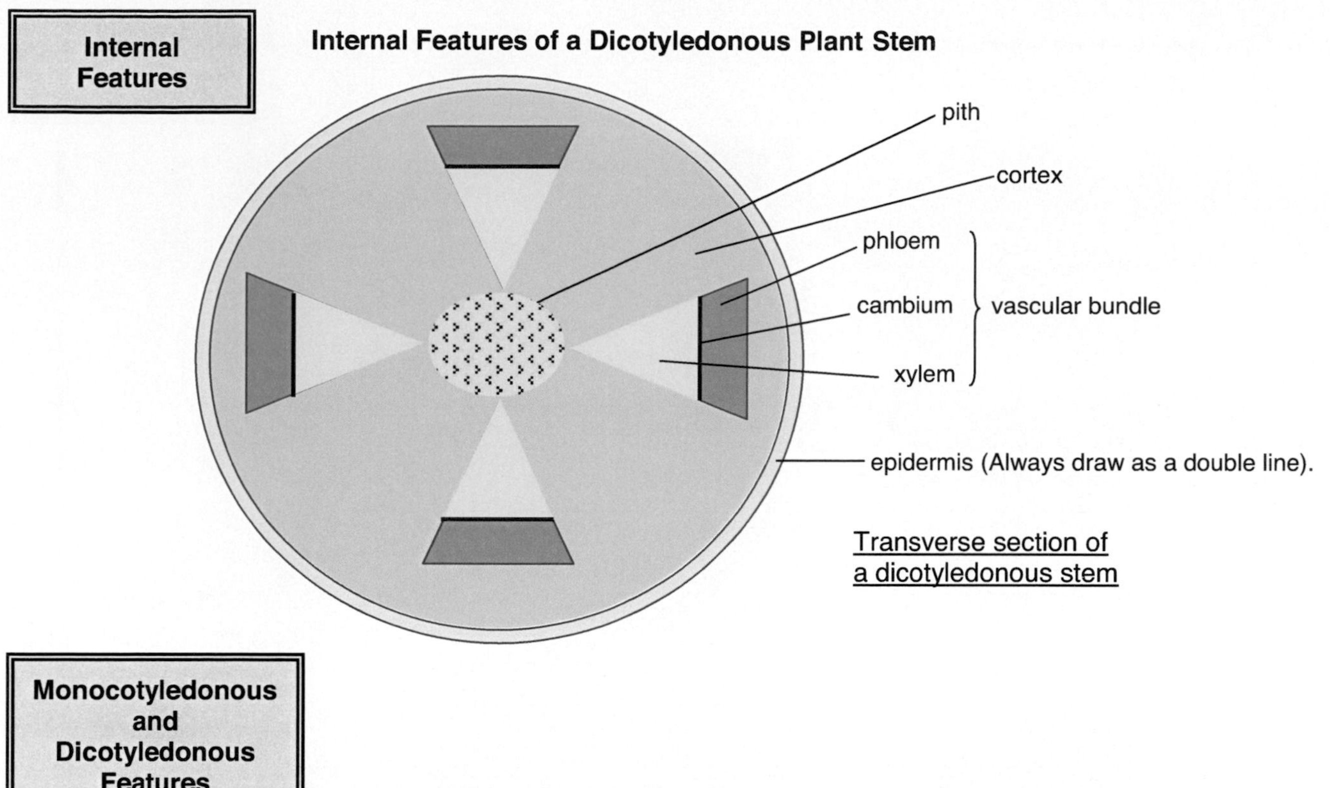
pith
cortex
phloem
cambium
xylem
vascular bundle
epidermis (Always draw as a double line).

Transverse section of a dicotyledonous stem

Monocotyledonous and Dicotyledonous Features

Differences between Monocotyledonous and Dicotyledonous Plants

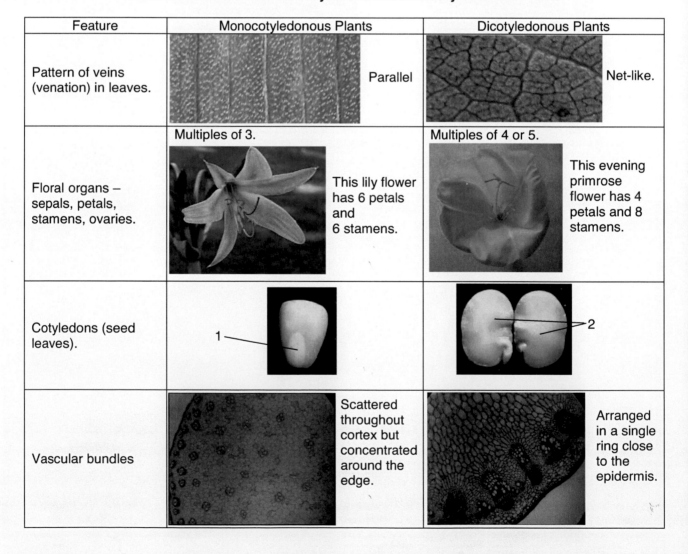

Feature	Monocotyledonous Plants	Dicotyledonous Plants
Pattern of veins (venation) in leaves.	Parallel	Net-like.
Floral organs – sepals, petals, stamens, ovaries.	Multiples of 3. This lily flower has 6 petals and 6 stamens.	Multiples of 4 or 5. This evening primrose flower has 4 petals and 8 stamens.
Cotyledons (seed leaves).	1	2
Vascular bundles	Scattered throughout cortex but concentrated around the edge.	Arranged in a single ring close to the epidermis.

Leaf Structure

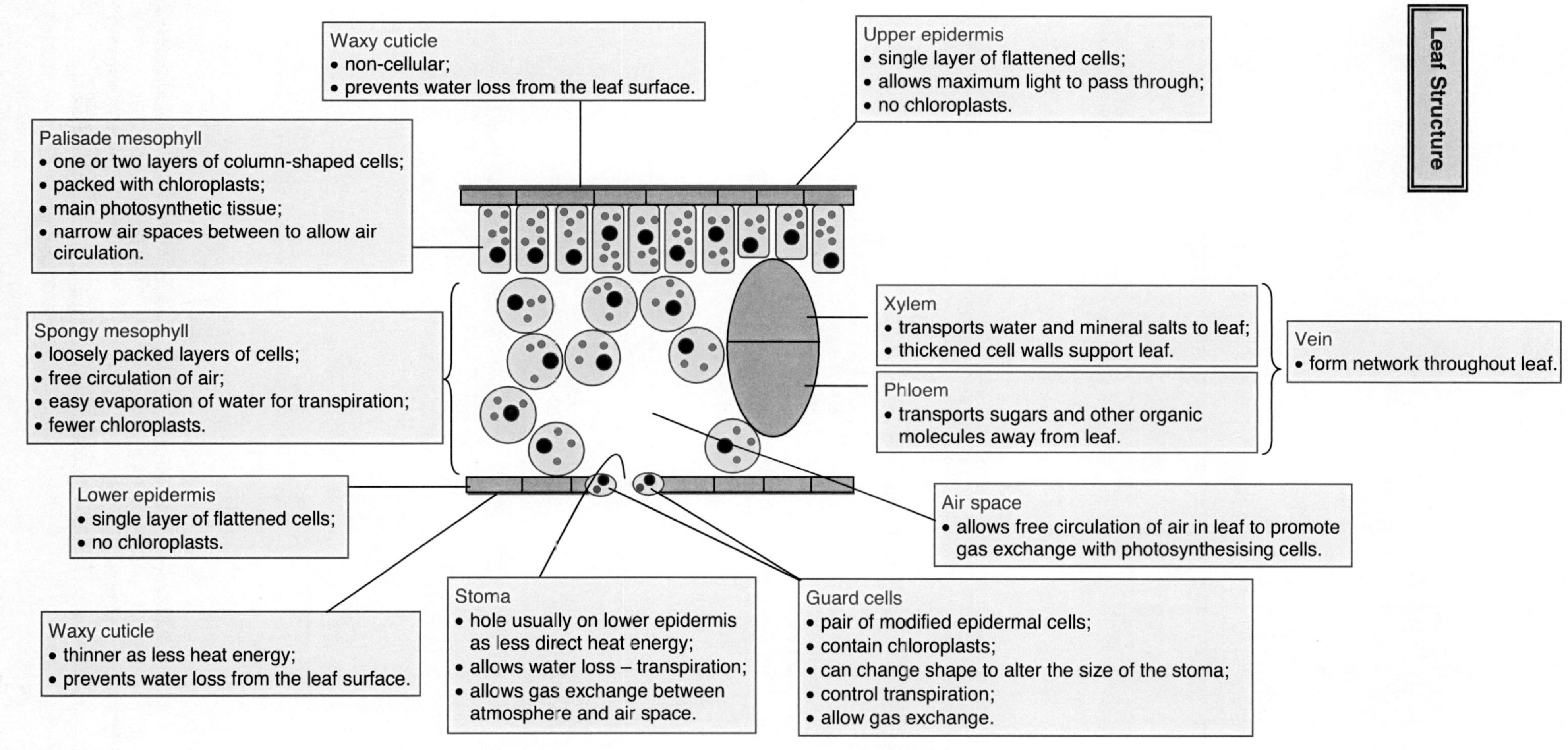

Waxy cuticle
• non-cellular;
• prevents water loss from the leaf surface.
Upper epidermis
• single layer of flattened cells;
• allows maximum light to pass through;
• no chloroplasts.
Palisade mesophyll
• one or two layers of column-shaped cells;
• packed with chloroplasts;
• main photosynthetic tissue;
• narrow air spaces between to allow air circulation.
Spongy mesophyll
• loosely packed layers of cells;
• free circulation of air;
• easy evaporation of water for transpiration;
• fewer chloroplasts.
Xylem
• transports water and mineral salts to leaf;
• thickened cell walls support leaf.
Phloem
• transports sugars and other organic molecules away from leaf.
Vein
• form network throughout leaf.
Lower epidermis
• single layer of flattened cells;
• no chloroplasts.
Air space
• allows free circulation of air in leaf to promote gas exchange with photosynthesising cells.
Waxy cuticle
• thinner as less heat energy;
• prevents water loss from the leaf surface.
Stoma
• hole usually on lower epidermis as less direct heat energy;
• allows water loss – transpiration;
• allows gas exchange between atmosphere and air space.
Guard cells
• pair of modified epidermal cells;
• contain chloroplasts;
• can change shape to alter the size of the stoma;
• control transpiration;
• allow gas exchange.

Vertical Section of Dicotyledonous Leaf with Functions of Regions

Modifications of Roots, Stems and Leaves

Modifications of Roots, Stems and Leaves

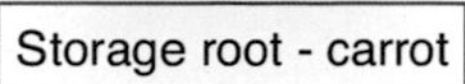

Storage root - carrot

In both of these either the root or stem is swollen and the cortex cells are packed with starch grains and other nutrients.

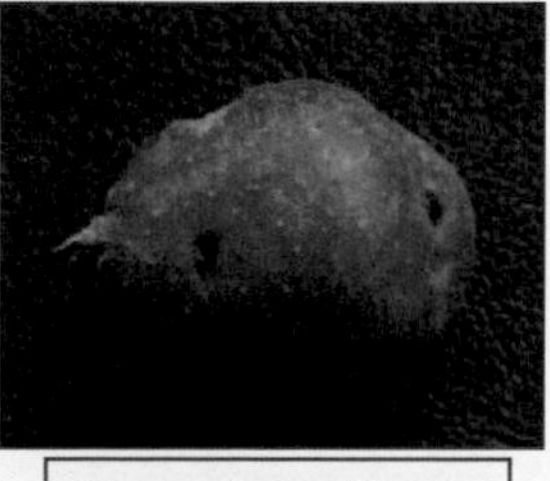

Stem tuber - Potato

Bulb – onion. This is made up of layers of leaf bases that have swollen up and the cells are packed with starch grains and other nutrients. There is only a tiny amount of chlorophyll as this is not needed.

Tendrils - Sweet Pea. The tendrils are modified leaves which, when they touch a surface, curl around and so help support the plant.

Growth from Meristems

Growth from Meristems

Dicotyledonous plants have apical and lateral meristems.

Key similarities

- Meristematic tissue contains small unspecialised cells that can undergo mitosis;
- After cytokinesis one cell differentiates and the other remains in the meristem;
- They result in growth of the plant;

Key differences

- Apical meristems are found at the shoot and root tips;
- They result in growth in length of the shoot or root;
- Lateral meristems are the strips of cambium in the vascular bundles (see page 158);
- They result in growth of diameter of the shoot or root.

Phototropism

Phototropism

Be careful not to confuse tropism with trophic as in trophic level.

Key points

- Phototropism is growth of the plant either towards or away from a directional source of light;
- Shoots generally show a positive phototropic response, ie they bend towards the light;
- The value of this is that it may bring the leaves into a better position for photosynthesis;
- Roots, if they show a response, are generally negatively phototropic;
- It is controlled by the plant growth regulator called auxin;
- Auxin stimulates growth by increasing the length of cells behind the apical meristem;
- The precise mechanism is unclear. It may be that auxin accumulates on the shaded side which stimulates more growth than on the illuminated side, or that the light stimulates the synthesis of auxin inhibitors on the illuminated side so growth is slower.
- Auxins can be used artificially, such as in rooting powders to stimulate growth of roots in cuttings.

The Root System

The Root System

Key points

Roots have large surface area for water and mineral ion uptake due to –

- a large amount of branching;
- root tips covered with large numbers of fine root hairs – extensions of epidermal cells.

Entry of Mineral Ions

1. Diffusion;
2. Mass flow;
3. Active transport;
4. Mutualistic fungal hyphae.

Notes.

1. Remember that this has to be facilitated diffusion.
2. As water moves into the root by osmosis the dissolved mineral ions are carried in this flow. This is called mass flow.
3. Active transport requires specific integral protein channels and energy from ATP. (See page 16).
4. Many species of fungi grow on roots and the relationship is mutualistic, ie both the fungus and the host plant benefit. The benefit to the plant is that the fungus, through fine thread-like structures called hyphae, has a very large surface area for taking up mineral ions and most of these are passed on to the plant.

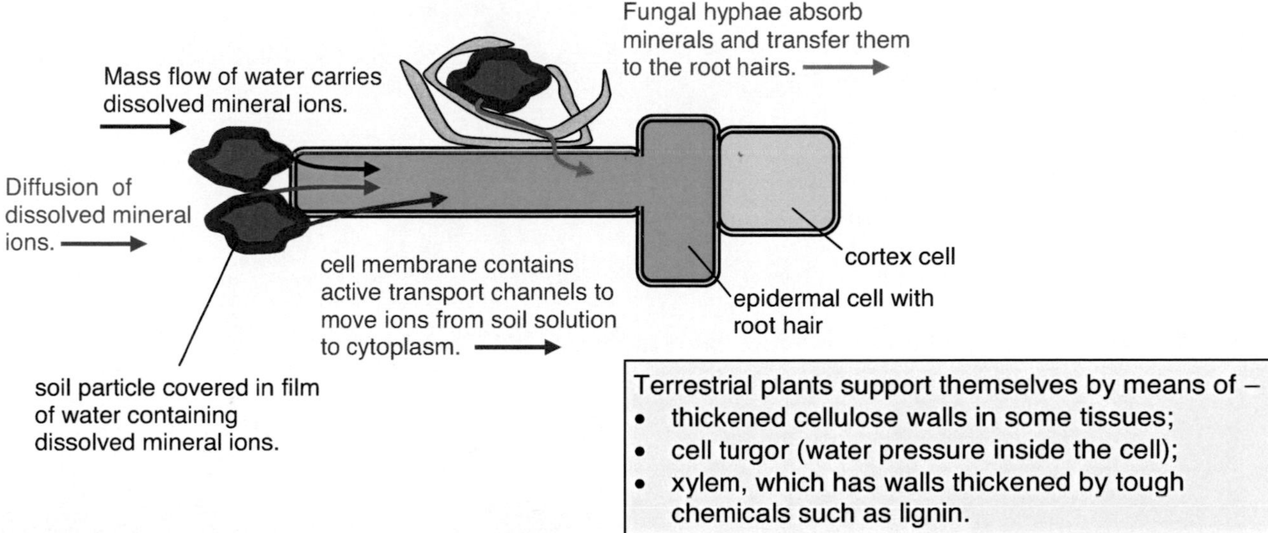
Fungal hyphae absorb minerals and transfer them to the root hairs.
Mass flow of water carries dissolved mineral ions.
Diffusion of dissolved mineral ions.
cell membrane contains active transport channels to move ions from soil solution to cytoplasm.
cortex cell
epidermal cell with root hair
soil particle covered in film of water containing dissolved mineral ions.

Terrestrial plants support themselves by means of –

- thickened cellulose walls in some tissues;
- cell turgor (water pressure inside the cell);
- xylem, which has walls thickened by tough chemicals such as lignin.

Revision Monocots and dicots

Complete the shaded boxes

Feature	Monocotyledonous Plants	Dicotyledonous Plants
Pattern of veins (venation) in leaves.		
Number of floral organs – sepals, petals, stamens, ovaries.		
Number of cotyledons (seed leaves).		
Type of root system.		

What is meristematic tissue?

Name the two meristematic regions in dicotyledonous plants.

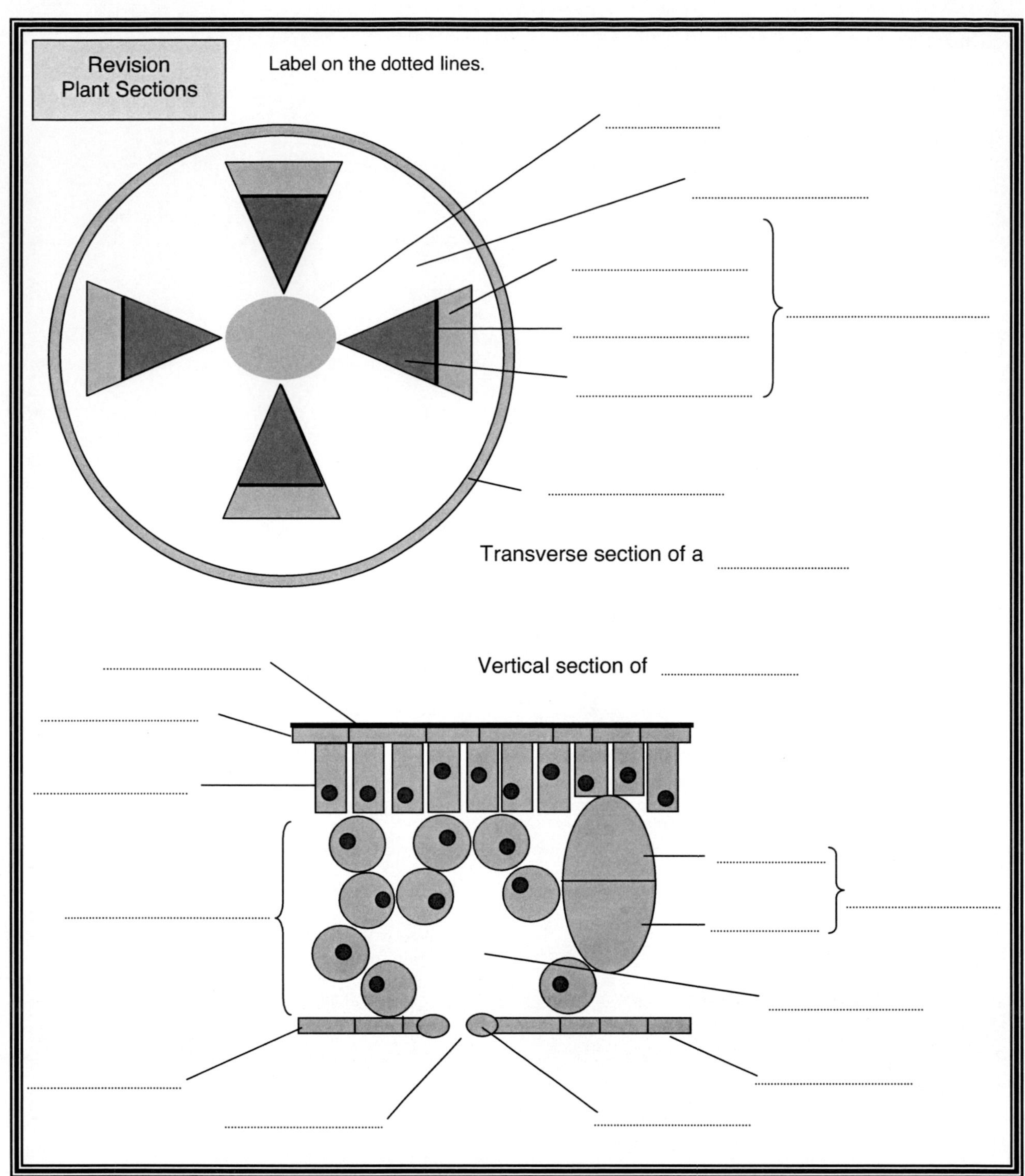
Revision
Plant Sections
Label on the dotted lines.
Transverse section of a
Vertical section of

Name the process when light shining on one side of a plant causes growth towards the light.	Name the plant growth regulator that controls this pattern of growth.

List 3 ways terrestrial plants support themselves.

State the 2 ways the root system provides a large surface area.

List 4 ways mineral ions move from soil to root.

Water Transport in a Plant

Water Transport through the Plant

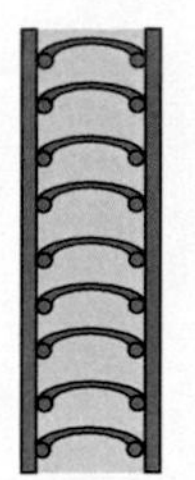

Vertical section through a typical xylem vessel, showing thickened walls and rings of thickening.

2 Water evaporates from the surface of the spongy mesophyll cells into the air spaces and then leaves via the stomata. As a molecule evaporates it pulls another molecule behind it. This transpiration pull extends to the xylem vessels in the veins of the leaf and stem.

3 Water is pulled up the stem in xylem vessels as the transpiration stream. The water molecules are held together by hydrogen bonds. (Refer back to page 27). This is called cohesion and is a very powerful force as the columns of water in tall trees are continuous. The strengthening in the walls of the xylem vessels is necessary to prevent them collapsing. (Same principle as the supporting cartilage in the air passages to the lungs). Also water molecules adhere to the sides of the xylem vessels and other cells, and this adhesion creates a strong force which holds up the considerable mass of water.

1 Water enters roots through osmotic uptake by root hairs.
This creates root pressure that pushes water a short distance up the stem.
The root hairs create a large surface area.

Guard cells can absorb or lose water. This allows them to regulate transpiration by altering the size of the stoma.

The plant growth regulator (hormone) abscisic acid causes the closing of stomata.

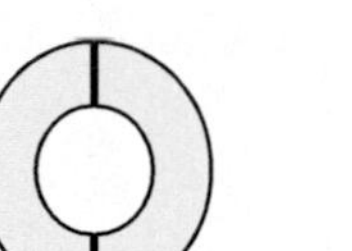

Guard cells gain water:
- stoma large
- transpiration high.

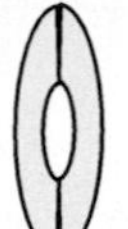

Guard cells lose water:
- stoma small
- transpiration low.

Plant hormones are now called plant growth regulators.

Transpiration

Abiotic Factors Affecting Transpiration

Factor	Effect on Transpiration	Mechanism
Increasing light	Increases	▪ Guard cells gain water, enlarging stoma.
Increasing temperature	Increases	▪ More water evorates from spongy mesophyll cells; ▪ Humidity is decreased; ▪ Rate of diffusion through stomata increased.
Increasing wind	Increases	▪ Regions of air around stomata saturated with water vapour are blown away; ▪ Diffusion gradient increased.
Increasing humidity	Decreases	▪ Diffusion gradient through the stomata decreased.

Define transpiration

Xerophytes

Adaptations of Xerophytes	
Rolled leaves	These roll downwards so enclosing the stomata, which reduces transpiration.
Thick waxy cuticle	This reduces uncontrolled evaporation of water from the leaf's surface.
Water storage	Increased amount of cortex tissue that can store water. This often contains a bitter tasting chemical to prevent animals drinking it.
Deep roots	Absorb water from deep sources.

Translocation

Phloem Transport - Translocation

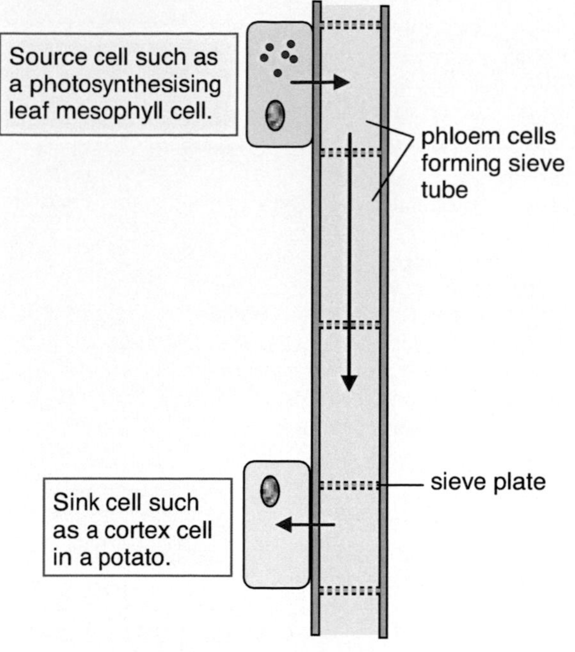
Source cell such as a photosynthesising leaf mesophyll cell.
phloem cells forming sieve tube
sieve plate
Sink cell such as a cortex cell in a potato.

Key features

- Phloem cells form long sieve tubes;
- Nuclei and most other organelles lost;
- Modified cytoplasm remains;
- Plasma membrane remains;
- End wall partially dissolved forming sieve plate;

Mechanism

- Solutes such as sucrose and amino acids from the source cell actively transported into the sieve tube; ⟶
- This creates an osmotic gradient so water (from xylem) enters the sieve tube increasing pressure;
- Solutes from the sieve tube actively transported out into the sink cell and converted to, eg. starch; ⟵
- This creates an osmotic gradient so water leaves the sieve tube decreasing pressure;
- The pressure gradient within the sieve tube causes a pressure flow from source to sink. ↓
- This can work in either direction, ie the source can be below ground eg. a root cell or seed, and the sink at the growing shoot tip or developing fruit.

Outline 4 adaptations shown by xerophytes.

State the role of stomata.	Name the leaf cells that form the stoma.	Name the hormone that causes the closing of stomata.	What is mass flow?

What is the effect on transpiration of – increasing light intensity? increasing humidity? increasing temperature? increasing wind speed?	What is the reason for each of your answers?

Flower Structure

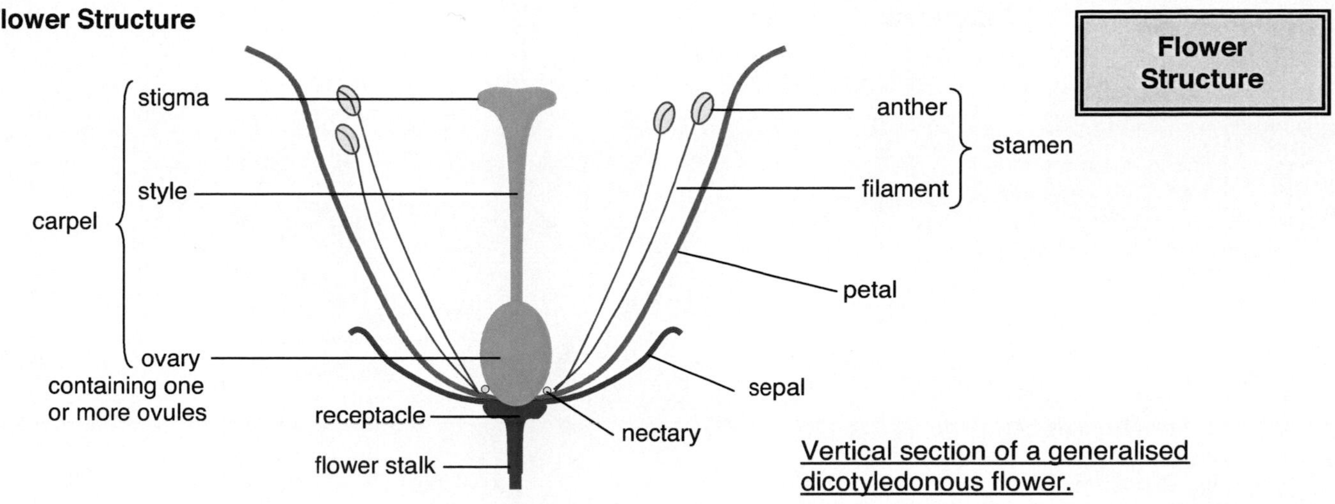
stigma
style
carpel
ovary
containing one
or more ovules
receptacle
flower stalk
nectary
sepal
petal
anther
filament
stamen

Vertical section of a generalised dicotyledonous flower.

Flower Structure

Pollination, Fertilisation, Seed Dispersal

Pollination	Fertilisation	Seed Dispersal
Transfer of pollen from an anther to the stigma.	Fusion of a male gamete from the pollen grain with a female gamete in an ovule inside the ovary.	Spreading the seeds away from the parent plant.

A Dicotyledonous Seed

Seed Structure

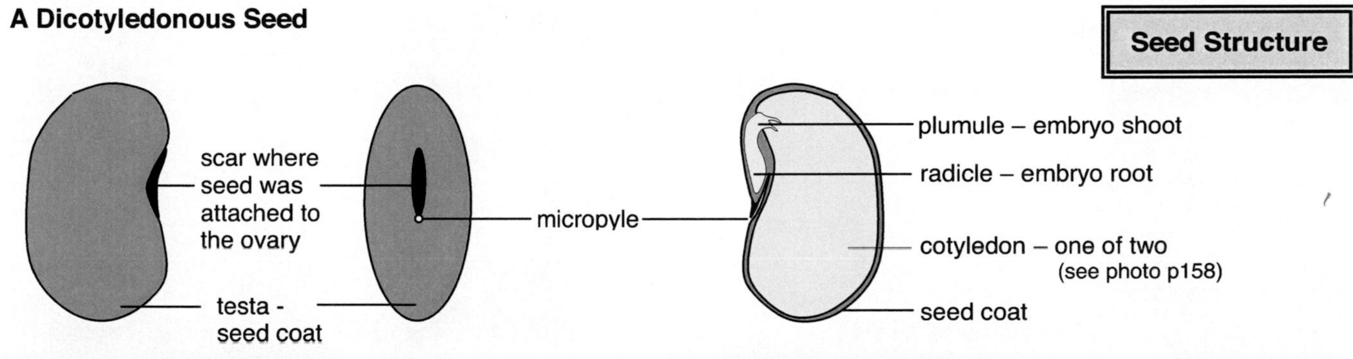
scar where
seed was
attached to
the ovary
testa -
seed coat
micropyle
plumule – embryo shoot
radicle – embryo root
cotyledon – one of two
(see photo p158)
seed coat

External structure

Internal structure

Examples : Garden pea, *Pisum sativum*
Broad bean, *Vicia faba*

What is translocation?

Is translocation an active or passive process?

In translocation what is meant by a source? State two examples.

In translocation what is meant by a sink? State two examples.

Name the process by which sugars and amino acids are moved into and out of the phloem.

Germination

Germination

4
These nutrient molecules then diffuse into the embryo and are used by the embryo for energy and growth.

↑

3
These enzymes digest the stored protein and starch in the endosperm releasing small nutrient molecules such as amino acids and maltose.

↑

2
The gibberellins diffuse into the aleurone layer where they stimulate the synthesis of amylase and protease enzymes.

↑

1
The seed absorbs water through the micropyle (imbibition) and this causes secretion from the cotyledon of plant growth regulators (hormones) called gibberellins.

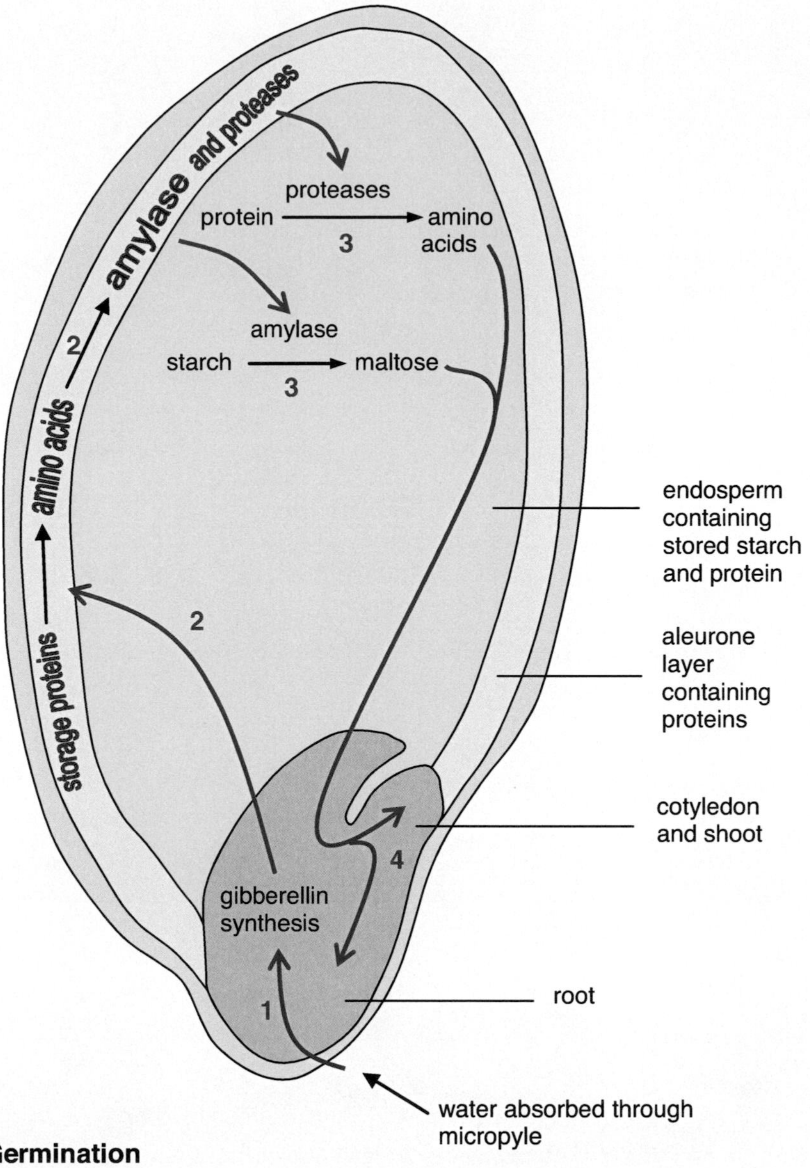

Conditions for Germination

1. Moisture
   See number 1 in the above diagram.
   Seeds dry out for dispersal. At germination the cells need to rehydrate so that metabolic reactions can take place.

2. Warmth
   Many of the metabolic events of germination use enzymes. These are sensitive to temperature. Temperature is often used as a trigger for germination – eg many seeds from temperate climates only germinate after being exposed to cold temperatures for several days before being given warmer temperatures. Hence they germinate in Spring.

3. Oxygen
   Many of the metabolic events of germination use energy. This is produced by aerobic respiration.

Control of Flowering

Key points

- Plants can be divided into two groups – long-day and short-day;
- This is controlled by phytochrome;
- There are two forms of phytochrome – P_r which absorbs red light and P_{fr} which absorbs far red light;
- In red or white light P_r is <u>rapidly</u> converted to P_{fr};
- In darkness P_{fr} is <u>gradually</u> converted back to P_r;
- P_{fr} promotes flowering in long-day plants;
- P_{fr} inhibits flowering in short-day plants.

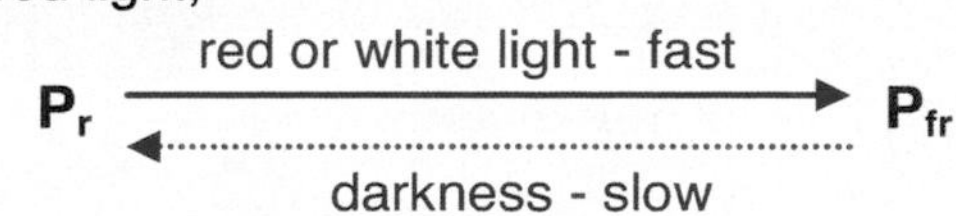
red or white light - fast
P_r
P_{fr}
darkness - slow

Lets see how this works.

Light period	Dark period	Quantity of P_r	Quantity of P_{fr}	Flowering
Long P_r converted to P_{fr} rapidly	Short Not much of the P_{fr} is converted back to P_r	Low	High	Long-day plants will flower. Short-day plants inhibited from flowering.

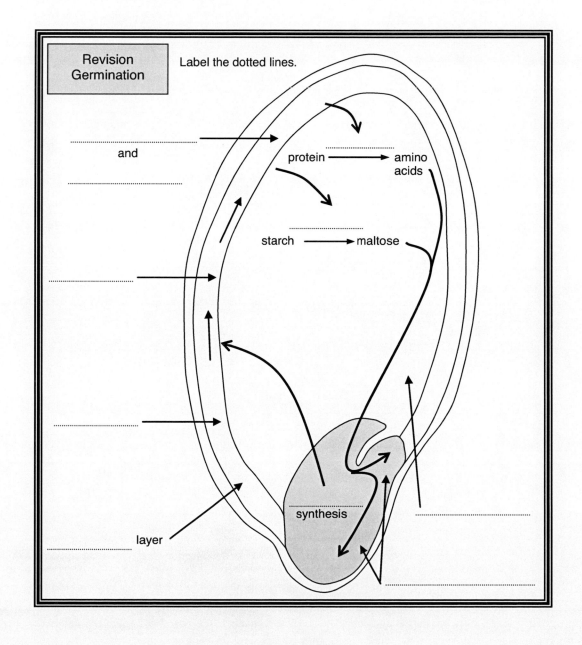

Revision Germination

Label the dotted lines.

.... and ....
protein → amino acids
....
starch → maltose
....
....
.... synthesis
....
.... layer
....

Revision
Flower Structure

Label the flower parts where indicated.

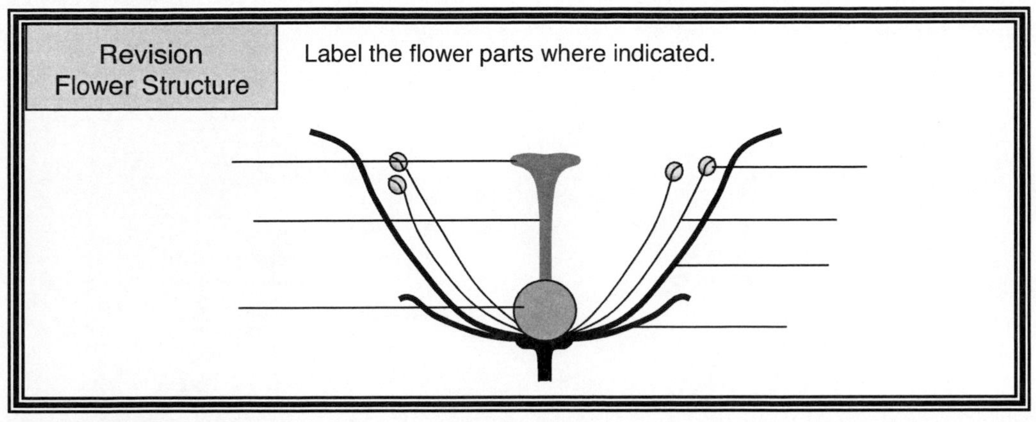

Revision
Seed Structure

Label the dotted lines.

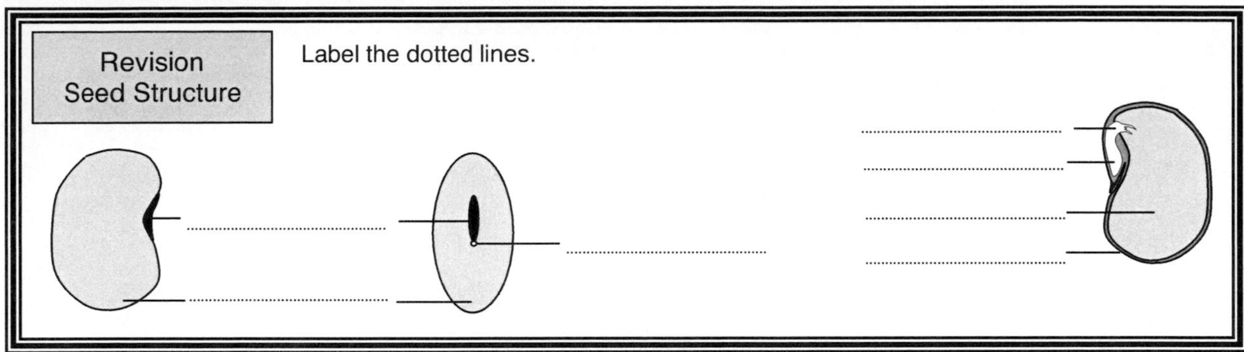

Distinguish between pollination and fertilisation.

What is seed dispersal?

List three conditions for seed germination.

What is the role of water when it is absorbed at the start of the germination process?

Name a dicotyledonous seed.

Why does a seed need warmth for germination?

Why does a seed need oxygen for germination?

Name the substance that controls flowering.

What happens when P_r absorbs red or white light?

What happens to P_{fr} in the dark?

Which group of plants flower when there is a high level P_{fr}?

Self-test Quiz on Topic 9

1. Which of the following statements is correct.
   a. Monocotyledons have flowering parts in 3s and dicotyledons have them in 4s or 5s.
   b. Monocotyledons have flowering parts in 4s or 5s and dicotyledons have them in 3s
   c. Leaf veins in both monocotyledons and dicotyledons are net-like.
   d. Dicotyledons have fibrous root systems.

2. The function of meristems is to
   a. generate new cells for growth.
   b. transport water within the plant.
   c. provide support in the stem,
   d. keep the plant happy.

3. A xerophyte is type of plant that
   a. possesses modified xylem tissue,
   b. loses its leaves in winter,
   c. has a reduced rate of photosynthesis,
   d. is adapted to dry conditions.

4. Water is taken into a plant
   a. through active uptake by the xylem tissue,
   b. through water loss as a result of respiration in the root cells,
   c. by osmosis through the root hairs,
   d. by the active removal of water causing transpiration in the leaves.

5. Which of the following statements about meristems is correct?
   a. Apical meristems protect the root as it grows through the soil.
   b. Lateral meristems produce new leaves.
   c. Lateral meristems bring about growth in diameter of the stems and roots.
   d. Apical meristems control translocation.

6. In a generalised dicotyledonous leaf the cells with the greatest number of chloroplasts are
   a. epidermal cells,
   b. palisade mesophyll cells,
   c. spongy mesophyll cells,
   d. guard cells.

7. Which of the following is not used to support a plant?
   a. Cell turgor.
   b. Thickened cellulose walls.
   c. Xylem.
   d. Epidermis.

8. Which of the following drawings represents a correctly labelled vertical section of a stem?

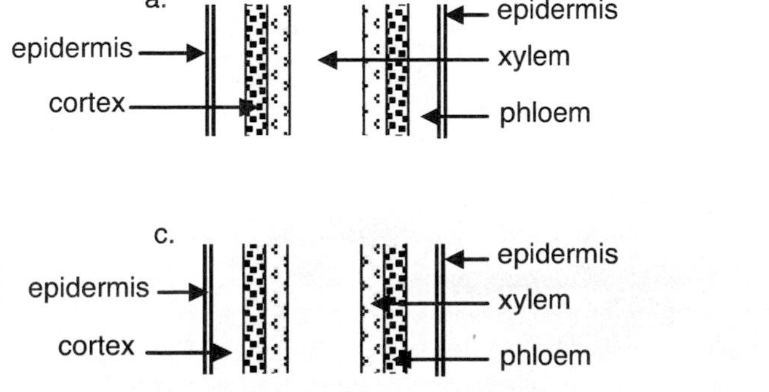

a.
epidermis
cortex
epidermis
xylem
phloem
c.
epidermis
cortex
epidermis
xylem
phloem

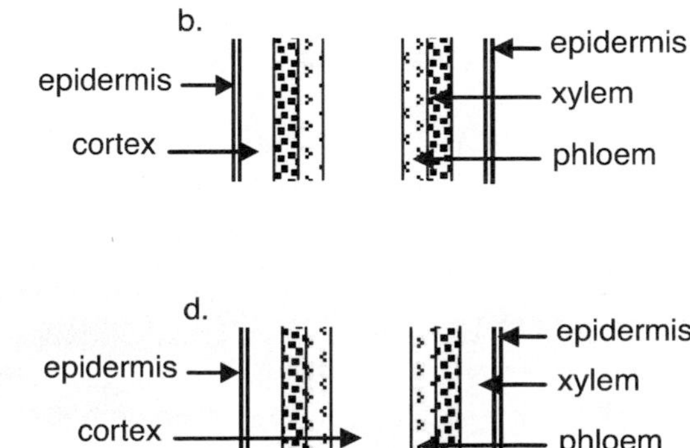

b.
epidermis
cortex
epidermis
xylem
phloem
d.
epidermis
cortex
epidermis
xylem
phloem

9. Which of the following is the best definition for transpiration?
    a. The loss of water vapour from the leaves and stem of the plant.
    b. The movement of water into the leaves of the plant.
    c. The transport of water through the phloem tissue.
    d. The uptake of water via the root hairs of the plant.

10. Translocation is best described as
    a. transport of food substances up the stem from storage cells in the root,
    b. loss of water vapour from the leaves of a plant,
    c. transport of biochemicals within the plant using energy,
    d. uptake of water from the roots via root hairs.

11. Which of the following statements is correct?
    a. The plant hormone abscisic acid stimulates photosynthesis in the leaves.
    b. The plant hormone auxin stimulates growth of the shoot towards light.
    c. Stimulation of the lateral meristems by light increases growth in diameter of the plant.
    d. Light reduces the growth inhibiting effect of auxin.

12. Which of the following statements is correct?
    a. Fertilisation is growth of the pollen on the stigma of the flower.
    b. Pollination is transfer of the male gamete to the ovule.
    c. Pollination is transfer of pollen from anther to stigma.
    d. Fertilisation is growth of the seed from the ovum.

13. Which of the following statements correctly describes seed dispersal?
    a. The transfer of seeds from anther to stigma.
    b. Formation of seeds from the ovules within the ovary.
    c. Release and spreading of seed from the parent plant.
    d. Growth of seeds following absorption of water.

14. During germination of a typical starchy seed which is the correct sequence of events?
    a. Water absorbed; amylase synthesised; gibberellins secreted; starch broken down to maltose.
    b. Water absorbed; proteins broken down to amino acids; gibberellins secreted; starch synthesised.
    c. Water absorbed; starch broken down to maltose; gibberellins synthesised; starch synthesised.
    d. Water absorbed; gibberellins secreted; amylase synthesised; starch broken down to maltose.

15. Which statement correctly describes a difference between transport cells in xylem tissue and phloem tissue.
    a. Xylem cells have completely lost their end walls but phloem cells still have an end wall.
    b. Xylem cells contained a modified cytoplasm but phloem cells contain normal cytoplasm.
    c. The nucleus in xylem cells is non-functional but the nucleus in phloem cells is important in regulating active transport.
    d. Phloem cells have thickened cellulose walls to assist in support.

16. Which of the following leaf cell types does <u>not</u> contain chloroplasts?
    a. Epidermis cells.
    b. Guard cells.
    c. Palisade mesophyll cells.
    d. Spongy mesophyll cells.

17. Which of the following statements about the control of flowering is correct?
    a. Long day plants flower because long days result in a high concentration of P_r.
    b. Long day plants flower because long days result in a high concentration of P_{fr}.
    c. P_{fr} causes flowering in long day plants because sunlight changes it to P_r.
    d. Short day plants flower because high levels of P_{fr} block the effect of P_r.

Topic 10

Genetics

AHL Genetics Introduction

AHL Genetics - Introduction

The major difference between HL and SL genetics is that SL dealt only with monohybrid crosses, that is crosses involving only one gene. Now we have to deal with a range of situations involving two characteristics, that is two genes, in an individual, eg brown hair <u>and</u> blue eyes. These are called dihybrid crosses.

What is an autosome?

Key point

- The two genes may be on separate chromosome pairs or together on the same chromosome pair. This second situation is called linkage simply because the genes are "linked" together.

The homologous pairs of chromosomes below illustrate these two situations.

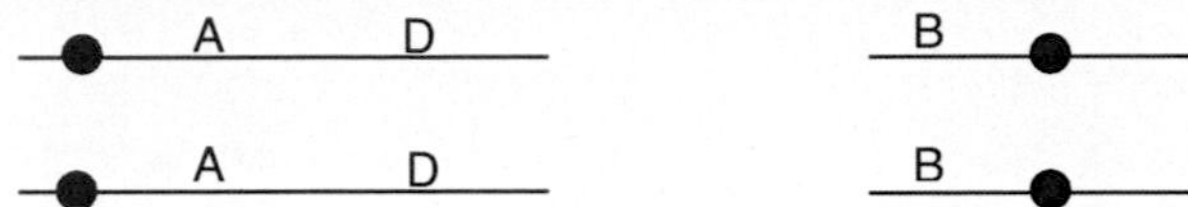
A D
A D
B
B

Here we have two pairs of homologous chromosomes, one pair carrying the genes A and D, and the other pair carrying the gene B. Genes A and B are unlinked as are genes D and B and they will assort independently. Genes A and D are however linked and will not assort independently.

Linkage in genetics problems will be covered later.

Representing Genotypes

Representing Genotypes

In a monohybrid cross the genotypes containing two alleles were represented as AA or Aa or aa. In a dihybrid cross four alleles are represented and consequently there are nine possible genotypes.

AABB	AaBB	aaBB
AABb	AaBb	aaBb
AAbb	Aabb	aabb

These are parental genotypes. What happens about gametes? The key point is that meiosis halves the number of chromosomes. Hence when the parent has four alleles the gamete has two alleles, <u>one</u> from <u>each</u> pair.

Parental genotype	Gametes	Number of types of gamete
AABB	AB	1
AAbb	Ab	1
aaBB	aB	1
aabb	ab	1
AaBB	AB and aB	2
Aabb	Ab and ab	2
AABb	AB and Ab	2
aaBb	aB and ab	2
AaBb	AB and Ab and aB and ab	4

Note the number of types of gamete. This is helpful in problem solving which will be dealt with later. Note also it is number of **types**; for genotype AABB you do not need to write gamete AB twice or four times – they are all the same and it wastes time in exams.

In the above examples the genotype letters have been written in a line. An alternative format is <u>A</u> <u>B</u>
A B

You will see that this resembles their positions on the homologous chromosomes, the short lines representing the locus on the chromosomes. Note that there are two separate lines because A and B are on two separate chromosomes. The great value of this format is that it can show visually whether the genes are linked or not, and if they are linked, in what way. Take the linked genes A and D, and the genotype AaDd.

In this format, AaDd, you cannot tell if A and D are linked on the same chromosome, or A and d are linked on the same chromosome. If you use the alternative format you can.

$\frac{A\ D}{a\ d}$ $\frac{A\ d}{a\ D}$ The continuous lines again represent the chromosome, so that in the first situation A is linked to D on the same chromosome, and in the second situation A is linked to d on the same chromosome. This point is absolutely crucial to linkage problems.

> This is the format that will be used in exams and so you must use it too.

Meiosis

Meiosis

Phase	Key Points
Prophase I	Supercoiling of chromosomes. Replicated chromosomes pair up in their homologous pairs to form a bivalent. Crossing over may occur.*[1] Spindle fibre network of microtubules start to form. Nuclear envelope begins to break down.
Metaphase I	Spindle fibre network complete. Bivalents line up on equator in a random way.*[2] Centromere attached to microtubules.
Anaphase I	Microtubules contract separating homologous pairs to opposite poles. Centromeres do **not** split.
Telophase I	These stages often merge with each other because they are opposite. The spindle fibre network breaks down and two new ones begin to form, often at right angles to the first one.
Cytokinesis I	*First cell division starts.*
Prophase II	
Metaphase II	Chromatids line up on equator. Centromeres attached to microtubules.
Anaphase II	Centromeres **do** split and sister chromosomes pulled to opposite poles.
Telophase II	Spindle fibre network breaks down. Nuclear envelope reforms. Chromosomes uncoil.
Cytokinesis II	*Second cell division into four haploid cells.*

*[1] and *[2] Both of these are important in producing genetic variety.

Since you have studied mitosis you already know most of meiosis. Meiosis has two phases, but the names are the same as in mitosis with I or II added. Likewise the key facts for each stage are very similar. I have kept the same pattern as in mitosis but indicated in blue where the five differences are.

Cell with two pairs of chromosomes

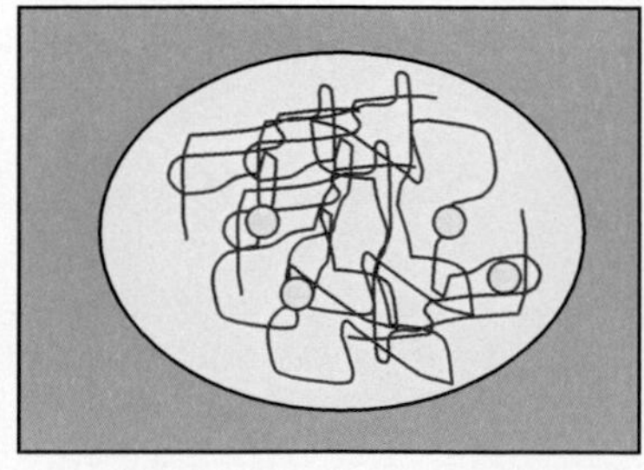

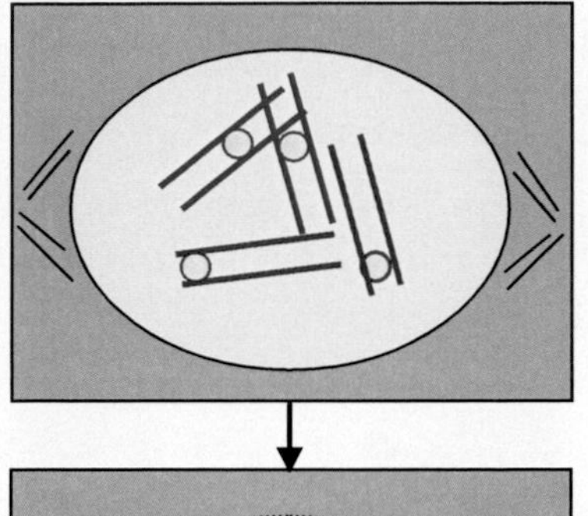

Prophase I

- Replicated DNA undergoes supercoiling and becomes visible under the light microscope;
- Spindle microtubules start to form;

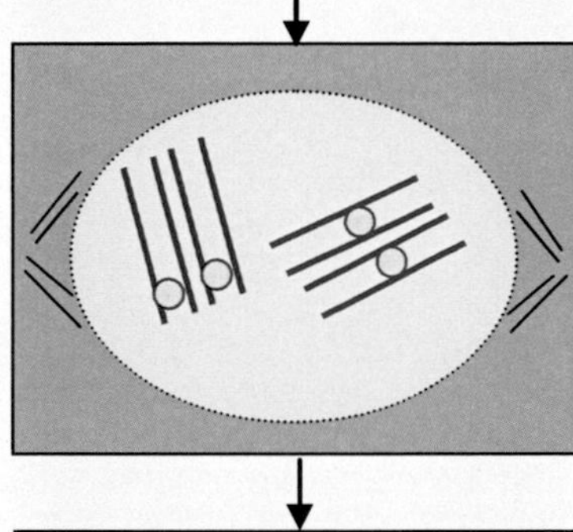

Later Prophase I

- Homologous chromosomes line up as pairs called bivalents. This is called synapsis. (This is a difference from mitosis).
- Crossing over may occur between non-sister chromatids within the bivalent leading to exchange of genetic material. (This is a difference from mitosis).
- Nuclear envelope breaks down.

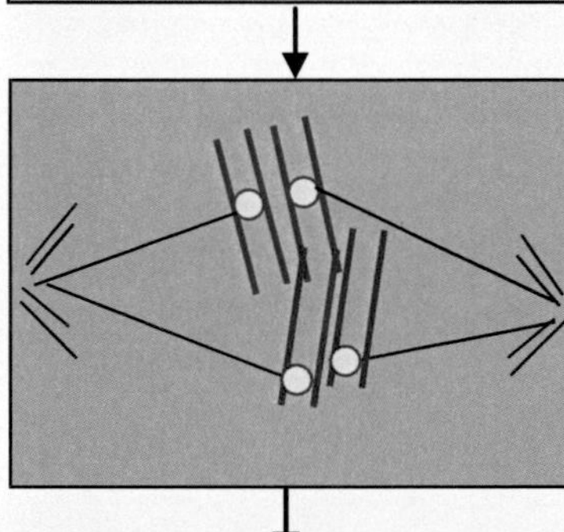

Metaphase I

- Microtubule network completed;
- Microtubules attach to centromeres;
- Bivalents move to central plate (equator) of cell. (This is a difference from mitosis).

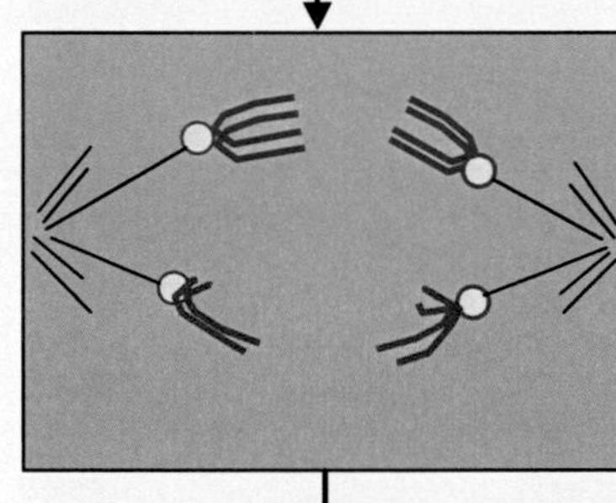

Anaphase I

- Centromeres do not split; (This is a difference from mitosis).
- Microtubules contract;
- Homologous chromosomes pulled to opposite poles. (This is a difference from mitosis).

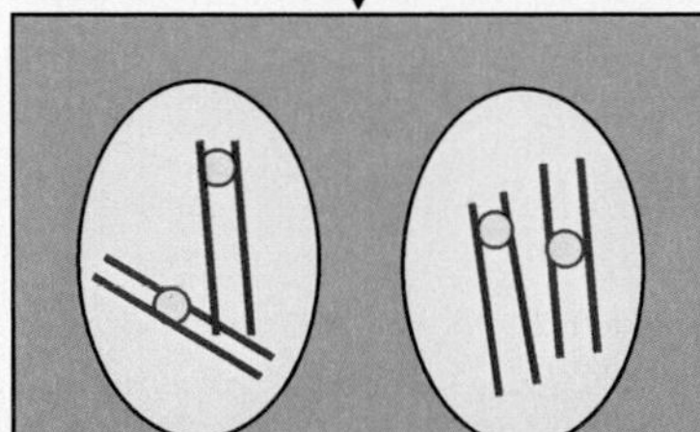

Telophase I

- Chromosomes uncoil;
- Spindle microtubules break down;
- Nuclear envelope reforms.

Note how each cell contains one chromosome from each homologous pair. The chromosome number has been halved so this is called a reduction division.

→ Second division
(There is no S phase)

Cytokinesis I

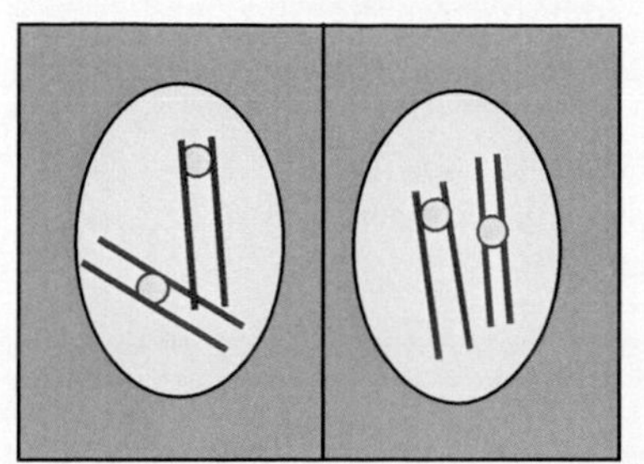

Each of these cells then undergoes the second division of meiosis.
Only one is shown below for simplicity.
The second division is very similar to mitosis.

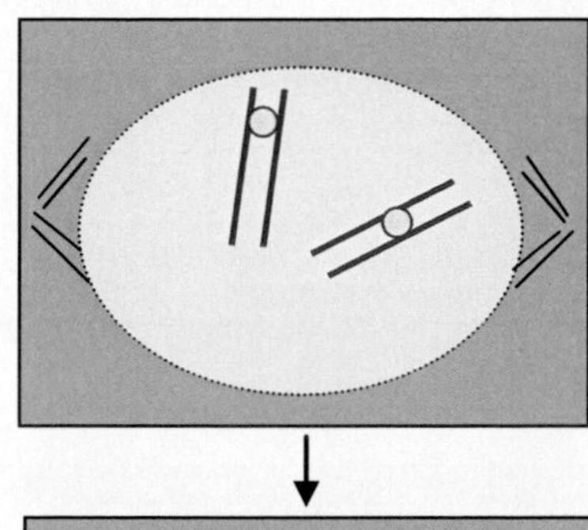

Prophase II

- The amount of supercoiling depends on the amount of uncoiling during telophase I;
- Spindle microtubules start to form;
- Nuclear envelope breaks down at end of prophase II.

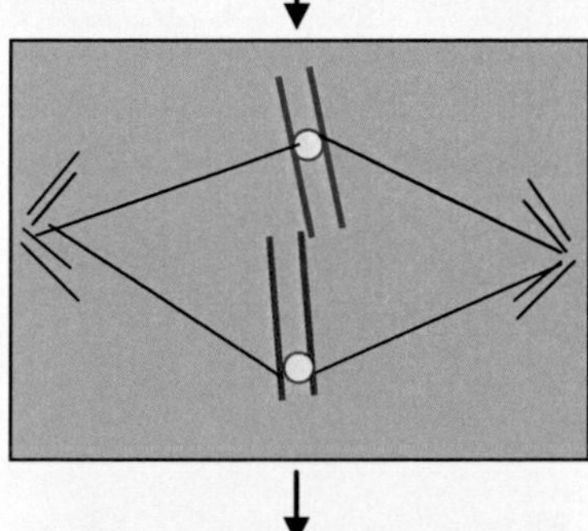

Metaphase II

- Chromosomes move to central plate (equator) of cell;
- Microtubule network completed;
- Microtubules attach to centromeres.

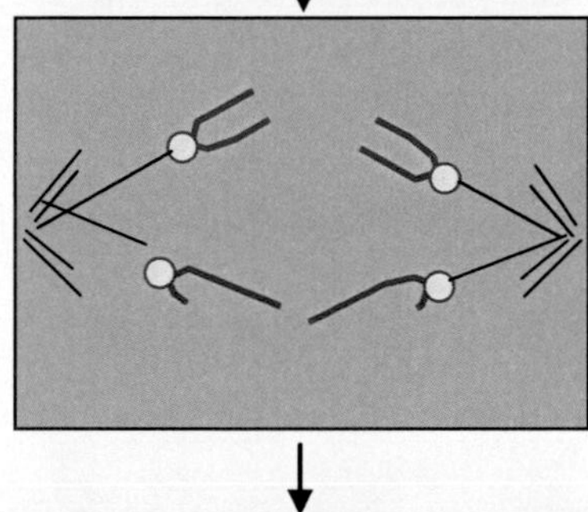

Anaphase II

- Centromeres **do** split;
- Microtubules contract;
- Chromosomes pulled to opposite poles.

A chromosome consists of a pair of sister chromatids, but as soon as the centromere splits the chromatids become chromosomes.

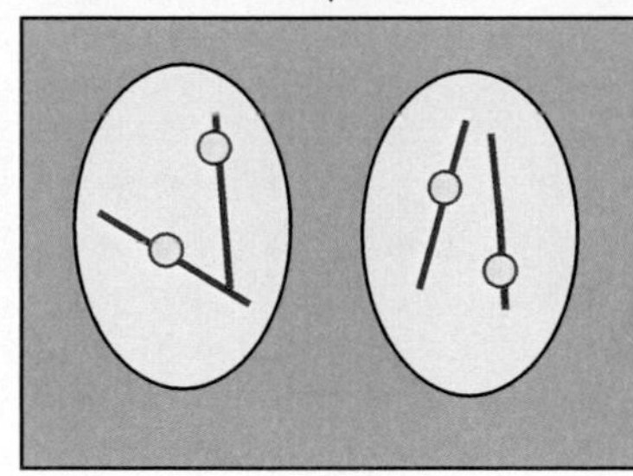

Telophase II

- Chromosomes uncoil;
- Spindle microtubules break down;
- Nuclear envelope reforms.

Cytokinesis II in both cells

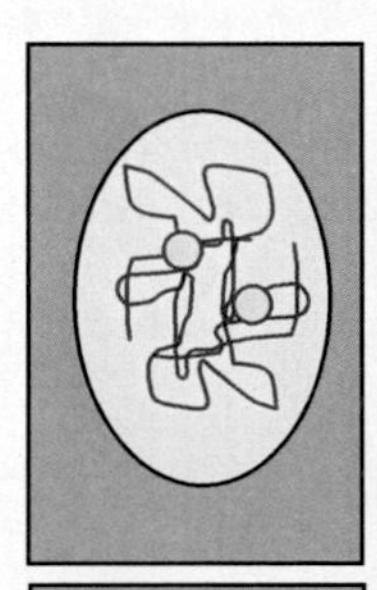

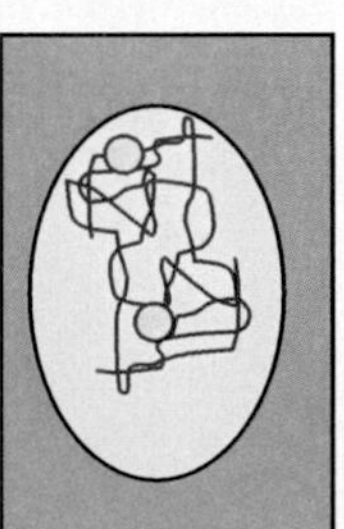

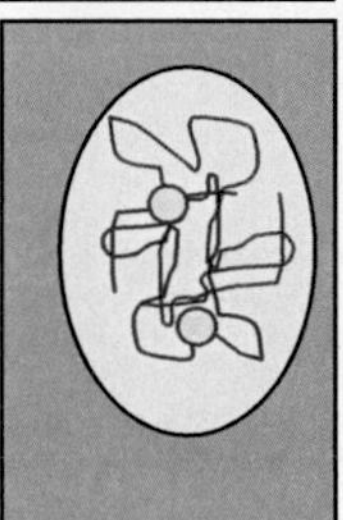

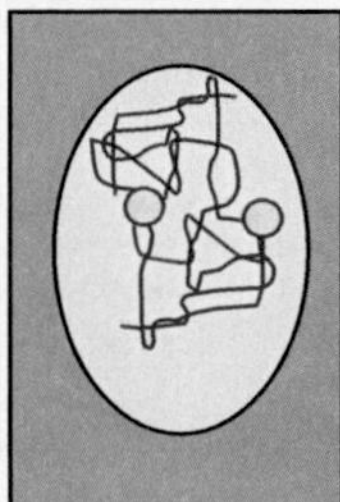

- <u>Four</u> cells from one original cell, each with one chromosome from each homologous pair.
- These are <u>haploid</u> cells.
- One or more may now undergo differentiation into gametes.
- In spermatogenesis all four differentiate into sperms.
- In oogenesis only one differentiates into a secondary oocyte.

Crossing Over

Crossing Over

The effect of this is to mix linked alleles .
We will start with the bivalent, the pair of homologous chromosomes that have replicated and lined up together.

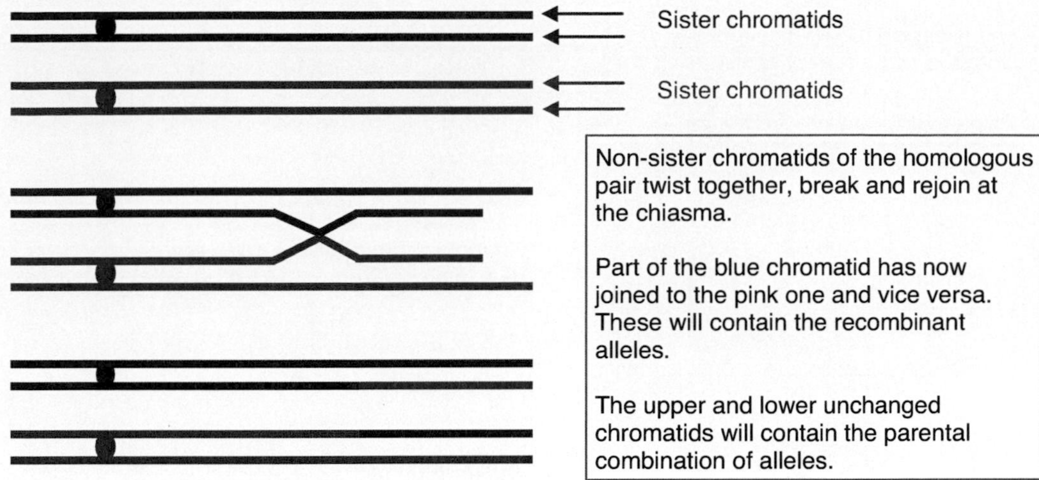
Sister chromatids
Sister chromatids
Non-sister chromatids of the homologous pair twist together, break and rejoin at the chiasma.
Part of the blue chromatid has now joined to the pink one and vice versa. These will contain the recombinant alleles.
The upper and lower unchanged chromatids will contain the parental combination of alleles.

How does this appear with actual alleles? We will use the genotype $\frac{A\ D}{a\ d}$.

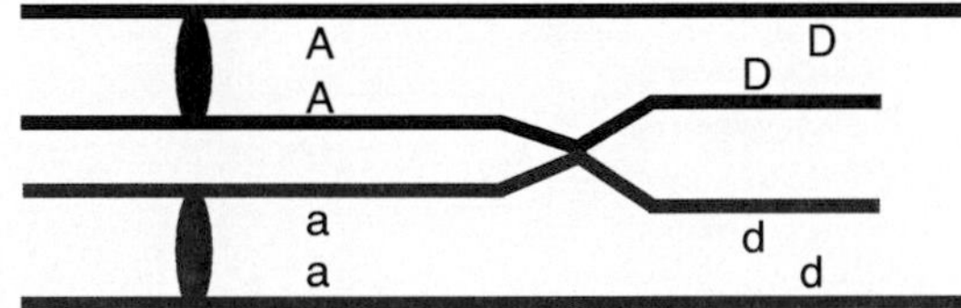
A
A
D
D
a
a
d
d

After completion of the crossing over process we get -

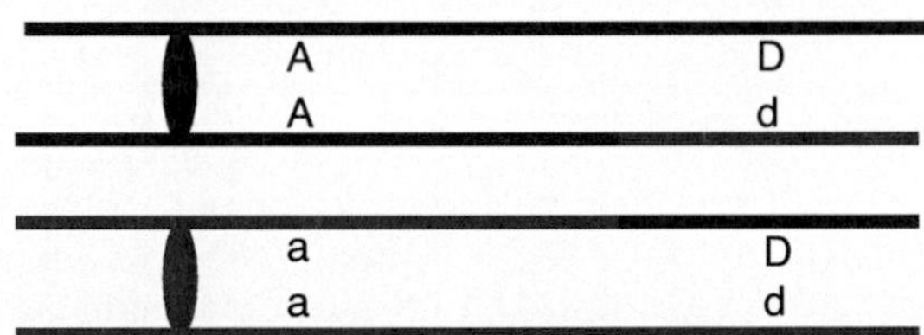
A
A
D
d
a
a
D
d

And finally after completion of meiosis we get the gametes containing AD; ad; Ad; aD – four different types. If you look back at the table on p172 and the genotype AaBb we get the similar four types of gamete. However, there is a crucial difference. The four types of gamete from AaBb are in equal proportions because the numbers are determined by the random positioning of the homologous pairs on the equator at metaphase I. (Refer to the section Mendel's Law of Independent Assortment on p178). With the linked genes the numbers of gametes are in two unequal pairs. The first two, AD and ad, are the **parental gametes** because that is way they are linked on the parental chromosomes. They are the large pair of numbers. The other two Ad and aD are the **recombinant gametes** because the alleles have *recombined* in a different way.

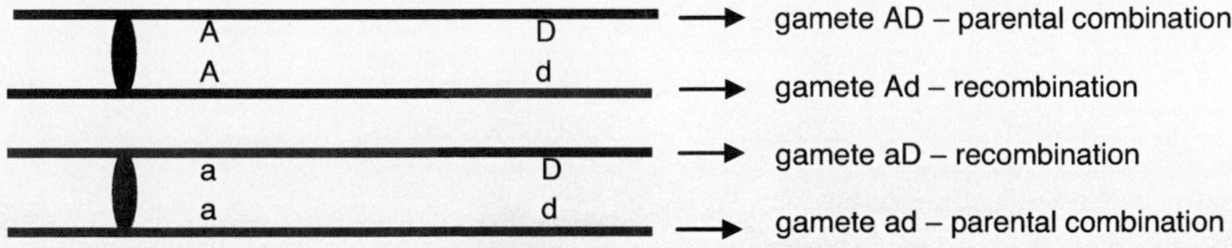
A
A
D
d
a
a
D
d
gamete AD – parental combination
gamete Ad – recombination
gamete aD – recombination
gamete ad – parental combination

As an example of where linkage and crossing over have occurred the numbers of gametes formed might be –

AD = 110 Ad = 5
ad = 110 aD = 5.

The large difference between the two pairs is because the probability of a cross-over occurring between the two gene loci is very small and the gametes Ad and aD will only appear if a cross-over has occurred between the two loci. A cross-over occurring anywhere else on the chromosome will not produce these two types of gamete.
The numbers of Ad and aD will be equal because the cross-over has to produce one of each. As usual any slight differences are due to random processes, for example, in a real cross we might get -

AD = 112   Ad = 4
ad = 108   aD = 6.

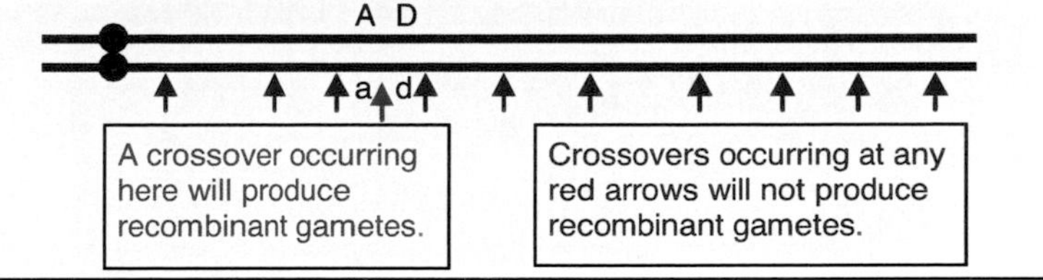
A D
a d
A crossover occurring here will produce recombinant gametes.
Crossovers occurring at any red arrows will not produce recombinant gametes.

Summary

Genotype $\frac{\underline{A}\ \underline{B}}{a\ b}$ gives gametes AB, Ab, aB, and ab in equal proportions.

Genotype $\frac{A\ D}{a\ d}$ with no crossing over gives gametes AD and ad in equal proportions,

but with crossing over gives gametes AD and ad (in equal proportions, large number), and also Ad and aD (in equal proportions, small number).

Meiosis and Variety

Meiosis and Variety

Key points

- Random alignment at metaphase I.
- Maternal and paternal chromosomes could go to either pole.
- This results in 2^n combinations of gametes, eg over 8 million in humans. (See page 178).
- Crossing over can occur between non-sister chromatids of homologous chromosomes.
- This separates combinations of alleles and creates new combinations of maternal and paternal alleles. (See page 176).
- A single cross-over doubles the number of combinations from random alignment.
- Cross-over positions are variable.
- Fertilisation combines maternal and paternal alleles.
- Fertilisation creates new combinations of alleles. This would be particularly significant if the alleles interacted in some way eg showed degrees of codominance.
- Fertilisation is random producing many combinations of maternal and paternal alleles, eg over 8 million squared (64 million million) in humans, ignoring crossovers.

Revision
Basic Genetics

Revise all the genetics terms – see page 62.
Try the problem below. The answer is at the bottom of the box.

Two different species of plant have both red and white flowered forms. When a red flowered form of species A is crossed with a white flowered form, the offspring have red flowers. With species B though, when the red form and the white form are crossed, the flowers are white but speckled with red. Explain the inheritance pattern of red and white in these two species. What will be the ratio of phenotypes for the F2 of species B?

In species A the inheritance pattern is normal Mendelian, with red being the dominant characteristic.
In species B red and white are codominant. In the F2 generation 50% will be white with red speckles, 25% red and 25% white.

Mendel's Law of Independent Assortment

Mendel's Law of Independent Assortment

There are several different ways of stating this. Two versions are given below so you can choose whichever you find easiest to understand and learn.

> Alleles of genes located on different chromosomes assort independently of one another.

> Either of a pair of alleles of a gene is equally likely to be inherited with either of another pair of alleles of a different gene.

This is one of the ways that meiosis produces variety.

Assume there are two pairs of chromosomes carrying the alleles J, j and ***K, k*** of the two genes Jay and Kay. Assume they have lined up on the equator at metaphase I as shown on the right.
(The sister chromatids are not shown for simplicity).

J ***K***
j ***k***
equator

After meiosis is complete we get the gametes -

J ***K***

j ***k***

Since each homologous pair of chromosomes behaves independently there is an equal chance they could line up on the equator differently.

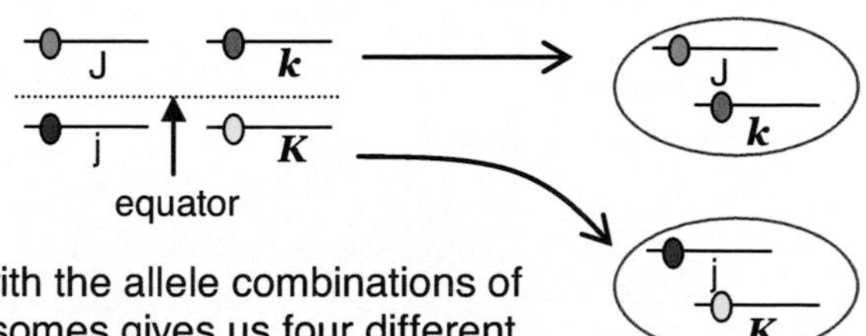

J
k
j
K
equator
J
k
j
K

This gives us equal numbers of gametes with the allele combinations of J***K***, J***k***, j***K***, j***k***. Thus two pairs of chromosomes gives us four different types of gamete.

Three pairs of chromosomes gives us eight different types of gametes.

$2^2 = 4$
$2^3 = 8$

From these two situations you may be able to determine a simple mathematical relationship. It is that the number of different types of gamete is 2^n, where n = the haploid number of chromosomes.
Thus for the fruit fly *Drosophila*, $2^4 = 16$, and for a human $2^{23} = 8,388,608$ different types of gamete.

What is a recombinant chromosome?

If two cross-overs occur between the two loci will there be recombinants in the offspring?

Revision Crossing Over

In the second diagram complete the chromosomes to show the position of the alleles after a crossover has taken place between the A and B loci.

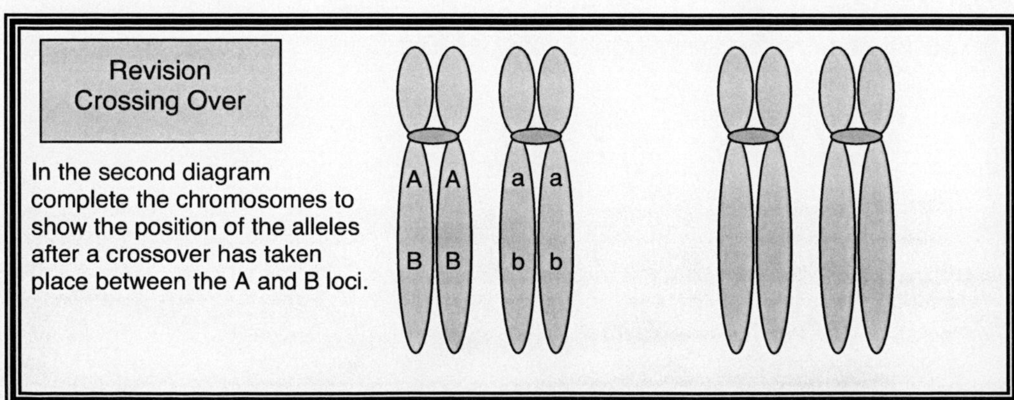

A
A
a
a
B
B
b
b

Dihybrid Crosses

The basic principles applied to solving dihybrid problems are the same as for monohybrid but there are some other points we need to look out for. Once again the problem can go forwards, ie you are given the parents and have to determine the offspring, or backwards, ie you are given the offspring and have to determine the parents.
Reminder – never use a letter for a gene where you cannot distinguish clearly between upper and lower case.

PROBLEM 1
A fly with pink eyes and short wings was crossed with a pure breeding one that had red eyes and long wings. Assuming that red eyes and long wings are dominant, determine genotype and phenotype ratios in both the F_1 and F_2 generations.

SOLUTION 1
Let R = red eyes and r = pink eyes
L = long wings and l = short wings
Pink and short are both recessive and hence the genotype must be homozygous. We are told that red and long is pure breeding and hence must also be homozygous.

	pink, short	x	red, long
P	rrll		RRLL
G	(rl)		(RL)
F_1		RrLl	

All the F_1 have the doubly heterozygous genotype RrLl and therefore red eyes and long wings.

	RrLl	x	RrLl
F_1	RrLl	x	RrLl
G	(RL) (Rl) (rL) (rl)		(RL) (Rl) (rL) (rl)

F_2

	RL	Rl	rL	rl
RL	RRLL	RRLl	RrLL	RrLl
Rl	RRLl	RRll	RrLl	Rrll
rL	RrLL	RrLl	rrLL	rrLl
rl	RrLl	Rrll	rrLl	rrll

9 red eyes, long wings R_L_

3 red eyes, short wings R_ll

3 pink eyes, long wings rrL_

1 pink eyes, short wings rrll

By arranging the gametes in this order notice how the Punnett grid produces a pattern with the 9 and the two 3s forming triangles, and the single double homozygous recessive in the bottom right corner.

The _ means the allele could either be dominant or recessive.

PROBLEM 2

In the mongoose red eyes and striped tail are dominant characteristics, with brown eyes and plain tail being the corresponding recessives.
A mongoose with brown eyes and plain tail was crossed with one with red eyes and striped tail. Over a period of years the total number of offspring was 30 made up as below.

7 red eyes, plain tail,
8 brown eyes, plain tail,
8 red eyes, striped tail,
7 brown eyes, striped tail.

Determine the genotypes of the parents.

SOLUTION 2

Since red and striped are dominant let R = red and T = striped. (Notice that S is not used because on plain paper the difference between S and s is not clear).
The genotype of the mongoose with brown eyes and plain tail has to be doubly homozygous recessive, rrtt.
The genotype of the other parent is R_T_ because it has red eyes and a striped tail.
If we look at the offspring we see that there are some that have brown eyes and striped tail. Thus they have the genotype rrtt. One r and one t have come from the rrtt parent and the other r and t must have come from the other parent. This means that this parent must have been RrTt.
Finally we prove this by drawing out the Punnett grid.

P RrTt x rrtt

G (RT) (Rt) (rT) (rt) (rt)

F_1

	RT	Rt	rT	rt
rt	RrTt	Rrtt	rrTt	rrtt
	red, striped	red, plain	brown, striped	brown, plain

1 RrTt red eyes, striped tail,
1 Rrtt red eyes, plain tail,
1 rrTt brown eyes, striped tail,
1 rrtt brown eyes, plain tail.

The actual numbers observed – 8, 7, 8, 7, - can be taken as a 1:1:1:1 ratio within experimental variation.
Thus our expected ratio fits with our actual results, confirming that the genotypes of the two parents are RrTt and rrtt.

Autosomal Gene Linkage

Autosomal Gene Linkage

Sex chromosomes are the pair that carry the genes to determine gender, whereas all the other chromosomes are called autosomes.

Define a linkage group.

Recall that linked genes are on the same chromosome – page 173. They therefore break Mendel's second law as they do not behave independently.
Problems will fall into one of two categories – linkage without crossing over and linkage with crossing over. Each is easy to recognise. In the first case the ratio produced is like that of a monohybrid cross, ie 1 : 1 or 3 : 1, and there are no recombinants. In the second case recombinants will be produced but the ratio will not be a standard Mendelian one.

PROBLEM 1

The snowy gull commonly has white feathers and a yellow beak, but some birds have black feathers and an orange beak. Black and orange are recessive and the genes are linked.
A pure breeding bird with white feathers and yellow beak was mated to one with black feathers and orange beak. The offspring had white feathers and yellow beak. Two of these were mated and 75% of the offspring had the dominant phenotypes and the other 25% had the recessive. Explain.

SOLUTION 1

White and yellow are dominant so we will use the letters H and Y to represent the alleles. (W would be an unsuitable letter to use).
The white, yellow bird is pure breeding and so has a homozygous genotype. Since black and orange are recessive the genotype of this bird must also be homozygous.
The genes are linked so we must use the alternative format for writing the genotype.

	white, yellow	x	black, orange
P	$\frac{H\,Y}{H\,Y}$		$\frac{h\,y}{h\,y}$
G_1	(HY)		(hy)
F_1		$\frac{HY}{hy}$	

	white, yellow	x	white, yellow
F_1	$\frac{HY}{hy}$	x	$\frac{HY}{hy}$
G_2	(HY) (hy)		(HY) (hy)

F_2

	HY	hy
HY	$\frac{HY}{HY}$ white feathers, yellow beak	$\frac{HY}{hy}$ white feathers, yellow beak
hy	$\frac{HY}{hy}$ white feathers, yellow beak	$\frac{hy}{hy}$ black feathers, orange beak

White feathers, yellow beak, and black feathers, orange beak are in the ratio 3:1
White, yellow and black, orange are parental combinations. Note the absence of recombinations.

PROBLEM 2

Transparent wings and clubbed antennae are autosomally linked dominant alleles in the fairy fly. Grey wings and smooth antennae are the characteristics resulting from being homozygous for both the recessive alleles.
A fly with grey wings and smooth antennae was mated to an unknown fly and all of the offspring had transparent wings and clubbed antennae.
These offspring were all mated to flies with grey wings and smooth antennae and the total offspring were –

227 transparent wings, clubbed antennae,
10 transparent wings, smooth antennae,
231 grey wings, smooth antennae,
7 grey wings, clubbed antennae.

Determine the genotypes of all the flies.

SOLUTION 2

The clear give-away is the non-Mendelian ratio in the numbers of offspring – this is the classic one large pair of numbers and one small pair of numbers indicating linkage and crossing over.
We are told transparent and clubbed are the dominant characteristics so we assign the letters T and B to the alleles. t and b are the recessive alleles for grey and smooth.
The grey, smooth fly has to have the genotype $\frac{tb}{tb}$.
Since all the offspring are transparent, clubbed (the dominant characteristics) we can assume that the other parent must be pure breeding transparent, clubbed otherwise we would get some offspring showing recessive characteristics. The genotype must be $\frac{TB}{TB}$.

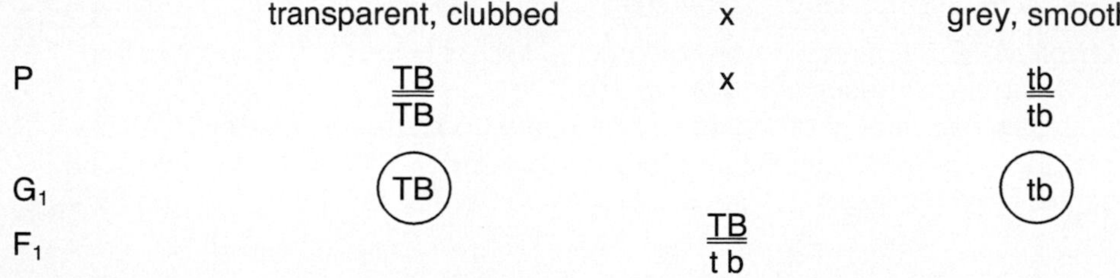
transparent, clubbed x grey, smooth
P TB/TB x tb/tb
G_1 TB tb
F_1 TB/t b

The second cross is again with the homozygous recessive tb/tb.

P TB/t b x tb/tb

G_1 (TB) (tb) (Tb) (tB) (tb)

F_1

	TB	tb	Tb	tB
tb	TB/tb	tb/tb	Tb/tb	tB/tb
	transparent, clubbed 227	grey, smooth 231	transparent, smooth 10	grey, clubbed 7

These are the parental combinations and form the large pair of numbers.

These are the recombinants and form the small pair of numbers.

The unknown fly thus had the genotype TB/TB and the other two parent flies the genotype tb/tb.

Polygenic Inheritance

Polygenic Inheritance

Key points

- When two or more genes contribute to the inheritance of one characteristic.
- The basic Mendelian principles still apply but the end result can be continuous variation as opposed to the discontinuous variation that we have considered up to now.

Example 1

Seed colour in wheat is controlled by around six genes. For this first example we will look at the effect of just two of these at two pairs of unlinked loci, but the second example of human skin colour on the next page does look at the effect of six genes. The seed colour can vary from white through to dark red, so we can use the letters W and R to represent the genes. The genotype WWWW will produce a white seed whereas the genotype RRRR will produce a dark red seed.

Genotype	Seed colour
WWWW	white
WWWR	pale pink
WWRR	mid pink
WRRR	dark pink
RRRR	red

We are going to cross two wheat plants that produce mid pink seeds and have the genotype W/R W/R

Therefore each parent can produce four different types of gamete – WW, WR, WR, and RR.

F_1

	WW	WR	WR	RR
WW	WWWW	WWWR	WWWR	WWRR
WR	WWWR	WWRR	WWRR	WRRR
WR	WWWR	WWRR	WWRR	WRRR
RR	WWRR	WRRR	WRRR	RRRR

	Seed colour				
	white WWWW	pale pink WWWR	mid pink WWRR	dark pink WRRR	red RRRR
Number	1	4	6	4	1

If we now plot this as a bar chart we get a normal distribution, or continuous variation, albeit rather narrow.

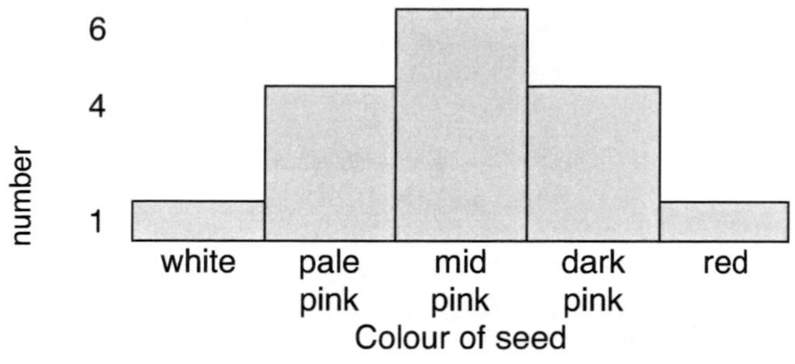
6
4
1
number
white
pale pink
mid pink
dark pink
red
Colour of seed

What are the gametes produced by these genotypes? Answers at bottom of page.

1. A B / a b
2. AB / a b with no crossing over
3. AB / a b with crossing over

What is the key point to look for in a genetics problem with linkage and no crossing over?

What is the key point to look for in a genetics problem with linkage and crossing over?

1. AB, Ab, aB, ab. 2. AB, ab 3. AB, ab, Ab, aB.

Example 2

Polygenes determine human skin pigmentation. It is thought that around 20 pairs of loci are involved but for this illustration I will show only 3 pairs with alleles A,B,C and a,b,c.

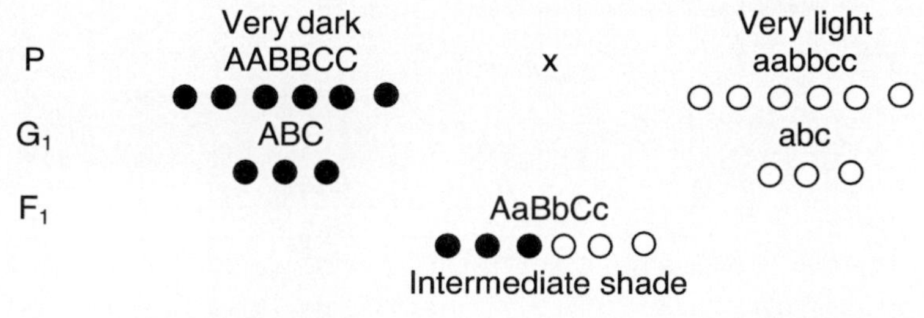

P
Very dark
AABBCC
x
Very light
aabbcc
G_1
ABC
abc
F_1
AaBbCc
Intermediate shade

P AaBbCc x AaBbCc

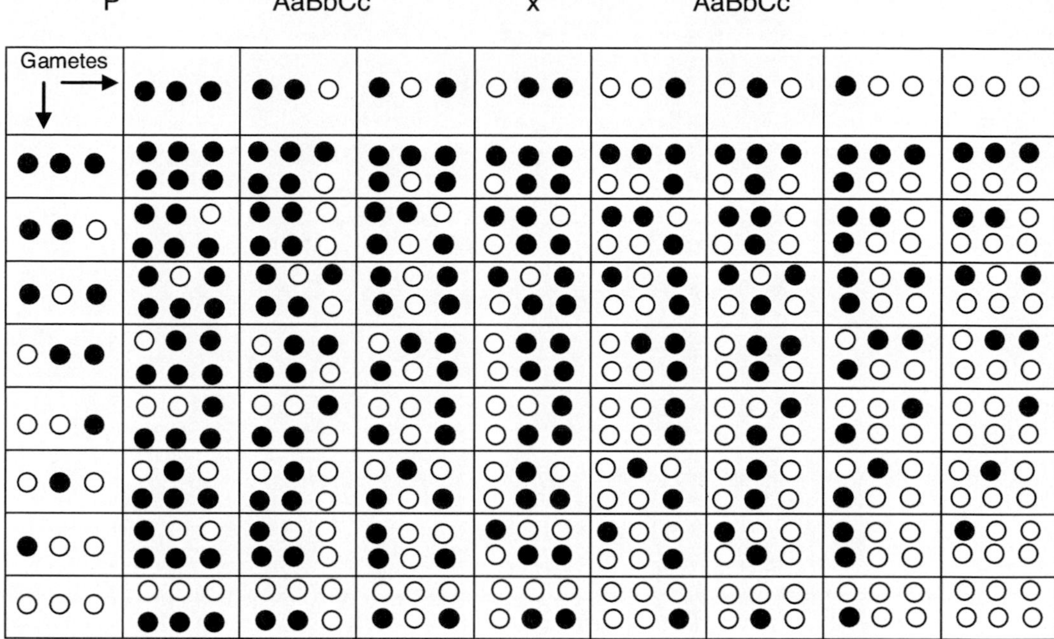

Gametes

When these are grouped we end up with the numbers below.

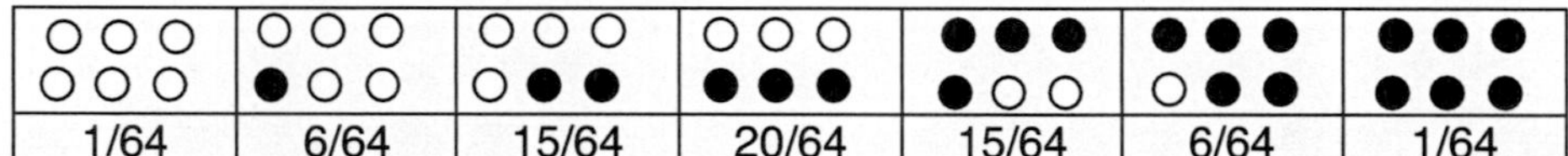

1/64
6/64
15/64
20/64
15/64
6/64
1/64

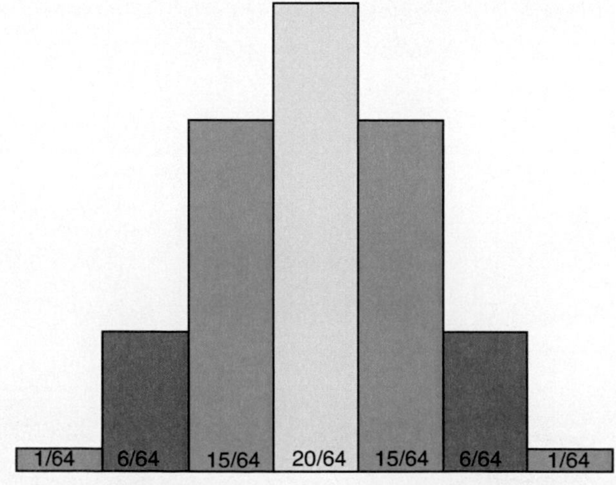

1/64
6/64
15/64
20/64
15/64
6/64
1/64

This looks closer to a normal distribution. It should be obvious therefore that the greater the number of genes controlling the characteristic the closer the distribution will be to a normal distribution.

Self-test Quiz on Topic 10

1. During which phase of meiosis do the centromeres break?
   a. Metaphase I,
   b. Metaphase II,
   c. Anaphase I,
   d. Anaphase II.

2. Chiasma formation and crossing over take place during
   a. Prophase I,
   b. Prophase II,
   c. Metaphase I,
   d. Anaphase I.

3. An animal cell has a diploid number of 6. How many genetically different types of gamete could it produce assuming no crossing over takes place?
   a. 216,
   b. 27,
   c. 36,
   d. 8.

4. Recombination can best be defined as
   a. the appearance amongst the offspring of combinations of characteristics due to mutations,
   b. the reassortment of alleles as a result of crossing over,
   c. combinations of characteristics in the offspring due to random alignment during metaphase I,
   d. formation of new characteristics as a result of non- disjunction during anaphase II.

5. Autosomes are
   a. those chromosomes that carry homologous genes,
   b. those chromosomes that do not determine the sex of the individual,
   c. those chromosomes that do determine the sex of the individual,
   d. the only chromosomes that can carry out the process of crossing over.

6. A linkage group is
   a. the group of chromosomes found in any one nucleus,
   b. the combinations of genes produced as a result of crossing over,
   c. all the genes found on one chromosome.
   d. all the different alleles of a gene,

7. Polygenic inheritance can result in
   a. continuous variation,
   b. mutations,
   c. crossing over,
   d. formation of linkage groups.

8. The purpose of crossing over is to
   a. mix alleles between chromosomes of the homologous pair,
   b. mix alleles between sister chromatids,
   c. increase the phenotypic variation in the parents,
   d. mix genes between the chromosomes of non homologous pairs.

9. The gametes that can be produced from the genotype RrTt are
   a. Rr, RT, rt and Tt.
   b. RTrt
   c. RrTt.
   d. RT, Rt, rT and rt.

10. During which phase of meiosis does the reduction division occur?
    a. Metaphase I.
    b. Anaphase I.
    c. Anaphase II.
    d. Telophase I.

11. Which statement is correct about Mendel's law of independent assortment?
    a. Only unlinked genes can combine randomly.
    b. All genes show independent assortment.
    c. Genes in different linkage groups always stay together.
    d. Alleles of genes on homologous chromosomes behave independently.

12. An organism has the genotype $\frac{\underline{A\ b}}{a\ B}$. The table shows genotypes and numbers for the gametes. Which is the correct line?

a.	AB 100	Ab 105	aB 101	ab 99
b.	AB 14	Ab 210	aB 208	ab 12
c.	AB 135	Ab 45	aB 45	ab 15
d.	AB 210	Ab 14	aB 12	ab 208

Genetics Problems
(The answers to all these problems are in Appendix 6, pages 235 - 239).

Most genetics problems are about fruit flies, mice or maize, so to be different most of these problems are plants and animals from my imagination! The genetics is no different though.

1. The genotypes in a particular variety of tomato were TtHh, Tthh, ttHh and tthh. The genes are not linked. Which two pairs would a plant breeder select in order to obtain a phenotype ratio of 1:1:1:1?

2. In the Squishy plant yellow fruit is dominant over green, and bumpy fruit dominant over smooth.
Explain how a cross between a plant with green bumpy fruits and one with yellow smooth fruits gave –
25 plants with green bumpy fruits,
26 plants with green smooth fruits,
24 plants with yellow bumpy fruits,
25 plants with yellow smooth fruits.

3. The Administrator beetle (*Regis tra*) has black wing cases and short antennae. Two beetles with these characteristics were crossed and the offspring were –
19 black, short antennae,
6 black, long antennae,
5 white, short antennae,
1 white, long antennae.
Determine the genotypes of the parents.

4. Frumpy plants have small flowers with green petals and these are the dominant characteristics. Large white flowers are recessive, and the genes are not linked. A plant with small green flowers was crossed with one with large white flowers and the offspring had either small green flowers or large green flowers.
Determine the genotypes of the parents.
If the plants with large green flowers were allowed to self pollinate, determine the genotypes and phenotype ratio of the offspring.

5. A plant breeder crossed a Pogwort with red flowers with one with white flowers and all the offspring were pink. Determine the flower colours and proportions of the F_2 generation.

6. A Tarsus rat was taken from a group that was known to breed true for black and straight hair. It was then bred with a rat of unknown genotype and the offspring were –

Black, straight hair	1315
Red, curly hair	1370
Red, straight hair	21
Black, curly hair	19

Determine the genotype of the unknown parent and give a genetic explanation of the results.

7. The Zye Goat has yellow legs and large eyes as dominant characteristics. White legs and small eyes are recessive. The genes are linked and crossing over occurs in both sexes. A goat with the dominant phenotype was test crossed. The results are below.

	F_1 results
Yellow legs, large eyes	275
Yellow legs, small eyes	6
White legs, large eyes	8
White legs, small eyes	290

Explain genetically how these results were produced and state which of the F_1 are the recombinants.

8. There are two types of Zom Bee, one with red legs and one with blue legs. The characteristic is carried on the X chromosome. If red is dominant, what is the F_2 ratio if red-legged female bees are crossed with blue-legged males, the F_1 males all being red-legged? (Genetically, Zom Bees are the same as the fruit fly Drosophila).

9. Blue flowers of the Whoopsy Daisy are dominant to white, and tall plant recessive to short. A tall white flowered plant crossed with a short blue flowered plant gave the following offspring.

Short, blue	11
Tall, white	12
Short, white	113
Tall, blue	110.

Explain these results fully.

10. In the Dead Sloe (*Rigor mortis*) the allele for round fruit is dominant over long fruit, and the allele for complex flower recessive to simple flower. A cross was made between two varieties, Purplepear (long fruit and simple flower) and Grapecluster (round fruit and complex flower). All the F_1 plants produced round fruits and had simple flowers.
A test cross on the F_1 gave the following results.

Round fruit, simple flowers	23
Long fruit, simple flowers	93
Round fruit, complex flowers	89
Long fruit, complex flowers	19

(a) Explain these results fully.

(b) If the alleles were not linked what numbers would you predict for each phenotype for the F_1 test cross. Base your calculation on the same total number of offspring as the actual test cross.

11. The Paraceta Mole has dominant alleles for white fur and black feet but there are recessive alleles for yellow fur and pink feet.
A pure breeding (remember that this means homozygous) white mole with black feet was crossed with a yellow mole with pink feet. As expected all the offspring were white with black feet. When these offspring were crossed amongst themselves many times they produced a total of 113 white with black feet, 32 yellow with pink feet, 7 white with pink feet and 8 yellow with black feet. What do these results indicate and what numbers would you have expected in the F_2?

Topic 11

Human Health and Physiology

Defence Against Infectious Diseases

Blood Clotting

Clotting

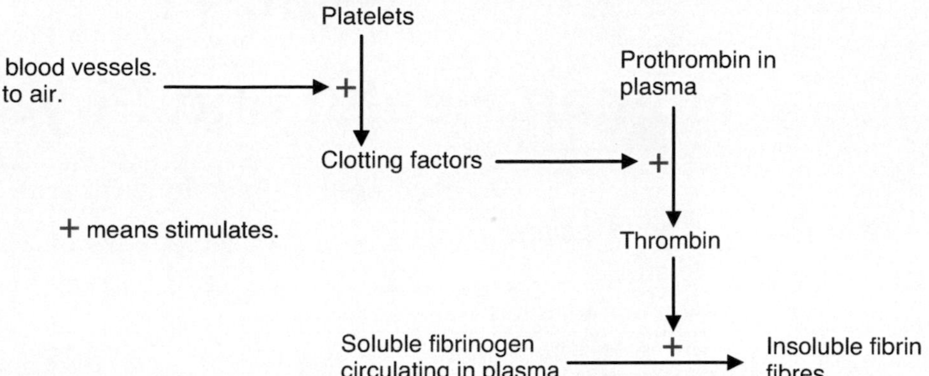

Platelets
Damaged blood vessels.
Exposure to air.
Prothrombin in plasma
Clotting factors
+ means stimulates.
Thrombin
Soluble fibrinogen circulating in plasma
Insoluble fibrin fibres

Fibrin is an insoluble fibrous protein. The fibres become entangled and create a mesh in which red blood cells become trapped, blocking blood flow.

Immunity

Immunity

Key components

Cells -

- macrophages;
- B-cells;
- Helper T-cells;
- Memory cells;
- Plasma cells.

Principles

- Antigen presentation;
- Clonal selection;

Define active immunity.

Define passive immunity.

Clonal Selection

Clonal Selection

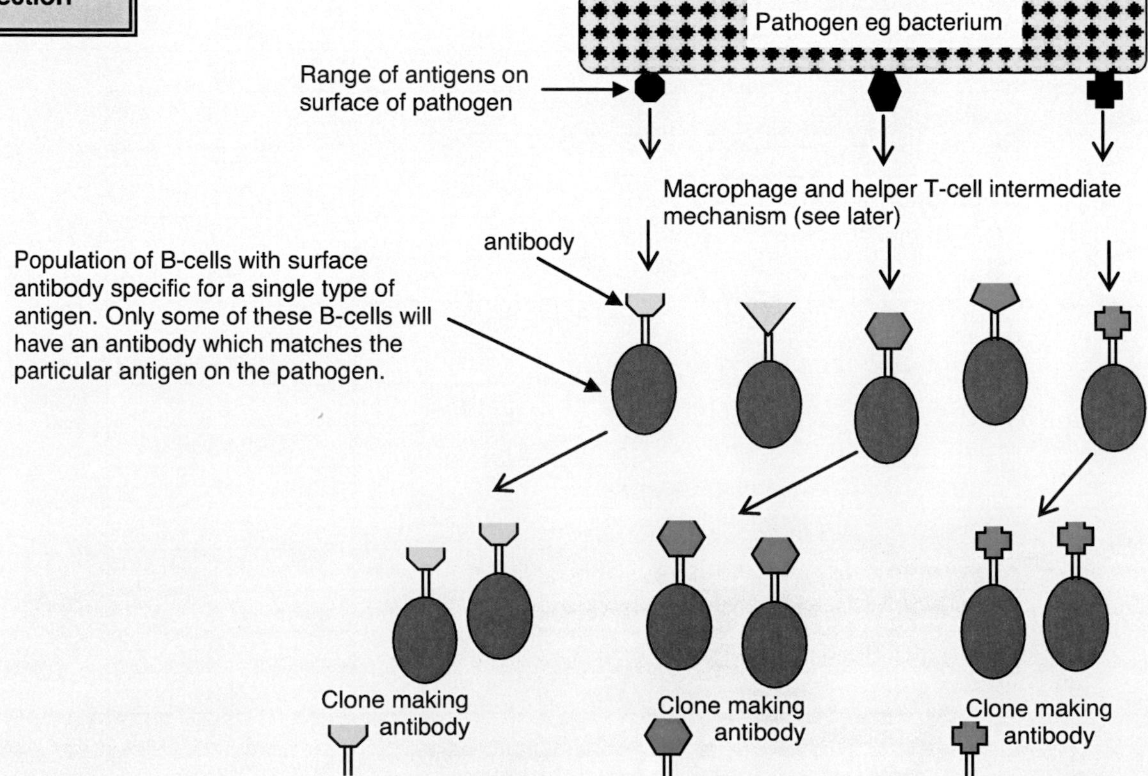

Pathogen eg bacterium
Range of antigens on surface of pathogen
Macrophage and helper T-cell intermediate mechanism (see later)
antibody
Population of B-cells with surface antibody specific for a single type of antigen. Only some of these B-cells will have an antibody which matches the particular antigen on the pathogen.
Clone making antibody
Clone making antibody
Clone making antibody

Key points

- A B-cell is *selected* by binding to its specific antigen;
- This then results in it forming a *clone*. Hence the term **clonal selection**.
- B-cells that have the wrong type of receptor, the second and fourth ones in the previous diagram, are not selected and do not form clones.
- The pathogen *challenges* the immune system.
- The immune system *responds*. Hence the term '**challenge and response**'.

The pathogen shown in the diagram has three different antigens and thus three clones of B-cells are produced. This is called a *polyclonal response*. Compare this to monoclonal antibodies on page 194.

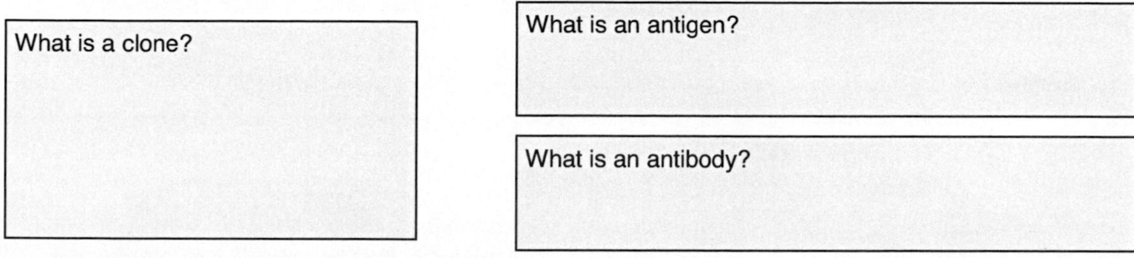

What is a clone?
What is an antigen?
What is an antibody?

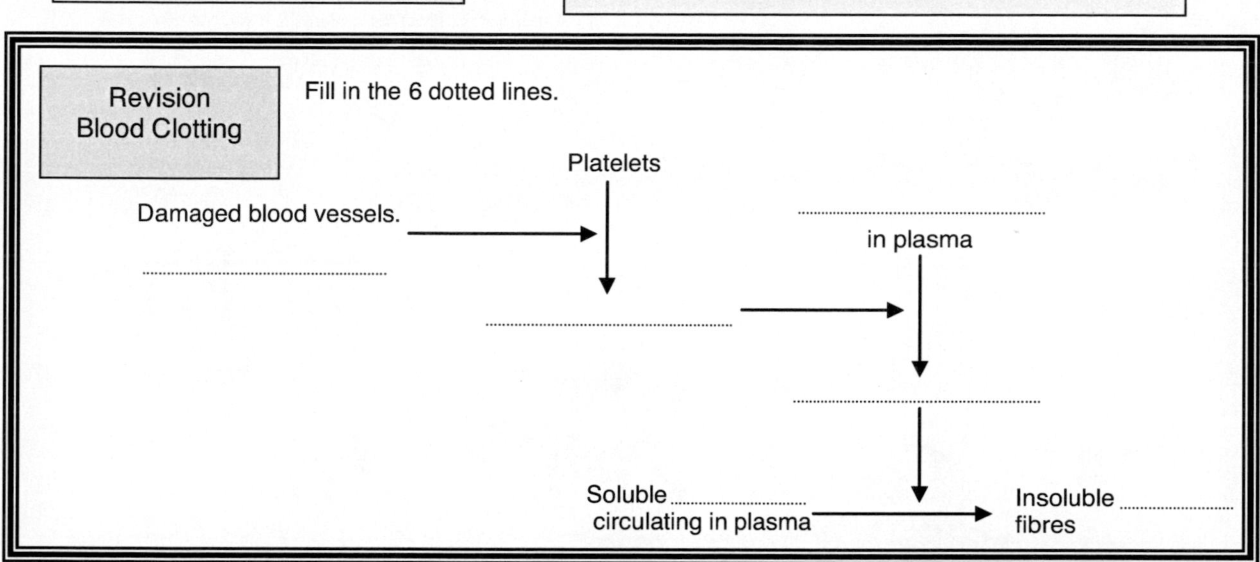

Revision
Blood Clotting
Fill in the 6 dotted lines.
Platelets
Damaged blood vessels.
in plasma
Soluble
circulating in plasma
Insoluble
fibres

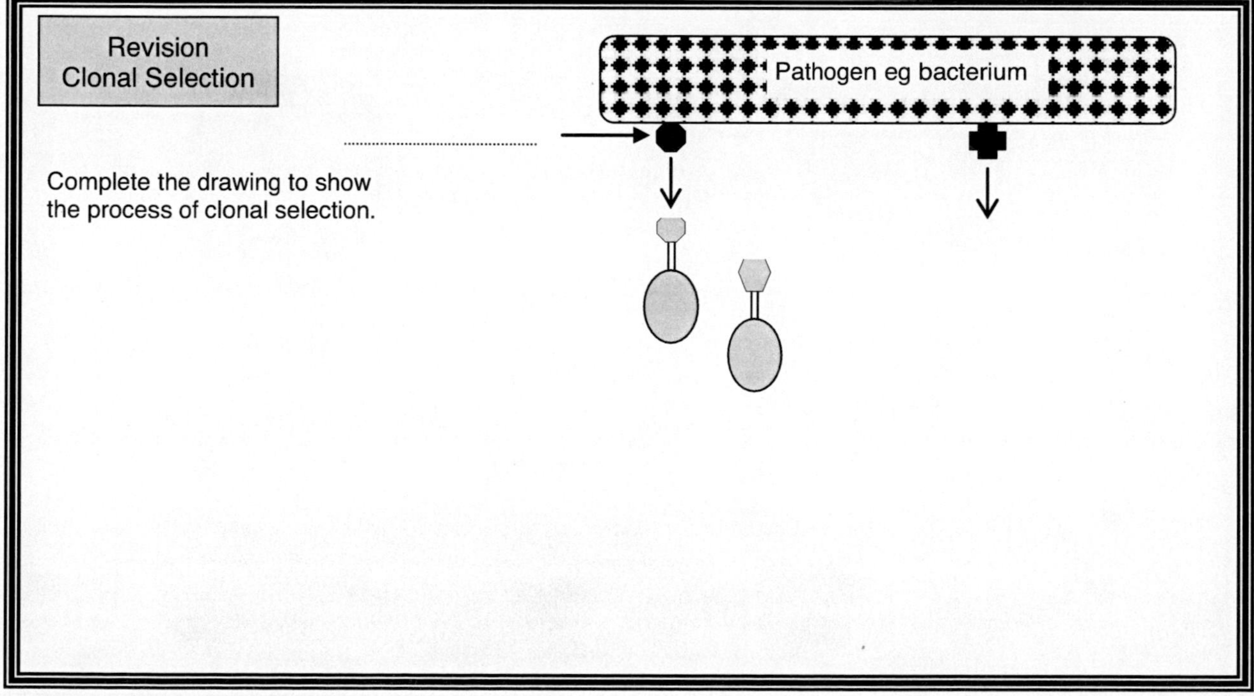

Revision
Clonal Selection
Pathogen eg bacterium
Complete the drawing to show the process of clonal selection.

Antibody Production

Antibody Production

Key points

- Each B-cell only produces antibody with a single type of receptor.
- Each helper T-cell (T_H-cell) only has a single type of specific receptor on its surface.
- Both B-cells and T_H-cells produce clones of active cells and memory cells.
- The active cells only remain active for a short period of time; the memory cells remain dormant for many years.
- T_H-cells are activated by chemicals during macrophage presentation.
- B-cells are only activated by chemicals from T_H-cells.
- Activated B-cells are called plasma cells.

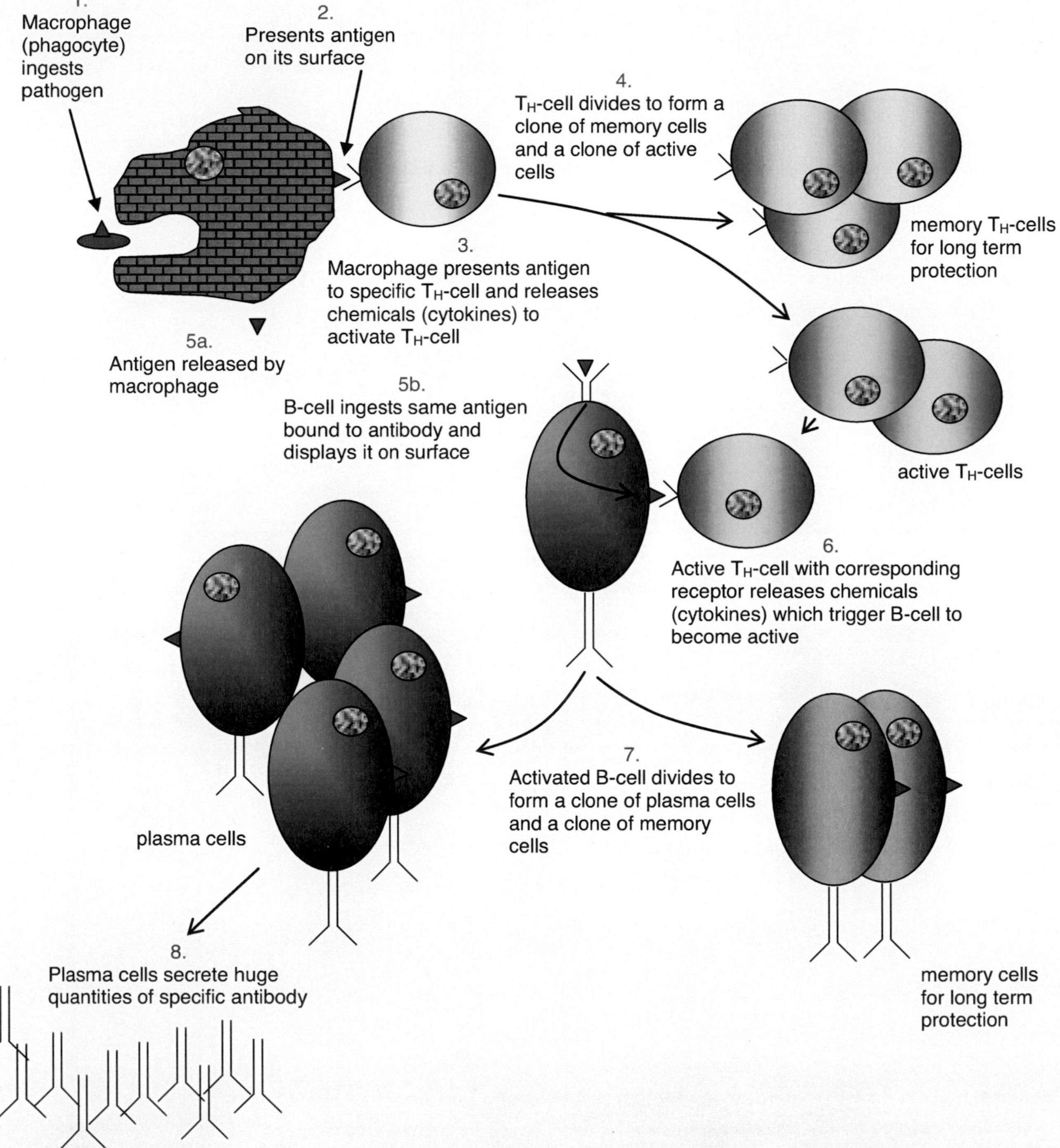

1. Macrophage (phagocyte) ingests pathogen
2. Presents antigen on its surface
3. Macrophage presents antigen to specific T_H-cell and releases chemicals (cytokines) to activate T_H-cell
4. T_H-cell divides to form a clone of memory cells and a clone of active cells
memory T_H-cells for long term protection
5a. Antigen released by macrophage
5b. B-cell ingests same antigen bound to antibody and displays it on surface
active T_H-cells
6. Active T_H-cell with corresponding receptor releases chemicals (cytokines) which trigger B-cell to become active
7. Activated B-cell divides to form a clone of plasma cells and a clone of memory cells
plasma cells
memory cells for long term protection
8. Plasma cells secrete huge quantities of specific antibody

Vaccination

Vaccination

Principles

- Stimulation of B-cells and helper T-cells produces memory cells;
- Memory cells bring about a rapid secondary response.

A vaccine contains a form of the pathogen or toxin that has been modified (attenuated) such that it is unable to harm the body. However it still triggers the immune response leading to clones of memory cells. This <u>immunological</u> <u>memory</u> means that if the real pathogen invades the body it is rapidly destroyed before it causes harm.

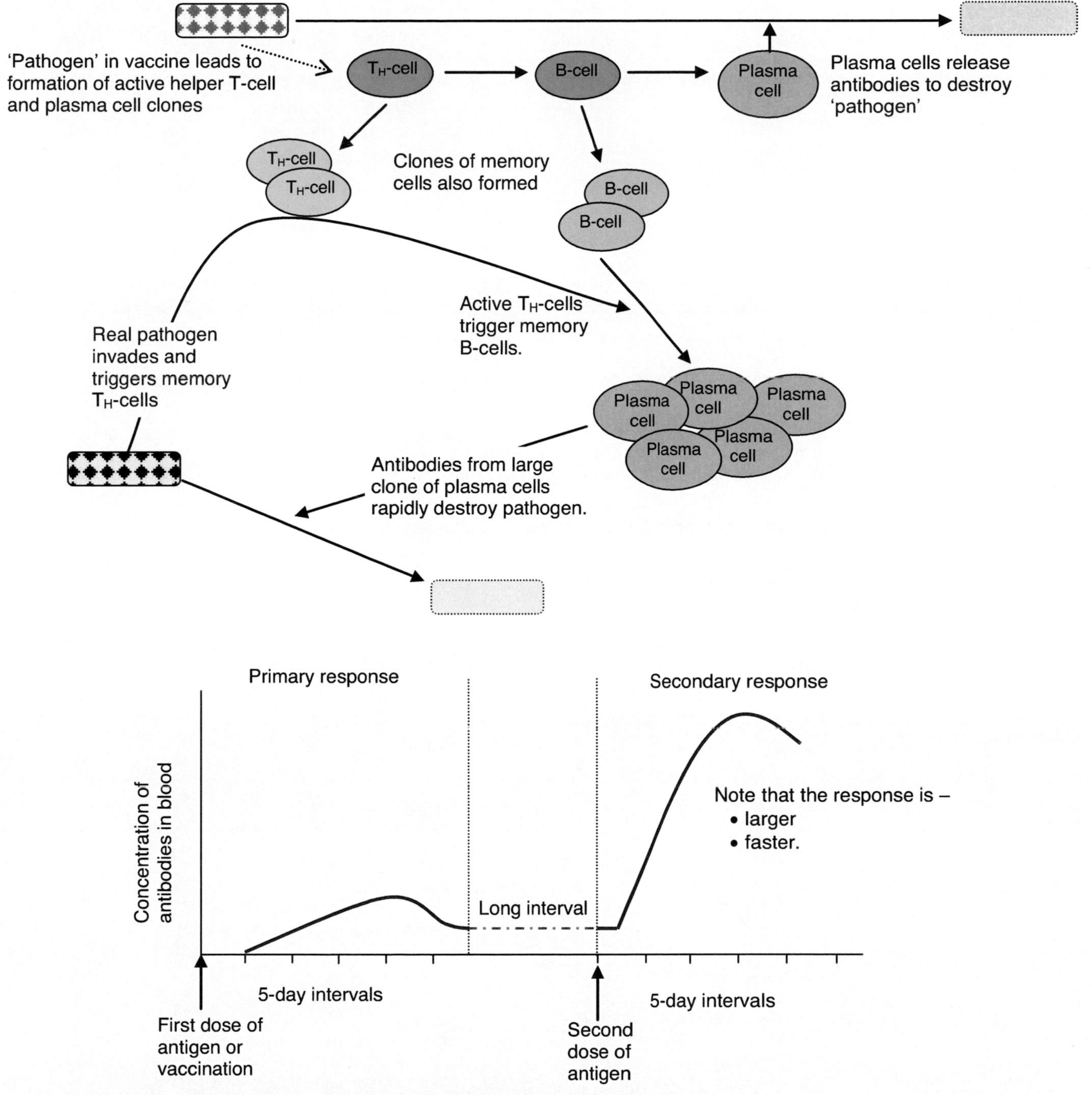

'Pathogen' in vaccine leads to formation of active helper T-cell and plasma cell clones
T_H-cell
B-cell
Plasma cell
Plasma cells release antibodies to destroy 'pathogen'
T_H-cell
T_H-cell
Clones of memory cells also formed
B-cell
B-cell
Active T_H-cells trigger memory B-cells.
Real pathogen invades and triggers memory T_H-cells
Plasma cell
Plasma cell
Plasma cell
Plasma cell
Plasma cell
Antibodies from large clone of plasma cells rapidly destroy pathogen.
Primary response
Secondary response
Concentration of antibodies in blood
Note that the response is –
• larger
• faster.
Long interval
5-day intervals
5-day intervals
First dose of antigen or vaccination
Second dose of antigen

To which type of cell does a macrophage 'present' antigen?	Name the two types of clone produced by an activated B-cell.	How many types of antibody does a single B-cell clone produce?	Do activated Helper T-cells produce antibodies?

Benefits and Dangers of Vaccination

Benefits	Dangers
▪ Reduced deaths from virulent pathogens such as tuberculosis; ▪ Decreases health-care costs; ▪ Prevention of epidemics and pandemics; ▪ Reduced side effects as a result of infection by some pathogens eg Mumps may cause sterility in men; ▪ Assist in eradication of a disease. (So far this has only been achieved with Smallpox).	▪ Immunity from a vaccine may not be as effective as that derived from a true infection resulting in serious illness later in life; ▪ Some vaccines may result in harmful side effects. In the UK the MMR (combined Measles, Mumps, Rubella) vaccine has caused a major debate as to whether it may cause autism. ▪ An attenuated vaccine may become virulent; ▪ Some vaccines contain mercury which may have a toxic effect; ▪ The immune system may become overloaded.

Monoclonal Antibodies

Monoclonal Antibodies

Remember that a pathogen will usually bring about a polyclonal response since it has several antigens, but each plasma cell (active B-cell) only produces a single type of antibody.

Key point

- Monoclonal antibodies are the antibodies from a single clone of plasma cells.

Key points

- A myeloma cell is a cancerous tumour of a plasma cell;
- Myeloma cells divide repeatedly in culture but do not produce antibody;
- Plasma cells have a short life span;
- Plasma cells only produce a specific antigen.

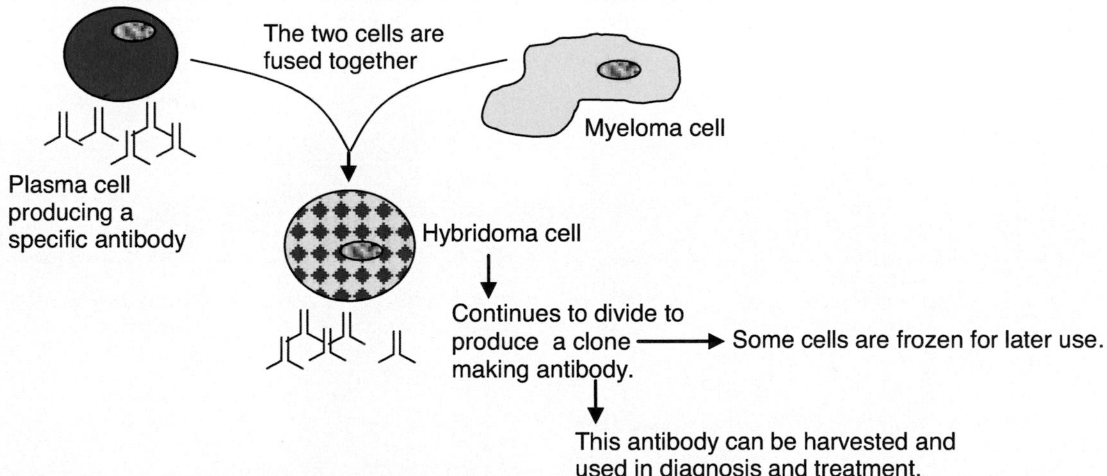
The two cells are fused together
Myeloma cell
Plasma cell producing a specific antibody
Hybridoma cell
Continues to divide to produce a clone making antibody.
Some cells are frozen for later use.
This antibody can be harvested and used in diagnosis and treatment.

Uses

Diagnosis - Pregnancy testing.
- Detect HCG present in the urine. (See p218).

Test for suspected heart attack.
- Damaged heart muscle cells release a specific cardiac enzyme into the blood.

Treatment - After being bitten by a rabid dog or bat.
- The rabies virus can be fatal before the immune system has time to respond. Monoclonal antibodies are injected along with the rabies vaccine. The antibodies quickly destroy the virus and the vaccine produces a longer term immunity.

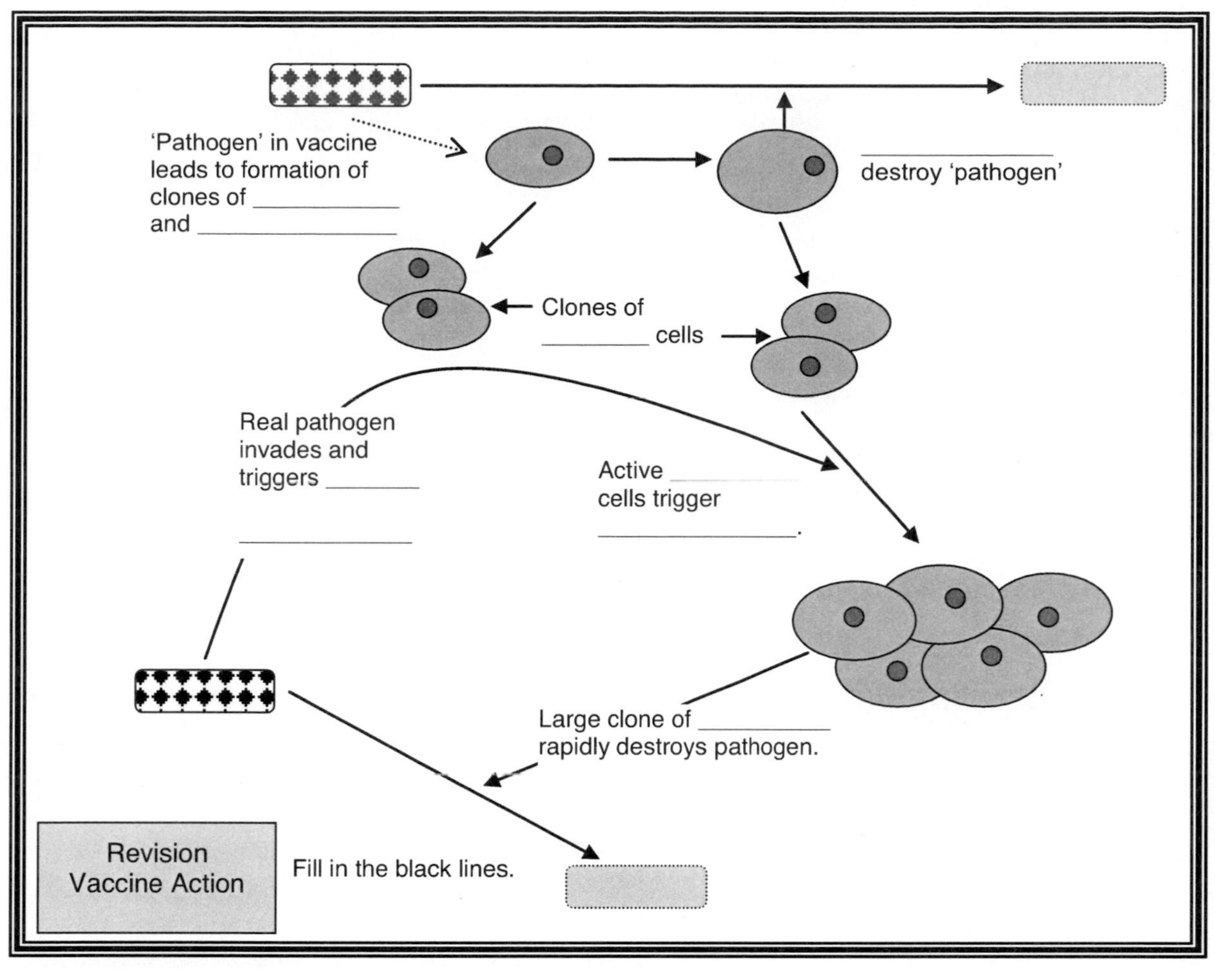
'Pathogen' in vaccine leads to formation of clones of ___________ and ______________
destroy 'pathogen'
Clones of ________ cells
Real pathogen invades and triggers ________
Active ________ cells trigger ______________.
Large clone of __________ rapidly destroys pathogen.
Revision Vaccine Action
Fill in the black lines.

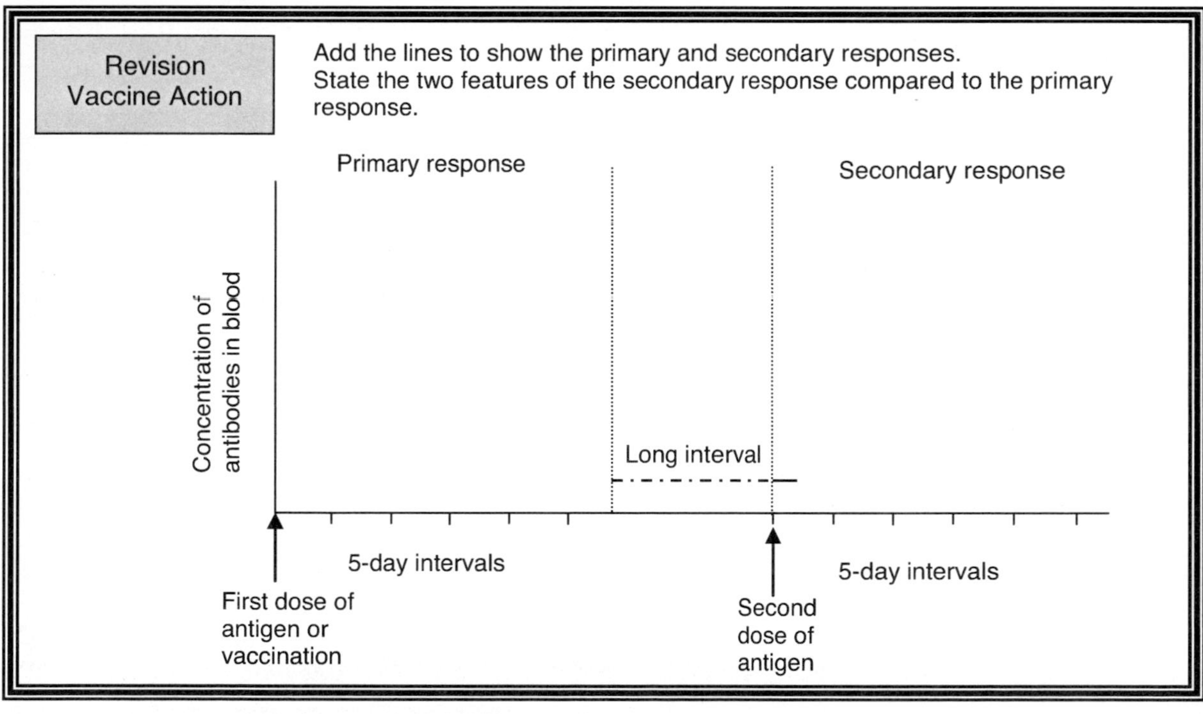
Revision Vaccine Action
Add the lines to show the primary and secondary responses.
State the two features of the secondary response compared to the primary response.
Primary response
Secondary response
Concentration of antibodies in blood
Long interval
5-day intervals
5-day intervals
First dose of antigen or vaccination
Second dose of antigen

Self-test Quiz on Defence Against Infectious Diseases

1. Which of the following statements about macrophages is <u>not</u> true?
   a. Lysosomes play an important part in their function.
   b. They are found in both the blood stream and tissue fluid.
   c. They activate helper T-cells.
   d. They produce antibodies.

2. Which of the following happens during the clotting process?
   a. Platelets in the plasma release fibrin when exposed to air.
   b. Fibrinogen in the plasma stimulates the release of clotting factors.
   c. Clotting factors from platelets convert prothrombin to thrombin.
   d. Macrophages release thrombin which results in the formation of fibrin fibres in the blood.

3. According to the clonal selection theory
   a. an animal contains large numbers of B-cells each producing a specific but different type of antibody,
   b. each B-cell produces many types of antibody,
   c. antigens form clones when selected by the specific B-cell,
   d. when a T-cell is selected by an antigen it will produce a specific type of antibody.

4. Which of the following does <u>not</u> have a role in antibody production?
   a. Helper T-cells.
   b. Macrophages.
   c. B-cells.
   d. Erythrocytes.

5. Which of the following statements is correct?
   a. Active immunity results in the production of antibodies.
   b. Passive immunity requires the presence of antigens.
   c. Active immunity only occurs following vaccination.
   d. Both passive and active immunity involve B-cells.

6. Antibodies are produced by
   a. helper T-cells,
   b. macrophages,
   c. plasma cells,
   d. erythrocytes.

7. Memory cells are important in that
   a. they prevent the body from being invaded again by the same pathogen,
   b. they permit the body to respond more rapidly to later invasions by the same pathogen,
   c. they allow the body to reduce the number of different types of B-cell,
   d. a wider range of antibodies can be produced to destroy invading pathogens.

8. Monoclonal antibodies are
   a. antibodies produced by B-cells,
   b. antibodies produced by a single clone of B-cells,
   c. antibodies that destroy only viruses,
   d. antibodies that are produced by tumour cells.

9. A vaccine is usually effective at preventing a serious disease because
   a. it increases the number of macrophages in the plasma;
   b. it contains antibodies which remain in the plasma;
   c. it stimulates the production of memory cells;
   d. it maintains a high level of active plasma cells in the blood.

10. Monoclonal antibodies are manufactured by
    a. joining a plasma cell to a tumour cell;
    b. joining a macrophage to a helper T-cell;
    c. culturing plasma cells collected from a blood sample;
    d. joining a helper T-cell to a tumour cell.

11. If a person has been vaccinated and then comes into contact with the disease, which of the following statements would apply?
    a. The secondary response is the same size as the primary response.
    b. The secondary response is larger and faster than the primary response.
    c. The primary response is larger and faster than the secondary response.
    d. The secondary response is larger but slower than the primary response.

Muscles and Movement

[The table below considers the skeletal muscles. Muscles in the body not attached to bones are cardiac muscle and muscles of the gut and reproductive system.]

Structure and Function

Structure	Function
Nerves	▪ Carry impulses to and from the brain to co-ordinate muscular activity; ▪ Motor neuron impulses stimulate muscles to contract; ▪ Nerve impulses control timing and speed of muscle contraction.
Muscles	▪ Contain receptors that send information via sensory neurons to the brain about the position of the muscle; ▪ Contract to bring about movement at a joint; ▪ Work in antagonistic pairs on each side of a joint.
Bones	▪ Bones meet at a joint and act as levers; ▪ Different types of joint between bones control the range of movement; ▪ Provide rigid anchorage for muscles through tendons.
Tendons	▪ Join muscle to bone.
Ligaments	▪ Tough inelastic structures holding bones of joint together.

Elbow Joint

The Human Elbow Joint

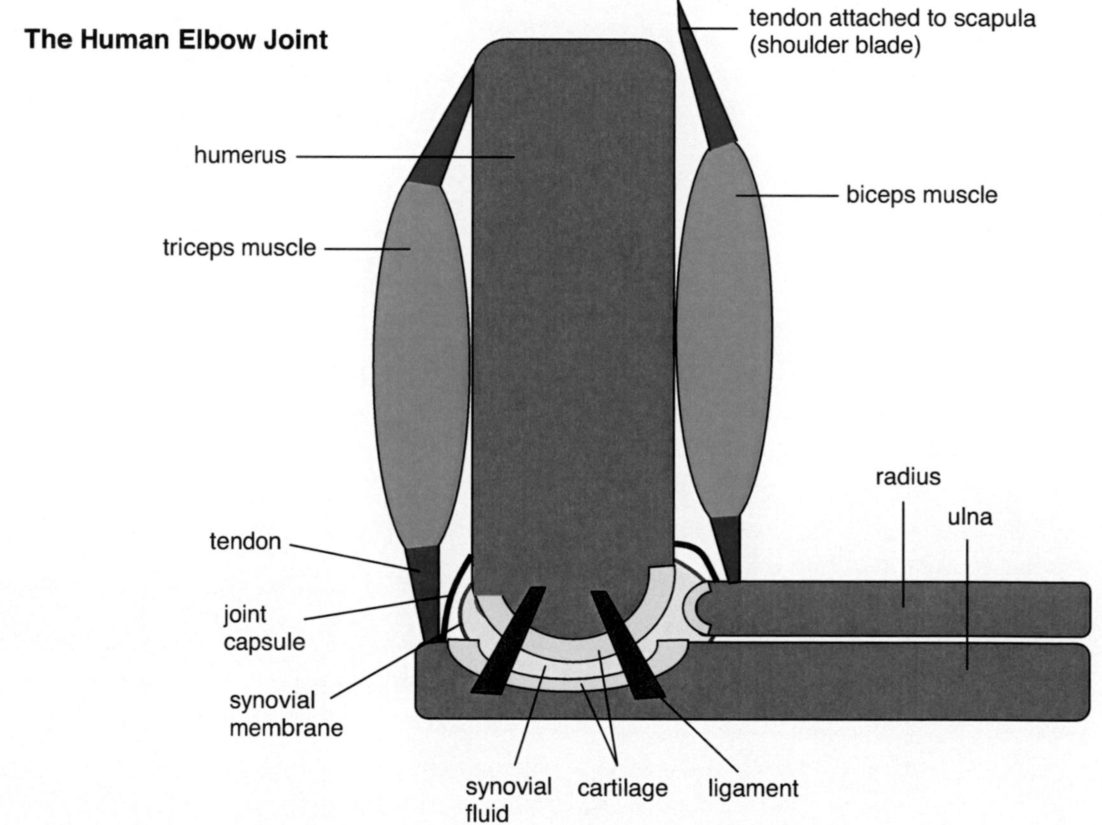
tendon attached to scapula (shoulder blade)
humerus
biceps muscle
triceps muscle
radius
ulna
tendon
joint capsule
synovial membrane
synovial fluid
cartilage
ligament

Structure	Function
Bones - Humerus Ulna Radius	Rigid structures providing anchors for muscles; Create fulcrum at joint.
Muscles - Biceps = flexor muscle – bends joint Triceps = extensor muscle – straightens joint	Provide forces to move joint; Act as antagonistic pair.
Cartilage	Smooth strong covering on articulating surfaces of joint.
Synovial fluid	Lubricates articulating surfaces of cartilage; Shock absorber.
Joint capsule	Encloses joint to protect it.

Revision
Elbow Joint

Label all the structures indicated with plain lines.

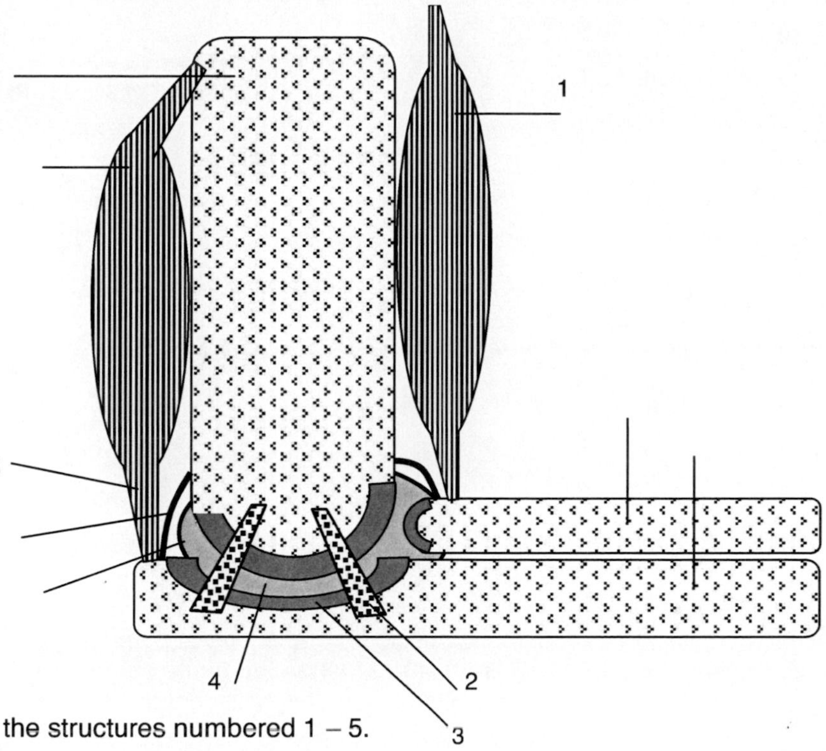

1

5

4 2 3

State the function of the structures numbered 1 – 5.

1.

2.

3.

4.

5.

The Hip and Knee Joints

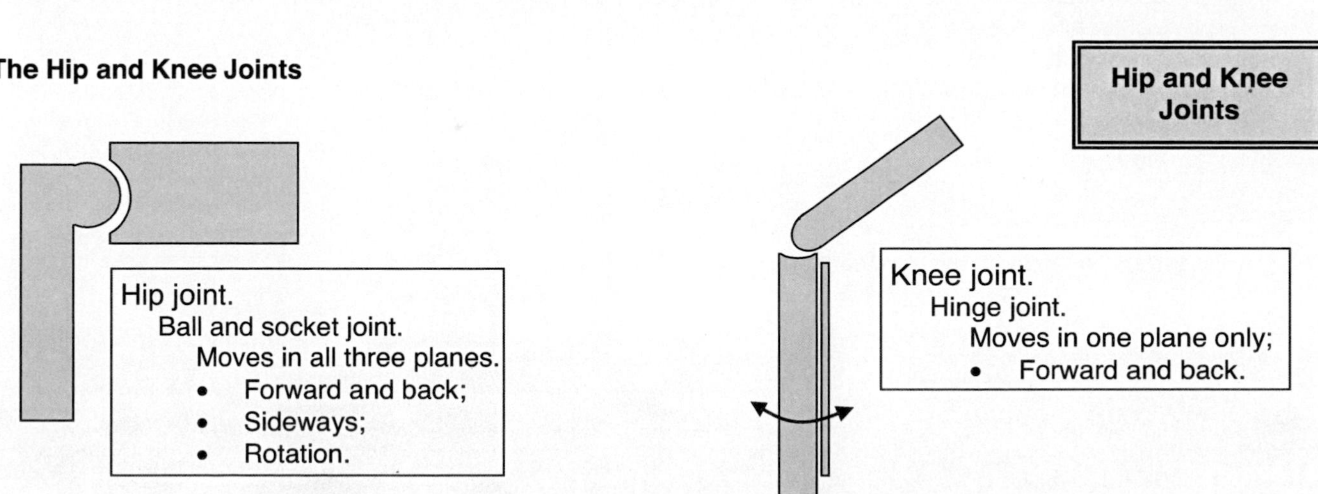

Hip and Knee Joints
Hip joint.
Ball and socket joint.
Moves in all three planes.
• Forward and back;
• Sideways;
• Rotation.
Knee joint.
Hinge joint.
Moves in one plane only;
• Forward and back.

Muscle Structure

Muscle Structure

Key components

- Tendon
- Fibres
- Myofibrils

A muscle fibre is a group of modified muscle cells where many cells have joined end to end to form a single mass of cytoplasm with many nuclei. (Refer back to The Cell Theory on page 10).

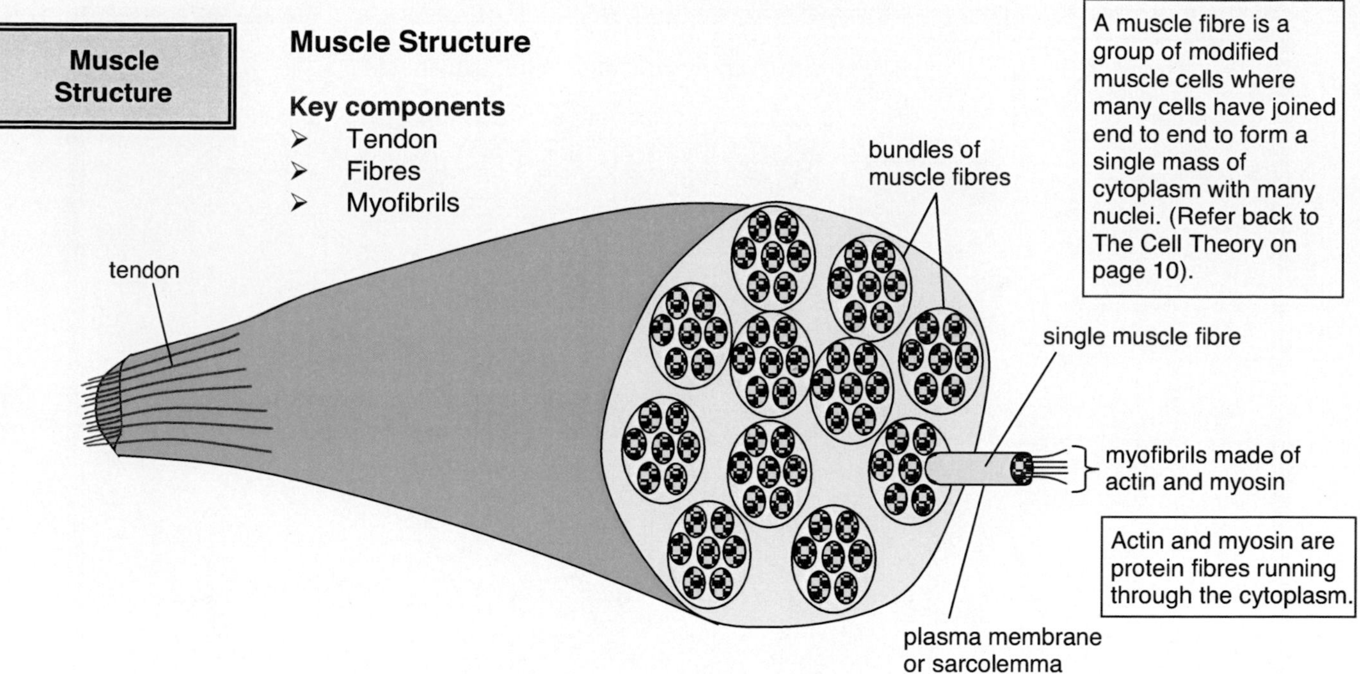
tendon
bundles of muscle fibres
single muscle fibre
myofibrils made of actin and myosin
plasma membrane or sarcolemma

Actin and myosin are protein fibres running through the cytoplasm.

If we remove a single muscle fibre and look at it under the electron microscope we can see a distinct banding pattern (hence the name striated muscle). This banding is due to the arrangement of filaments of two different thicknesses.

Banding pattern of skeletal muscle.

Relate this pattern to the positions of the actin and myosin filaments in the diagram underneath.

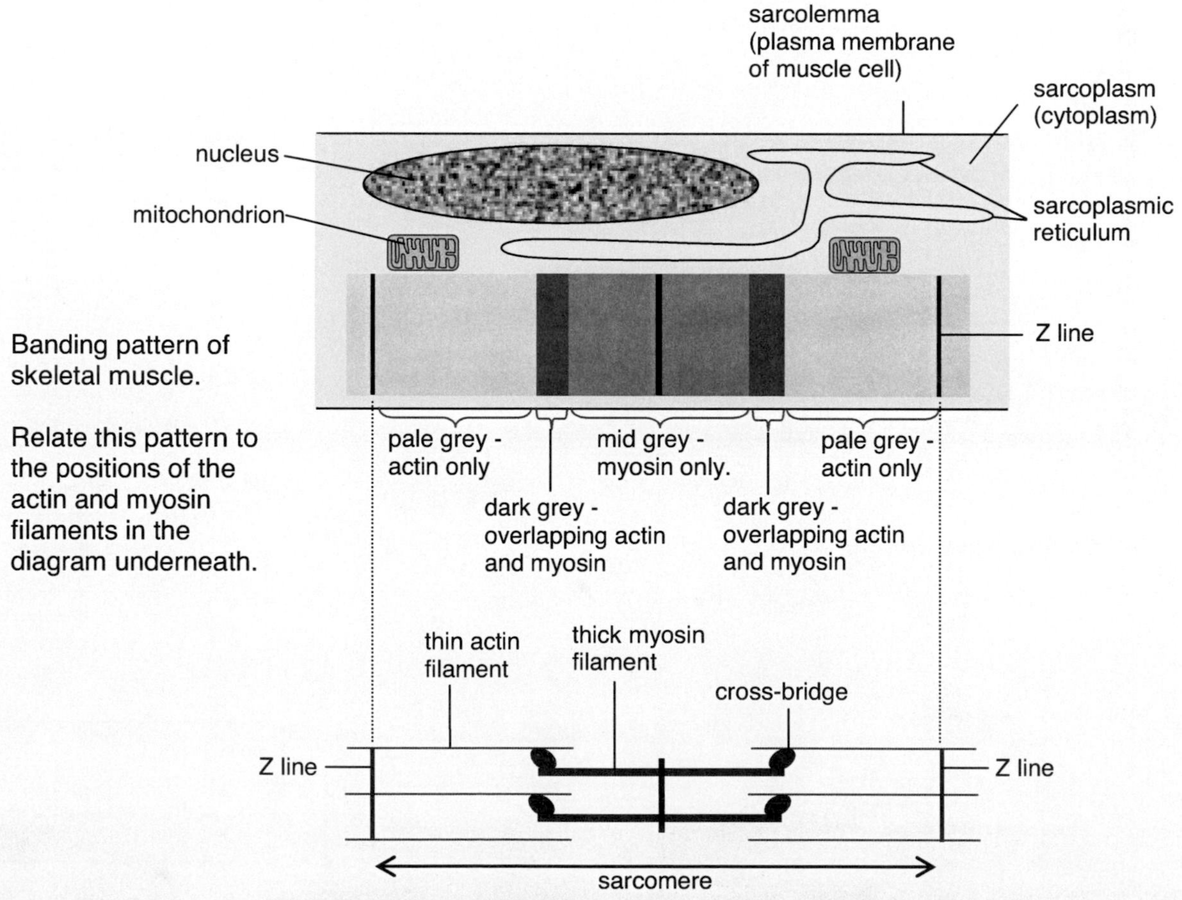
sarcolemma (plasma membrane of muscle cell)
sarcoplasm (cytoplasm)
nucleus
mitochondrion
sarcoplasmic reticulum
Z line
pale grey - actin only
mid grey - myosin only.
pale grey - actin only
dark grey - overlapping actin and myosin
dark grey - overlapping actin and myosin
thin actin filament
thick myosin filament
cross-bridge
Z line
Z line
sarcomere

The Z line is in the middle of the actin. A sarcomere runs from one Z line to the next. *(A of Actin and Z are opposite ends of the alphabet).*

Cross-bridge Formation During Muscle Contraction

Cross-bridge Formation

Key components

- Actin (thin) filament;
- Myosin (thick) filament;
- Myosin head;
- Sarcoplasmic reticulum;
- Calcium ions;
- (Troponin;
- Tropomyosin).

Troponin and tropomyosin are not in your syllabus but including them makes more sense of the role of calcium ions and cross-bridge formation.

Key points

- Arranged along the myosin filaments are projecting heads;
- The actin filament has special binding sites for the myosin heads;
- Binding of the myosin head to the actin binding site forms a cross-bridge;
- These binding sites are covered by a spiral filament of the protein tropomyosin;
- Troponin is attached to the tropomyosin;
- Calcium ions bind to troponin, pulling the tropomyosin off the myosin binding sites;
- Calcium ions are stored by active transport in the sarcoplasmic reticulum;
- Depolarisation of the sarcoplasmic reticulum membrane opens voltage gated calcium channels allowing calcium ions to flow out and to bind to troponin.

Troponin and tropomyosin. Which is which? Remember that tropomyosin is a long fibrous molecule like myosin.

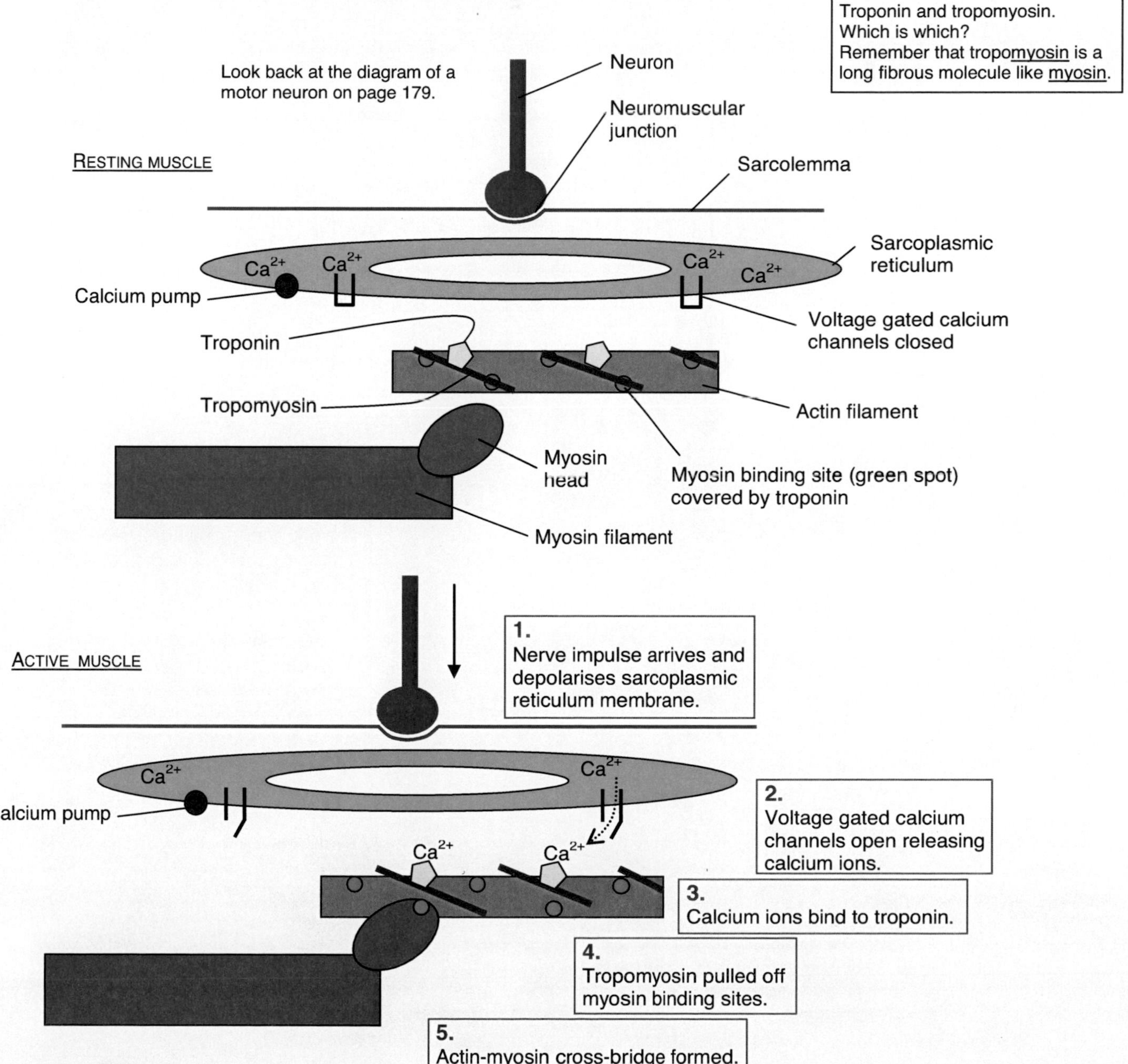
Look back at the diagram of a motor neuron on page 179.
Neuron
Neuromuscular junction
RESTING MUSCLE
Sarcolemma
Sarcoplasmic reticulum
Ca^{2+}
Ca^{2+}
Ca^{2+}
Ca^{2+}
Calcium pump
Voltage gated calcium channels closed
Troponin
Tropomyosin
Actin filament
Myosin head
Myosin binding site (green spot) covered by troponin
Myosin filament
ACTIVE MUSCLE
1. Nerve impulse arrives and depolarises sarcoplasmic reticulum membrane.
Ca^{2+}
Ca^{2+}
Calcium pump
2. Voltage gated calcium channels open releasing calcium ions.
Ca^{2+}
Ca^{2+}
3. Calcium ions bind to troponin.
4. Tropomyosin pulled off myosin binding sites.
5. Actin-myosin cross-bridge formed.

The Sliding Filament Mechanism

The Sliding Filament Mechanism

Key points

- When a cross-bridge forms it can bend pulling the actin filament;
- When ATP binds to myosin it breaks the cross-bridge;
- The myosin head contains the enzyme ATPase which hydrolyses ATP;
- When the cross-bridge breaks the myosin head resets to its original position;
- The cross-bridge reforms further along the actin and the process repeats;
- The Z lines move closer together, ie the sarcomere shortens.

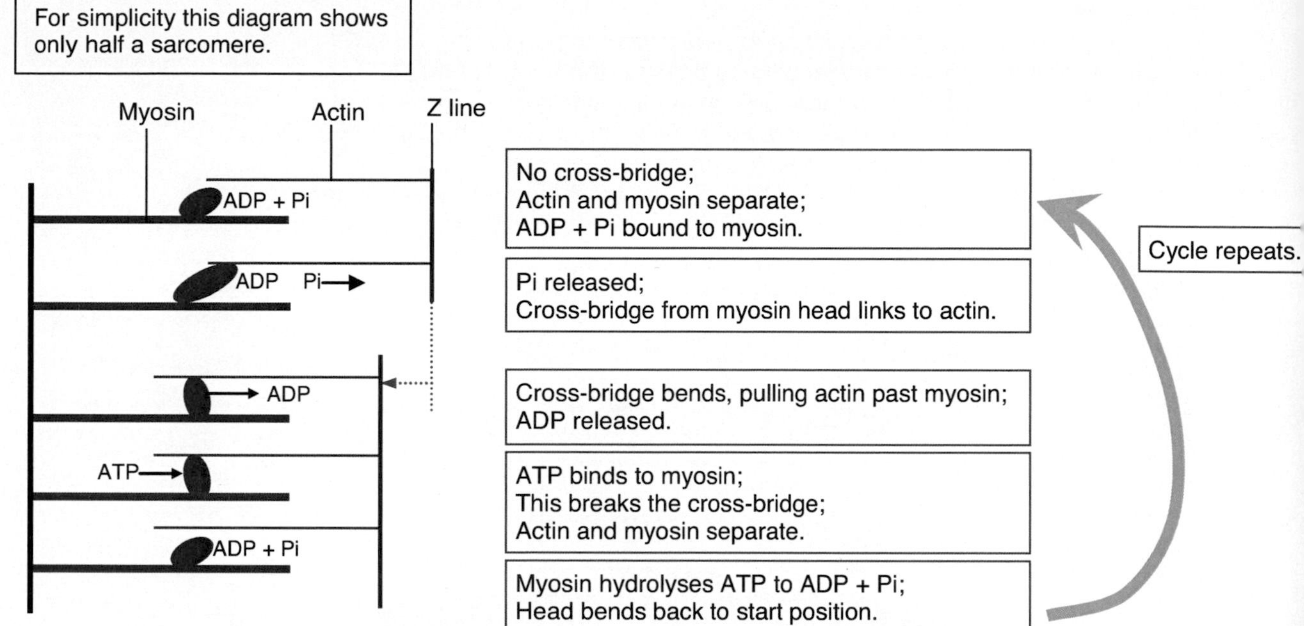

For simplicity this diagram shows only half a sarcomere.
Myosin
Actin
Z line
ADP + Pi
ADP
Pi
ADP
ATP
ADP + Pi
No cross-bridge;
Actin and myosin separate;
ADP + Pi bound to myosin.
Pi released;
Cross-bridge from myosin head links to actin.
Cross-bridge bends, pulling actin past myosin;
ADP released.
ATP binds to myosin;
This breaks the cross-bridge;
Actin and myosin separate.
Myosin hydrolyses ATP to ADP + Pi;
Head bends back to start position.
Cycle repeats.

Banding Patterns

Changes to the Banding Pattern during Muscle Contraction

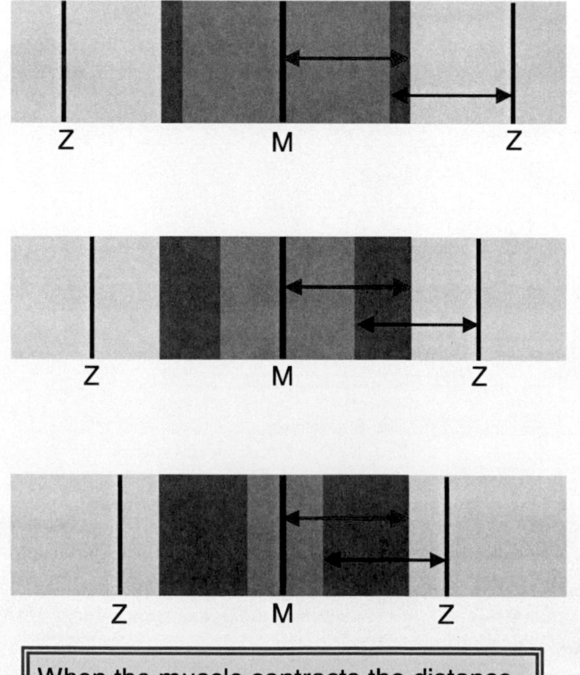

Z
M
Z
Z
M
Z
Z
M
Z
When the muscle contracts the distance between adjacent Z lines has decreased.

Relaxed

Notice that as the muscle contracts the distance between the Z line and the **m**iddle line called **M** is getting smaller.

The blue arrow shows the length of the actin filaments and the red arrow shows the length of the myosin filaments. Neither of these have actually changed in length but the dark grey region where they overlap gets bigger.

Contracted

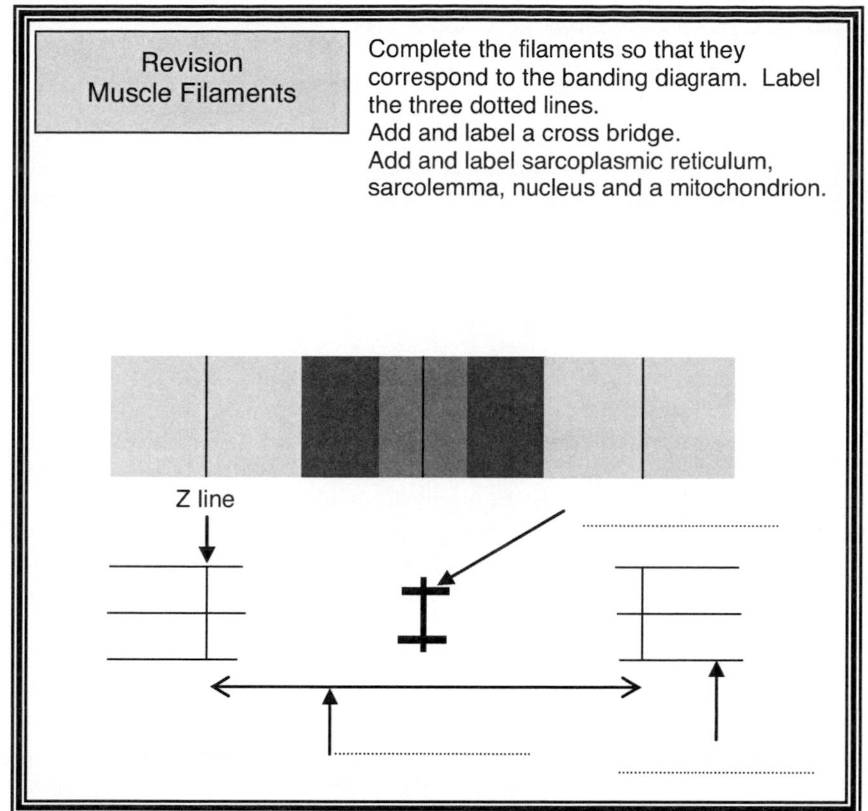
Revision
Muscle Filaments
Complete the filaments so that they correspond to the banding diagram. Label the three dotted lines.
Add and label a cross bridge.
Add and label sarcoplasmic reticulum, sarcolemma, nucleus and a mitochondrion.
Z line

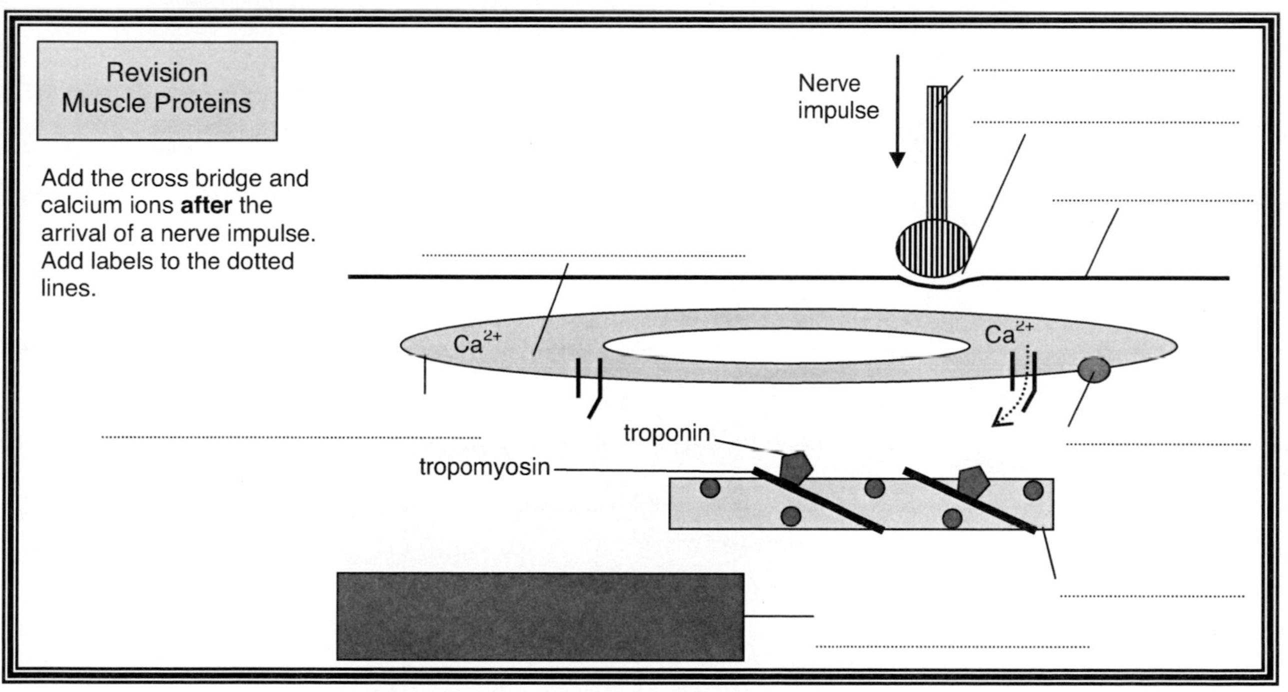
Revision
Muscle Proteins
Add the cross bridge and calcium ions **after** the arrival of a nerve impulse. Add labels to the dotted lines.
Nerve impulse
Ca^{2+}
Ca^{2+}
troponin
tropomyosin

Self-test Quiz on Muscles and Movement

1. When depolarisation of the axon membrane occurs,
   a. sodium ions flow out of the axoplasm,
   b. potassium ions flow into the axoplasm,
   c. chloride ions flow into the axoplasm,
   d. sodium ions flow into the axoplasm.

2. Recovery of the resting potential after depolarisation is achieved by
   a. diffusion of sodium ions out of the axoplasm,
   b. an active linked sodium / potassium pump,
   c. active transport of negative protein ions into the axoplasm,
   d. diffusion of chloride ions out of the axoplasm.

3. During the process of synaptic transmission which of the following does <u>not</u> occur?
   a. Chemical gated sodium channels on the presynaptic membrane open.
   b. Chemical gated sodium channels on the postsynaptic membrane open.
   c. Voltage gated calcium channels on the presynaptic membrane open.
   d. Neurotransmitter is released from the presynaptic membrane.

4. Which of the following statements is true about skeletal muscle?
   a. The thick filament is made up of actin and myosin,
   b. Each muscle cell contains a single nucleus,
   c. The sarcomeres shorten in length when the muscle contracts,
   d. Neurotransmitter is stored in the sarcoplasmic reticulum.

5. During contraction of skeletal muscle
   a. calcium ions diffuse out of the sarcoplasmic reticulum,
   b. calcium ions are actively transported out of the sarcoplasmic reticulum,
   c. calcium ions bind to myosin,
   d. calcium ions bind to actin.

6. During contraction of skeletal muscle
   a. ATP is used to form the cross bridges between the actin and myosin,
   b. voltage gated calcium ion channels on the sarcoplasmic reticulum are opened,
   c. depolarisation of the sarcoplasmic reticulum causes it to release sodium ions into the muscle cells,
   d. the actin and myosin filaments become shorter.

7. Which of the following statements is correct?
   a. ligaments join muscle to bone,
   b. cartilage joins muscle to bone,
   c. tendons join bone to bone,
   d. ligaments join bone to bone.

8. The function of synovial fluid is to
   a. fill the gap between presynaptic and postsynaptic membranes,
   b. act as a lubricant at a joint,
   c. allow phagocytes to move between cells,
   d. act as a lubricant within muscle myofibrils.

9. Which of the following statements is correct?
   a. The biceps is attached to the ulna.
   b. The triceps is attached to the ulna.
   c. The joint capsule secretes synovial fluid.
   d. The knee joint is a ball and socket.

The Kidney

Kidney Structure

Key points

- ➢ Carries out both excretion and water regulation;
- ➢ Blood filtrate passes into tubules within the kidney and these adjust the amount of urea, salts and water.
- ➢ Thus under different conditions the concentration of the urine varies.
- ➢ Examples -
  - urine first thing in the morning is concentrated because you sweated a lot during the night;
  - drinking a lot on a cold day produces a lot of dilute urine;
  - not drinking enough on a hot day and exercising produces a little concentrated urine.

Kidney Structure

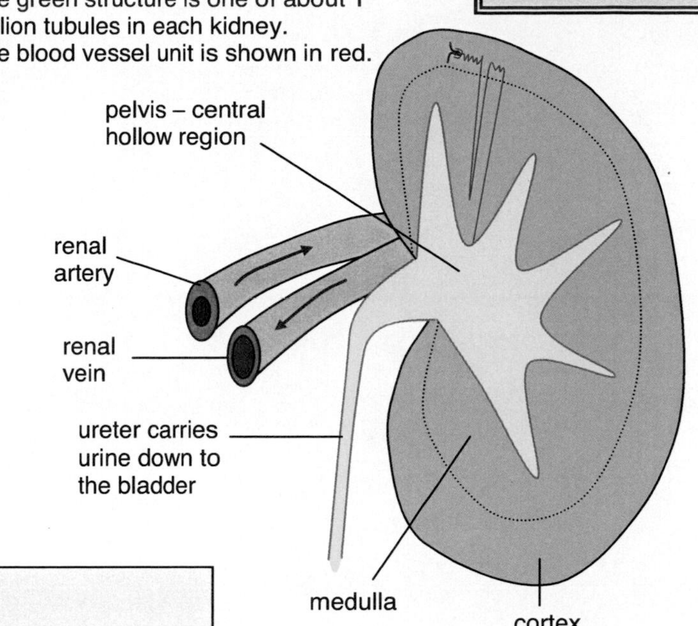

The green structure is one of about 1 million tubules in each kidney.
The blood vessel unit is shown in red.
pelvis – central hollow region
renal artery
renal vein
ureter carries urine down to the bladder
medulla
cortex

Define excretion.

Excretion

Excretion

Key points

- ➢ Metabolic pathways produce waste products that could be toxic or damage molecular structures if allowed to accumulate, eg urea breaks weak non-covalent bonds in proteins leading to denaturing;
- ➢ Excretion is the removal of these substances.

Kidney Tubule

The Kidney Tubule

Bowman's capsule

glomerulus

proximal convoluted tubule

renal arteriole

renal venule

afferent vessel

efferent vessel

collecting duct

loop of Henle

to ureter

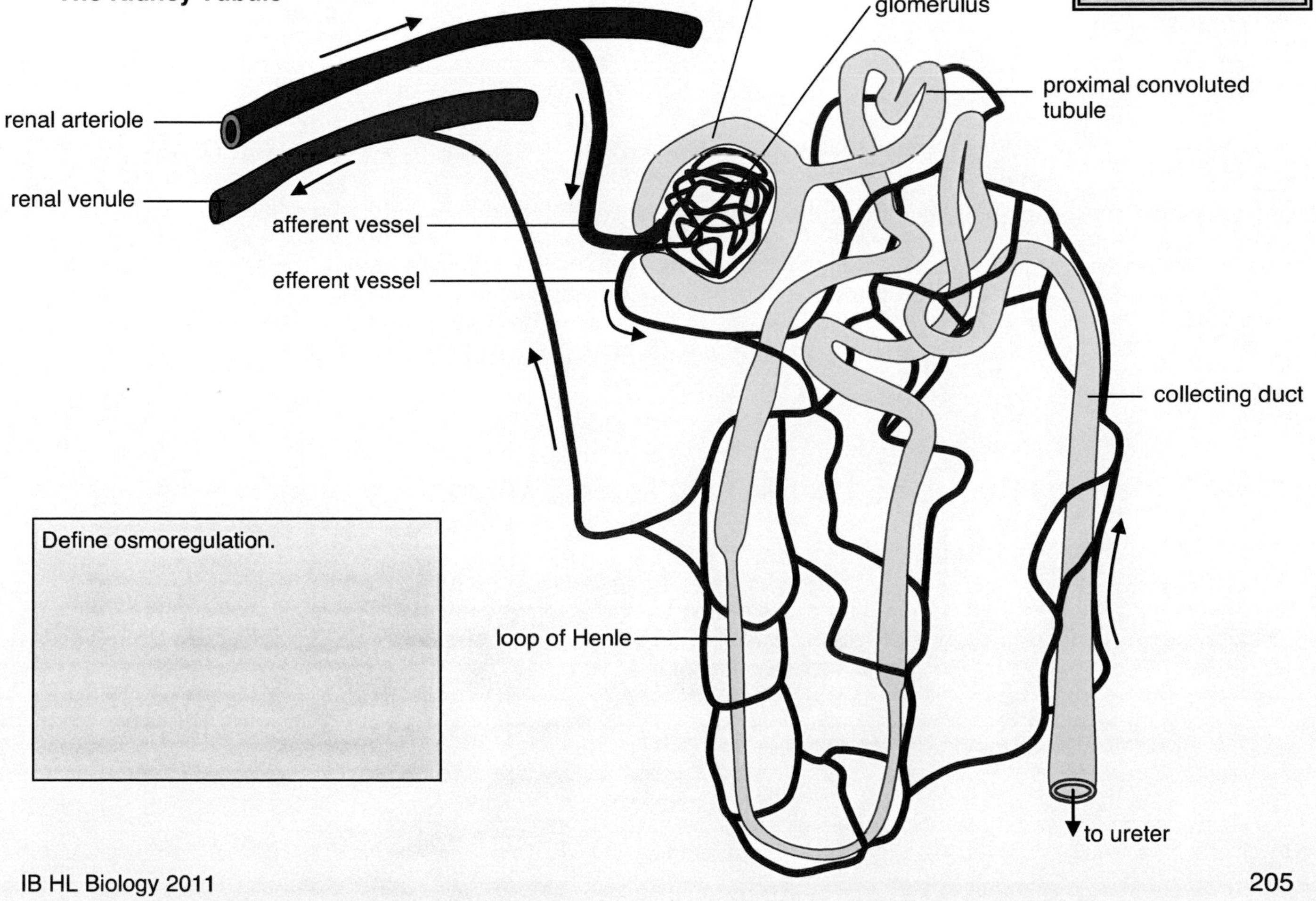

Define osmoregulation.

Ultrafiltration

Ultrafiltration

Ultrafiltration is filtration at the molecular level.

Key components

- ➢ Bowman's capsule;
- ➢ Podocytes
- ➢ Glomerulus;
- ➢ Fenestrated capillary;
- ➢ Basement membrane.

afferent vessel from renal arteriole

space inside Bowman's capsule

blood flow

podocyte layer

glomerulus

efferent vessel to capillaries around tubule

Name the two blood vessels attached to the kidney.

Name the tube carrying urine to the bladder.

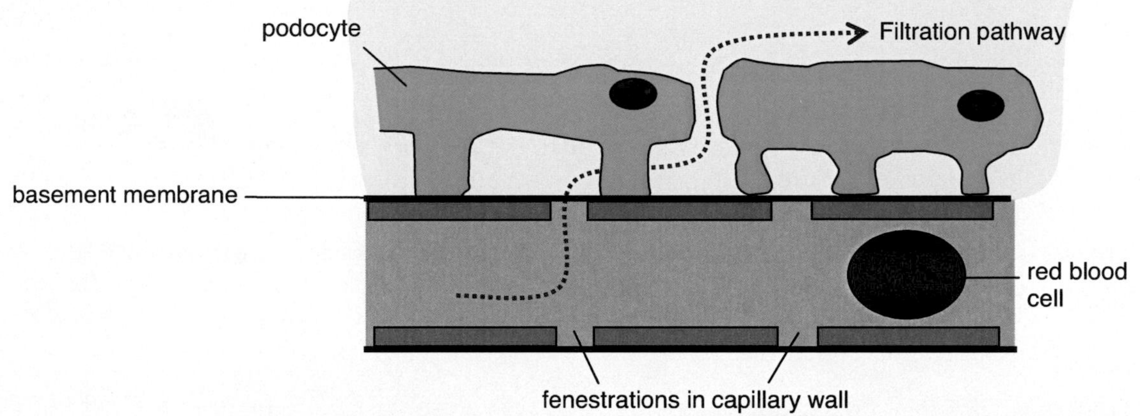
space inside Bowman's capsule containing filtrate
podocyte
Filtration pathway
basement membrane
red blood cell
fenestrations in capillary wall

- Glomerulus has a large surface area.
- Large molecules in the blood can enter the fenestrations (gaps) between the capillary cells but are unable to pass through the basement membrane.
- Thus the basement membrane acts as the 'ultra-filter' and is the only barrier between the filtrate and the blood, allowing small solute molecules such as glucose and urea through but not large ones such as large proteins*.
- The podocytes (cells with feet) allow the filtrate to pass rapidly and easily into the space of Bowman's capsule as there are gaps between the cells.

* Smaller proteins such as the glycoprotein HCG can pass through and is used in the pregnancy test.

Key points

- ➢ Passive;
- ➢ Unselective

  Thus the filtrate will contain approximately the same proportions of all the small soluble molecules as the blood leaving the glomerulus.
- ➢ High glomerular pressure.

  This is due to the blood vessel leaving the glomerulus, the efferent arteriole, being narrower than the incoming vessel, the afferent arteriole. (See previous page). This creates a high pressure in the glomerulus causing filtrate to leave the blood.

Efferent = **E**xit

Name the three regions of the kidney.

What is ultrafiltration?

Reabsorption

Reabsorption

The kidney tubule can be divided into three reabsorption regions –

1. Proximal convoluted tubule,
2. Loop of Henle,
3. Collecting duct.

1. PROXIMAL CONVOLUTED TUBULE

Proximal Tubule

Key points

- Desirable substances taken back into blood by **selective reabsorption**;
- Glucose and salts reabsorbed by active transport;
- Water reabsorbed by osmosis;
- Other solutes reabsorbed by diffusion;
- All glucose (under normal conditions) is reabsorbed;
- About 80% of the filtrate is reabsorbed here.

Key features

- Long, to increase surface area;
- Surrounded by capillaries;
- Cells lining tubule have adaptations shown on the diagram.

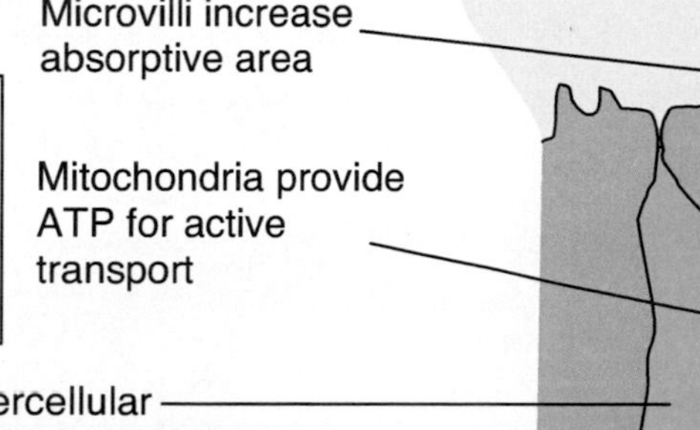
Microvilli increase absorptive area
Tubule lumen
Mitochondria provide ATP for active transport
selective reabsorption
Intercellular and subcellular spaces increase surface area for export
Capillary lumen
Active transport channels in plasma membrane

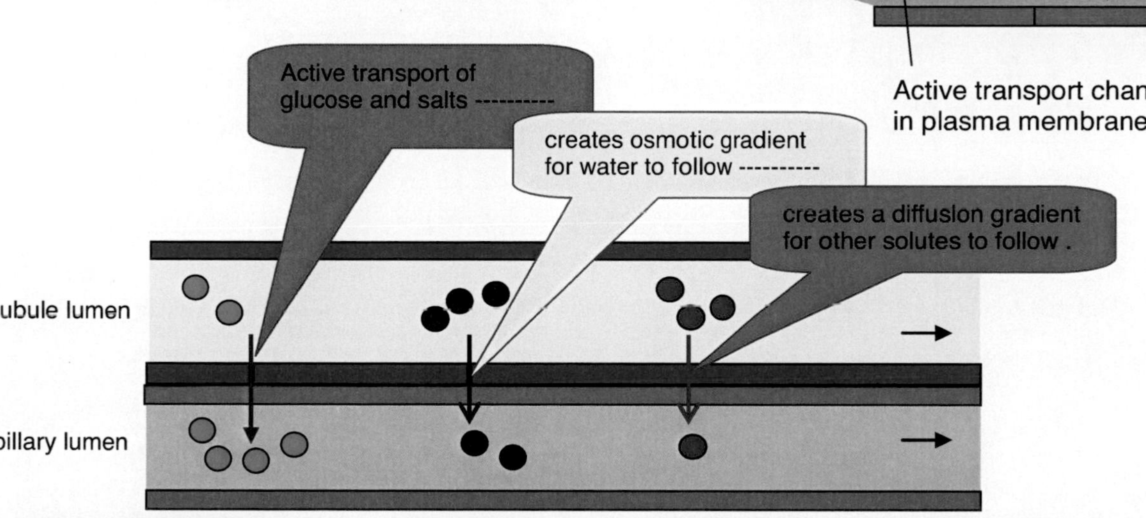
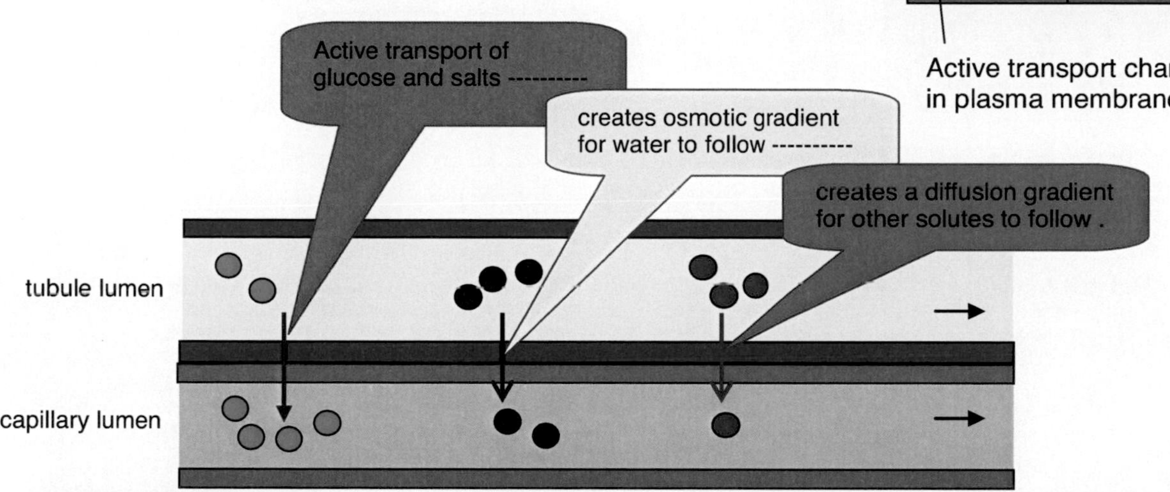
Active transport of glucose and salts ----------
creates osmotic gradient for water to follow ----------
creates a diffusion gradient for other solutes to follow .
tubule lumen
capillary lumen

Revision
Kidney Structure

Draw and label a vertical section through the kidney to show the internal regions and attached tubes.

Loop of Henle

2. LOOP OF HENLE

Principles

- The primary function of the loop of Henle is to create an osmotic gradient within the medullary region of the kidney;
- Some water and salt reabsorption occurs.

Try and visualise this drawing in three dimensions. In reality it is not flat like this. The tubule is surrounded by interstitial fluid and there are many capillaries – look back at p205.

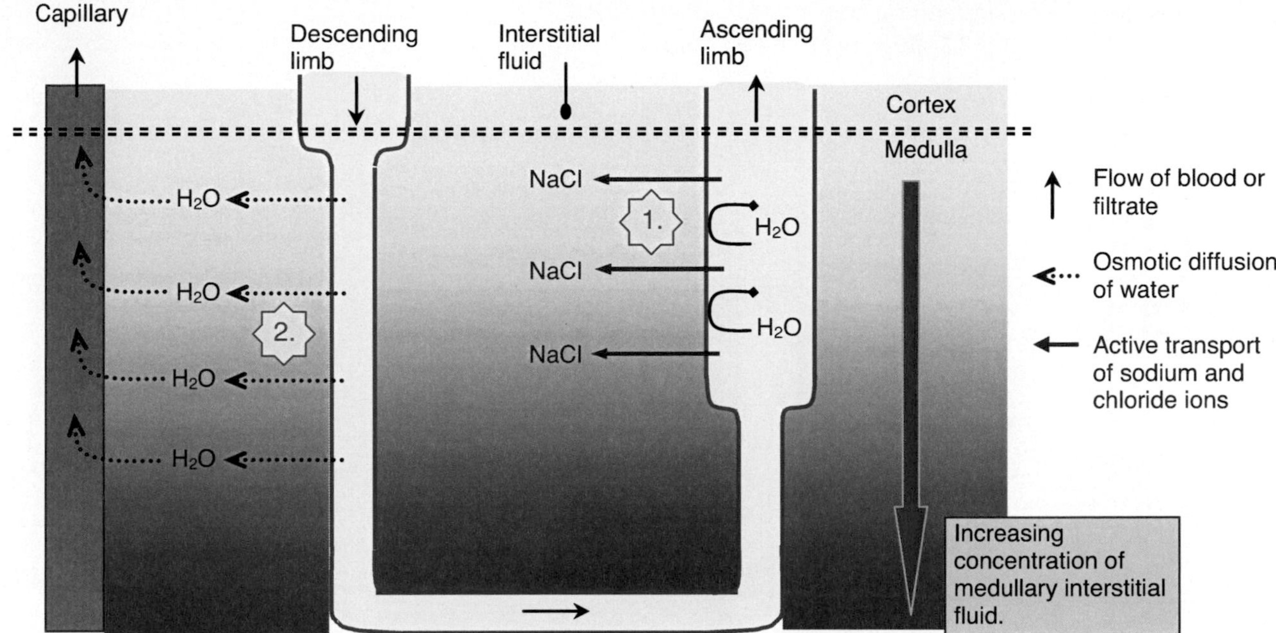

Capillary
Descending limb
Interstitial fluid
Ascending limb
Cortex
Medulla
NaCl
NaCl
NaCl
1.
2.
H2O
H2O
H2O
H2O
H2O
H2O
Flow of blood or filtrate
Osmotic diffusion of water
Active transport of sodium and chloride ions
Increasing concentration of medullary interstitial fluid.

1.

The cells of the ascending limb actively transport salt out into the interstitial fluid. (This is a linked Na^+:K^+:Cl^- symport pump).
In theory water should follow as an osmotic gradient has been created, but the walls of the ascending limb are impermeable to water.

2.

The walls of the descending limb <u>are</u> permeable to water. As a result of the salt being pumped into the interstitial fluid the resulting osmotic gradient causes water to leave the descending limb. This water is removed by the blood in an ascending capillary.

Salt continues to enter the loop in the filtrate in the descending limb but less leaves the loop in the filtrate in the ascending limb and so it accumulates in the interstitial fluid of the medulla. This is called a counter-current multiplier. (Counter-current because the flows are opposite in the descending and ascending limbs).

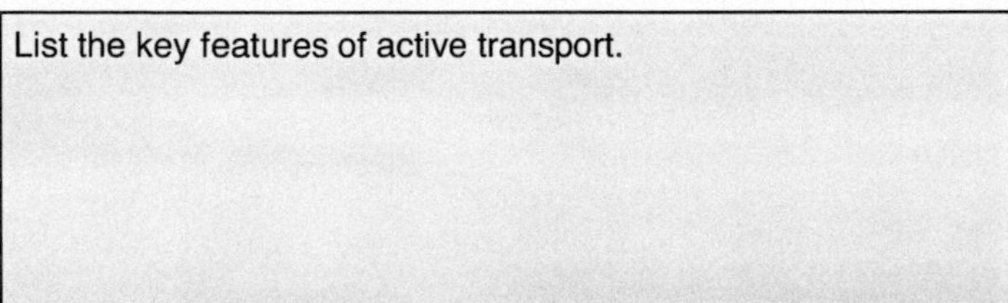

List the key features of active transport.

List the five features of proximal convoluted tubule cells that promote reabsorption.

3. Collecting Duct

Collecting Duct

Principles

- The walls have a variable permeability to water;
- The hormone ADH from the pituitary gland increases the permeability;
- Water flows down the osmotic gradient created by the loop of Henle.

1.
As filtrate flows down the collecting duct the surrounding interstitial fluid is increasingly more concentrated (hypertonic). Thus there is an osmotic gradient between the filtrate and the interstitial fluid.

In the absence of ADH there are few water channels and the duct wall is impermeable to water. This results in isotonic or hypotonic (dilute) urine.

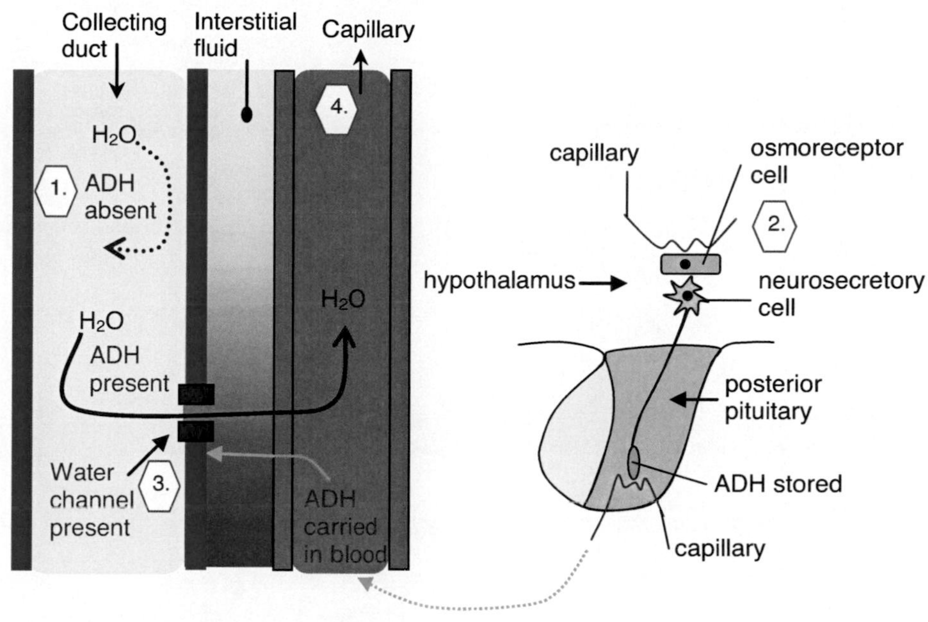

Collecting duct
Interstitial fluid
Capillary
4.
H_2O
1.
ADH absent
H_2O
ADH present
H_2O
Water channel present
3.
ADH carried in blood
capillary
osmoreceptor cell
2.
hypothalamus
neurosecretory cell
posterior pituitary
ADH stored
capillary

2.
If the blood concentration rises osmoreceptors in the hypothalamus stimulate neurosecretory cells to release ADH from the posterior pituitary gland which travels in the blood stream to the collecting duct.

3.
Water channels in the duct wall are inserted by the presence of ADH so water leaves the filtrate by osmosis and is removed by the blood.
This results in hypertonic (concentrated) urine.

4.
Note that the blood flow is opposite to the filtrate flow. This is so that there is always an osmotic gradient between the filtrate and the blood.

The half-life of ADH is only 15 -20 minutes so this allows water balance to be tightly controlled.

Revision Ultrafiltration

Label the dotted lines.

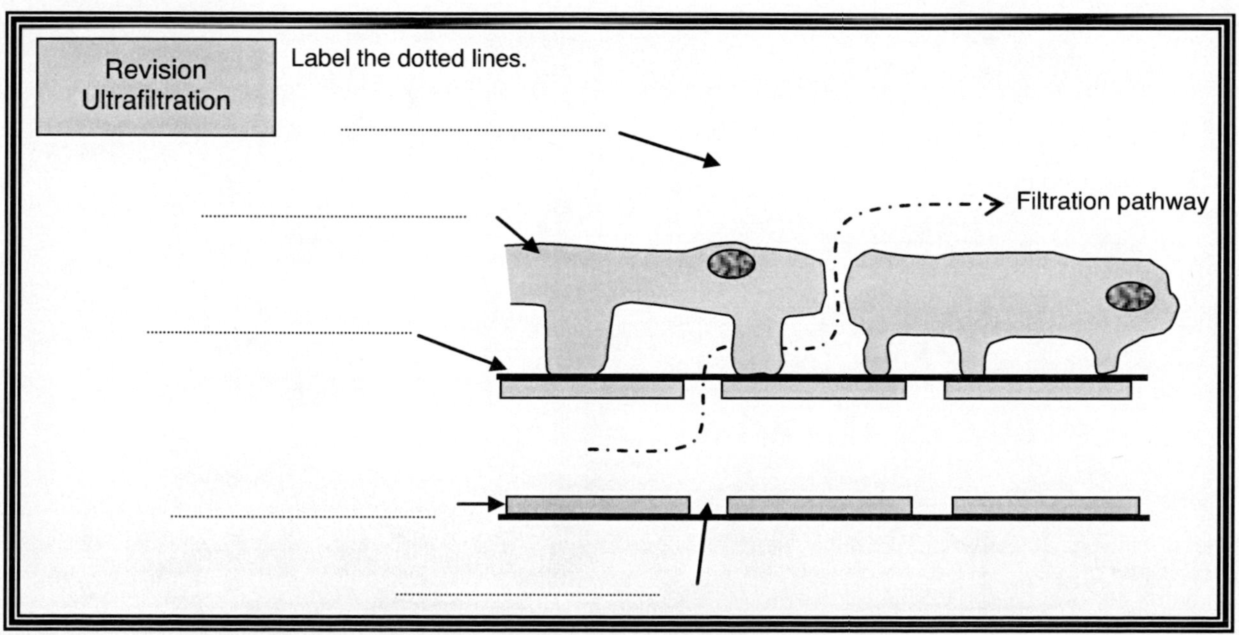

Filtration pathway

Name the three reabsorptive regions of the nephron.

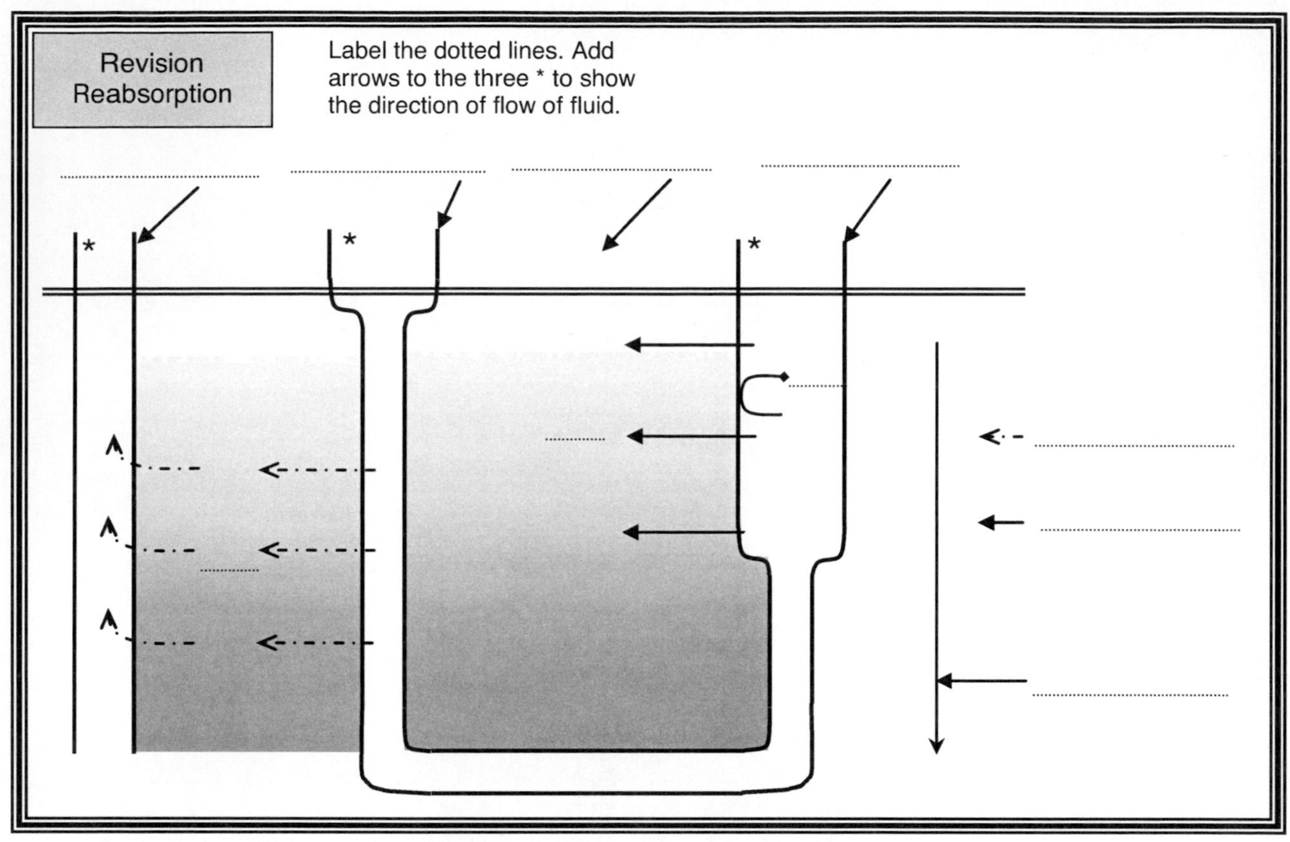
Revision
Reabsorption
Label the dotted lines. Add arrows to the three * to show the direction of flow of fluid.

Revision
Reabsorption

State where this type of cell is found on label A and the blood vessel label B. Label the dotted lines showing the special adaptations of this cell.

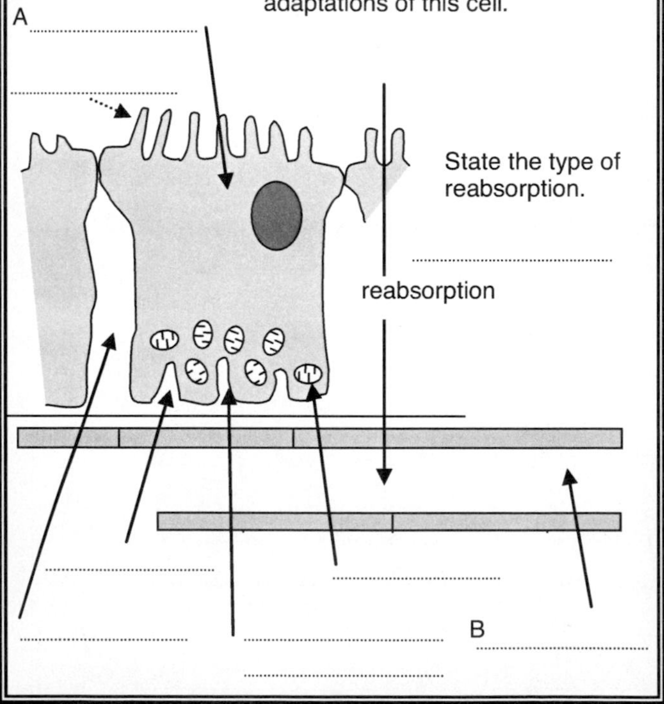

A ....

State the type of reabsorption.

.... reabsorption

B ....

Revision
Reabsorption

Label the dotted lines.

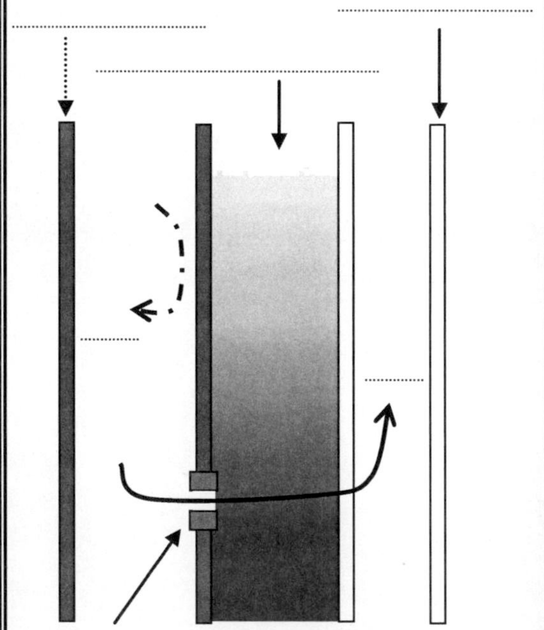

.... is present due to the .... of the hormone ....

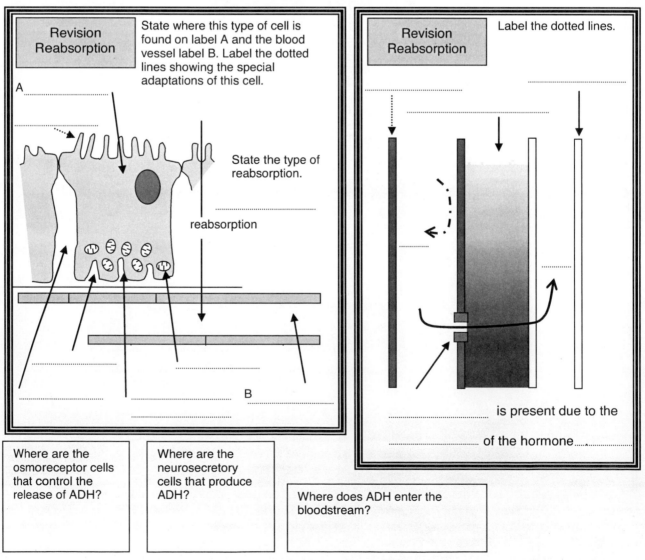

Where are the osmoreceptor cells that control the release of ADH?

Where are the neurosecretory cells that produce ADH?

Where does ADH enter the bloodstream?

Composition of Fluids

Composition of Fluids

Substance	Blood plasma	Glomerular filtrate	Urine
Proteins	Normal concentration.	None to very little (remember HCG) because most plasma proteins are too large to pass through the basement membrane in Bowman's capsule.	None to very little. If any substantial amount of protein is present this could indicate damage to the kidney.
Glucose	Normal concentration.	Glucose is small enough to pass through the basement membrane and so its concentration is approximately equal to that in the plasma.	Normally none. In a healthy person all the glucose is reabsorbed in the proximal convoluted tubule. In a diabetic some may be present.
Urea	Normal concentration.	Urea is small enough to pass through the basement membrane and so its concentration is approximately equal to that in the plasma.	Higher concentration due to reabsorption of water. However ideally all the filtered urea would be excreted but because it is a small molecule over half of that filtered gets reabsorbed back into the blood.

Diabetics

Diabetics

Diabetes is the inability to prevent glucose levels in the plasma from becoming too high due to a failure of the insulin homeostatic mechanism.

In the proximal convoluted tubule there are active transport proteins that pick up the glucose molecules as they flow past in the filtrate. If the number of glucose molecules in the filtrate is very high because the plasma concentration in the glomerulus was very high, then some of them will get missed and leave the proximal tubule. After here there are no glucose transport proteins and so this glucose will end up in the urine. Imagine someone is throwing tennis balls at you and you have to catch them and put them in a box. As the rate of balls coming to you increases there will come a time when a ball zooms past you because just at that moment you had a ball in both hands.

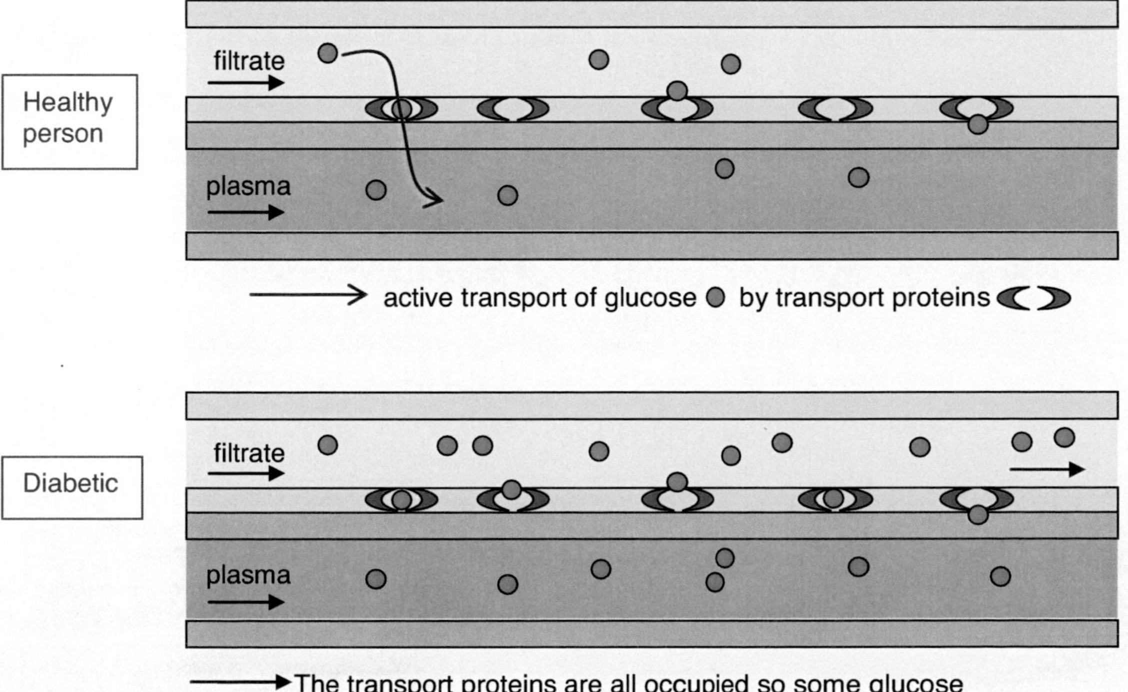
Healthy person
filtrate
plasma
active transport of glucose by transport proteins
Diabetic
filtrate
plasma
The transport proteins are all occupied so some glucose molecules have gone past and will appear in the urine.

Self-test Quiz on The Kidney

1. In which region of the kidney will glomeruli be found?
    a. Ureter.
    b. Cortex.
    c. Medulla.
    d. Pelvis.

2. In the kidney the ureter is connected directly to the
    a. cortex,
    b. medulla,
    c. pelvis,
    d. renal vein.

3. The reason why some desert mammals have very long loops of Henle is because
    a. it allows them to conserve water,
    b. it reduces the loss of nutrients,
    c. they can stay in their burrows during the heat of the day,
    d. they can increase the amount of urea lost.

4. Which of the following is <u>not</u> a characteristic feature of the cells of the proximal tubule?
    a. microvilli,
    b. cilia,
    c. large numbers of mitochondria,
    d. subcellular spaces.

5. Which of the following statements is correct?
    a. The collecting duct actively absorbs water.
    b. The active transport of glucose creates a gradient for salt to diffuse from the plasma to the proximal tubule,
    c. Glucose is returned to the blood stream by active transport from the descending limb of the loop of Henle.
    d. The osmotic gradient in the medulla created by the loop of Henle permits reabsorption of water from the collecting duct.

6. Which of the following statements is correct?
    a. There is relatively more urea in the renal vein than in the renal artery.
    b. The glomerular filtrate contains more glucose than the filtrate in the collecting duct.
    c. The filtrate pressure in Bowman's capsule is higher than the blood pressure in the glomerulus.
    d. There is the same amount of glucose in the renal vein as there is in the renal artery.

7. Glucose may be present in the urine of a diabetic because
    a. the quantity of glucose in the filtrate exceeds the transport capacity of the proximal tubules.
    b. they produce more glucagon which raises plasma glucose.
    c. the glucose transport mechanism in the proximal tubules fails to function.
    d. there is insufficient insulin to activate the transport channels in the proximal tubules.

8. Ultrafiltration means
   a. that only molecules below a certain size can pass through the filtration membrane,
   b. that filtration takes place under pressure in the glomerulus,
   c. the process of filtration is very efficient,
   d. active transport is involved in the process of transferring glucose and salts from the glomerulus to Bowman's capsule.

9. The hormone that controls water uptake in the collecting duct is
   a. insulin.
   b. adrenalin.
   c. antidiuretic hormone.
   d. glucagon.

10. The hormone that controls water uptake in the collecting duct is released from the
   a. hypothalamus.
   b. posterior pituitary gland.
   c. anterior pituitary gland.
   d. kidney.

11. Water is absorbed in the collecting duct when ADH is present. Which of the following is <u>not</u> a mechanism by which water moves from the filtrate to the blood.
   a. Facilitated diffusion.
   b. Active transport.
   c. Osmosis.
   d. Diffusion.

12. Glucose is not normally found in the urine because
   a. it is unable to leave the glomerulus;
   b. it is actively removed from the filtrate in the loop of Henle;
   c. it diffuses out of the filtrate into the blood;
   d. it is actively transported into the blood from the proximal convoluted tubule.

13. Pressure in the glomerulus is maintained due to –
   a. the efferent vessel being narrower than the afferent vessel.
   b. some of the filtrate being removed in the proximal convoluted tubule.
   c. the afferent vessel being narrower than the efferent vessel.
   d. active transport of solutes into Bowman's capsule.

14. Proteins are not normally found in the urine because –
   a. proteins are not present in the plasma;
   b. proteins leaving the glomerulus are broken down into amino acids before being released into the filtrate.
   c. proteins in the plasma are mostly too large to pass through the basement membrane of the capillaries.
   d. they are actively transported out of the filtrate by the cells of the proximal convoluted tubule.

15. Which of the following statements is correct?
   a. Sodium ions are actively transported out of the ascending limb and actively transported into the descending limb.
   b. As sodium ions are actively transported out of the ascending limb water follows due to osmosis.
   c. Sodium ions are actively transported out of the descending limb causing water to diffuse into the descending limb.
   d. As sodium ions are actively transported out of the ascending limb water moves by osmosis out of the descending limb.

16. Which of the following statements is correct?
    a. If the blood concentration rises the less water is reabsorbed in the proximal tubule.
    b. ADH released from the pancreas increase the uptake of water in the descending limb.
    c. ADH released from the pituitary gland causes water reabsorption in the collecting duct.
    d. When blood concentration falls ADH is released from the pituitary gland and water channels are inserted in the collecting duct walls.

17. Solutes are transferred from the filtrate in the proximal tubule to the plasma by
    a. active transport and diffusion;
    b. active transport and osmosis;
    c. osmosis and diffusion;
    d. diffusion only.

18. Filtration in Bowman's capsule is made more efficient by the presence of
    a. fenestrated capillaries;
    b. podocytes;
    c. increased glomerular pressure;
    d. all of the above.

Reproduction

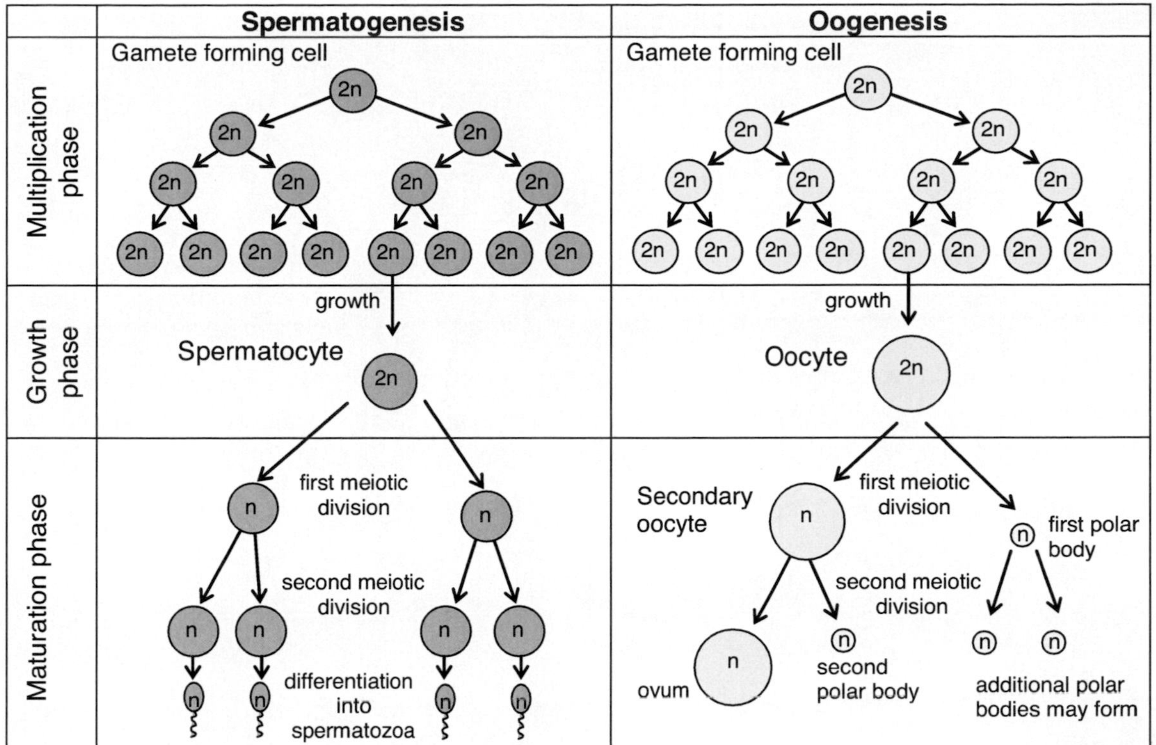
Spermatogenesis
Oogenesis
Multiplication phase
Growth phase
Maturation phase
Gamete forming cell
2n
growth
Spermatocyte
Oocyte
first meiotic division
second meiotic division
n
differentiation into spermatozoa
Secondary oocyte
first polar body
ovum
second polar body
additional polar bodies may form

Comparing Spermatogenesis and Oogenesis

Comparing Spermatogenesis and Oogenesis

Key points

Similarities

- Involve mitosis at the start.
- Involve cell growth.
- Involve FSH and LH.
- Involve meiosis.
- Involve differentiation - sperm : acrosome, midpiece, tail.
  - egg : cortical granules.

Differences

- Polar bodies are structures that remove the excess genetic material during oogenesis and do not develop further into gametes. They are not formed during spermatogenesis.
- Each gamete forming cell in a male produces four gametes, whereas that in a female only produces one gamete plus 2 or 3 polar bodies.
- The human uterus is best at carrying only one embryo and hence only one oocyte is released. However large numbers of sperm are released as most are lost on the journey from vagina to oviduct.
- Sperm production is continuous throughout the month whereas oocyte production follows a monthly cyclical pattern.
- Both testes produce sperm, whereas ovulation tends to occur from alternate ovaries each month.
- Spermatogenesis commences at puberty whereas the start of oogenesis is prenatal.
- Spermatogenesis continues until death whereas oogenesis stops at menopause.
- Spermatogenesis involves Sertoli or nurse cells whereas oogenesis does not.
- In spermatogenesis meiosis is a continuous process leading to haploid cells. In oogenesis meiosis pauses after prophase II and completion of the second division is stimulated by penetration of the oocyte membrane by the sperm. Thus the cell released at ovulation is the secondary oocyte and not an ovum.

Hormone	Site of Production	Function in Boys
Luteinising hormone (LH)	Anterior pituitary	Stimulates secretion of testosterone by interstitial cells
Follicle stimulating hormone (FSH)	Anterior pituitary	Stimulates initial stages of spermatogenesis
Testosterone	Interstitial cells of the testes	Brings about puberty and maintains secondary sexual characteristics; Stimulates final stages of spermatogenesis

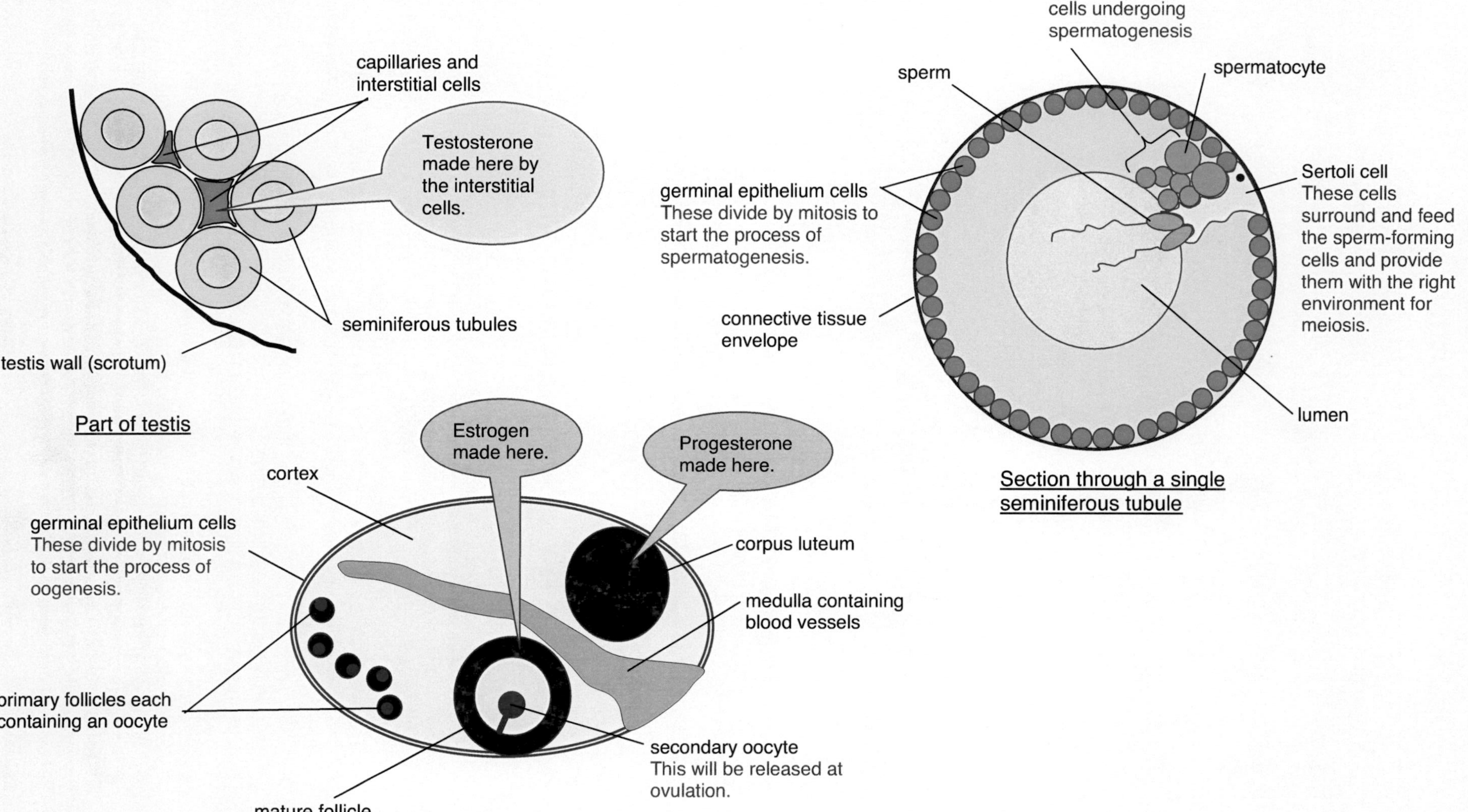
capillaries and interstitial cells
Testosterone made here by the interstitial cells.
seminiferous tubules
testis wall (scrotum)
Part of testis
cells undergoing spermatogenesis
sperm
spermatocyte
germinal epithelium cells
These divide by mitosis to start the process of spermatogenesis.
Sertoli cell
These cells surround and feed the sperm-forming cells and provide them with the right environment for meiosis.
connective tissue envelope
lumen
Section through a single seminiferous tubule
Estrogen made here.
Progesterone made here.
cortex
germinal epithelium cells
These divide by mitosis to start the process of oogenesis.
corpus luteum
medulla containing blood vessels
primary follicles each containing an oocyte
secondary oocyte
This will be released at ovulation.
mature follicle
Section through ovary

Semen Production

Semen is the mixture of sperms and secretions from accessory glands along the male reproductive tract.

Structure	Function
Epididymis	Storage structure in each testis where the sperm mature and become motile.
Seminal vesicles	Produce seminal fluid. Thick due to mucus and protein. Contains fructose as an energy source for sperm. Contains prostaglandins. These are hormones that stimulate contractions of the female reproductive tract. This helps movement of the sperm into the oviducts.
Prostate gland	Produces prostate fluid. Thin alkaline fluid to neutralise acidity in vagina. Contains a clotting enzyme that converts the protein in seminal fluid into a gelatinous mass. This helps protect the sperm from the hostile environment of the vagina.

Semen Production

Where is the epididymis?

Where are the seminal vesicles?

Where is the prostate gland?

Structure of the Sperm

Sperm Structure

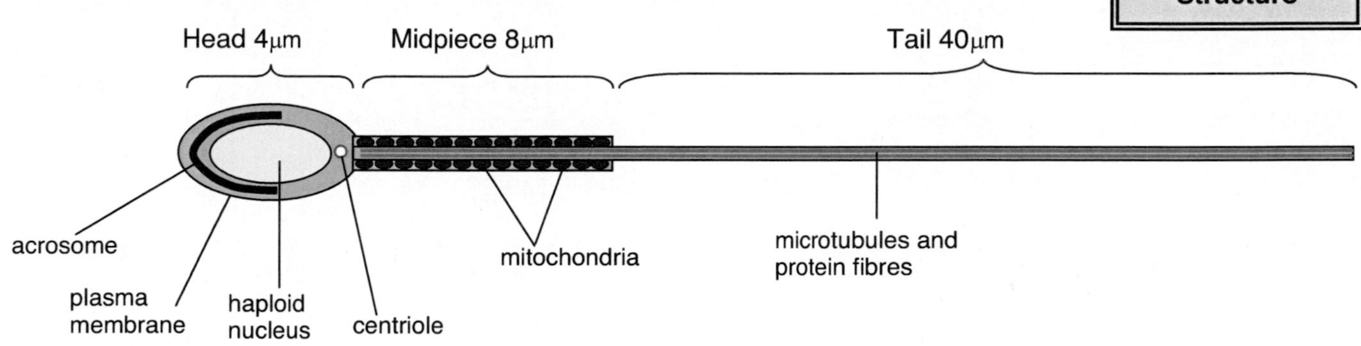
Head 4μm
Midpiece 8μm
Tail 40μm
acrosome
plasma membrane
haploid nucleus
centriole
mitochondria
microtubules and protein fibres

Structure of the Egg

Egg Structure

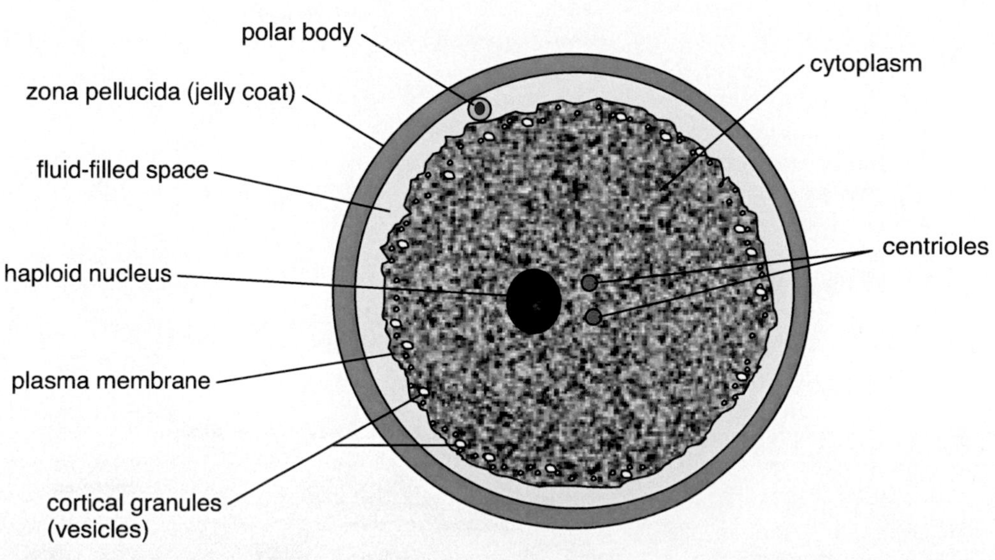
polar body
zona pellucida (jelly coat)
fluid-filled space
haploid nucleus
plasma membrane
cortical granules (vesicles)
cytoplasm
centrioles

Fertilisation

Fertilisation and the Acrosome and Cortical Reactions

Final maturation of the sperm, called <u>capacitation</u>, occurs in the female genital tract.

1.
- Sperm head contacts zona pellucida;
- Binds to specific glycoproteins;
- Calcium pump activated causing uptake of calcium ions into sperm head.
- This causes the acrosome (a very large lysosome) to release enzymes by exocytosis.*
- These enzymes include a carbohydrase and a protease.

zona pellucida (jelly coat)

fluid-filled space

plasma membrane

cortical granules (vesicles)

2.
- Enzymes allow penetration by the sperm head of the zona pellucida, the fluid-filled space and the plasma membrane of the oocyte.
- This triggers completion of the second meiotic division of the oocyte.

3.
- Penetration of the plasma membrane by the sperm head triggers release of Ca^{2+} stored in endoplasmic reticulum;
- This causes exocytosis* of the enzymes in the cortical granules into the fluid-filled space, the cortical reaction.
- These enzymes do two things –
  - remove the sperm binding glycoproteins on the surface of the zona pellucida;
  - cause changes to proteins in the zona pellucida, creating the fertilisation membrane which prevents other sperm from entering the cytoplasm.

4.
Fertilisation membrane spreads over surface of plasma membrane.

5.
Fusion of the sperm nucleus with the egg nucleus is delayed for several hours until the final stages of oogenesis are completed – see page 215, last bullet point of Differences.

* You came across this same process earlier – an influx of Ca^{2+} causes vesicles of neurotransmitter to bind to the pre-synaptic membrane – see page 101.

HCG

HCG - Human Chorionic Gonadotrophin

Key facts

- ➢ Produced by the developing placenta;
- ➢ Production starts soon after implantation;
- ➢ Maintains corpus luteum so production of progesterone continues;
- ➢ High levels of progesterone and estrogen prevent the endometrium from breaking down;
- ➢ HCG is small enough to pass through the basement membrane of the glomerulus. It can be detected in the urine with the use of monoclonal antibodies as a pregnancy test. (See page 194).

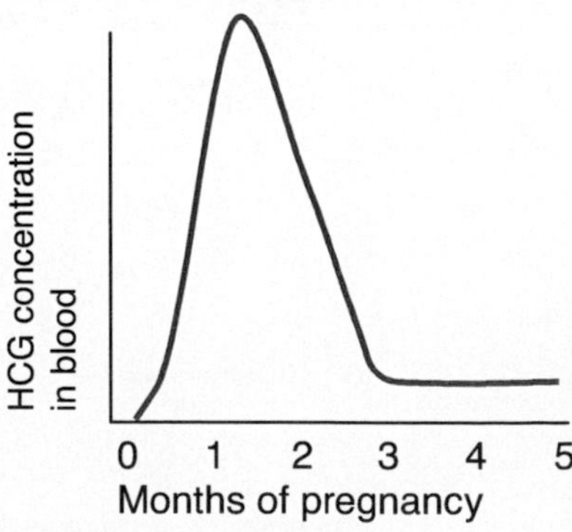
HCG concentration in blood
0
1
2
3
4
5
Months of pregnancy

Early Embryo Development

Early Embryo Development

zygote → blastocyst

Single diploid cell

Several mitotic divisions

Hollow ball of cells

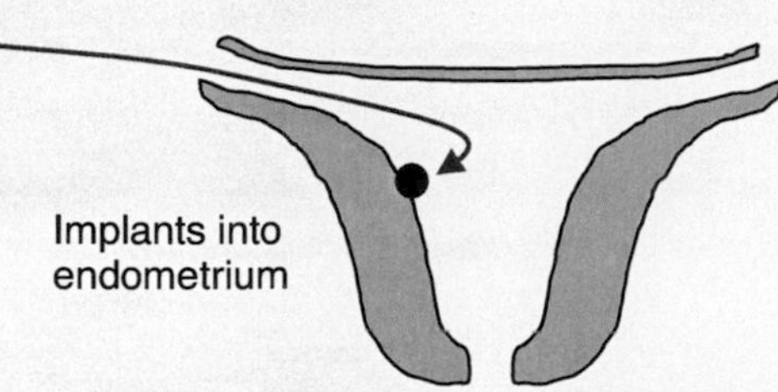
Implants into endometrium

The Placenta

Key facts

- Barrier between maternal blood and fetal blood;
- Exchange site for molecules between maternal blood and fetal blood;
- Is an endocrine organ – HCG, estrogen, progesterone, human placental lactogen (stimulates mammary development);
- Has complete hormonal control of pregnancy by week 12. (Note in graph on previous page that the level of HCG has dropped to a very low level by week 12 as it is no longer required to maintain the corpus luteum).

The fetus is supported and protected by the amniotic sac and fluid.

Nutrients and waste materials are exchanged between fetal blood and maternal blood through the placenta.

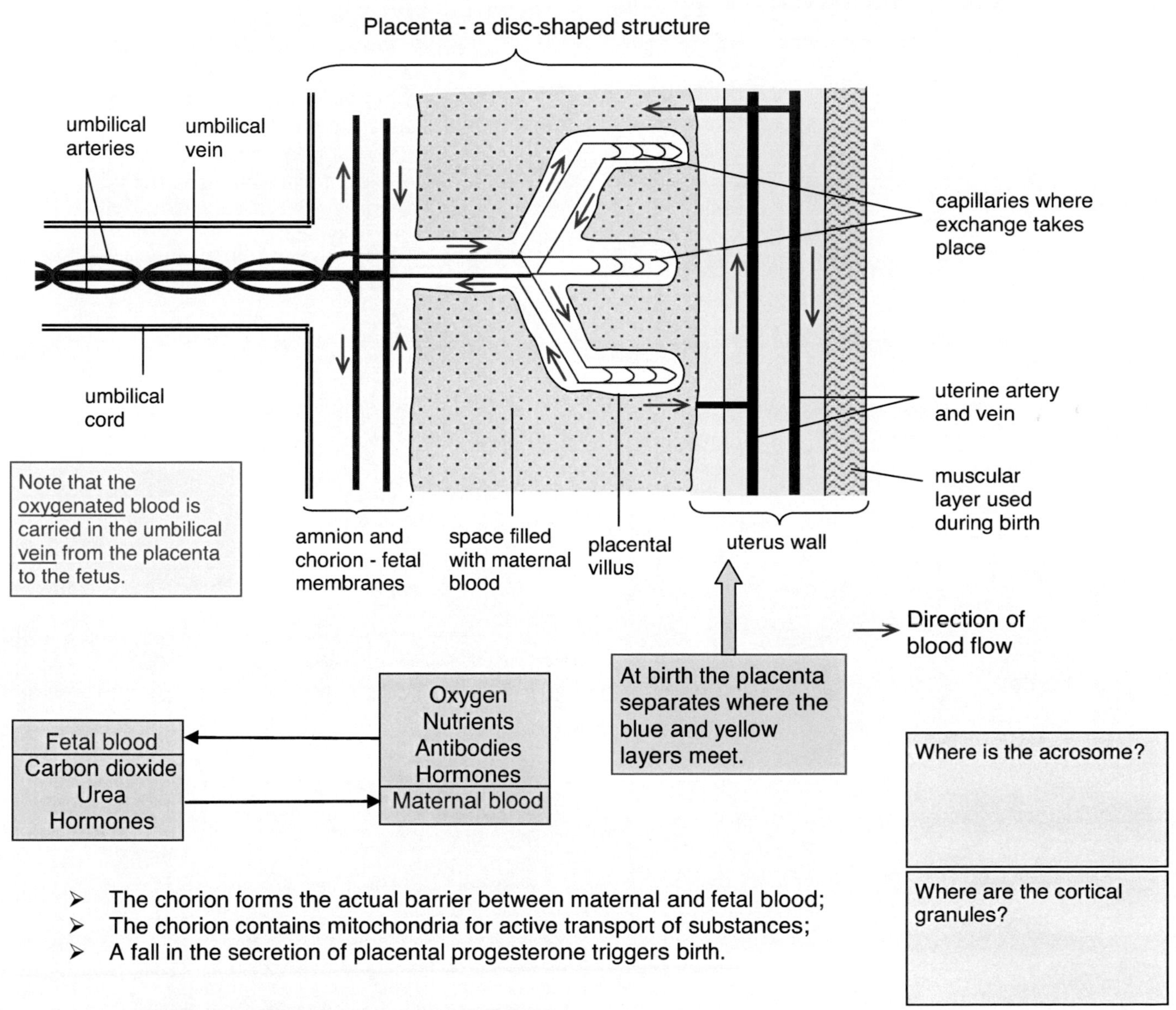
Placenta - a disc-shaped structure
umbilical arteries
umbilical vein
umbilical cord
capillaries where exchange takes place
uterine artery and vein
muscular layer used during birth
amnion and chorion - fetal membranes
space filled with maternal blood
placental villus
uterus wall
Direction of blood flow
Note that the oxygenated blood is carried in the umbilical vein from the placenta to the fetus.
At birth the placenta separates where the blue and yellow layers meet.
Fetal blood
Carbon dioxide
Urea
Hormones
Oxygen
Nutrients
Antibodies
Hormones
Maternal blood
Where is the acrosome?
Where are the cortical granules?

- The chorion forms the actual barrier between maternal and fetal blood;
- The chorion contains mitochondria for active transport of substances;
- A fall in the secretion of placental progesterone triggers birth.

Prolactin, a hormone from the anterior pituitary gland, increases after birth and stimulates milk production.

Birth and its Hormonal Control

Birth and its Hormonal Control

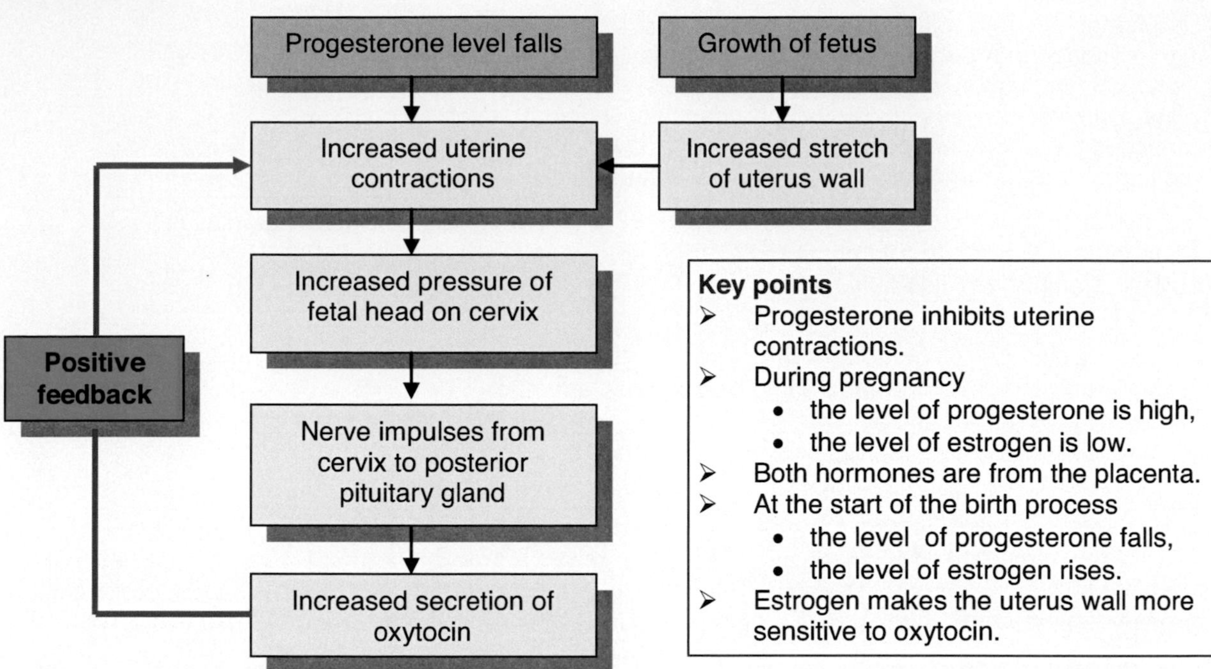

Progesterone level falls
Growth of fetus
Increased uterine contractions
Increased stretch of uterus wall
Increased pressure of fetal head on cervix
Positive feedback
Nerve impulses from cervix to posterior pituitary gland
Increased secretion of oxytocin

Key points

- Progesterone inhibits uterine contractions.
- During pregnancy
  - the level of progesterone is high,
  - the level of estrogen is low.
- Both hormones are from the placenta.
- At the start of the birth process
  - the level of progesterone falls,
  - the level of estrogen rises.
- Estrogen makes the uterus wall more sensitive to oxytocin.

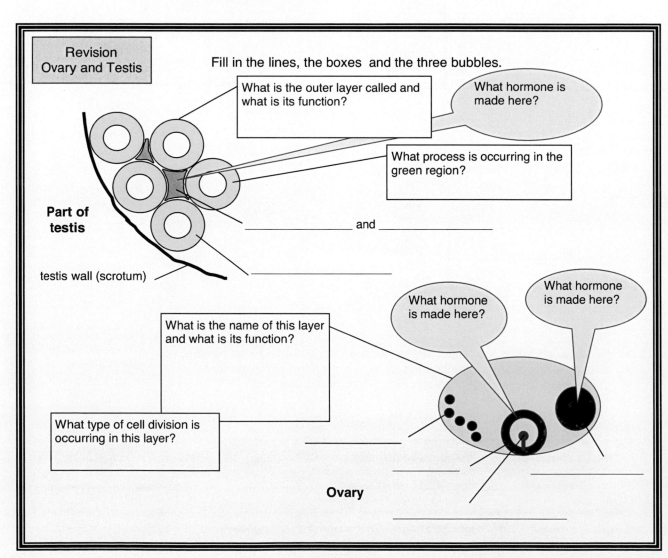

Revision
Ovary and Testis

Fill in the lines, the boxes and the three bubbles.

What is the outer layer called and what is its function?

What hormone is made here?

What process is occurring in the green region?

Part of testis

________________ and ________________

testis wall (scrotum)

____

What hormone is made here?

What hormone is made here?

What is the name of this layer and what is its function?

What type of cell division is occurring in this layer?

____

Ovary

When is the first polar body formed?

When is the second polar body formed?

In which part of the sperm are mitochondria found?

Name the barrier separating maternal and fetal blood.

List three substances passing from maternal to fetal blood.

List three substances passing from fetal to maternal blood.

Does the umbilical vein carry deoxygenated or oxygenated blood?

List three hormones produced by the placenta.

What are the lengths of the head, midpiece and tail of a sperm?

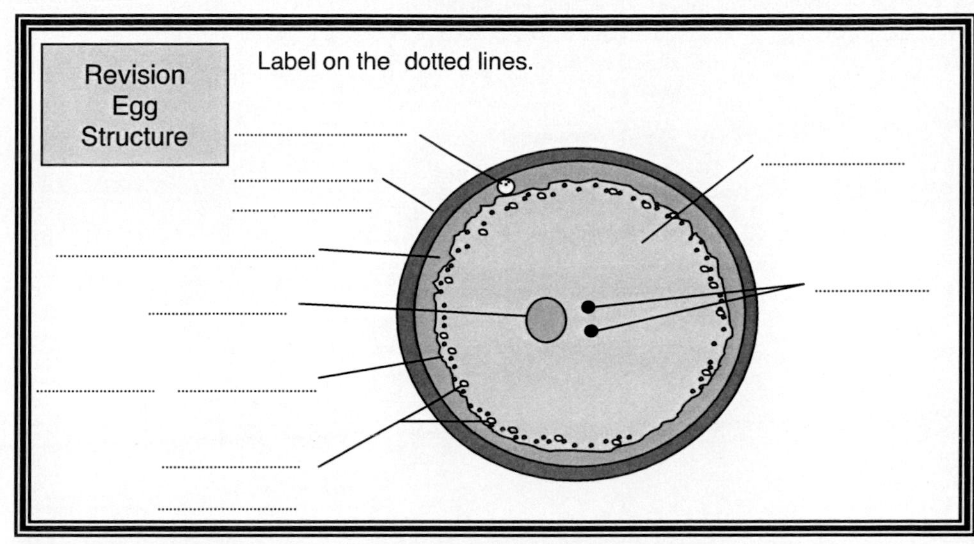

Revision
Egg
Structure
Label on the dotted lines.

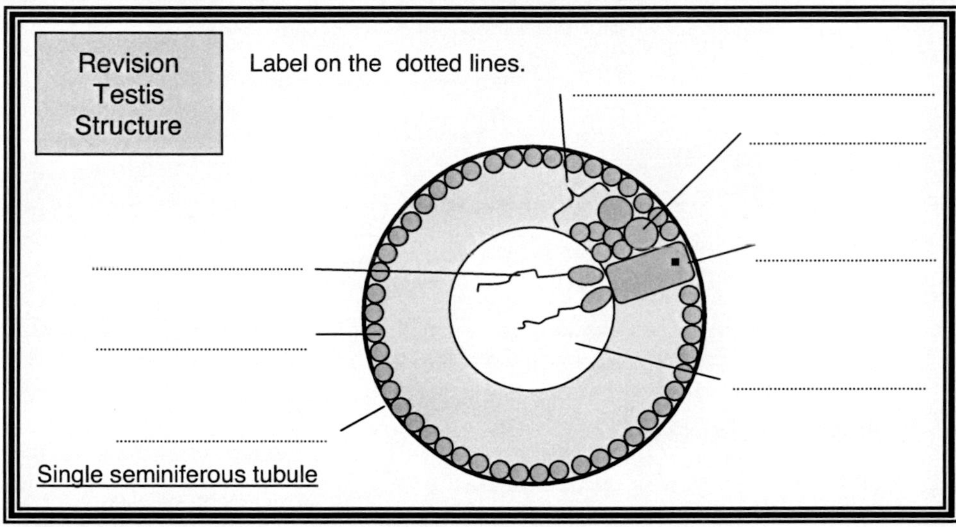

Revision
Testis
Structure
Label on the dotted lines.
Single seminiferous tubule

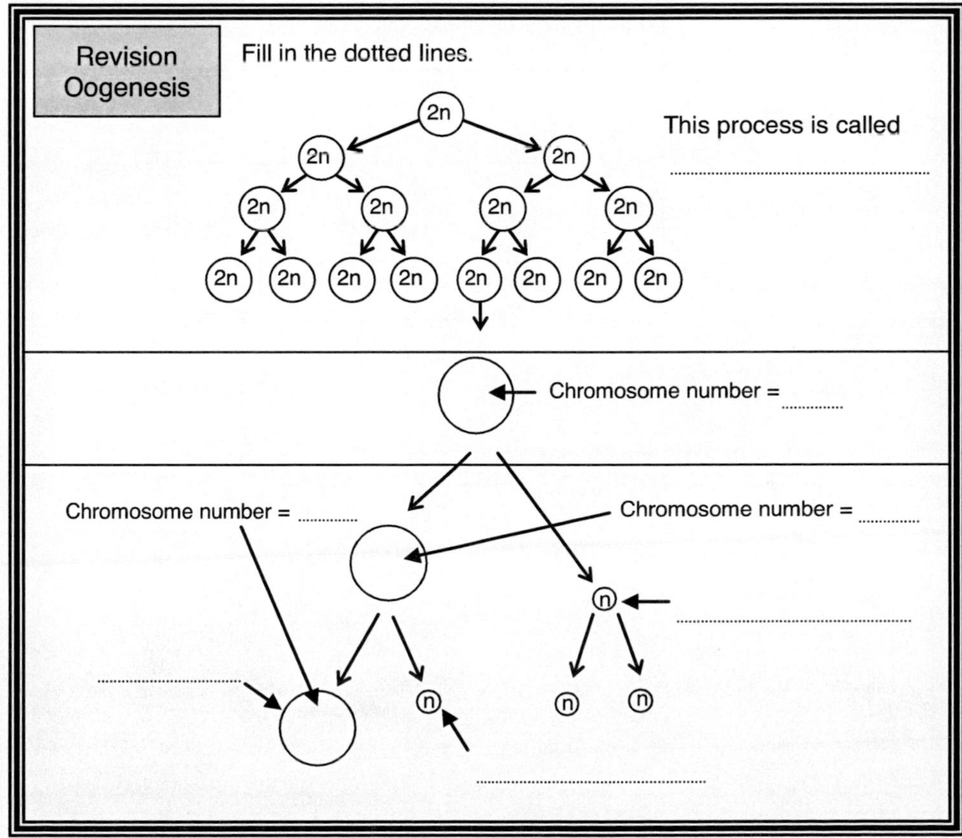

Revision
Oogenesis
Fill in the dotted lines.
2n
This process is called
Chromosome number =
Chromosome number =
Chromosome number =
n

Revision Fertilisation

Label in the places indicated and fill in the boxes with the details of what happens at each step.

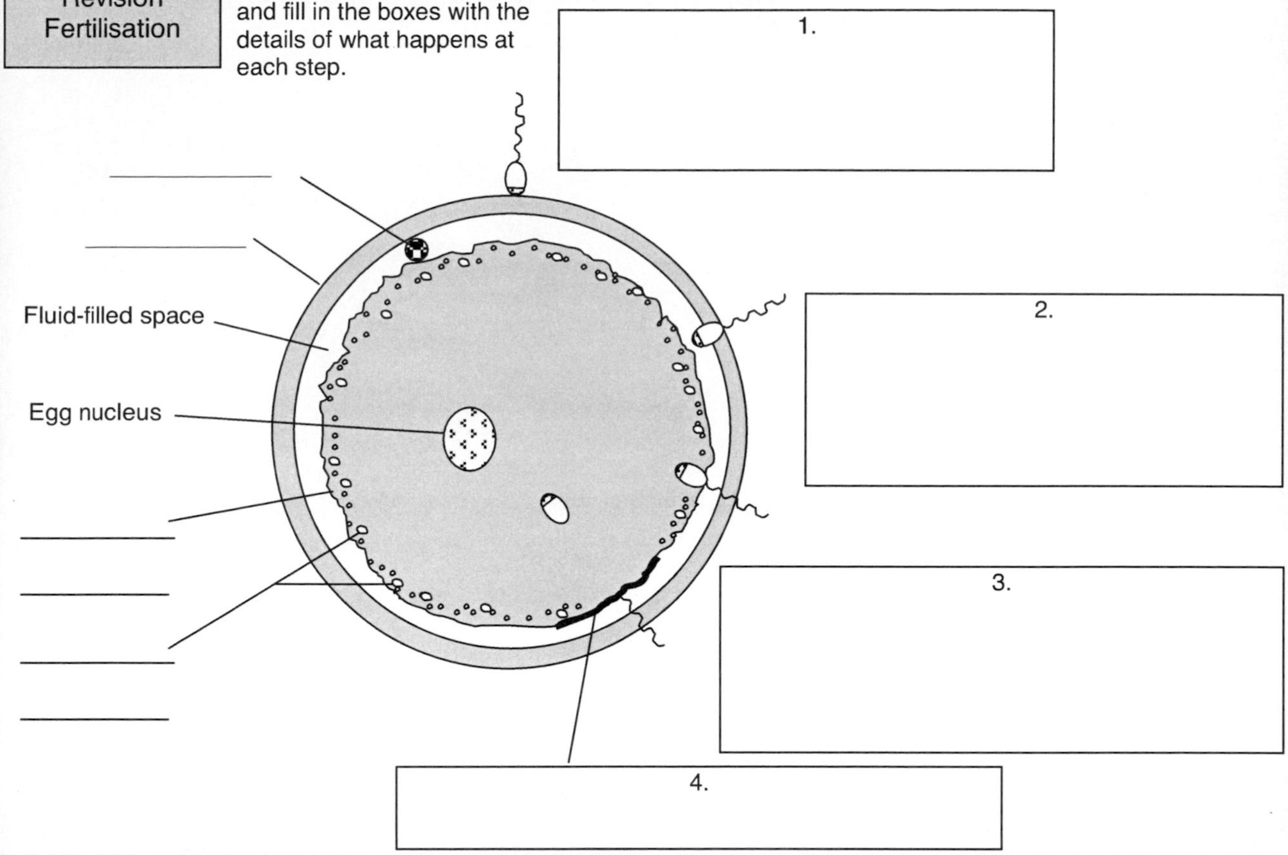

1.

2.

3.

4.

Fluid-filled space

Egg nucleus

Revision Semen Production

Fill the details of the functions of the three structures.

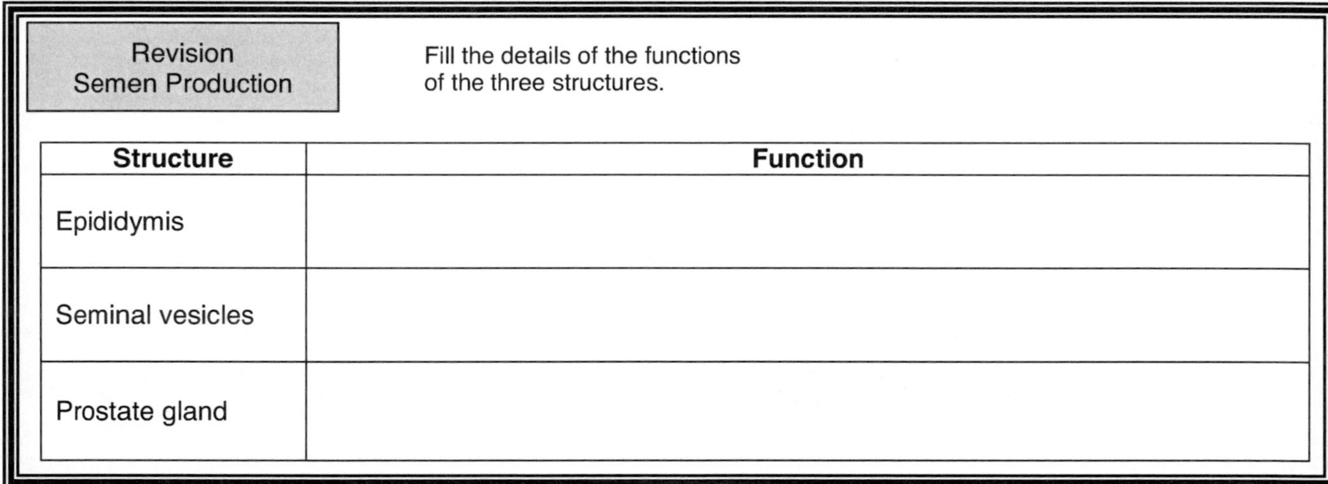

Structure	Function
Epididymis	
Seminal vesicles	
Prostate gland	

Revision Sperm Structure

Label on the dotted lines.

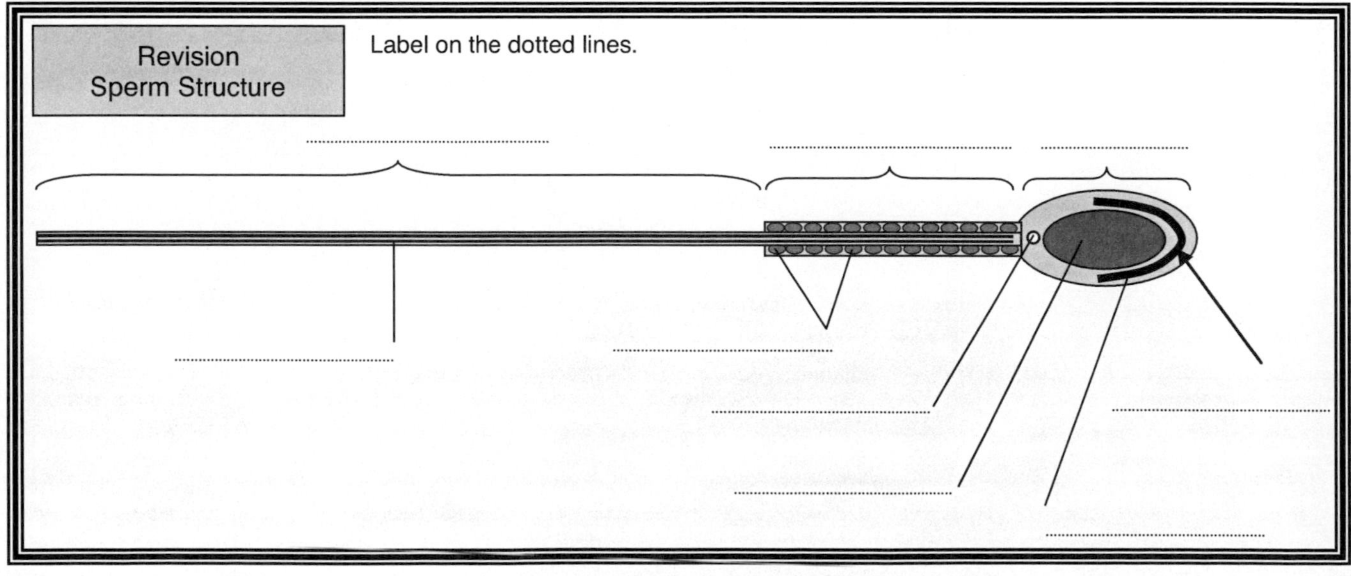

Revision
Reproductive Hormones

Complete the shaded boxes and fill in the missing words on the 5 dotted lines.

Hormone	Site of Production	Function in Boys
Luteinising hormone (LH)		
	Anterior pituitary	Stimulates .... stages of ....
Testosterone		Brings about .... and maintains secondary sexual characteristics; Stimulates .... stages of ....

Self-test Quiz on Reproduction

1. Follicle stimulating hormone (FSH) is produced in
   a. the female pituitary gland only,
   b. the pituitary gland of both males and females,
   c. the female pituitary gland and the ovaries,
   d. the ovaries only.

2. Testosterone is produced by
   a. the seminiferous tubules,
   b. the testis wall,
   c. the interstitial cells,
   d. the pituitary gland.

3. The first polar body is formed during
   a. meiosis in the ovaries,
   b. mitosis in the ovaries,
   c. meiosis in the testes,
   d. very low body temperatures.

4. The blastocyst is the structure which is
   a. formed after several mitotic divisions of the fertilised egg.
   b. formed by fusion of the sperm with the egg.
   c. produced after the fertilised egg divides by meiosis.
   d. formed by the release of the cortical granules after fertilisation.

5. During oogenesis the sequence of events is
   a. meiosis I, meiosis II, cell growth, mitosis,
   b. mitosis, meiosis I, meiosis II, cell growth,
   c. mitosis, cell growth, meiosis I, meiosis II,
   d. cell growth, mitosis, meiosis I, meiosis II,

6. The structures responsible for the formation of semen are
   a. seminiferous tubules, interstitial cells and seminal vesicles,
   b. seminal vesicles and seminiferous tubules,
   c. prostate gland, seminiferous tubules and interstitial cells,
   d. prostate gland, seminal vesicles and epididymis.

7. During the process of fertilisation
   a. the acrosome reaction is followed by the cortical reaction,
   b. the acrosome reaction forms the fertilisation membrane,
   c. the cortical reaction allows penetration of the sperm head through the egg plasma membrane,
   d. enzymes released from the cortical granules stimulate formation of the first polar body.

8. Which one of the following pairs of hormones is <u>not</u> secreted by the placenta?
   a. HCG and estrogen.
   b. Estrogen and progesterone,
   c. Progesterone and LH.
   d. HCG and progesterone.

9. The energy for the sperm to swim is released by
   a. the mitochondria in the uterus lining,
   b. the mitochondria in the midpiece region of the sperm,
   c. the zona pellucida,
   d. the Graafian follicle.

10. The acrosome of the sperm
    a. carries the genetic information,
    b. provides the energy for the sperm to swim,
    c. causes ovulation,
    d. contains enzymes that facilitate fertilisation.

11. The developing spermatozoa in the testes are nourished by
    a. Sertoli cells.
    b. interstitial cells.
    c. secretions from the seminal vesicles.
    d. secretions from the prostate gland.

12. The function of polar bodies is to
    a. remove the excess genetic material.
    b. increase the number of eggs formed.
    c. increase the chances of the sperm finding the egg.
    d. increase the food stores in the egg for use by the embryo.

13. Which of the following statements about the placenta is correct?
    a. This is where the fetal blood and mother's blood mix.
    b. This acts as a barrier to all substances in the mother's blood.
    c. This acts as a barrier to toxins produced by the fetus preventing them from passing into the mother's blood.
    d. This is where nutrients in the mother's blood are absorbed by the fetal blood.

14. Human chorionic gonadotrophin (HCG) is the hormone that
    a. allows the blastocyst to implant in the uterus,
    b. stimulates ovulation by inhibiting the release of FSH,
    c. stimulates the ovary to maintain production of progesterone,
    d. promotes re-growth of the uterus lining after menstruation.

15. The fertilisation membrane is formed from
    a. the cortical granules;
    b. the acrosome;
    c. the zona pellucida;
    d. the plasma membrane of the egg.

16. Which of the following statements about the placenta is correct?
    a. Fetal capillaries are in spaces filled with maternal blood;
    b. Maternal and fetal capillaries lie alongside each other;
    c. Maternal blood flows into the fetal capillaries from the uterine artery.
    d. Deoxygenated blood is brought to the placenta through the umbilical vein.

17. Birth is initiated by
    a. a rise in the level of oxytocin,
    b. a fall in the level of progesterone,
    c. a rise in the level of FSH,
    d. a fall in the level of estrogen,

18. Which of the following statements is correct about birth?
    a. Contraction of the uterine muscle causes a fall in the level of progesterone.
    b. Oxytocin has a positive feedback effect on the pituitary gland.
    c. Progesterone stimulates uterine contractions.
    d. Oxytocin increases uterine contractions through positive feedback.

Appendix 1

Command Terms

Objective 1

Define	Give precise meaning of a word or phrase as concisely as possible.
Draw	Represent by means of pencil lines (add labels unless told not to do so.
Label	Add labels to diagrams.
List	Give a sequence of names or other brief answers with no elaboration, each one clearly separated from the others.
Measure	Find a value for a quantity.
State	Give a specific name, value or other brief answer (no supporting argument or calculation is necessary).

Objective 2

Annotate	Add brief notes to a diagram, drawing or graph.
Apply	Use an idea, equation, principle, theory or law in a new situation.
Calculate	Find an answer using mathematical methods (show the working unless instructed no to do so).
Describe	Give a detailed account, including all the relevant information.
Distinguish	Give the differences between two or more different items.
Estimate	Find an approximate value for an unknown quantity based on the information provided and scientific knowledge.
Identify	Find an answer from a number of possibilities.
Outline	Give a brief account or summary (include essential information only).

Objective 3

Analyse	Interpret data to reach conclusions.
Comment	Give a judgement based on a given statement or result of a calculation.
Compare	Give an account of similarities and differences between two (or more) items, referring to both (all) of them throughout (comparisons can be given using a table).
Construct	Represent or develop in graphical form.
Deduce	Reach a conclusion from the information given.
Derive	Manipulate a mathematical equation to give a new equation or result.
Design	Produce a plan, object, simulation or model.
Determine	Find the only possible answer.
Discuss	Give an account including, where possible, a range of arguments, assessments of the relative importance of various factors or comparisons of alternative hypotheses.
Evaluate	Assess the implications and limitations.
Explain	Give a clear account including causes, reasons or mechanisms.
Predict	Give an expected result.
Show	Give the steps in a calculation or derivation.
Sketch	Represent by means of a graph showing a line and labelled but unscaled axes but with important features (for example, intercept) clearly indicated.
Solve	Obtain an answer using algebraic and/or numerical methods.
Suggest	Propose a hypothesis or other possible answer.

Appendix 2

Definitions

Action potential	The reversal and then restoration of the electrical potential across the plasma membrane of a nerve cell as electrical impulse passes along it.
Active immunity	Immunity due to the production of antibodies by the organism itself after stimulation by antigens.
Active site	The specific region of an enzyme to which the substrate or substrates bind.
Allele	A specific form of a gene, occupying the same gene locus as other alleles of that gene, but differing from other alleles by small differences in its base sequence.
Carrier	An individual that has a recessive allele of a gene.
Cell respiration	Release of energy in the form of ATP from the controlled breakdown of organic compounds within the cell.
Clone	A group of genetically identical organisms or a group of cells derived from a single parent cell.
Codominant alleles	Pairs of alleles that both affect the phenotype when present in the heterozygous state.
Community	A group of populations living and interacting with each other in an area.
Denaturation	A structural change in a protein that results in a loss (usually permanent) of its biological properties.
Diffusion	The passive movement of a substance from a region of high concentration to a region of low concentration.
Dominant allele	An allele that has the same effect on the phenotype when in either the homozygous or heterozygous state.
Ecology	The study of relationships between living organisms and between living organisms and their environment.
Ecosystem	A community and its abiotic environment.
Enzyme	Globular protein capable of catalysing a specific chemical reaction.
Evolution	The process of cumulative change in the heritable characteristics of a population.
Excretion	Removal from the body of waste products of metabolic pathways.
Gene	A heritable factor that controls a specific characteristic.
Gene mutation	A change in the sequence of bases in a gene.
Genome	The whole of the genetic information of an organism.
Genotype	The alleles possessed by an organism.
Habitat	The environment in which a species normally lives or the location of a living organism.
Heterozygous	Having two different alleles at a gene locus.
Homologous chromosomes	A pair of chromosomes with the same genes but not necessarily the same alleles of those genes.
Homozygous	Having two identical alleles at a gene locus.
Linkage group	All those genes on a particular chromosome.
Locus	The specific position on a homologous chromosome of a gene.
Osmoregulation	The control of the water balance of the blood, tissue fluid or cytoplasm of a living organism.
Osmosis	The passive movement of water molecules across a partially permeable membrane from a region of lower solute concentration to a region of higher solute concentration.
Passive immunity	Immunity due to the acquisition of antibodies from another organism, via the placenta, colostrum or by injection, in which active immunity has been stimulated.
Pathogen	An organism or virus that causes a disease.
Phenotype	The characteristics of an organism.
Polygenic inheritance	The transmission of a characteristic influenced by several genes.
Population	A group of organisms of the same species that live in the same area at the same time.
Recessive allele	An allele that only has an effect on the phenotype when it is in the homozygous state.
Resting potential	The electrical potential across the plasma membrane of a nerve cell that is not conducting a nerve impulse.
Sex Linkage	The pattern of inheritance characteristic of genes located on the sex chromosomes.
Species	A group of organisms that can interbreed and produce fertile offspring.
Test cross	Testing a phenotypically dominant phenotype to determine if it is heterozygous or homozygous.
Transpiration	The loss of water vapour from the leaves and stems of a plant.
Trophic level	The position of an organism in a food chain.

Appendix 3

Table of critical values for the Student t-test

Degrees of freedom	Significance level				
	20% 0.2	10% 0.1	**5%** **0.05**	2% 0.02	1% 0.01
18	1.33	1.73	**2.10**	2.55	2.88
19	1.32	1.73	**2.09**	2.54	2.86
20	1.32	1.73	**2.09**	2.53	2.85
21	1.32	1.72	**2.08**	2.52	2.83
22	1.32	1.72	**2.07**	2.51	2.82
23	1.31	1.71	**2.07**	2.50	2.81
24	1.31	1.71	**2.06**	2.49	2.80
25	1.31	1.71	**2.06**	2.49	2.79
26	1.31	1.71	**2.06**	2.48	2.78
27	1.31	1.70	**2.05**	2.47	2.77
28	1.31	1.70	**2.05**	2.47	2.76
29	1.31	1.70	**2.04**	2.46	2.76
30	1.31	1.70	**2.04**	2.46	2.75
40	1.30	1.68	**2.02**	2.42	2.70
50	1.30	1.67	**2.00**	2.40	2.67
60	1.29	1.67	**2.00**	2.39	2.66
120	1.28	1.65	**1.98**	2.15	2.61

Note that at the bottom of the table the degrees of freedom jumps by 10 but the significance values change only by a small amount. It is therefore not worth including all the intermediate values.

Degrees of freedom = $(n_1 + n_2) - 2$, where n_1 and n_2 are the number of values for each set of data.

Appendix 4

Electron Micrographs

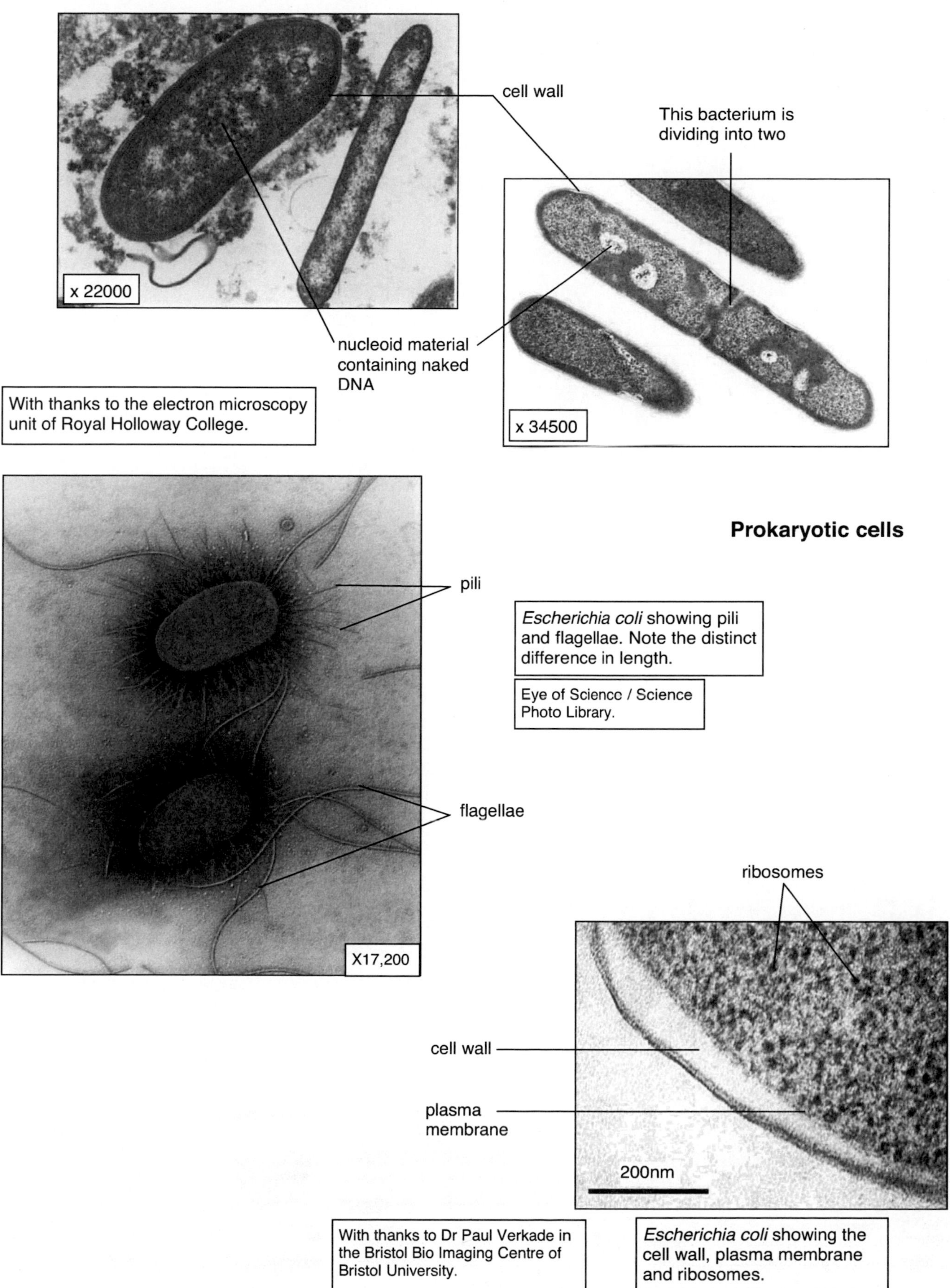
cell wall
This bacterium is dividing into two
x 22000
nucleoid material containing naked DNA
x 34500
Prokaryotic cells
pili
flagellae
X17,200
ribosomes
cell wall
plasma membrane
200nm

With thanks to the electron microscopy unit of Royal Holloway College.

Escherichia coli showing pili and flagellae. Note the distinct difference in length.

Eye of Science / Science Photo Library.

With thanks to Dr Paul Verkade in the Bristol Bio Imaging Centre of Bristol University.

Escherichia coli showing the cell wall, plasma membrane and ribosomes.

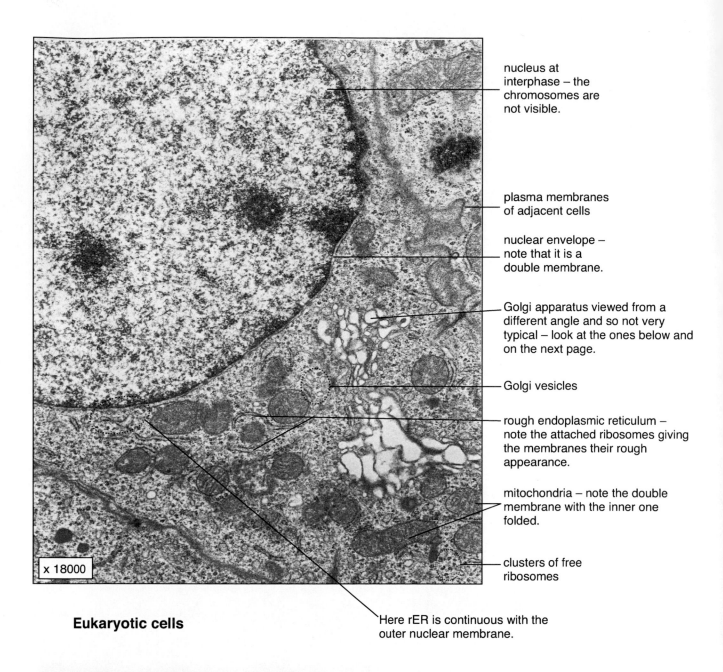

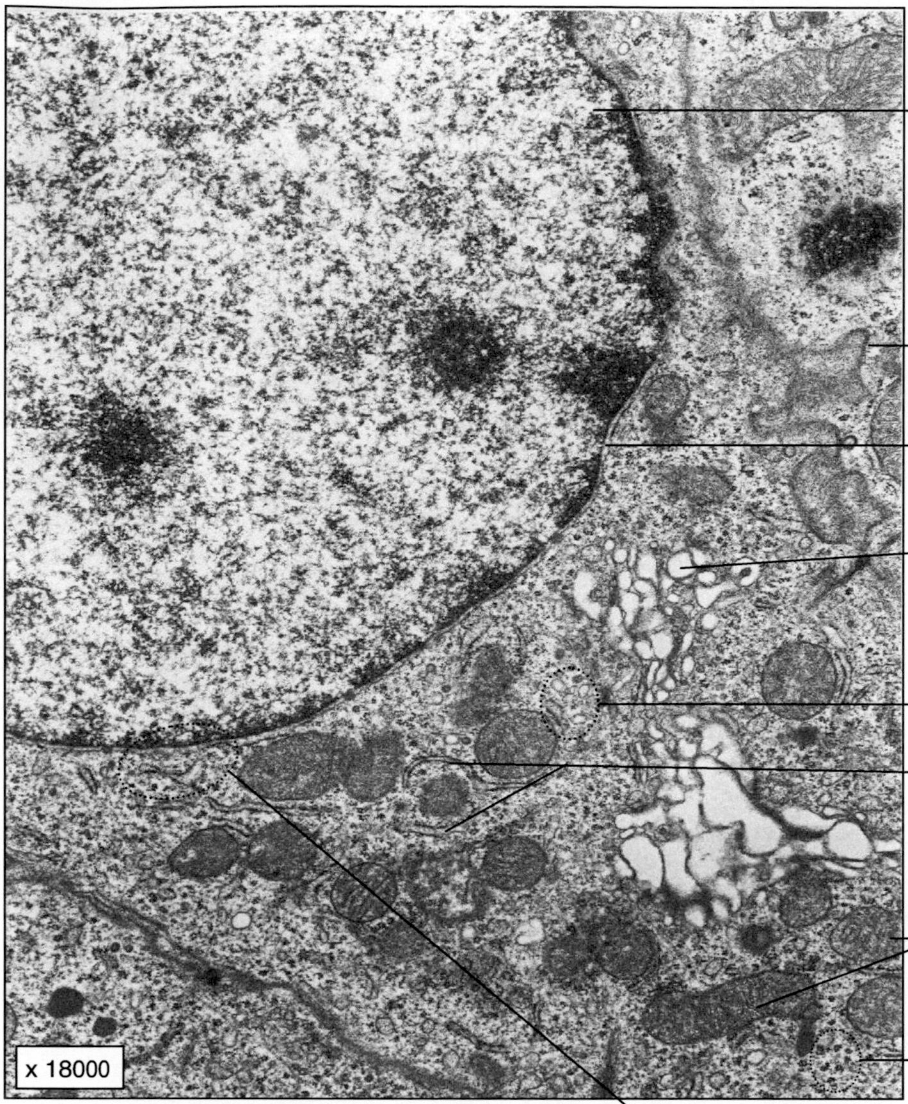

x 18000

nucleus at interphase – the chromosomes are not visible.

plasma membranes of adjacent cells

nuclear envelope – note that it is a double membrane.

Golgi apparatus viewed from a different angle and so not very typical – look at the ones below and on the next page.

Golgi vesicles

rough endoplasmic reticulum – note the attached ribosomes giving the membranes their rough appearance.

mitochondria – note the double membrane with the inner one folded.

clusters of free ribosomes

Here rER is continuous with the outer nuclear membrane.

Eukaryotic cells

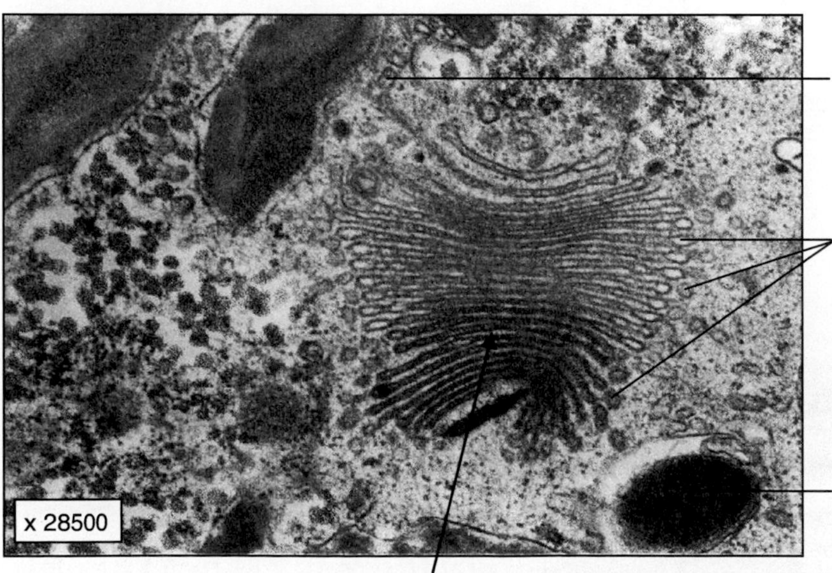
x 28500
Here vesicles containing unprocessed proteins from the rER are joining on.
Note the vesicles budding off on both sides. These will either become lysosomes or they will be transporting processed proteins to the plasma membrane either for incorporation into the membrane (eg glycoproteins), or for exocytosis (eg hormones, digestive enzymes).
fat droplet – these usually stain black in electron micrographs.
Golgi apparatus

Eukaryotic cells

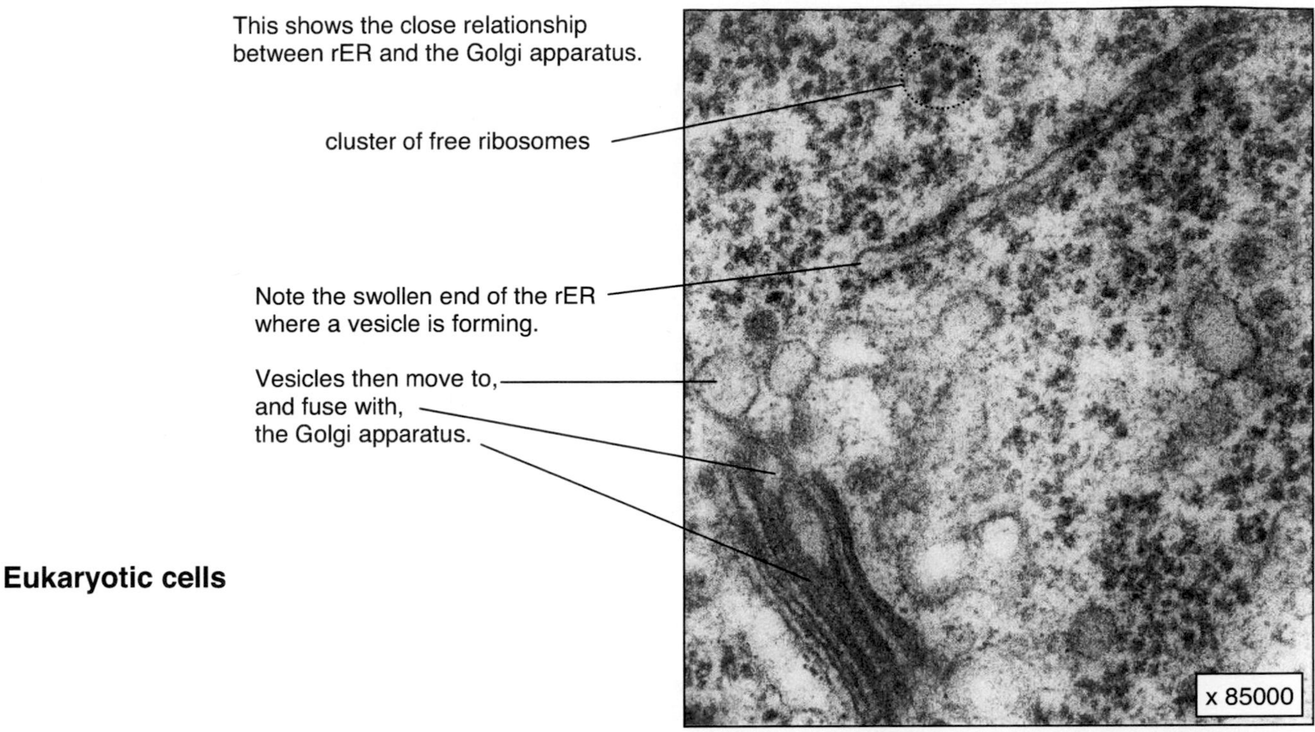

This shows the close relationship between rER and the Golgi apparatus.
cluster of free ribosomes
Note the swollen end of the rER where a vesicle is forming.
Vesicles then move to, and fuse with, the Golgi apparatus.
x 85000

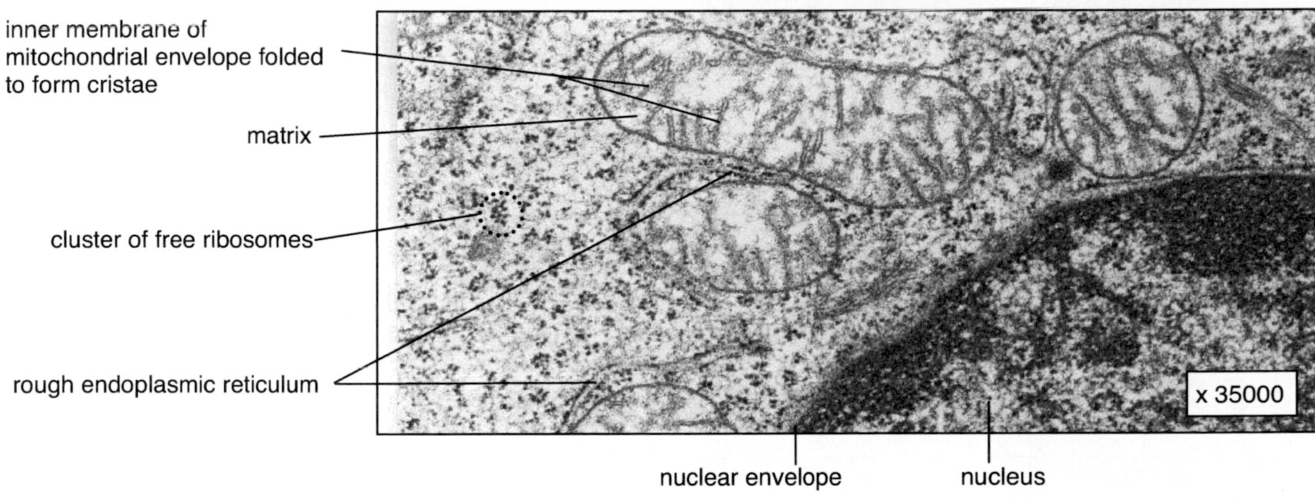

inner membrane of mitochondrial envelope folded to form cristae
matrix
cluster of free ribosomes
rough endoplasmic reticulum
x 35000
nuclear envelope
nucleus

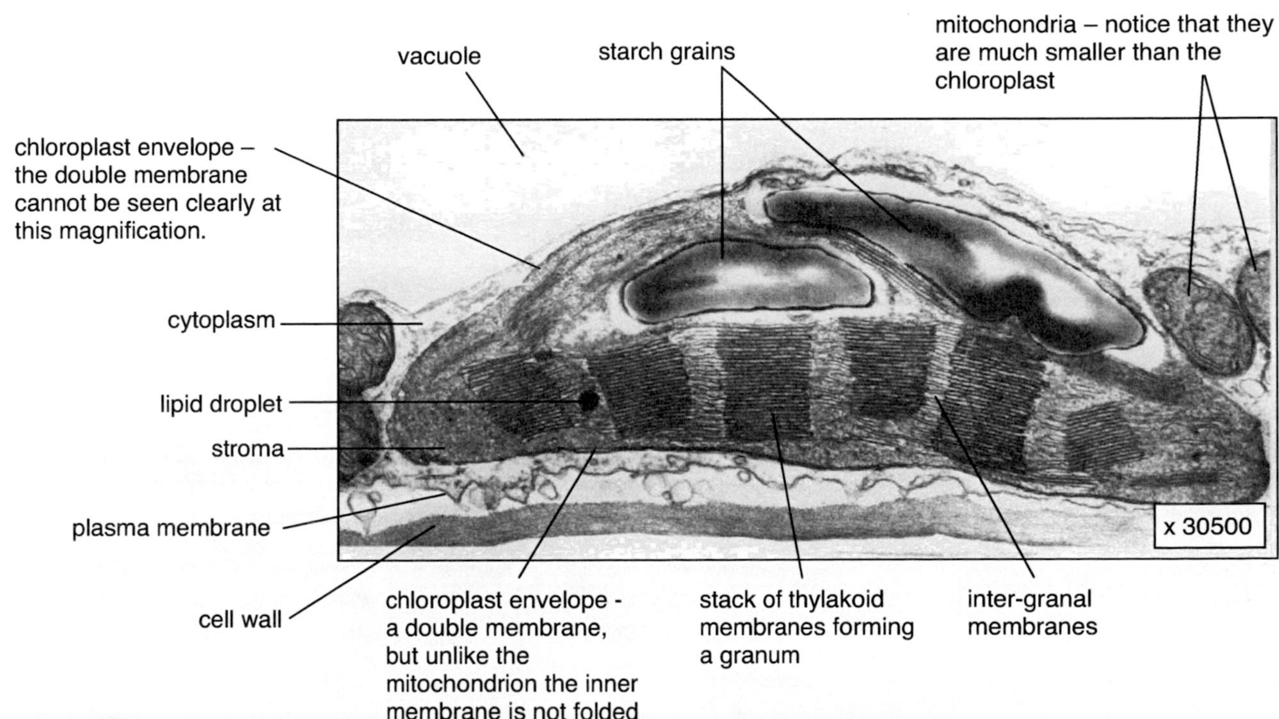

vacuole
starch grains
mitochondria – notice that they are much smaller than the chloroplast
chloroplast envelope – the double membrane cannot be seen clearly at this magnification.
cytoplasm
lipid droplet
stroma
plasma membrane
cell wall
x 30500
chloroplast envelope - a double membrane, but unlike the mitochondrion the inner membrane is not folded
stack of thylakoid membranes forming a granum
inter-granal membranes

Appendix 5

How to maximise your marks in multiple choice questions.

- Take great care to read the instructions and fill in the answer sheet in exactly the way required. This paper is marked by machine.
- Always check the answer you fill in is for the correct question number.
- Don't go fast. It is much better to work carefully through each question rather than go back. This is because your mind has become pre-programmed for the answer you have already chosen.
- If a question looks as though it might take some time leave it and go on to the next. Each question is worth the same mark and you will therefore gain if you get more questions completed.
- Always read every answer and actively eliminate the wrong ones. Examiners can put in tricks. Many of the questions in this guide do that. These include an answer that looks good and may be a correct statement but is not the answer to the question. Also watch for negatives – 'Which one is not ------'
- Never leave a blank space on the answer sheet. If you really don't know then guess. At least you have a 25% chance of the mark whereas if you put nothing you have 0% chance.

Answers to Self-test Quizzes.

Topic 1

1. Degrees of freedom = 10 + 10 -2 = 18; Critical value 2.10; No significant difference.
2. Degrees of freedom = 26 + 26 -2 = 50; Critical value 2.00; Significant difference.

3a. Degrees of freedom = 30 + 30 -2 = 58; Critical value 2.00; Significant difference.

3b. Degrees of freedom = 15 + 12 -2 = 25; Critical value 2.06; No significant difference so he was wrong.

3c. Degrees of freedom = 22 + 19 -2 = 39; Critical value 2.02; No significant difference so she was right.

4. She was right to say the standard deviation was small but not very small. 33% of 47 is 15.5 and 13 is very close to this, so it is actually close to being a large standard deviation.

5. a. 6. c.

	Topic													
	2	3	4	5	6	7	8	9	10	Defence	Muscles	Kidney	Reproduction	
1	d	a	a	b	c	d	b	a	d	d	d	b	b	1
2	b	b	d	d	a	a	d	a	a	c	b	c	c	2
3	d	b	c	c	a	c	b	d	d	a	a	a	a	3
4	d	d	c	a	b	c	b	c	b	d	c	b	a	4
5	a	c	b	b	d	d	a	c	b	a	a	d	c	5
6	c	c	a	a	c	a	d	b	c	c	b	b	d	6
7	a	b	a	b	d	b	b	d	a	b	d	a	a	7
8	d	c	d	a	b	a	c	c	a	b	b	a	c	8
9	a	b	b	a	d	a	c	a	d	c	b	c	b	9
10	c	a	a	c	a	d	a	c	b	a		b	d	10
11	b	c	b	c	c	c	d	b	a	b		b	a	11
12	d	a	c	a	c	a	d	c	b			d	a	12
13	d	c	a	c	b	b	b	c				a	d	13
14	a	b	a	d	d	c		d				c	c	14
15	a	d	c	b	a	a		a				d	a	15
16	d	c	d	a	b	d		a				c	a	16
17	b	b	d	c	d	b		b				a	b	17
18	a	a	c	c	d	a						d	d	18
19	c	d	a	b	a	d								19
20	d	c	c	a	a	b								20
21	c	a	b		b	b								21
22	a	c	a		c	c								22
23	c	c	d		d	d								23
24	b	d	c		c									24
25	a	b	d		a									25
26		a	c		c									26
27		b			c									27
28		a			b									28
29		c			b									29
30		b												30
31		a												31

Appendix 6

Answers to Genetics Problems in Topic 4

1. The majority of all the young mice is black so that tells us that black is dominant. Therefore let B = black and b = grey. The grey male mouse must have the genotype bb because grey is recessive. Since about half the offspring of the first black female are grey she must have the grey allele in her genotype. Thus she is heterozygous, Bb. The second female only produces black offspring and so, given the numbers, it is likely that she is homozygous BB.

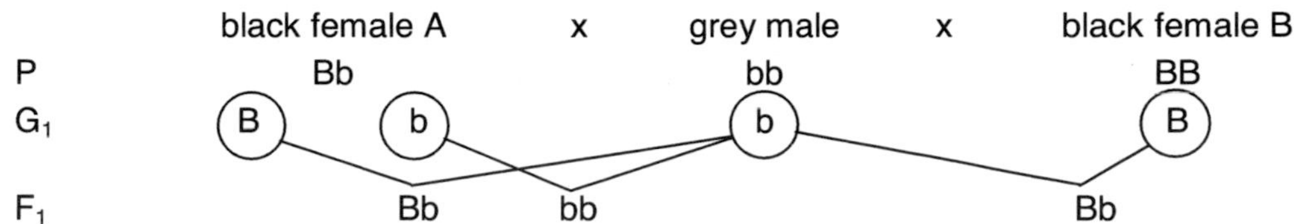

black female A
x
grey male
x
black female B
P
Bb
bb
BB
G1
B
b
b
B
F1
Bb
bb
Bb

2. The F_1 Bandycoot babies were all yellow but orange ones appeared in the F_2. This tells us that yellow must be dominant and orange recessive. Therefore let Y = yellow and y = orange. The heterozygous parent is thus Yy. The test for heterozygosity is a test cross, that is with the homozygous recessive yy. A YY genotype will not give any orange offspring whereas about half the offspring will be orange with a Yy genotype.

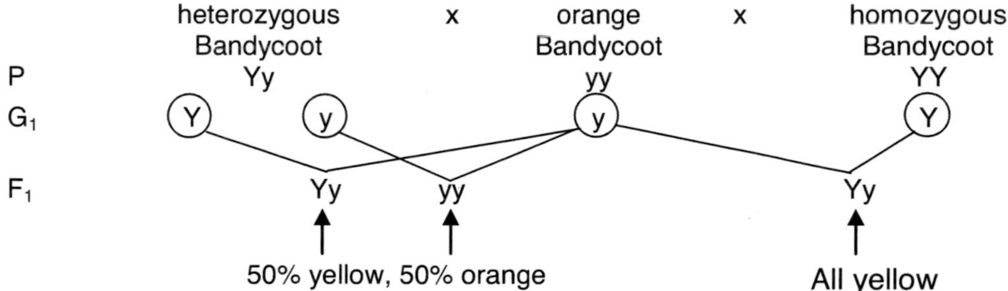

heterozygous Bandycoot
x
orange Bandycoot
x
homozygous Bandycoot
P
Yy
yy
YY
G1
Y
y
y
Y
F1
Yy
yy
Yy
50% yellow, 50% orange
All yellow

3. We are told that green is dominant so let G = green and g = blue.
The blue-eyed beetle must therefore have the genotype gg. Its parents were both green-eyed and either had the genotype GG or Gg. However since the beetle must inherit one allele from each parent both parents must be Gg.
The female beetle is green eyed but the first baby Boring beetle is blue eyed. Hence her genotype must be Gg.
If they have another baby beetle it could be green-eyed with the genotype Gg.

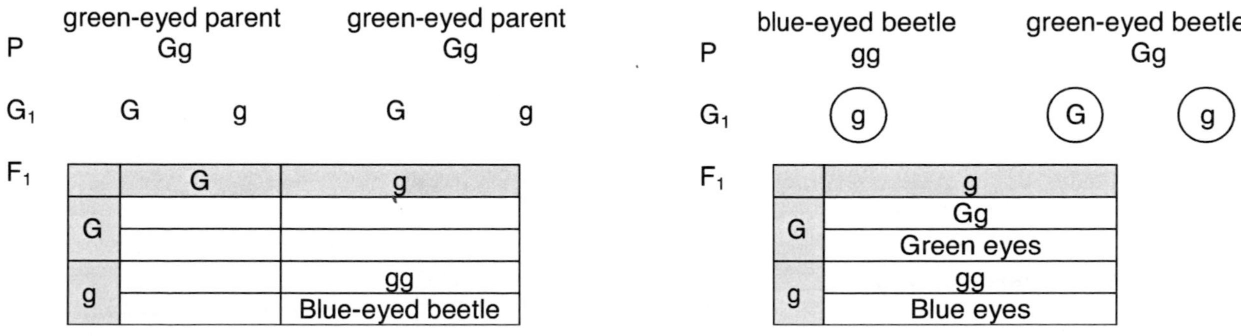

green-eyed parent
green-eyed parent
P
Gg
Gg
G1
G
g
G
g
F1
blue-eyed beetle
green-eyed beetle
P
gg
Gg
G1
g
G
g
F1

	G	g
G		
g		gg Blue-eyed beetle

	g
G	Gg Green eyes
g	gg Blue eyes

> Note that the Punnett grid has both genotype and phenotype for the offspring. On larger grids it makes it easier to determine the offspring, and less prone to making mistakes.

4. Since all the first generation Quolls had luminous eyes, luminous must be dominant. Therefore let L = luminous and l = blue. Furthermore since the first generation did not contain any blue-eyed Quolls we can assume that the luminous-eyed parent was homozygous, LL.

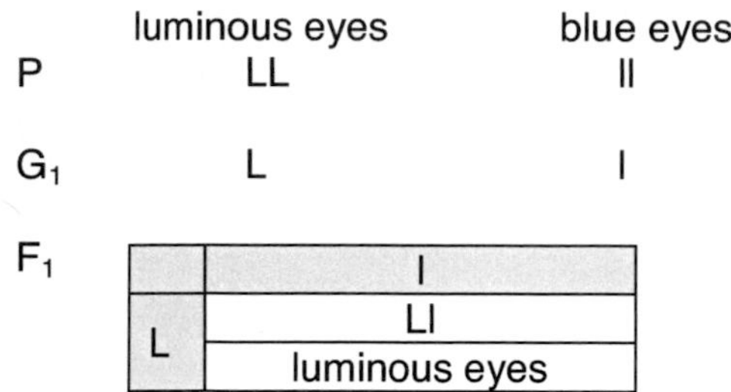

luminous eyes
blue eyes
P
LL
ll
G_1
L
l
F_1
l
L
Ll
luminous eyes

Lonely Quoll though met a blue-eyed Quoll, and since blue eyes must have the genotype ll this would produce 50% blue-eyed offspring.

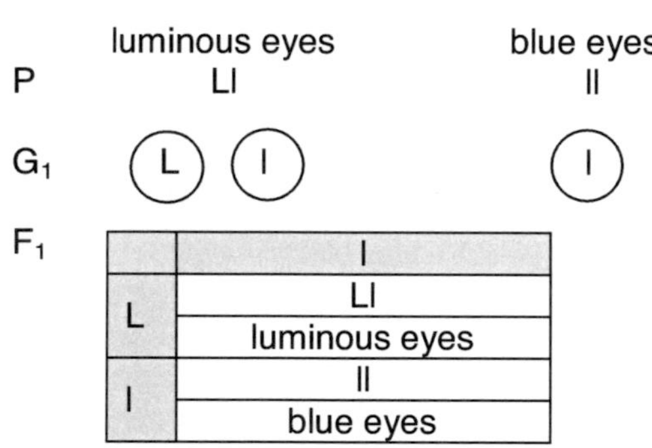

luminous eyes
blue eyes
P
Ll
ll
G_1
L
l
l
F_1
l
L
Ll
luminous eyes
l
ll
blue eyes

These offspring all met luminous-eyed Quolls and since their offspring were also all luminous-eyed we can again assume they were homozygous, LL.

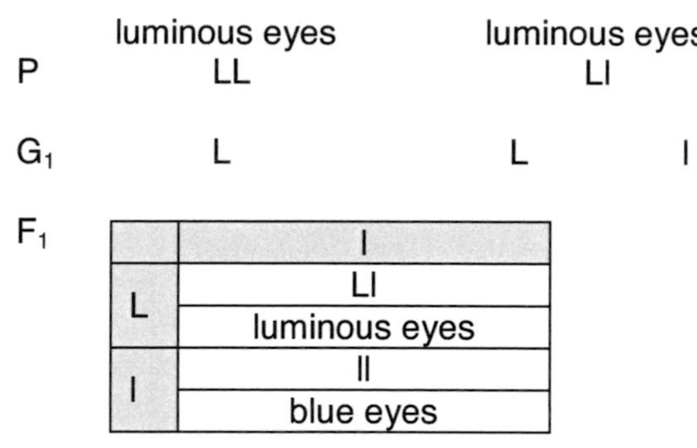

luminous eyes
luminous eyes
P
LL
Ll
G_1
L
L
l
F_1
l
L
Ll
luminous eyes
l
ll
blue eyes

5.

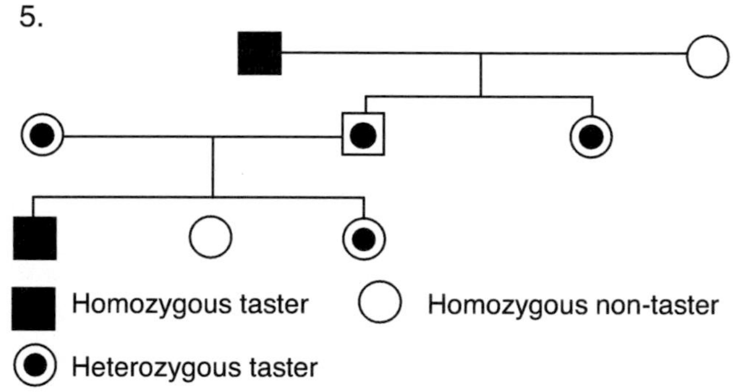

Homozygous taster
Homozygous non-taster
Heterozygous taster

6. If Grandpa was blood group O then his genotype had to be ii. His son Horace married a person who was also group O and therefore genotype ii. Their two daughters were group B and this I^B allele therefore had to have come from their father Horace. This meant that his genotype was I^B?, but since his father could only have given him an i allele we can deduce his genotype was $I^B i$. This means that the I^B allele must have come from his mother, making her genotype I^B?.
Grandpa's second child was group A, and using a similar argument we can deduce that the I^A allele must have come from Grandma. Finally therefore we can deduce that Grandma's genotype was $I^A I^B$ and hence her blood group AB.
This therefore makes it impossible for Grandpa and Grandma to have a group O child – all their children have to be either group A or group B.

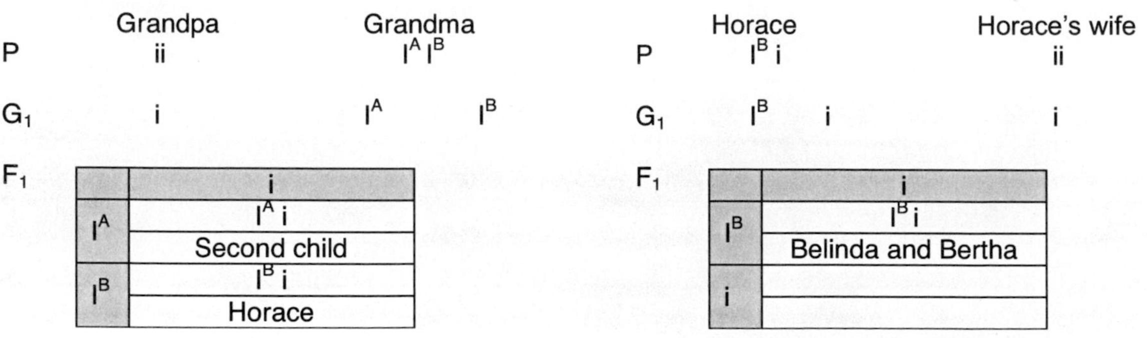

Grandpa
Grandma
P
ii
$I^A I^B$
G_1
i
I^A
I^B
F_1
i
I^A
$I^A i$
Second child
I^B
$I^B i$
Horace
Horace
Horace's wife
P
$I^B i$
ii
G_1
I^B
i
i
F_1
i
I^B
$I^B i$
Belinda and Bertha
i

7. We are told the characteristic is sex linked. Female Dingbats are XX and the males XY. The baby Dingbat is a female and therefore inherited one of her X chromosomes from the father. This chromosome carried the web allele, and her other X chromosome from her mother carried the normal allele. Since baby has normal feet we can deduce that normal is dominant. Males always inherit their X chromosome from their mother, and since both her X chromosomes carry the normal allele he too will have normal feet.
Let N = normal.

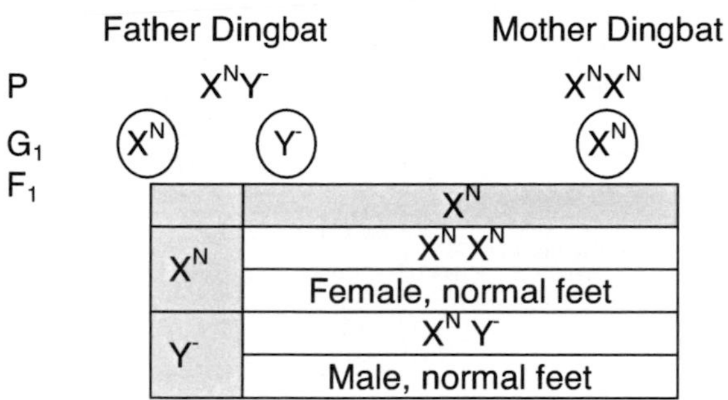
Father Dingbat
Mother Dingbat
P
X^NY^-
X^NX^N
G_1
X^N
Y^-
X^N
F_1

	X^N
X^N	$X^N X^N$ Female, normal feet
Y^-	$X^N Y^-$ Male, normal feet

Answers to Genetics Problems in Topic 10

1. There are only four possible phenotypes and the offspring include each type. Hence both parents must possess recessive alleles for each gene. The Punnett grid must have four F_1 boxes and this can be obtained either with a 4 x 1 grid, meaning one parent gives 4 types of gamete and the other one type, or a 2 x 2 grid meaning that both parents give 2 types of gamete.

4 x 1 grid.

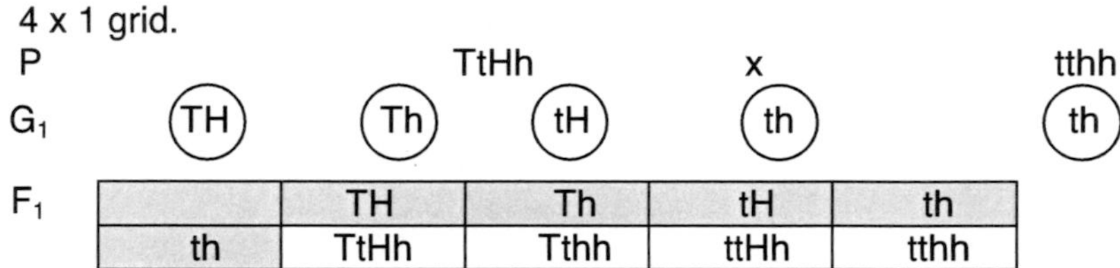
P
TtHh
x
tthh
G_1
TH
Th
tH
th
th
F_1

	TH	Th	tH	th
th	TtHh	Tthh	ttHh	tthh

Tthh and ttHh both give two types of gamete. We could not have Tthh x Tthh as this gives a 3:1 phenotype ratio (there is no H). Similarly ttHh x ttHh gives a 3:1 phenotype ratio (there is no T). However Tthh x ttHh does give the required ratio.

2 x 2 grid.

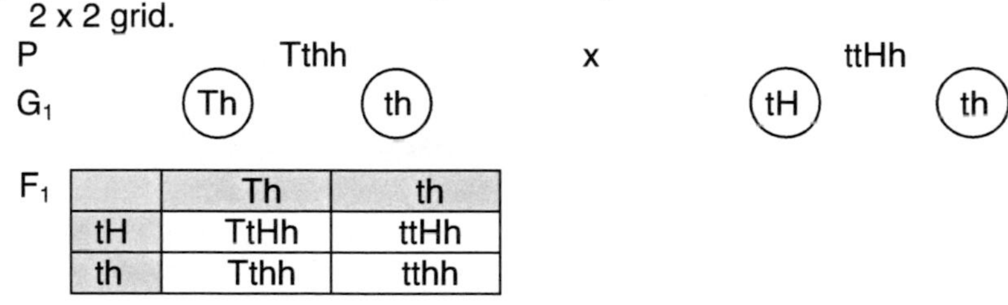
P
Tthh
x
ttHh
G_1
Th
th
tH
th
F_1

	Th	th
tH	TtHh	ttHh
th	Tthh	tthh

Thus there are two possible answers to this problem.

2. Let Y = yellow and B = bumpy as these are the dominant characteristics.
The genotype of the green bumpy plant is yyB?, and that of the yellow smooth plant is Y?bb. We have to put in the question marks as we do not yet know whether these are homozygous or heterozygous. We can though deduce that they must be heterozygous in order for the recessive characteristic to show in the offspring, eg. if yyB? was yyBB then there would be no smooth offspring, and similarly if Y?bb was YYbb there would be no green offspring.

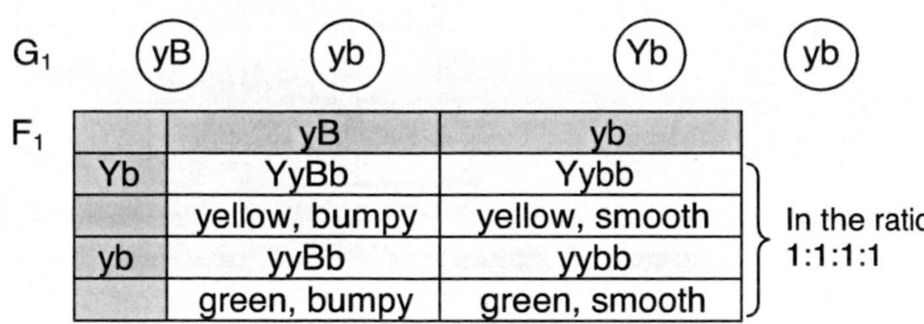
green, bumpy
yellow, smooth
P
yyBb
x
Yybb
G_1
yB
yb
Yb
yb
F_1
In the ratio 1:1:1:1

	yB	yb
Yb	YyBb yellow, bumpy	Yybb yellow, smooth
yb	yyBb green, bumpy	yybb green, smooth

In the ratio 1:1:1:1

Note here how the Punnett grid is big enough to include the phenotypes. This is a quicker and more accurate / efficient way of linking genotype and phenotype.

3. We are not told which characteristics are dominant but we can easily deduce this because black wing cases and short antennae form the largest number of offspring. Thus let B = black and H = short. (Remember that S is a bad letter to choose).
The ratio is closest to 9:3:3:1, which gives a total of 16. Only a 4 x 4 grid gives 16 and so we know that each parent must form four different types of gamete. The only genotype that does this is the double heterozygous, BbHh.

F_1

	BH	Bh	bH	bh
BH	BBHH	BBHh	BbHH	BbHh
	black, short antennae	black, short antennae	black, short antennae	black, short antennae
Bh	BBHh	BBhh	BbHh	Bbhh
	black, short antennae	black, long antennae	black, short antennae	black, long antennae
bH	BbHH	BbHh	bbHH	bbHh
	black, short antennae	black, short antennae	white, short antennae	white, short antennae
bh	BbHh	Bbhh	bbHh	bbhh
	black, short antennae	black, long antennae	white, short antennae	white, long antennae

9 B_H_ black, short antennae
3 bbH_ white, short antennae,
3 B_hh black, long antennae,
1 bbhh white, long antennae.

Look back at the coloured Punnett grid on page 179.

4. Let A = small, a = large; G = green, g = white.
The genotype of the plant with large white flowers has to be aagg since these alleles are recessive. This produces one type of gamete. Since the offspring were either small, green flowers or large, green flowers we can deduce that the other parent did not have a white allele but did have a large allele, ie. AaGG, thus producing two types of gamete.

F_1

	AG	aG
ag	AaGg	aaGg
	small, green flowers	large, green flowers

F_1 large, green flowers aaGg x large, green flowers aaGg

G_2 (aG) (ag) (aG) (ag)

F_2

	aG	ag
aG	aaGG	aaGg
	large, green flowers	large, green flowers
ag	aaGg	aagg
	large, green flowers	large, white flowers

The F_2 ratio is 3 large, green flowers to 1 large, white flowers.

5. Since the offspring were all pink this tells us that the Pogwort flower colour genes are codominant, C^R and C^W. The red and white flowered parents therefore had to be homozygous.

P red $C^R C^R$ x white $C^W C^W$

G_1 (C^R) (C^W)

F_1 $C^R C^W$ pink

F_1 pink $C^R C^W$ x pink $C^R C^W$

G_2 (C^R) (C^W) (C^R) (C^W)

F_2

	C^R	C^W
C^R	$C^R C^R$	$C^R C^W$
	red flowers	pink flowers
C^W	$C^R C^W$	$C^W C^W$
	pink flowers	white flowers

1 red : 2 pink : 1 white.

6. The numbers of offspring – one large pair and one small pair - clearly tells us that there is linkage and crossing over. We are not told which characteristics are dominant but we can easily deduce it. We are told that the black straight haired rat was true breeding and therefore must be homozygous. If it was homozygous dominant all the offspring would have black straight hair. Hence black and straight must be recessive. Therefore let R = red and Y = curly.
This means the other rat had to have red curly hair and also had to be heterozygous for both genes. The next problem to solve is which way are the alleles linked. Again this is easy to tell as the large numbers are the parental combinations, ie. black is linked to straight and red is linked to curly.

	black, straight		red, curly
P	r y / r y		R Y / r y

G_1: (r y) — (R Y) (r y) Parental gametes — (R y) (r Y) Recombinant gametes

F_1

	R Y	r y	R y	r Y
r y	R Y / r y	r y / r y	R y / r y	r Y / r y
	1315 red, curly	1370 black, straight	21 red, straight	19 black, curly

Parental combinations (red, curly; black, straight) — Recombinants (red, straight; black, curly)

7. Once again the data clearly shows linkage and crossing over. Let Y = yellow and L = large. The numbers tells us the linkage pattern. In cross 1 yellow is linked to large and white to small, and in cross 2 yellow is linked to small and white to large.

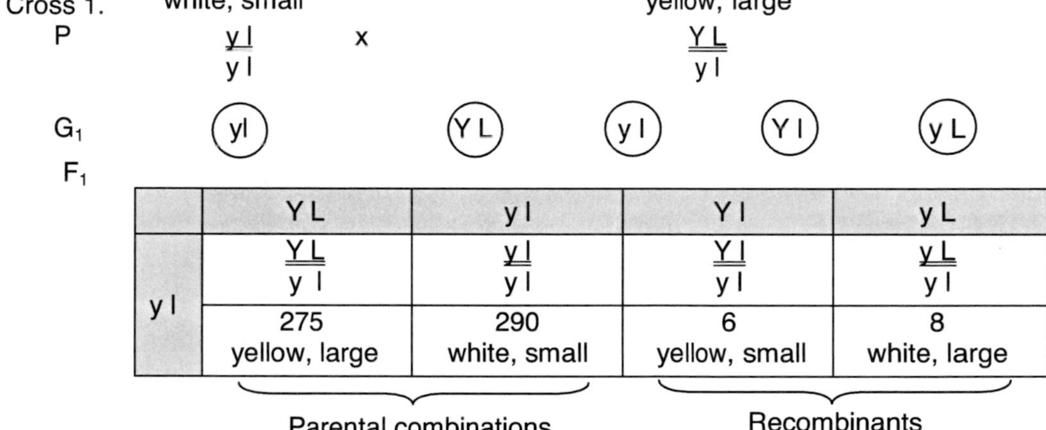

Cross 1.

	white, small		yellow, large
P	y l / y l	x	Y L / y l

G_1: (yl) — (Y L) (y l) (Y l) (y L)

F_1

	Y L	y l	Y l	y L
y l	Y L / y l	y l / y l	Y l / y l	y L / y l
	275 yellow, large	290 white, small	6 yellow, small	8 white, large

Parental combinations (yellow, large; white, small) — Recombinants (yellow, small; white, large)

8. Since Zom Bees are the same as the fruit fly the female is XX and male XY. We are told red is dominant. The female bee has red legs but we are not told if she is homozygous or heterozygous. However we can deduce this because we are told that all the F_1 males have red legs. If she was heterozygous then there would be some males with blue legs since they inherit their X chromosome from the female parent.

female, red
P X^RX^R
x
male, blue
X^rY^-
G_1 X^R
X^r
Y^-

Remember that using Y^- is a helpful way of preventing an allele being put on the Y chromosome by mistake.

F_1

	X^R
X^R	$X^R X^R$ female, red legged
Y^-	X^RY^- male, red legged

	female, red		male, red
F_1	X^RX^r	x	$X^R Y^-$
G_2	X^R X^r		X^R Y^-

F_2

	X^R	X^r
X^R	$X^R X^R$ female, red legged	$X^R X^r$ female, red legged
Y^-	X^RY^- male, red legged	X^rY^- male, blue legged

Thus in the F_2 we have a ratio of –
2 female, red legged,
1 male, red legged,
1 male, blue legged.

9. The offspring numbers tell us that the genes are linked and crossing over has occurred. Let B = blue and H = short. The tall white flowered plant is homozygous recessive, but the short blue flowered plant must be heterozygous for both genes in order for the F_1 to show recessive phenotypes. The numbers also tell us that short is linked to white and tall to blue.

	tall, white		short, blue
P	$\frac{\text{h b}}{\text{h b}}$	x	$\frac{\text{H b}}{\text{h B}}$

G_1 (h b) (Hb) (hB) (HB) (hb)

F_1

	Hb	hB	HB	hb
h b	$\frac{\text{H b}}{\text{h b}}$	$\frac{\text{h B}}{\text{h b}}$	$\frac{\text{H B}}{\text{h b}}$	$\frac{\text{h b}}{\text{h b}}$
	113 short, white	110 tall, blue	11 short, blue	12 tall, white

10.(a) Let R = round and L = simple.
Purplepear, (long fruit and simple flower), will have the genotype rrL? and Grapecluster (round fruit and complex flower), will have the genotype R?ll. Since the F_1 all had simple flowers and produced round fruits that means that the parents had to be homozygous for these alleles. The numbers again tell us there is linkage with crossing over.

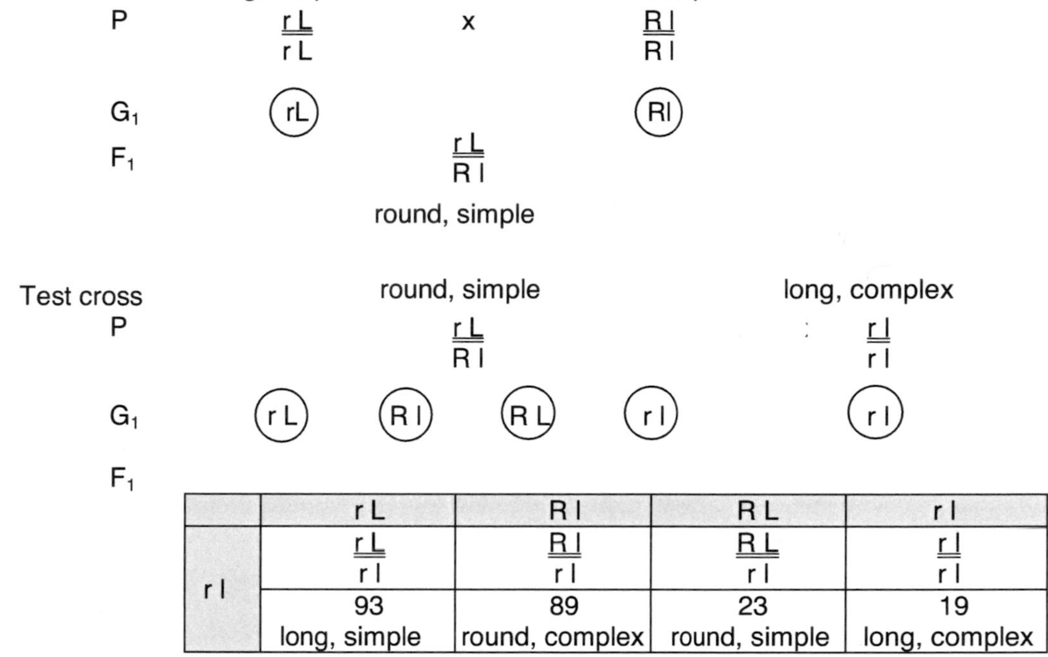

long, simple
round, complex
P
rL / rL
x
Rl / Rl
G1
rL
Rl
F1
rL / Rl
round, simple
Test cross
round, simple
long, complex
P
rL / Rl
rl / rl
G1
rL
Rl
RL
rl
rl
F1

	rL	Rl	RL	rl
rl	rL / rl	Rl / rl	RL / rl	rl / rl
	93 long, simple	89 round, complex	23 round, simple	19 long, complex

These theoretical results fit in with the experimental results.

(b) If the genes were not linked we would get the following ratio because it is double heterozygous x homozygous recessive – RrLl x rrlll.
1 round fruit, simple flowers :1 round fruit, complex flowers :1 long fruit, simple flowers : 1 long fruit, complex flowers. The reason for this is that, being unlinked, the alleles can assort independently and hence obey Mendel's second law.
Total number = 93 + 89 + 23 + 19 = 224. Each phenotype would be ¼ of this which is 56.

11. Let H = white and B = black so h = yellow and b = pink
The white mole with black feet is homozygous and so must have the genotype HHBB. It can only produce HB gametes. The yellow mole with pink feet must have the genotype hhbb and can only produce the gametes hb. This means all the offspring must have the genotype HhBb. If the genes are unlinked these F_1 will produce the gametes HB, Hb, hB and hb in equal numbers and the usual 4 x 4 Punnett grid will result in the ratio 9 white fur, black feet : 3 white fur, pink feet : 3 yellow fur, black feet : 1 yellow fur, pink feet. The actual ratio produced is approximately 16 white, black : 5 yellow, pink : 1 white, pink : 1 yellow, black. This is clearly nothing like the expected ratio and this would indicate that the genes are linked. If this is the case then the genotype of the F_1 is $\frac{\underline{HB}}{hb}$. This means there would be large numbers of the HB and hb gametes, and small numbers of the Hb and hB gametes. This would produce a higher than expected number of yellow moles with pink feet and a smaller number of the white/pink and yellow/black combinations, which is in fact what was produced.
The total number of offspring is 113 + 32 + 7 + 8 = 160 so with unlinked genes the expected numbers would be –

9/16 white fur black feet = 90,
3/16 white fur pink feet =30,
3/16 yellow fur black feet 30,
1/16 yellow fur pink feet =10.

Appendix 7

The Carbon Cycle

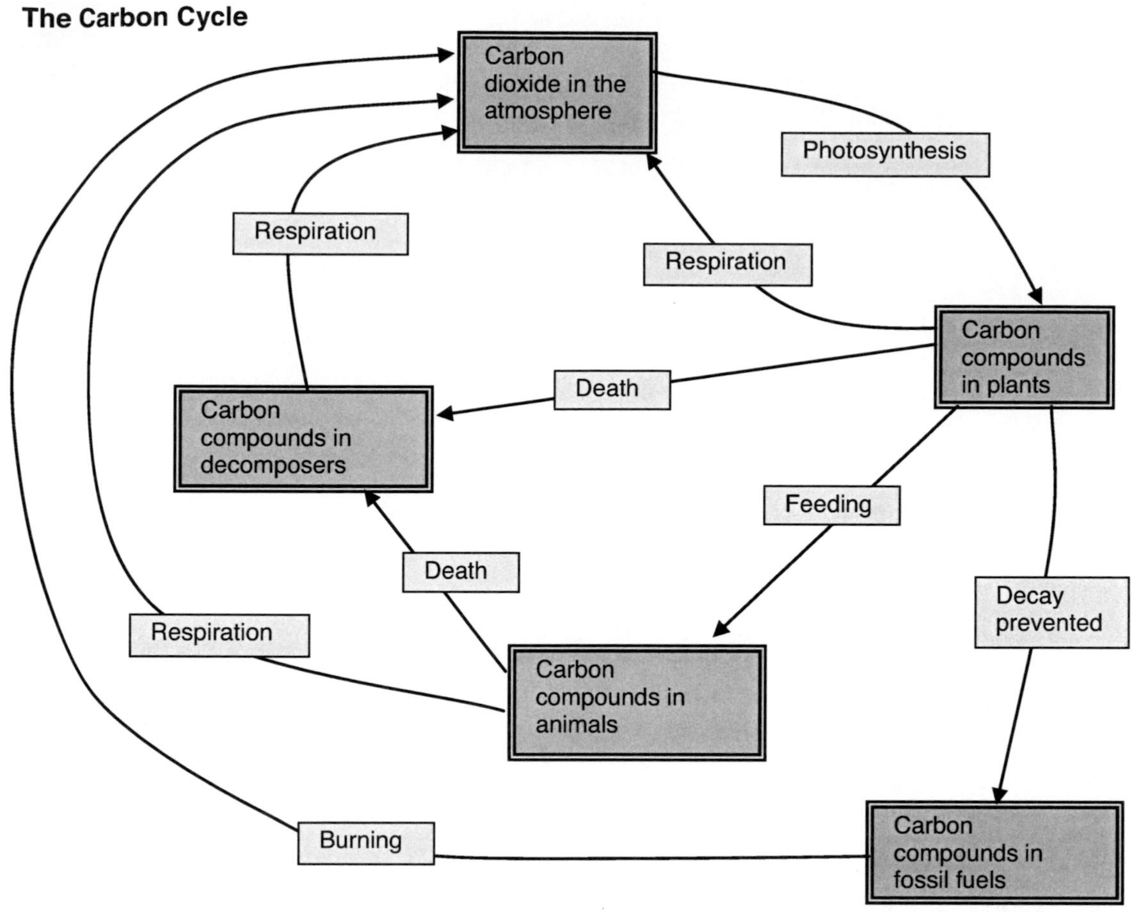

Carbon dioxide in the atmosphere
Photosynthesis
Respiration
Respiration
Carbon compounds in plants
Death
Carbon compounds in decomposers
Feeding
Death
Decay prevented
Respiration
Carbon compounds in animals
Burning
Carbon compounds in fossil fuels

Appendix 8

The mRNA Codon Table

First letter		Second letter: U		C		A		G		Third letter
		U		**C**		**A**		**G**		
U		UUU	Phenyl-alanine	UCU	Serine	UAU	Tyrosine	UGU	Cysteine	U
		UUC		UCC		UAC		UGC		C
		UUA	Leucine	UCA		**UAA**	***Stop codon***	**UGA**	***Stop codon***	A
		UUG		UCG		**UAG**	***Stop codon***	UGG	Tryptophan	G
C		CUU	Leucine	CCU	Proline	CAU	Histidine	CGU	Arginine	U
		CUC		CCC		CAC		CGC		C
		CUA		CCA		CAA	Glutamine	CGA		A
		CUG		CCG		CAG		CGG		G
A		AUU	Iso-leucine	ACU	Threonine	AAU	Asparagine	AGU	Serine	U
		AUC		ACC		AAC		AGC		C
		AUA		ACA		AAA	Lysine	AGA	Arginine	A
		AUG	Methionine	ACG		AAG		AGG		G
G		GUU	Valine	GCU	Alanine	GAU	Aspartic acid	GGU	Glycine	U
		GUC		GCC		GAC		GGC		C
		GUA		GCA		GAA	Glutamic acid	GGA		A
		GUG		GCG		GAG		GGG		G

It is useful to remember these two shaded ones, start AUG and stop UAG.

Note how the amino acids are in groups. Therefore in general it is the first two bases that are critical, eg GG - = glycine. Only two amino acids have a single codon.

Appendix 9

Essays – maximising your marks

- Allow 5 minutes to plan and 30 minutes to write each of the two essays.
- Read each sub-section carefully and look at the marks allocated. Each relevant fact gains a mark so 5 marks means you have to include five facts. Essays are commonly in three sub-sections – Objective 1, Objective 2, and Objective 3. The time required to gain say 5 marks for a list is much less than the time required to gain 5 marks in a discussion - plan your time carefully.
- Ensure you follow the command term precisely – hence the importance of knowing them. They are in Appendix 1 but more advice is given below for some of the more difficult ones.
  - '**Draw**' means –
    - A large, clearly and fully labelled drawing taking up about half a side.
    - You must draw in pencil.
    - The pencil must be HB.
    - I would strongly advise labelling in pencil – mistakes can then easily be changed.
    - Use a ruler for the label lines.
    - Include a title.
    - Make sure that you have practised all those diagrams where the syllabus says 'Draw'. These are listed below and all are included in this guide.

- The ultrastructure of *E. coli*..
- The ultrastructure of a liver cell.
- The structure of a membrane.
- Structure of water molecules to show polarity and hydrogen bonding.
- Identify diagrams of amino acids, glucose and ribose, and fatty acids. Learning to draw them will help you with this.
- The simple molecular structure of DNA.
- The carbon cycle.
- A sigmoid growth curve.
- The digestive system.
- The heart.
- The ventilation system – gross structure of thorax plus detail of alveolus.
- A motor neuron and myelin sheath.
- Male and female reproductive systems.
- Structure of a peptide bond.
- The structure of the mitochondrion as seen in electron micrographs.
- The structure of the chloroplast as seen in electron micrographs.
- Plan diagrams to show tissue distribution in stem and leaf of a generalised dicotyledonous plant.
- The structure of a dicotyledonous animal pollinated flower.
- The external and internal structure of a named dicotyledonous seed.
- The structure of a sarcomere including Z lines, thin and thick filaments and banding.
- The structure of the kidney.
- The structure of a mature sperm and egg.

Label

- A diagram of the human elbow joint.

Annotate

- A diagram of the ultrastructure of *E. coli* with functions of named structures.
- A diagram of the ultrastructure of a liver cell with functions of named structures.
- A graph showing levels of hormones of the menstrual cycle, ovulation, menstruation and thickening of the endometrium.
- A diagram of a glomerulus and associated nephron to show functions.
- A diagram of the testis to show location and function of interstitial cells, germinal epithelium, developing spermatozoa and Sertoli cells.
- A diagram of the ovary to show the location and function of germinal epithelium, primary and mature follicles and secondary oocyte.

- ❖ **'Compare'**
- Look for similarities and differences.
- There do not have to be the same number of each.
- Do NOT simply describe each in turn.
- Useful words = *both* when looking at similarities;
  whereas when looking at differences.

> This Command Term commonly turns up in Paper 2, Q1. Here are two example answers.
>
> **Both** white and blue flowers attract equal numbers of bees.
> Leaves in the sun have a mean surface area of $20cm^2$ **whereas** leaves in the shade have a mean surface area of $30cm^2$.

- ❖ 'Discuss'
- Include comments for and against the topic.
- Suggest ideas or hypotheses if relevant.
- Balance relative importance of factors.
- Give a final concluding statement but not necessarily a personal choice.
- Useful words = *however, on the other hand.*
- ❖ **'Evaluate'**
- Give your judgement of the value or importance of the topic.
- Does it have advantages?
- Does it have disadvantages?
- What is the balance between the two?
- ❖ **'Explain'**
- This may be the cause or reason for something to happen.
- Useful words = *because, thus.*
- Or it may be the mechanism behind something happening.
- Useful words = *therefore, and so.*

◆ Wherever possible illustrate your answer with simple diagrams. These help to make your answer more clear.

◆ The 2 additional marks for the essay are for -
- expressing relevant ideas clearly,
- linking of these ideas in a logical sequence.

◆ Read through the examples given below carefully. You will see how each starts with basic points and then more and more information is added, each sentence relating to the next. Gradually a complete picture is built up to cover the precise requirements of the command term.

1. *List what a plant needs in order to carry out photosynthesis and what the products of the process are. [7]*

Needs.
Water,
Carbon dioxide
Light of sufficient intensity and containing red and blue wavelengths,
Sufficient warmth.

Products
Oxygen,
Glucose which is converted into other substances.

2. *Describe enzyme activity using the lock and key model. [5]*

Your answer must include a diagram such as that on page 42.

Enzymes are large protein molecules folded in such a way as to have a special region called the active site. The shape of the active site is unique for each enzyme as it corresponds to the shape of the substrate that fits into it. The analogy is that a key will only work in a lock if the two have the same shape. In a mixture of substrate and enzyme the substrate binds into the active site and the reaction takes place. An example of this is the enzyme amylase which acts on starch to break it down into maltose. Amylase will only act on starch as only starch has the right shape to fit into the active site of amylase. Maltose can be broken down further into two glucose molecules, but this requires a different enzyme.

3. Outline the events in meiosis that reduce the number of chromosomes in the nucleus by half. [8]

Look back at pages 173 - 175. The key process is the first part of meiosis. You must have diagrams to illustrate your answer.

During prophase I the replicated chromosomes pair up in their homologous pairs. Each of these is called a bivalent. In metaphase I the bivalents line up on the equator and a spindle fibre attaches to each chromosome. During anaphase I the homologous pairs are pulled apart by contraction of the spindle fibres and the centromeres do not split. This is called the reduction division as the number of chromosomes is halved in each cell after cytokinesis I has taken place.
Now follows the second division which separates the sister chromatids because a spindle fibre attaches to each side of the centromere. During anaphase II the centromeres do split. After cytokinesis II each nucleus contains half the amount of genetic material as in the original nucleus.

4. Explain how energy is transferred and transformed in food chains. [8]

Energy enters a food chain as light energy because of the process of photosynthesis carried out by green plants. This energy is stored as organic compounds such as glucose, cellulose, and amino acids, in the plant. Some of this stored chemical energy is used up by the plant during chemical transformations such as respiration, protein synthesis, and lost as heat. Some will be transferred to a herbivore when the plant is eaten. Chemical reactions are generally inefficient and therefore heat energy is lost in the transfer from one compound to another.
Not all of what is eaten enters the herbivore as some is passed out in the faeces. What is digested and absorbed becomes assimilated into the herbivore. However the herbivore also uses up some of this energy during chemical transformations such as muscle activity and this is again lost as heat. Only about 10% of the available plant energy becomes converted into herbivore. A similar process happens in the next step when a carnivore eats the herbivore, though this energy transfer can be a little more efficient because less energy is lost in the faeces.
When the plants and animals die and decay the stored energy is transferred to decomposers, but they also lose heat energy through their respiration.
Finally all the energy that entered the ecosystem as light energy leaves as heat energy.

5. Discuss the possible effects of increased atmospheric carbon dioxide concentration on food webs. [7]

Carbon dioxide is a requirement for photosynthesis. If its concentration in the atmosphere increased then this could lead to an increase in the rate of photosynthesis. (Growers increase the amount of carbon dioxide in their greenhouses to increase crop production). If photosynthesis increased then there would be more plant material available for herbivores allowing them to increase. This in turn would lead to an increase in the number of carnivores and also decomposers at the end. How each trophic level in the web changed would be determined by the actual organisms involved. The web might become stable at new levels for each organism, but on the other hand it could change dramatically with certain plants out-competing others leading to changes in herbivores and carnivores.
Carbon dioxide is also a greenhouse gas and its increasing concentration in the atmosphere would seem to be resulting in global warming. A rise in temperature can make previously cooler places suitable for plants that prefer warmer temperatures. For example the tree-line could move up a mountain and in the process destroy the original vegetation and the food webs that existed there. A human population that lived in cool highlands above the mosquito line could, in a warming climate, find themselves invaded by this insect along with malaria. The food web has changed.
There are indications that global warming is affecting the climate in other ways. Rain belts in particular could shift with drier areas becoming wetter and wetter areas becoming drier. In each place the food webs would have to change.
At present the overall effects of increasing carbon dioxide on food webs are unclear. What is now clearly established is that the levels are increasing and are having effects in many parts of the world. We should be acting to reduce carbon dioxide output, but in the meantime we need to collect as much ecological data as possible.

6. *Explain how proteins act as enzymes, including control by feedback inhibition in allosteric enzymes. [9]*

A polypeptide is made of a linear sequence of amino acids. These can fold into a three-dimensional shape – tertiary level structure – and two or more of these can combine to form quaternary level structure. Most enzymes are at this level. The three dimensional structure allows for the formation of an indentation in the surface of the molecule that acts as the active site. This is where the substrate or substrates bind. The shape of this active site can either correspond immediately to the shape of the substrate – the lock and key model – or mould to the shape of the substrate as it binds – the induced fit model. *[Simple diagrams should be included to show these – p42 and p131].* The active site only uses a very small proportion of the amino acids forming the protein, maybe as few as 4 or 5. They are though critical because the different R groups have different properties. Some are electrically neutral, some are positive or negative, some are hydrophobic, and some are hydrophilic. A polar molecule such as maltose will require an active site that is hydrophilic, whereas a non-polar molecule such as triglyceride will require an active site that is hydrophobic.
In an anabolic reaction the two or more substrates bind to the active site and the activation energy is lowered allowing them to combine. An example would be RuBP carboxylase combining ribulose bisphosphate and carbon dioxide. Reactions of this type are usually endothermic.
Many metabolic pathways are in the form of chains or rings, the product of one reaction acting as the substrate for the next, eg. A → B → C → D. If D is not used then it will accumulate and this could affect cell functioning. Furthermore it may be a waste of energy if these are endergonic reactions. It would be sensible therefore to control the sequence by blocking the reaction from A to B by enzyme 1. If E1 is an allosteric enzyme then this could be done by D – as D accumulates it inhibits E1 by allostery. Allosteric enzymes exist in two forms – active and inactive – and they alternate between them. Furthermore they have two binding sites, the active site and the allosteric effector site. *[A simple diagram should be included to show this – p128].* If an allosteric inhibitor binds to the effector site then it will lock the enzyme in the inactive state therefore preventing the reaction from taking place. This is a form of non-competitive inhibition. In the example above D is the allosteric inhibitor. If D now starts to get used up then it leaves the allosteric site and so the reaction A → B can now continue. Because D is a product later in the metabolic chain it is called feedback inhibition.

7. *Outline the changes that lead to the depolarisation of an axon as an action potential travels along a neuron. [5]*

[Diagram as on page 100]
When the axon is at rest there is a potential difference across the axon membrane of around 70mV, the outside of the axon being positive due to a high concentration of sodium ions. During the action potential, voltage gated sodium channels open and a few sodium ions rapidly diffuse in, reversing the potential difference. The sodium gates then close. This happens only over a narrow band of the axon membrane. The sodium gates adjacent to the point of the action potential are opened by the reverse in the potential difference, and these in turn open the next sodium gates. Thus a wave of opening and closing sodium gates occurs as the action potential moves along the axon.

8. *Explain how the structure of the mitochondrion allows it to carry out its function efficiently. [6]*

[Labelled drawing of mitochondrion]
The function of the mitochondrion is to carry out aerobic respiration. There are two parts to this. The first part is Krebs cycle which takes place in the matrix. This is a solution similar to cytoplasm and contains all the enzymes both for Krebs cycle and the preceding link reaction. The starting point is pyruvate and this is transported from the cytoplasm through specific facilitated diffusion channels in the mitochondrial membranes.
The second part is oxidative phosphorylation and this takes part on the inner membrane. Embedded in the membrane are the electron carriers and proton pumps as well as ATP synthase which looks like a stalked particle. Embedding these molecules in the membrane allows them to be fixed next to each other therefore making it easy for the electrons to flow in the correct sequence. This inner membrane is highly folded therefore increasing its surface area. As electrons flow through the carriers, protons are pumped into the inter-membrane space and from here diffuse back into the matrix via ATP synthase. This flow of protons is aided by the fact that the inter-membrane space is narrow and so a high concentration of protons is easily built up.
The mitochondrion also contains its own DNA which is used to synthesise some of the proteins used in the above metabolic pathways.

9. *Discuss the theory of evolution by natural selections. [8]*

Various ideas had been put forward over a period of many years as to how the variety of life had arisen. Key amongst these was that of special creation by some form of god though these are just that, creation as opposed to natural selection. Some though argued that natural selection occurred after special creation. As more interest was shown in the process of inheritance another idea was that characteristics that were acquired could be passed on to offspring, but there was little evidence for this. The major step came in the mid nineteenth century when Darwin and Wallace put forward the idea of evolution by natural selection. Their argument was based on simple and readily repeatable observations and simple deductions from these observations. They observed that organisms tend to overproduce but over long periods of time the populations remained fairly stable. This meant that many offspring died in the struggle for survival. The next observation was that sexual reproduction produced variety amongst the offspring. Sometimes these differences gave a better chance of survival to some of the offspring and since these characteristics were inherited they would pass them on to their offspring. In this way the gene pool of the population changed, ie evolved. They supported their case by a large number of examples, the most easily understood one being the parallel with artificial selection by humans of domestic animals. There came more difficulty with longer periods of time as the only evidence there was from fossils. This is inevitably a very patchy record and it was easier for the protagonists to point to these gaps as flaws in the argument. However since then more and more fossils have come to light and the gaps are being filled.

10. *Explain why the light independent reactions of photosynthesis can only continue for a short time in the dark. [6]*

The light independent reactions (LIR) form a cyclic pathway that is driven by two products of the light dependent reactions (LDR). These are ATP and NADPH + H^+. The NADPH + H^+ is used to reduce glycerate 3-phosphate (GP) to triose phosphate (TP), and the ATP supplies energy for this conversion. If the LDR stops then so does the formation of both ATP and NADPH + H^+. Thus reduction of GP stops and so no more TP is formed. The TP is used to reform ribulose bisphosphate (RuBP) and so formation of this too stops. Once all of the existing RuBP has been converted into GP by reacting with carbon dioxide no further reactions at all will take place. The amount of GP levels off at maximum and the amount of RuBP and TP drop to zero.

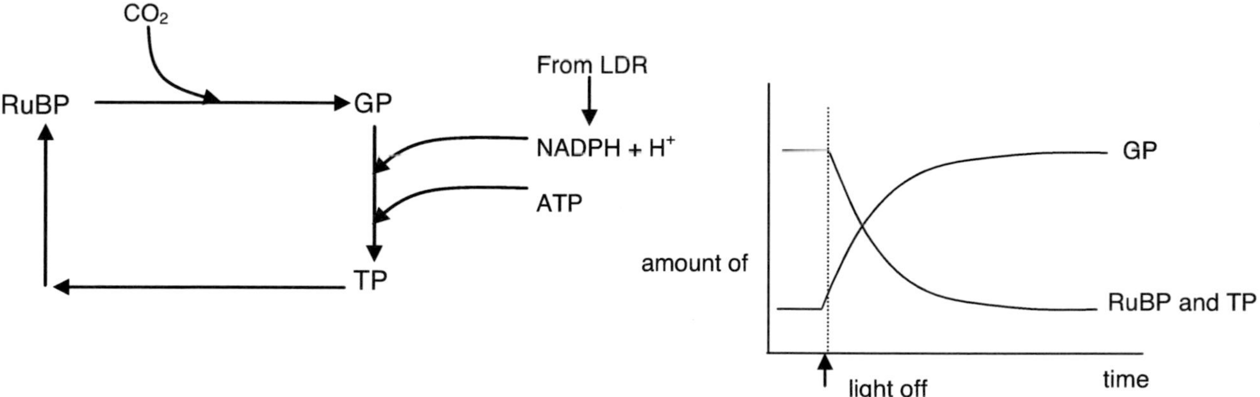

CO_2
RuBP
GP
From LDR
NADPH + H^+
ATP
TP
amount of
GP
RuBP and TP
light off
time

11. *Outline how enzymes in the cytoplasm are produced. [6]*

Enzymes that function in the cytoplasm are produced on free ribosomes. mRNA, produced by transcription in the nucleus, attaches to a free ribosome subunit. This now becomes attached to the second subunit and also a tRNA molecule carrying the amino acid corresponding to the start codon on the mRNA. The tRNA is held in place by complementary base pairing between the mRNA codon and the tRNA anticodon. The second tRNA molecule with its amino acid binds to the ribosome and now a peptide bond can be formed between the two amino acids. The ribosome then shifts one triplet along the mRNA in a 5' – 3' direction so that the third tRNA molecule can bind. This process is repeated until the ribosome reaches a stop codon on the mRNA. At this point the ribosome breaks free and the completed polypeptide is released into the cytoplasm. Most enzymes are quaternary level and so the additional polypeptides will need to be combined.

12. *Compare transmission of an electrical impulse along a neuron with transmission across a synapse. [8]*

The key difference between the two is that transmission along the neuron uses the movement of sodium and potassium ions whereas across the synapse it is the movement of a chemical compound, a neurotransmitter.
At rest the neuron uses an active sodium-potassium pump to maintain a high concentration of sodium ions outside the neuron membrane and this, along with the high concentration of negative ions in the axoplasm, creates a potential difference across the membrane. On the other hand at the synapse there is a high concentration of sodium ions in the fluid filled synaptic gap.
When a voltage gated sodium channel in the neuron membrane is opened sodium ions flow into the axoplasm and the membrane becomes polarised in the opposite direction. This depolarisation triggers the opening of a voltage gated potassium channel which is important in returning to the resting potential. In addition depolarisation causes the opening of a voltage gated sodium channel further along the neuron. In this way the impulse travels along the neuron. At the synapse however depolarisation results in the opening of voltage gated calcium channels. The inflow of calcium ions causes vesicles of neurotransmitter to bind to the presynaptic membrane and burst. The neurotransmitter diffuses across the gap and binds to a receptor. It is this binding that now causes a chemical rather than a voltage gated sodium channel to open and allow sodium ions to flow into the axoplasm and depolarise the postsynaptic neuron. Potassium channels are not involved in synaptic transmission.

Appendix 10

How to read a nomogram

A nomogram is usually a series of three lines that can be in various positions. Reading one is very simple. In the question you are given values for two of the lines and asked to deduce some data from the third. (Sometimes there is a fourth line but the principle is the same). Examples –

1. *If the temperature of the water is 15°C what is the % saturation when the oxygen concentration is 4cm^3 l^{-1}?*

To answer this use a ruler to draw a straight line .... between 15°C and 4cm^3 l^{-1} and then simply read off the % saturation – 57%.

2. *Determine the temperature change that causes a change in % saturation from 25 to 35 while the oxygen concentration remains at 2cm^3 l^{-1}.*

To answer this use a ruler to draw two straight lines, -.-.-.-.-.-.-.-.-.- one from 2cm^3 l^{-1} through 25% up to the temperature line, and the other from 2cm^3 l^{-1} through 35% up to the temperature line. Read off the two temperatures and calculate the change. 8°C to 25°C is a rise of 17°C.

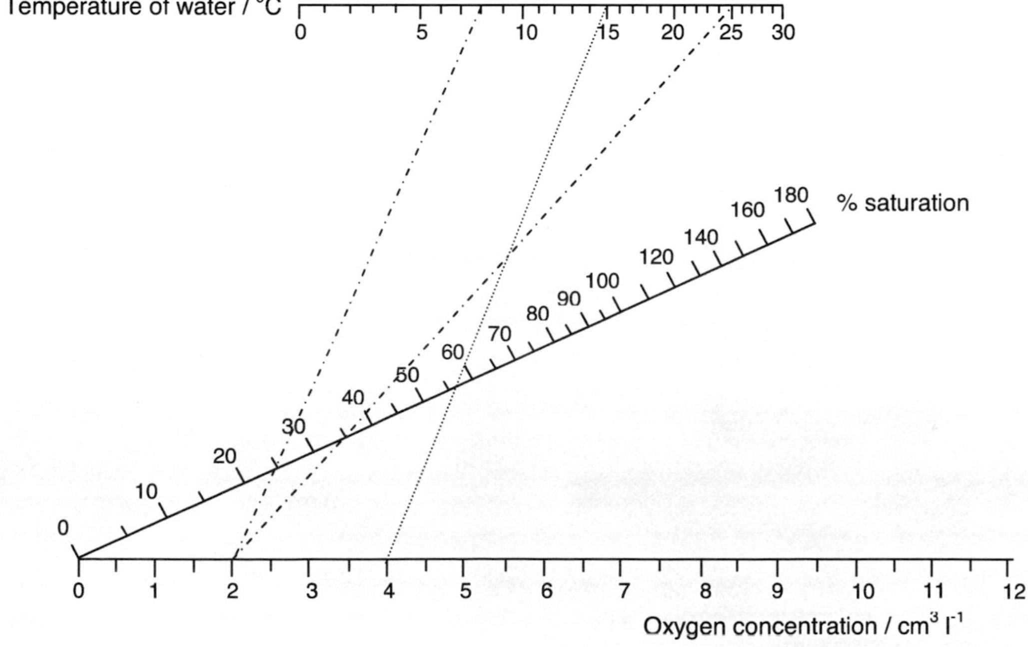
Temperature of water / °C
0
5
10
15
20
25
30
% saturation
0
10
20
30
40
50
60
70
80
90
100
120
140
160
180
0
1
2
3
4
5
6
7
8
9
10
11
12
Oxygen concentration / cm³ l⁻¹

Appendix 11

External Assessment Specifications

Component	Overall weighting %	Duration hours	Format and syllabus coverage
Paper 1	20	1	40 multiple choice questions on the core.
Paper 2	36	2¼	Section A One data-based question and several short-answer questions on the core and AHL (all compulsory). Section B **<u>Two</u>** extended response questions on the core and AHL from a choice of four.
Paper 3	20	1¼	Several short answer questions and one extended response question in each of the **<u>two Options</u>** studied (all compulsory).

Appendix 12

Exam Tool Kit and Mobile Phones

Having invigilated many exams it never ceases to surprise me what vital items students forget to bring in. If you never use an item then fine, but if you need it and haven't got it then it creates stress. If English is not your first language then for some exams you are allowed to take in a basic language dictionary. Check with your IB co-ordinator first though.
I would suggest taking the following into EVERY exam, ie ALL subjects, in a large <u>transparent</u> pencil case –

- ❑ 2 or 3 black pens,
- ❑ several spare cartridges if you use liquid ink,
- ❑ highlighter (for highlighting key words and points in questions),
- ❑ 15cm transparent ruler with a good clean edge – for labelling drawings,
- ❑ 30cm transparent ruler with a good clean edge – for graphs,
- ❑ 2 HB propelling pencils,
- ❑ clean pencil eraser,
- ❑ compass with a sharp pencil ready fitted,
- ❑ pencil sharpener,
- ❑ set square and protractor,
- ❑ calculator (put new batteries in). For Paper 1 Multiple Choice papers you are not allowed a calculator but for Paper 2 you are. These papers run consecutively so your exam supervisor will make the arrangements for you to have your calculator for Paper 2.

Mobile phones, iPods and other electronic communication devices.

<u>NEVER TAKE THESE INTO THE EXAM ROOM</u>. This is a serious breach of exam regulations and you may have that exam paper removed from your record. This means <u>failing your Diploma</u>.

Good luck!

Appendix 13

ABSORPTION	Taking in chemical substances through cell membranes or layers of cells.
ABSORPTION SPECTRUM	The pattern of absorption of light (by photosynthetic pigments) at different wavelengths.
ACTION SPECTRUM	The pattern of a chemical action (eg photosynthesis – production of oxygen) at different wavelengths of light.
ACTIVATION ENERGY	The energy barrier that prevents a reaction between chemical substances. Enzymes are biological catalysts that lower the energy needed to overcome the barrier and destabilise reactants so that the reaction can occur.
ADHESION	The attraction between water molecules and any surface they touch, such as soil particles, the surface of a root hair or the wall of xylem vessels.
AEROBIC	A process that requires oxygen.
ALLELE	One specific form of a gene, differing from other alleles by one or a few bases only and occupying the same gene locus as other alleles of the gene.
AMNIOCENTESIS	A medical procedure in which cells from the fetus are obtained from the amniotic fluid to enable genetic and biochemical analysis of the fetal cells.
ANAEROBIC	A process that can occur in the absence of oxygen.
ANTAGONISTIC	Opposite. Usually refers to muscles attached on each side of a joint, eg the biceps and triceps on each side of the elbow joint.
ANTIBIOTIC	A chemical substance, most commonly derived from a fungus, that selectively destroys bacteria. It is ineffective against viruses.
ASEXUAL REPRODUCTION	A form of reproduction which does not involve gametes and the offspring are genetically identical to the parent. It is due to mitosis.
ATP	Adenosine triphosphate. The energy 'currency' molecule used by cells.
ATTENUATED	A pathogen that has been treated in some way so that it will not cause disease. Attenuated pathogens are used in most vaccines.
AUTOSOME	A chromosome that is not a sex chromosome.
BASE	An organic molecule used in the structure of the nucleic acids DNA and RNA, and also other molecules such as ATP, NAD. There are 5 different types, adenine, cytosine, guanine, thymine and uracil. Abbreviations are A, C, G, T, U.
BINARY FISSION	Where an organism divides into two to produce two new individuals. Limited to bacteria and unicellular eukaryotes.
BINOMIAL	A system of classification where each organism is given a unique Latin name of genus and species, eg. modern human is *Homo sapiens.*
BIOMASS	The total dry mass of organic matter in an area.
BLASTOCYST	The hollow ball of cells formed from the fertilised egg which implants into the endometrium.
CARBOHYDRASE	An enzyme that digests disaccharides or polysaccharides.
CAUSAL RELATIONSHIP	A relationship between one event (A) and another (B) in which A precedes and causes B.
CELL CYCLE	A cycle involving several phases – interphase, which in turn is subdivided into G_1, S, and G_2 sub-phases, followed by mitosis (nuclear division), then cytokinesis (cell division), and back to interphase. One of the two cells then usually undergoes differentiation while the other one remains in the cycle.
CHIASMA / CHIASMATA	The point(s) at which homologous chromosomes remain in contact as chromatids move apart during prophase I of meiosis. Crossing over occurs here.
CHORIONIC VILLUS SAMPLING (CVS)	A medical procedure that extracts a tiny sample of the chorion from a pregnant woman to enable genetic and biochemical analysis of the embryo cells.
CLONE	A group of organisms of identical genotype, or a group of cells descended from a single parent cell as a result of repeated mitotic divisions.
CLONAL SELECTION	The selection of a specific B-cell for an antigen, and its subsequent division into a clone.
CODON	A triplet of bases in mRNA that codes for a specific amino acid during translation.
COHESION	A force of attraction between two molecules of the same type.
COMPLEMENTARY BASE PAIRING	The specific pairs of bases formed between the two strands of DNA, between DNA and RNA, between double stranded RNA or between mRNA and tRNA. Bases are linked by hydrogen bonds. A pairs with T or U, and G pairs with C.
COMPOUND	A substance made from two or more elements chemically combined.
CONDENSATION	A type of chemical reaction which releases water, eg formation of a dipeptide from two amino acids.
CONFORMATIONAL CHANGE	A change, temporary or permanent, in the shape of a protein, eg during binding of a substrate or allosteric effector to an enzyme, or during active transport.
CORRELATION	A relationship between two variables where a change in one causes a corresponding or proportional change in the other.
COTYLEDON	A modified leaf found in the seed.

Covalent bond	A strong chemical bond between molecules, eg between the sugar and phosphate, and the sugar and base in a nucleotide.
Crossing over	The exchange of alleles between non-sister chromatids of homologous chromosomes as a result of chiasmata formation. The process separates alleles that were previously linked.
Degeneration	Break down of an unused structure, eg sperm or polar body.
Dichotomous	Branching into two.
Dicotyledonous	The group of plants that have two cotyledons in the seed. The cotyledons store food which is used during germination.
Differentiation	The changes a cell undergoes from being unspecialised to being specialised for a particular function.
Digestion	Chemical breakdown of food by enzymes in the gut.
Diploid	A nucleus with two complete sets of chromosomes.
Disaccharide	A carbohydrate/sugar consisting of two smaller sugar molecules joined during condensation by a covalent bond, eg sucrose.
DNA ligase	An enzyme that joins two fragments of DNA such as Okasaki fragments on the lagging strand during DNA replication, or in biotechnology such as formation of a recombinant plasmid.
Domesticated	An animal that is used by humans for a specific purpose and usually lives in close or fairly close proximity to humans. They are often specially bred.
Egestion	Removal of undigested food and other materials through the anus.
Electrophoresis	Movement of charged molecules, such as DNA fragments, in an electric field.
Element	A substance which cannot be broken down into a simpler substance, eg. Fe, Ca.
Emergent property	A property which has arisen from the interaction of component parts: the whole is greater than the sum of its parts.
Emigration	The moving away from a population to a different locality.
Endocytosis	Process by which eukaryotic cells take up material from the outside by infolding / invagination of the plasma membrane to form vesicles enclosing the external material.
Endometrium	The lining of the uterus into which an embryo implants. It is shed during menstruation and then rebuilt.
Endosperm	The food storage tissue in the seed of monocotyledonous plants (monocotyledons). The food is used during germination.
Envelope	A double membrane around three specific organelles – nucleus, mitochondrion and chloroplast.
Error bar	Used to show the range or standard deviation of a set of values.
Erythrocyte	Red blood cell.
Ethical	Relating to or dealing with morals or the principles of morality.
Eukaryote	A cell that has a true nucleus, ie the chromosomes contained within a double membrane or envelope.
Evaporation	The formation of water vapour from liquid water.
Excretion	Removal of the waste products of metabolism.
Exothermic	A chemical reaction during which heat energy is released.
Exocytosis	The process by which molecules are secreted from eukaryotic cells. They are packaged in membrane bound vesicles which then fuse with the plasma membrane releasing their contents to the outside of the cell.
Exon	Any part of the eukaryotic DNA sequence that codes for part of a polypeptide.
Exponential growth	A rate of growth where numbers of individuals double per unit time, ie 1, 2, 4, 8, 16 etc.
Fenestrated	Having small spaces through which substances can pass. Describes capillaries where there are gaps between adjacent cells.
Filtrate	A solution formed after passing through a filter. In biology the 'filter' is usually a membrane such as the basement membrane between the glomerular cells and the Bowman's capsule podocytes in the kidney.
Flagellum	A long thin structure use to propel unicellular organisms.
Forensic investigation	An investigation to answer questions of interest to a legal system, most often in relation to a crime.
Fulcrum	The point about which a lever turns.
Gender	Being male or female.
Gene	A length of DNA which codes for a polypeptide.
Germinal epithelium	The layer of cells which divide by mitosis and eventually give rise to gametes. In the ovary this is the outer layer of the ovary and in the testes it is the outer layer of the seminiferous tubules.

Germination The period when a seed changes from being dormant to the initial stages of growth into a seedling.

GMO Genetically modified organism – an organism that is made of cells that contain DNA from another species.

Haploid A nucleus with a single set of chromosomes.

Hierarchy of taxa A series of different levels of groups of organisms which share characteristics within each group at each level. The higher the level the fewer the number of shared characteristics.

Homologous structures Structures which have the same evolutionary origin but may or may not have the same function, eg leg of a human and leg of a bird; arm of a human and wing of a bird.

Hybridoma A cell produced by the fusion of an antibody-producing cell (plasma cells) with a myeloma (tumour) cell.

Hydrogen bond A weak chemical bond between the small positive charge on a hydrogen atom and the small negative charge on either an oxygen or a nitrogen atom.

Hydrolysis A type of chemical reaction which uses water in order to separate two molecules, eg formation of two amino acids from a dipeptide.

Hydrophilic All or part of a molecule that is able to form hydrogen bonds with water.

Hydrophobic All or part of a molecule that repels water.

Hypothalamus Region of the brain just above the pituitary gland. Contains centres controlling osmoregulation, temperature regulation, sexual activity, and sleep.

Immigration The arrival in a population of a few members from a different locality.

Immunity Resistance to the onset of a disease after infection by the pathogen which causes the disease.

Immunological memory The ability of the body to remember and respond to a subsequent invasion of the same pathogen.

Implantation The blastocyst embeds in the endometrium (lining of the uterus).

Ingestion Taking in food through the mouth.

Inheritance The transfer of genetic information from parents to offspring.

Interstitial fluid Also called tissue fluid. A filtrate from the blood that surrounds cells. It is similar to plasma but does not contain the larger plasma proteins.

Intron A part of the DNA sequence that does not code for part of a polypeptide.

Ion A charged particle.

Ionic bond A weak bond between a negative charge on a molecule and a positive charge on another molecule, eg between COO^- and NH_3^+ on amino acids in different regions of a polypeptide.

Karyotyping Determining the number, types and forms of chromosomes in a cell by matching size and banding pattern to a standard pattern.

Leucocyte White blood cell. There are two types – phagocytes which engulf and digest bacteria and cell debris, and lymphocytes such as B-cells and T-cells which are associated with antibody production.

Lignification Deposition of a tough material, lignin, in the cellulose cell wall of plant cells to strengthen them. Lignification makes plants 'woody'.

Lipase An enzyme that digests lipids.

Lymph A fluid found in the lymphatic system. Its composition is similar to that of tissue fluid. The lymph coming from the gut is high in lipids.

Lymphatic system A network of vessels throughout the body. It collects excess tissue fluid and returns it to the blood at the subclavian veins. The vessels pass through many lymph nodes which store lymphocytes.

Lysis Splitting of a molecule or structure, eg hydrolysis means splitting using water; photolysis means splitting using light; haemolysis means splitting of a red blood cell.

Metabolism All the chemical reactions which take place in the body of an organism. These include both breaking down reactions (catabolism) such as converting glycogen or starch into glucose, or building up reactions (anabolism) such as making glucose from carbon dioxide and water, or protein synthesis from amino acids.

Micropyle A tiny hole in the seed coat of a seed. It allows uptake of water into the seed at the start of germination.

Monoclonal antibody Antibody produced in the laboratory from a clone of hybridoma cells, each of which produces the same specific antibody.

MONOCOTYLEDONOUS The group of plants that only have a single cotyledon in the seed. Unlike dicotyledonous plants the cotyledon does not store food.

MONOHYBRID CROSS A genetic cross involving only a single gene.

MONOSACCHARIDE The simplest type of sugar, eg ribose, glucose.

MORTALITY Death.

MUCUS Slimy material rich in glycoproteins.

MUCOUS MEMBRANE Any epithelial layer secreting mucus.

MULTIPLE ALLELES More than two alleles for a gene.

MYELIN SHEATH A fatty sheath around axons formed by Schwann cells. Gaps between the cells form the nodes of Ranvier.

MYELOMA CELL The cancerous form of a plasma cell. Plasma cells are the active antibody-producing form of B-cells.

MYOFIBRIL The protein fibres/filaments of actin and myosin in a muscle fibre.

MYOGENIC Referring to cardiac (heart) muscle – contracts of its own accord, ie without an external nervous stimulus.

NATALITY Birth.

NEGATIVE FEEDBACK The control of a process by the results or effects of the process in such a way that an increase or decrease in the results or effects is always reversed.

NOMENCLATURE Providing agreed scientific names for organisms/species.

NON DISJUNCTION Failure of homologous chromosomes to separate at meiosis I, or failure of sister chromatids to separate at meiosis II or mitosis.

NON-POLAR AMINO ACID An amino acid with a side chain which is not charged and cannot form hydrogen bonds.

NORMAL DISTRIBUTION A bell shaped curve on a graph which is symmetrical about the mean.

NUCLEOSIDE Consists of a sugar and a base, ie a nucleotide without the phosphate.

NUCLEOTIDE One unit of a nucleic acid. Consists of a sugar, base and phosphate.

ORGAN A group of at least two tissue types combined to carry out a function together, eg plant root or flower, animal kidney or skin.

ORGANELLE A structure found within a cell which has a specific function, eg mitochondrion, nucleus.

ORGANIC Compounds containing carbon that are found in living organisms, excluding hydrogen carbonates, carbonates and oxides of carbon.

ORGAN SYSTEM An integrated group of organs with a shared function, eg reproductive system, excretory system.

PANCREATIC ISLETS Small patches of endocrine pancreatic cells secreting the hormones insulin and glucagon. They are surrounded by the exocrine pancreatic cells secreting digestive enzymes.

PARTIALLY PERMEABLE MEMBRANE A membrane that only allows certain substances to pass through it. (The terms semi permeable and selectively permeable are old terms and should not be used).

PASSIVE A process that does not require the use of energy.

PEDIGREE CHART A diagram showing a family tree for an organism, including phenotypes and genotypes. It uses standard symbols.

pH The measure of the acidity or alkalinity of a solution. Neutral is a pH of 7, acids have a pH of less than 7 and alkalis a pH of more than 7.

PHAGOCYTIC The name of a cell which takes in material by phagocytosis, ie a phagocyte.

PHAGOCYTOSIS A form of endocytosis where the material being taken in is in the form of particles.

PHOSPHORYLATION The addition of a phosphate group to an organic compound.

PHOTOLYSIS A type of reaction which uses light energy in order to split water molecules during photosynthesis.

PINOCYTOSIS A form of endocytosis where the material being taken in is liquid or in solution.

PLASMID A small circular piece of DNA found in the cytoplasm of bacteria distinct from the chromosome.

PODOCYTE A specialised cell lining Bowman's capsule. The cells have extensions ('feet') which ceate gaps allowing the filtrate which has passed through the basement membrane to pass easily into the capsular space.

POLAR AMINO ACID An amino acid with a charged side chain which can form hydrogen bonds.

POLLINATION The transfer of pollen grains from the anther to the stigma. Cross pollination is when two different plants are involved; self pollination is when the pollen and stigma are on the same plant, either the same flower or two different flowers.

POLYPEPTIDE A chain of amino acids joined by peptide bonds.

POLYSACCHARIDE A chain, which may be branched, of monosaccharides, eg starch, glycogen.

PRE-NATAL Before birth.

PROKARYOTE A cell that does not have a true nucleus, ie the genetic material is not surrounded by a nuclear envelope. Bacteria are prokaryotes.

Term	Definition
Protease	An enzyme that digests protein.
Protein	A large polypeptide. May also be made up of two or more polypeptide chains.
Recombinant	An offspring that has combinations of genes or characteristics different from those of its parents.
Recombination	The reassortment of genes or characteristics into combinations different from those of its parents.
Reduction division	A nuclear division in which the number of chromosomes is halved.
Restriction enzyme (endonuclease)	A bacterial enzyme that cuts DNA at very specific base sequences, often producing 'sticky ends'. Used extensively in recombinant DNA technology.
Secretion	A substance that has been manufactured by a cell for a specific function, eg a hormone, digestive enzyme, mucus, and then released from that cell by exocytosis.
Selective breeding	The development by humans of breeds of plants or animals with particular desirable characteristics.
Selective reabsorption	Absorption into the blood stream of specific required/useful substances from the proximal convoluted tubule of the kidney.
Sex chromosome	A chromosome used in sex determination in organisms with a chromosomal mechanism of sex determination. In humans the chromosomes are X and Y. The female is XX and the male XY.
Significance	In a statistics test the significance is whether one variable has an effect on another variable or if the result is simply due to chance. In Biology the most common level of significance is 0.05 or 5%.
SI units	Length – metre, m; (centimetre, cm;) millimetre, mm = 10^{-3}m; micrometre, μm = 10^{-6}m; nanometre, nm = 10^{-9}m; Volume – litre, l; centimetre cubed, cm^3.
Solute	A substance which dissolves in a solvent to form a solution.
Solution	The liquid formed when a solute dissolves in a solvent.
Solvent	A liquid that dissolves a solute to form a solution. Water is the solvent in biological systems.
Standard deviation	The spread of data about the mean of a set of values. 68% of the values fall within ±1 standard deviation of the mean; 95% of the values fall within ±2 standard deviations of the mean.
Stem cell	An undifferentiated cell in an embryo or adult that can undergo unlimited division and can give rise to one or several different cell types.
Stem tuber	A swollen stem, often underground, which is used for vegetative propagation, a form of asexual reproduction. Example – potato.
Sticky end	A short sequence of unpaired bases at the end of a DNA molecule produced by cutting with a restriction enzyme.
Striated muscle	Skeletal muscle. The arrangement of the protein fibres (myofibrils) gives the muscle a striped (striated) appearance in an electron micrograph.
Substitution mutation	The replacement of a base in DNA with a different base.
Substrate	The chemical substance on which an enzyme acts.
Subunit	An identifiable part of a large molecule or structure. Together the subunits form a more complex structure such as a quaternary level protein or a ribosome.
Supercoiling	The repeated coiling of the DNA/protein strand during prophase to form the short fat chromosome that can be seen under the light microscope.
Syndrome	Clinically recognizable features - signs observed by a physician, or symptoms described by the patient.
Taxon / Taxa	A group of organisms within a hierarchy.
t-test	A statistical test to determine if there is a significant difference between two sets of data.
Tendril	A specialized stem, leaf or petiole (leaf stalk) of climbing plants with a long thin shape which can curl around structures it touches to support the plant.
Testa	The seed coat. It is a tough outer covering layer which protects the seed.
Therapeutic	A procedure or medication used to treat or cure a disease.
Tissue fluid	Also called interstitial fluid. A filtrate from the blood that surrounds cells. It is similar to plasma but does not contain the larger plasma proteins.
Trisomy	Having three of one particular chromosome.
Turgor	The level to which a plant cell is swollen due to its water content. As the cell takes up water the turgor pressure in the cell increases until it becomes fully turgid and water uptake stops. Turgid cells are important in supporting non-woody plants and parts of plants such as leaves

ULTRAFILTRATION — Filtration at the molecular level through a membrane. Only molecules below a certain size can pass through the membrane.

ULTRASTRUCTURE — The detailed structure of cells as seen in the electron microscope.

UNICELLULAR ORGANISM — An organism consisting of only one cell that carries out all the functions of life.

UNIVERSAL — Found in all living organisms. The genetic code is referred to as universal because the same triplet code of bases is used for the amino acids.

VESICLE — A structure (organelle) found in the cytoplasm bound by a single membrane. May be formed by breaking off from the rER or Golgi apparatus, or by endocytosis.

WATER POTENTIAL — The ability of a solution to lose water. Water will always move from a region of high water potential to one of lower water potential. Pure water has a maximum water potential of 0, and adding solute lowers the water potential so solutions have a negative water potential. The more solute is added the more negative the water potential.